DIANA

AND

ENAMOURED DIANA

Oxford University Press, Ely House, London W. 1

GLASGOW NEW YORK TORONTO MELBOURNE WELLINGTON
CAPE TOWN SALISBURY IBADAN NAIROBI LUSAKA ADDIS ABABA
BOMBAY CALCUTTA MADRAS KARACHI LAHORE DACCA
KUALA LUMPUR HONG KONG TOKYO

A CRITICAL EDITION OF YONG'S
TRANSLATION OF
GEORGE OF MONTEMAYOR'S

DIANA

AND

GIL POLO'S
ENAMOURED DIANA

————◄••►————

Judith M. Kennedy

OXFORD
AT THE CLARENDON PRESS
1968

PRINTED IN GREAT BRITAIN
AT THE UNIVERSITY PRESS, OXFORD
BY VIVIAN RIDLER
PRINTER TO THE UNIVERSITY

TO

MY PARENTS

PREFACE

MONTEMAYOR's pastoral romance *Diana* ranks as one of the masterpieces of the Golden Age of Spanish literature, and has always enjoyed an eminent reputation in Europe. In Elizabethan England *Diana* was highly popular and influential, but its fame suffered an eclipse as the appeal of the pastoral tradition in which it stands waned. Augustan wit and eighteenth-century rationalism were inimical to the idealistic spirit of Renaissance pastoral, and in the nineteenth and twentieth centuries English-speaking readers have responded more readily to the limited aspects of pastoral in the nature poetry of Wordsworth and Frost than to the rich texture of the amorous and courtly golden world. Recently, however, there has been an increasing interest in the genre which attracted and stimulated some of the greatest writers in the English language, and, in particular, modern critics have been turning more and more frequently to *Diana* to assist them in defining and understanding the use of the pastoral convention in the works of such authors as Shakespeare, Sidney, and Spenser.

Hitherto both the re-establishment of *Diana* as a classic in the English-speaking world and the researches of literary scholars have been hampered by the inaccessibility of a translation. The only complete English translation is that by Bartholomew Yong, published in 1598, and never until now reprinted in its entirety. It is hoped that the present critical edition will serve not only to make a definitive text of Yong's translation available to students of Elizabethan literature, but also to win for this charming and sophisticated romance the wider audience among English-speaking readers which it deserves.

A critical text of Yong's translation of Gil Polo's *Enamoured Diana* is included in this edition, for three main reasons: Gil Polo's romance provides a satisfying conclusion to some of Montemayor's unfinished stories; it reveals an attitude towards love within the pastoral convention which is complementary to Montemayor's; and it is in itself a highly successful work of literary art.

The Introduction to the present edition seeks to give some indication of the history and reputation of pastoral romance, of the art of *Diana*, and of the skill and readability of Yong's translation; and to provide a survey of the influence of *Diana* on English literature in the later sixteenth and seventeenth centuries. The Commentary seeks to elucidate possible difficulties in the text, and to indicate the accuracy of Yong's translation of the Spanish. I should like to thank the Delegates and Secretary of the Clarendon Press for their generosity in allowing me free scope to determine the extent of the Introduction and Commentary, despite the length of the text itself.

The debts incurred during the course of a study originally undertaken as a thesis can never be fully acknowledged. My indebtedness to the works of many scholars whose studies have a bearing on *Diana* and Renaissance pastoral I have tried to indicate in the footnotes and bibliography, but I should also like to attempt, however inadequately, to thank some of those who more personally have assisted me.

I owe thanks to the courtesy and helpfulness of the librarians of the Bodleian Library, the British Museum, the Cambridge University Library, the Library of Congress, the libraries of Trinity College, Cambridge, of the University of Saskatchewan, and of the Hispanic Society of America, and particularly to Mr. J. Feeley, of St. Thomas More College, University of Saskatchewan.

I also owe thanks to the many kind friends at Oxford and at the University of Saskatchewan who readily gave of their time and knowledge to help me with problems of translation and legal interpretation; to Professor A. K. R. Kiralfy, for permission to quote his opinion on a point of law; to the Canada Council, for two grants enabling me to return to England to complete this edition and prepare it for publication; and to the Principal and Fellows of Somerville College, Oxford, for their sustaining and long-continued support.

I am most deeply grateful to Mr. D. G. Neill, Mr. R. D. F. Pring-Mill, and Miss Jean Robertson, for their encouragement, and for invaluable advice and assistance with revisions; to Mr. John Buxton, for his constant guidance and stimulation, and

particularly for his unfailing kindness and patience as a super-
visor; and to Miss M. M. Lascelles, to whom I owe, among
uncountable and incalculable debts, the suggestion for this
edition of *Diana*.

J. M. K.

St. Thomas More College
University of Saskatchewan
Saskatoon, Canada

CONTENTS

LIST OF ABBREVIATIONS   xiii

INTRODUCTION
    i. Montemayor, and the Antecedents of *Diana*   xv
    ii. The Reputation of Pastoral Romance   xxiii
    iii. A Brief Examination of *Diana*   xxvii
    iv. *Diana* in England   xxxi
    v. Life of Bartholomew Yong   lviii
    vi. Yong as Translator   lxv
    vii. Textual Introduction   lxxiii

DIANA OF GEORGE OF MONTEMAYOR   1

ENAMOURED DIANA, by Gaspar Gil Polo   243

APPENDIX
    The Spanish texts of Montemayor and Gil Polo used by Yong   419

COMMENTARY   422

CHECK-LIST OF WORDS GLOSSED OR ANNOTATED   454

LIST OF MANUSCRIPTS AND BOOKS   457

INDEX OF FIRST LINES OF POEMS   466

LIST OF ABBREVIATIONS

Báez   Jorge de Montemayor, *Los siete libros de la Diana*, ed. E. M. Báez. Madrid, 1955.

Chapuis ⎫
Colin ⎭ *La Diane de G. de Montemayor. Divisee en trois parties, & traduites d'Espagnol en François* [Pt. 1 by N. Colin, pt. 2 and 3 by G. Chapuis]. *Reveuë & corrigee, etc.* Tours, 1592.

Estrada   Jorge de Montemayor, *Los siete libros de la Diana*, ed. F. L. Estrada, *Clásicos Castellanos*, 2nd ed., Madrid, 1954.

Ferreres   Gaspar Gil Polo, *Diana Enamorada*, ed. R. Ferreres, *Clásicos Castellanos*, Madrid, 1953.

Grove   Sir George Grove, *Grove's dictionary of music and musicians*, 5th ed., ed. by Eric Blom, 9 vols. and suppl. 1954, 61.

Minsheu   John Minsheu, *A dictionarie in Spanish and English, first published into the English tongue by Ric. Percivale Gent. Now enlarged, etc.* 1599.

Wilson   *Diana de Monte Mayor done out of Spanish by Thomas Wilson Esquire, In the yeare 1596.* British Museum Add. MS. 18638.

OED   *The Oxford English Dictionary.*

MLN   *Modern Language Notes.*

MLR   *Modern Language Review.*

PMLA   *Publications of the Modern Language Association of America.*

Unless otherwise stated, all translations are the editor's.

INTRODUCTION

1. *Montemayor, and the Antecedents of* Diana

MONTEMAYOR's *Diana* took Europe by storm in the latter part of the sixteenth century. Before 1600 there had appeared twenty-six editions of the Spanish text, eleven editions of various French translations, and the English version by Yong. By this time the Germans also were convinced of its lasting worth, and seven editions of German translations appeared during the seventeenth century. There was also a Dutch translation in 1652. There are eighty-two entries of editions and translations in Estrada's bibliography of *Diana*, to which may be added his own edition (1954), and that of E. Moreno Báez (Madrid, 1955).

The author of this best seller, Jorge de Montemayor,[1] was Portuguese, born about 1520 at Montemor-o-Velho, near Coimbra. From the place of his birth he takes his name, though in a Castilian form, for he was Spanish by choice, and (except for a few brief passages in the seventh book of *Diana*) wrote in Spanish, not in his native tongue. Very little is known about his family or his early years, and most knowledge of his youth is drawn from the evidence of his own writings. In a verse letter to his friend Sa de Miranda, he says that he drew a very small share of learning from his education, and most of that was 'style, creativity, and skill' (estilo, ingenio i arte). He spent all his time in music, by which he supported himself, since, as he says deprecatingly, his poetic muse was unequal to the task, and he was also a subject of cruel Love. In his reply to this letter Sa de Miranda highly praises Montemayor's musical ability, saying that by his singing he could move his audience to joy or tears. It was this talent which gained Montemayor entry to the Courts of Portugal and Spain. Montemayor's devotion to poetry is evident from his published works, and his acknowledgement of the power of love, celebrated in his secular poetry and in *Diana*, is emphatically attested by Fray Bartolomé Ponce: '. . . pues con amores vivió, | y aun con ellos se crió, | en amores se metió, | siempre en

---

[1] The account of Montemayor's life is drawn from Estrada.

ellos contempló, | los amores ensalcó | y de amores escrivió | y por amores murió. |'¹

In the letter to Sa de Miranda Montemayor says that he kept throughout his life the fondness he had acquired in childhood for reading the Holy Scriptures, and his first two published works were religious. His first work, as he himself says in the preface to it, was the *Diálogo espiritual,* published without place or date, and dedicated to King John III of Portugal. His first dated publication was the *Exposición moral sobre el psalmo LXXXVI,* Alcalá, 1548, in prose and verse, dedicated to the Princess Maria of Castile, daughter of Charles V. In the preface to this work Montemayor describes himself as a chorister in the chapel choir of this princess. It is not known at what date Montemayor arrived at the Court of Castile, although he may have accompanied Princess Maria of Portugal, when she came to marry Philip, later King Philip II, in 1543. A sonnet in his *Obras en verso* (1554) is dedicated to the death of this princess (1545).

Montemayor next came under the protection of the Princess Joanna, sister of Maria of Castile and of Philip. A document ratified on 15 November 1549 by her father Charles V when he was in Brussels shows the appointment of Montemayor as 'cantor contravaxo' in her church choir. He drew his annual salary of 40,000 maravedis until June of 1552.

He went to Portugal as usher to Princess Joanna when she married Prince John in 1552. It was probably during his stay at the Portuguese Court that he wrote the letter to Sa de Miranda, in which it appears that he was at this time troubled by his love for Marfida (the name by which he celebrates his mistress in much of his love poetry), and by the intrigues of Court life. Montemayor probably returned to Castile in 1554, when Prince John of Portugal died.

In 1554 appeared the first edition of Montemayor's collected poetical works, usually referred to as his *Cancionero,* published in Antwerp and dedicated to the Portuguese prince and his wife.

After Prince John's death, Princess Joanna became regent of Castile while Philip journeyed to England to marry Queen Mary.

¹ Preface to the *Clara Diana a lo divino,* quoted by Estrada, p. xxi. There is no neat equivalent in English for 'amores', but the passage may be rendered 'thus he lived always in love, and indeed he grew up in an atmosphere of love-affairs, he threw himself into them, he was always thinking about them, he extolled them, wrote of them, and died for them'.

It is possible that Montemayor accompanied Philip, though there is no definite record that he did. If Sireno (Syrenus), the hero of *Diana*, is identified with Montemayor, then certain passages in it, particularly the stanza in 'The song of the Nymph' (71. 31–36) might refer to this journey. The identification of Montemayor with Sireno is disputed, but there is excellent evidence in favour of it in an exchange of letters between Sireno and Rosenio printed at the end of the *Cantos* of Ausias March (which Montemayor translated), where Sireno is positively identified as Montemayor, and where his mistress is called Diana.

The prefatory matter to the edition of Montemayor's religious poems which appeared at Antwerp in 1558 states that the poet had been for a time in Flanders, so the many comments in his works on the evils of absence may refer to this rather than to a journey to England.

Montemayor also spent some time in Valencia. His translation of the poems of Ausias March is dated Valencia, 1560, and *Diana* is dedicated to the Valencian Juan Castellá de Vilanova, lord of Bicorb and Quesa.

By 1559, as appears from a conversation recounted by Fray Bartolomé Ponce, Montemayor had achieved the status of nobleman, 'hidalgo'.

In 1559 or 1560 Montemayor was in Milan, when an edition of *Diana* appeared which could not be sold or printed in that city without the author's licence. He died in Piedmont, probably in 1561. The preface to an edition of *Diana* Madrid, 1622 gives the date of his death as 26 February 1561. Fray Bartolomé Ponce tells us that he was killed by a friend in a duel over a love affair.

Montemayor's most famous work, *Los siete libros de la Diana*, was probably first published in 1559.[1] In it the main story is not completed, and at the end a continuation is promised. Montemayor died before he had time to fulfil this promise, but, not surprisingly, other authors were very ready to undertake the task, and in 1564 there appeared two independent continuations, one by Alonso Perez called, with his uniform lack of imagination,

---

[1] G. Ticknor in his *History of Spanish Literature*, 1849, has misled many Shakespearian scholars as to the title and date of *Diana*. Montemayor's work is never called *Diana Enamorada*, as he names it; this is the title of Gil Polo's continuation. He claimed to possess a copy printed at Valencia in 1542 (iii. 38, n. 5), but this is definitely a 'ghost'. In Book IV of *Diana* Montemayor refers to the widowhood of the Princess Joanna, whose husband died in 1554 (see above).

Segunda parte de la Diana, the other by Gaspar Gil Polo called *Diana Enamorada*. All three parts were translated by Bartholomew Yong and appeared in the handsome folio of 1598, but only Montemayor's and Gil Polo's are here reprinted. Critics agree unanimously that Perez's work is totally without merit. In Greg's words, Perez 'appears to exaggerate all the faults of the original in compensation for the lack of its merits'.[1] The present editor felt no compunction in joining with the curate and the barber in sending Perez's work 'to augment the number of the condemned' in the bonfire of Don Quixote's library,[2] thus saving readers from hours of bewildered boredom.

Enamoured Diana, on the other hand, is a charming work. Gil Polo brings the main story to a satisfactory conclusion, and the stories of his own invention are at least connected, however slightly, with those of Montemayor. His verse has been highly praised by Spanish critics: 'though he was less happy than Montemayor in invention, he far surpassed him in his verses, and almost succeeded in obscuring him'.[3] He was also greatly admired by Cervantes, who not only saves *Enamoured Diana* from the bonfire with the words 'Let . . . that of Gil Polo be kept as charily as if it were Apollo his own work';[4] but also in Calliope's song in *Galatea* (an imitation of the Song of Turia in Book III of *Enamoured Diana*) he devotes a laudatory stanza to Gil Polo.[5] The popularity of *Enamoured Diana* is evinced by the seventeen editions and seven translations (into Latin, French, English, and German) listed by Ferreres.

Both Perez and Gil Polo promised continuations of their work, but neither of these appeared. A work purporting to be a third part of *Diana*, by Hieronymo de Texeda, was published in Paris in 1627, but this, in Greg's words, 'is nothing more than a *rifacimento* of Gil Polo's continuation, altered apparently with a view to its forming a sequel to Perez' work'.[6] Rennert is a good deal harsher, adjudging it 'a work of no merit whatever, and . . .

---

[1] W. W. Greg, *Pastoral Poetry and Pastoral Drama*, 1906, p. 59.

[2] *Don Quixote*, tr. T. Shelton, Library of English Classics, 1900, i. 39 (ch. 6).

[3] Quintana, *Poesias Castellanas*, i. xxxiii, quoted H. A. Rennert, 'The Spanish Pastoral Romances', *PMLA*, vii (1892), 39, note.

[4] *Don Quixote*, loc. cit.

[5] *The Complete Works*, ed. J. Fitzmaurice-Kelly, tr. J. Ormsby, Glasgow, 1901-3, ii. 284-5.

[6] Op. cit., pp. 59-60.

interesting only as being one of the boldest examples of literary theft in the history of any literature'.[1]

Montemayor's work also gave rise to a host of imitations, both in Spain and abroad.[2] The main concern of this edition is the influence of *Diana* in England, but let us turn for a moment to examine its antecedents and progenitors, in Greek, Italian, and Spanish.

It is usually considered that the history of pastoral romance begins with two Greek works, Heliodorus' *Aethiopica* and Longus' *Daphnis and Chloe*. The first is the long and complicated tale of the love of Theagines and Cariclia, and is much concerned with adventure, shipwreck, and the marvellous: it contains practically nothing to give it a claim to the title of pastoral. The second is a comparatively simple tale of foundlings raised by shepherds, and later discovered to be children of rich parents: in this romance such essential features of pastoral as romantic love, love of nature, and the importance of the natural setting are prominent. But the influence of either of these romances on *Diana* is slight. The *Aethiopica* was not rediscovered until 1526, when the library of Mathias Corvin at Buda was pillaged,[3] the *editio princeps* is that of Basle, 1534, and it was translated into French by Amyot in 1547. Montemayor probably, however, knew this work, for it was the talk of Europe, and an anonymous translation into Spanish appeared in 1554.[4] *Daphnis and Chloe* can claim even less direct influence, since it was not widely read until Amyot's translation appeared in 1559, and 'By the time it became generally known the main features of renaissance pastoral were already fixed, and in motive and treatment alike it was alien to the spirit that animated the fashionable masterpieces'.[5] The modern pastoral romance is in effect a new birth from the 'blending of the eclogue with the mythological tale',[6] and although it is usually fathered on Sannazaro, the responsibility more properly lies with Boccaccio and his *Ameto*. The main intent of the *Ameto* is religious and

[1] 'The Spanish Pastoral Romances', *PMLA*, vii (1892), 39.

[2] See H. A. Rennert, op. cit., for a list of the Spanish imitations, with criticism and analyses.

[3] H. Genouy, L'"Arcadia" de Sidney dans ses rapports avec l'"Arcadia" de Sannazaro et la 'Diana' de Montemayor, Montpellier, 1928, p. 25.

[4] G. Ticknor, History of Spanish Literature, 1849, i. 223, note.

[5] W. W. Greg, op. cit., pp. 12–13.

[6] Ibid., p. 13.

allegorical rather than pastoral, but it has three features which make it important in the history of pastoral romance. First, it is set among woods and glades, its characters are nymphs and shepherds, and shepherds' festivals play an important part. Second, it introduces a succession of tales (while resting during the heat of the day at the festival, the nymph Lia, Ameto's beloved, and six other surpassingly beautiful nymphs tell the stories of their lives and loves, each of which is concluded by a song). The third important feature is 'the manner in which, undisturbed by its religious and allegorical machinery, it introduces us to a purely sensual and pagan paradise, in which love with all its pains and raptures reigns supreme'.[1]

Some hundred years later, Sannazaro, apparently with the works of Boccaccio, Petrarch, Ovid, Virgil, and Theocritus in front of him, wrote his *Arcadia*, arranged in twelve *prose* and *poesie*, with a proem and a final address 'A la Sampogna' (To the rustic flute) in which he outlines the scope of his work. As far as novel-writing is concerned, the *Arcadia* is no advance on the *Ameto*: the action is minimal, there is little or nothing which could be described as development of plot, character, or emotion, and though we hear the pains of love lamented, we are not allowed to see them inflicted. The Shepherdesses make only the most fleeting appearance on the horizon, and even this concession is made under the direct influence of Boccaccio. The great achievement of the *Arcadia* lies in Sannazaro's ability to convey an enchanting sense of the beauty of nature and the delights of the shepherd's life. We cannot resent the slender narrative while we are beguiled by the inviting cool of trees and fountains, there to be entertained by sweet songs, shepherds' sports, the picture of their piety, tales of hunting, and elegiac reminiscences of their loves. Indeed, the theme of Sannazaro's work is emotion recollected and commemorated in the tranquillity of the hills and groves of Arcadia. He tells his rustic flute that its proper place and function is to be played by shepherds, 'teaching the answering woods to resound the name of thy lady, and to lament bitterly with thee the harsh and unexpected chance of her untimely death'.[2]

A Spanish translation of the *Arcadia* was published at Toledo in

---

[1] W. W. Greg, *Pastoral Poetry and Pastoral Drama*, 1906, p. 43.
[2] *Arcadia*, a cura di E. Carrara, Turin, 1948, p. 163.

1547, and although the intent and effect of *Diana* are very different from those of the Italian romance, Montemayor is heavily and obviously indebted to Sannazaro. It is beyond the scope of this introduction to attempt a complete comparison, but a few points of similarity and departure may be noticed.

The pastoral setting of hills, trees, and crystalline fountains has been taken by Montemayor from Sannazaro, but is more lightly sketched; Montemayor does not show the deep love for nature which is apparent in the *Arcadia*. The 'pathetic fallacy' shown in the belief in the sympathy of inanimate objects with human emotions is perpetuated in *Diana*, but a step towards realism in setting has been made by discarding the classical features of pastoralism which Sannazaro allows to appear in the priest's invocation, 'do not permit our unworthy eyes ever to see in the woods the avenging nymphs, nor naked Diana bathing in the chill waters, nor at midday the wild Faun, when returning tired from the hunt, he runs enraged over the broad fields under the burning sun'.[1]

The sports proper to shepherds are another feature of the pastoral world, but whereas Sannazaro devotes considerable space to describing them, as, for example, in *Prosa XI*, Montemayor merely refers to them, using featness in such arts as a touchstone of the worthy and 'lovely' shepherd (cf. p. 25).

Montemayor takes from Sannazaro the magic water whose property it is to induce forgetfulness of unhappy love, and also the magic characteristics of Felicia and Alfeus. It is amusing to find that Sannazaro's 'famous old woman, most sagacious mistress of magic artifices',[2] who is described as a black witch, should become the wicked *male* conjurer Alfeus, while the wise priest-shepherd Enareto, with whom the 'famous old woman' is contrasted, becomes the sage Lady Felicia.

The most striking of Montemayor's departures from the example set by Sannazaro consists in the part played by women. In *Diana*, the women have advanced so far to the foreground that the men sometimes seem little more than objects for their affections and emotional torments. This is a complete reversal of the roles of the sexes in the *Arcadia*.

Genouy well summarizes the essential differences between the two authors: 'The pastoral atmosphere is then less marked and

[1] Ed. cit., p. 24.   [2] Ibid., p. 85.

more artificial in Montemayor. The Spanish author prefers to interest himself in the psychology of love; he does not limit himself to the expression of amorous complaints . . . nor to the mere evocation of the past, he makes his characters speak and act.'[1]

For inspiration and guidance in his delineation of amorous passions and in the conduct of stories, Montemayor turned to Boccaccio (whose *Decameron*, *Ameto*, and *Fiammetta* all had something to offer him) and to other *novellieri* such as Bandello, from whom he takes the story of Felismena. Genouy believes that his chief debt to the Italian *novellieri* lies in the idea of a succession of stories set in a slender framework: 'Thinking to find in this a source of interest for the reader, he had had the idea of providing a connecting thread, however fragile, between the various stories.'[2] The superficial device which binds the stories together may be fragile, but Montemayor's narrative skill has developed other methods of unification more interesting and stronger than the mere framework.[3]

Montemayor's romance differs sharply from medieval courtly romance and chivalric romance in his determination to sanction only the most virtuous aspects of the passion of love. He was influenced in his philosophy of love by Leone Ebreo, whose *Dialoghi d'Amore* provide the material for the discussions of love in Book IV of *Diana*, and by Castiglione.

In the native literature of the peninsular Montemayor could have found some hints for his own romance in the Portuguese *Menina e moça* of Bernardim Ribeiro, which itself shows the influence of Sannazaro's *Arcadia*, and in the vast chivalric romances such as *Amadis* and *Palmerin*, in which shepherds had already begun to mingle with more aristocratic characters.[4] Montemayor seems to find nothing incongruous in the introduction of knights and ladies to the pastoral scene: a licence which was approved and developed by Sidney in his *Arcadia*. We might also trace some influence of the native picaresque style in the wanderings of the various characters, and also in the opportunity for the introduction of picaresque adventures which Montemayor firmly, but it

[1] L'*"Arcadia' de Sidney dans ses rapports avec l'"Arcadia' de Sannazaro et la 'Diana' de Montemayor*, Montpellier, 1928, p. 80.
[2] Ibid., p. 120.   [3] See below, pp. xxvii–xxx.
[4] e.g. in the ninth book of *Amadis* and the first two parts of *Don Florisel de Niquea*. See Cervantes, *The Complete Works*, ed. J. Fitzmaurice-Kelly, tr. J. Ormsby, Glasgow, 1901–3, II. xx.

seems regretfully, rejects, where Felismena 'trotted directly to the Court, passing by the way many accidents, which (if time would give me leave to tell them) woulde not make you laugh a little to heare them' (p. 93).

From the fusion of these diverse antecedents Montemayor produced a masterpiece which provided inspiration for many authors and gave entertainment to a wide public for many years.

ii. *The Reputation of Pastoral Romance*

There is no dispute that *Diana* is a fine example of the genre of pastoral romance, but the appeal of this genre has fluctuated considerably. As early as Cervantes and Sorel there were those who revolted against its artificiality, although these two dissenters from prevailing taste also found something to admire and even imitate in the objects of their criticism.

In *Don Quixote*, even though Cervantes grants Montemayor 'the honour of being the best of that kind', he wishes 'that all that which treats of the wise Felicia, and of the enchanted water, be taken away, and also all the longer verses'.[1] In *The Dogs' Colloquy* his criticisms are even more general and far-reaching. Here his purpose is to show that the shepherds of pastoral romance bear no relation to the shepherds of real life, and he speaks disparagingly of 'the swoons of Sereno and the repentance of Diana', and 'that structure of intrigues and . . . that labyrinth of difficulties'.[2] Yet even in his indictment of the faults of romances, we feel his recognition of the charm they held for him, which worked so strongly upon him that he himself wrote a pastoral romance, *Galatea*.

From this I came to comprehend, what I think everybody must believe, that all those books are dreams well written to amuse the idle, and not truth at all, for, had they been so, there would have been some trace among my shepherds of that most happy life and of those pleasant meadows, spacious woods, sacred mountains, lovely gardens, clear streams and crystal fountains, and of those lovers' wooings as virtuous as they were eloquent, and of that swoon of the shepherd's in this spot, of the shepherdess's in that, of the bagpipe of one shepherd sounding here, and the flageolet of the other sounding there.[3]

[1] Tr. T. Shelton, Library of English Classics, 1900, i. 39 (ch. 6).
[2] *The Complete Works*, ed. J. Fitzmaurice-Kelly, tr. J. Ormsby, Glasgow, 1901-3, viii. 163.   [3] Ibid., p. 164.

In his anti-romance, *The Extravagant Shepherd* (1627), Sorel shows an equally critical spirit in Clarimond's attack upon *Diana*'s lack of order and verisimilitude,[1] but sweeps away his own objections by means of Philiris's charmingly high-handed answer to Clarimond: 'what he hath alleadged against *Diana of Montemajor* is of no great weight. Though the order of it should be disturbed, yet were the thing no less pleasant, and as for the Fables and Enchantments in it, all's pardonable.'[2]

Far different from these affectionate strictures are the distaste for and lack of understanding of pastoral romance shown by some more recent critics. One wonders why Atkinson undertook an extensive study of the form when he concludes that it is 'difficult to see the merits of Jorge de Montemayor and his school',[3] and C. V. Wedgwood shows a disdainful ignorance of and prejudice against the genre, when she classes *Diana* with *Huon of Bordeaux*, *Amadis of Gaul*, *Palmerin of England*, and *Guy of Warwick*, saying that 'A more fashionable or more intelligent public was pleased with *Don Quixote*',[4] and when she speaks of *Astrée* as 'that asphyxiating pastoral romance from France'.[5] Even critics more attuned to pastoral literature in general show a revulsion of feeling and lack of sympathy for the romance. With contemptuous irritation Reynier writes of 'Montemayor's shepherds who . . . forever sing their woes without doing anything to cure them',[6] and Greg completes his study of the form with these damning words: 'It remained throughout nerveless and diffuse, and, in spite of much incidental beauty, was habitually wanting in interest, except in so far as it renounced its pastoral nature.'[7]

Yet there are modern critics who show a truly sympathetic understanding of the attractions of pastoral romance, notably Miss M. M. Lascelles, who vigorously maintains that the form presents 'An ideal world—yes; but not the world of enervating daydream',[8] and in no age have such supporters been totally lacking.

[1] Tr. John Davies, 2nd ed. 1654, 3H3ᵛ.
[2] Ibid., 3K1ᵛ.
[3] 'Studies in Literary Decadence', *Bulletin of Spanish Studies*, iv (1927), 126.
[4] *Seventeenth Century English Literature*, 1950, p. 24.
[5] Ibid., pp. 24–25.
[6] G. Reynier, *Le Roman sentimental*, Paris, 1908, p. 312.
[7] *Pastoral Poetry and Pastoral Drama*, 1906, p. 154.
[8] 'Shakespeare's Pastoral Comedy', *More Talking of Shakespeare*, ed. J. Garrett, 1959, p. 76.

In what then does the charm of the pastoral romance consist? From the earliest days of pastoral literature men's minds have been captivated by the idea of a golden age when the world had the innocence of youth; when the whole earth and its inhabitants carried clouds of glory ever about them. It seemed that essential qualities of this golden age were simplicity and freedom from care, so the man caught in the toils of business and ambition in city and court turned longingly to the apparently simple and carefree life of the shepherd. This aspect of the charm of pastoral has been made immortal by Shakespeare's Forest of Arden, where they 'fleet the time carelessly, as they did in the golden world', and by Sidney's Arcadian Shepherd 'piping, as though he should never be old'. But this longing for golden innocence, this recognition of a better place existing at some other time, should not be construed as mere escapism seeking an outlet in pastoral literature. Even Greg's melodiously expressed idea of the origin of pastoral song in 'the yearning of the tired soul to escape'[1] is too easily converted by other critics to a condescending statement that 'Men took the pastoral in order to flee for a moment into Arcadia, to clothe in pleasant vagueness confessions of the delightful miseries of calf-love'.[2] Those who appreciate pastoral literature recognize that the golden world is not a simple anodyne or intoxicant, but a creation of the artistic imagination performing its highest function of poetic imitation of the ideal behind nature. Those who prefer Nature's brazen world of 'hard but ultimately deceiving fact' should not attempt to enter the Renaissance poet's world.[3]

The second distinguishing feature of most pastoral literature and all pastoral romance is a preoccupation with love. It is on the grounds of the universal and universally agreeable nature of this passion that d'Urfé bases the defence of his romance: 'If then to love is the true and natural action of our soul, who is the severe critic who will be able to find fault with me for going over in my memory the dear and sweet thoughts of the most agreeable actions that this Soul has ever produced in me?'[4] All aspects of the sorrows and joys of love can be appropriately sung in pastoral

---

[1] *Pastoral Poetry and Pastoral Drama*, 1906, p. 6.
[2] H. E. Cory, 'The Golden Age of Spenserian Pastoral', *PMLA*, xxv (1910), 241
[3] Sidney, *An Apology for Poetry*, ed. G. Shepherd, 1965, pp. 61, 100, 156.
[4] *L'Astrée*, Paris, 1647, iii, 'L'autheur A la Riviere de Lignon'.

verse, and appropriately discussed (even philosophically) in pastoral prose. Moreover, the atmosphere of the pastoral world is peculiarly suitable to the nurture and flowering of love. Fontenelle describes well the essential connexion between the two chief characteristics of pastoral, although he reduces the ideal innocence and simplicity of the golden world to a very human inclination for laziness:

> This is exactly what one imagines in the pastoral life. It will not admit ambition, nor anything that agitates the heart too violently; hence laziness has room to be content. But that sort of life, by its idleness and tranquillity, gives birth to love more easily than any other, or at least favours it more; and what sort of love? A love more simple, because one's mind is not so dangerously subtle; more diligent, because one is not busied with any other passion; more modest, because one is scarcely acquainted with vanity; more faithful, because when the liveliness of the imagination is less exercised, one has also fewer causes of uneasiness, of aversion, of caprice; that is to say, in a word, love purged of everything alien and faulty that the excesses of human whims have mingled with it.[1]

This refinement and purification of love has its counterpart in the refined and polished style of pastoral romance, but whereas the language is fashionable and sophisticated, the passion has been shorn of its normal complications. It is perhaps this contrast which leads Empson to say that 'The essential trick of the old pastoral . . . was to make simple people express strong feelings (felt as the most universal subject, something fundamentally true about everybody) in learned and fashionable language (so that you wrote about the best subject in the best way)',[2] and to conclude that the essence of the pastoral process is the 'putting the complex into the simple'.[3] Small wonder that a literature which presented the innocence of rustic simplicity combined with the most civilized polish of the highest society, and the most general and agreeable of all the passions without extraneous complications, should have been popular.

Pastoral romance is particularly suited to the full demonstration of these ideas. Verse provides an outlet for the direct expression of strong feeling; prose is the natural vehicle for the sophisticated

---

[1] Fontenelle, 'Discours sur la nature de l'églogue', Œuvres, Paris, 1818, iii. 57.
[2] Some Versions of Pastoral, 1935, p. 11.
[3] Ibid., p. 23.

discussion of the nature of love; the sheep, the whispering trees, the crystal streams and fountains are a constant reminder of the golden world; the very complexity of the plot is resolved in the essential simplicity of the unifying theme of love.

The world of pastoral romance is closely akin to the world of romantic comedy. Both share the charm of happy endings, of the feeling that past mistakes are not irretrievable. As Miss Lascelles points out, in pastoral romance, and notably in *Diana*, the benevolent oracle becomes the symbol of the second chance.[1] What notion could be more appealing to mortals constantly regretting past mistakes and ever incapable of undoing past actions?

These attractions have been sufficient to win admirers for the pastoral romance in all ages. 'These are Academies for the *Lover*, Schools of War for the *Souldier*, and Cabinets for the *Statesman*; they are the correctives of *passion*, the restoratives of *conversation*; they are the entertainments of the *sound*, and divertisements of the *sick*; in a word, the most delightful accommodations of *civill* life.'[2] Few critics are so inclusively and indiscriminately laudatory as John Davies of Kidwelly, but even more impressive are the tributes of those who see the faults of these works and still cannot resist their charm. Thus in the eighteenth century Florian finds that his heart capitulates even while his critical sense objects: '*Diana* is one of those works in which taste is often wounded, but in which the heart almost always rejoices.'[3] And in the twentieth century the same almost indefinable enchantment still enthralls the mind: 'For such romance, with its hint of improvisation to please a particular audience, seems to engage our imagination in such a way that, if the narrator cannot finish, it becomes an office of friendship to dream out his dream for him.'[4]

III. *A Brief Examination of* Diana

The narrative structure of Montemayor's *Diana* is neat and simple. There is a main story, the thread of which runs through all seven books, and which is still unresolved at the end, and there are three sub-stories, which are related in the first three books and

[1] 'Shakespeare's Pastoral Comedy', *More Talking of Shakespeare*, ed. J. Garrett, 1959, p. 75.
[2] H. d'Urfé, *Astrea*, tr. J. Davies, 1657–8, 'To the Reader', ii, A2ᵛ.
[3] 'Essai sur la Pastorale', *Estelle*, 2nd ed., Paris, 1788, p. 23, note.
[4] M. M. Lascelles, op. cit., p. 74.

resolved in the last three. The link between these stories is provided partly by the association of the characters, but mostly by
Felicia and her court. The central part played by Felicia is recognized by the devotion of the fourth book to her. Unfortunately,
since the edition of Valladolid in 1561, the balance of the structure
has been obscured by the printer's insertion of the Abindaraez
story into the fourth book, a flaw which Estrada has remedied by
printing this insertion as a footnote.

The stories are further unified by the recurrence of the themes
of love, suffering, constancy and inconstancy, faith and jealousy,
and disguise and deceit. The whole work, both narration and
discussion, is an examination of love, its causes and its effects.

The first appeal of Montemayor's *Diana* does not, however, lie
in its presentation of a philosophy of love, but in its narrative art,
and (to a lesser extent in translation) in its poetry.

The chief elements of Montemayor's narrative art are his ability
to sustain interest through suspense, his easy and economical
conduct of swiftly moving, multifarious action, his lively characterization (particularly of women), and his keen ear for the conversation of lovers.

The main story and its primary theme are presented in the
Argument. Diana is loved by Syrenus, whose love she returns,
and Sylvanus, whom she hates. When Syrenus is forced to be
absent for a while 'time, and *Dianas* hart with time were chaunged,
who then was married to another Shepherd called *Delius*, burying
him, whom she had but of late so greatly loved, in unjust oblivion'
(p. 10). This story, already in the past, is related in the first two
books through Syrenus's soliloquy, through conversation, and
through 'The song of the Nymph'. Interest in this story is sustained by the constant presence of Syrenus and Sylvanus, by the
reversal of their love in the fourth book, and by the introduction
of Diana herself and new light on her character and conduct in the
fifth book.

The theme of loyalty and fickleness is explored more thoroughly
in the sub-stories of the first and second books, those of Selvagia
and Felismena. There is such a wealth of examples of trifling
and inconstant love in the first story, that even Selvagia, in the
midst of her suffering, seems to find the situation amusing.
Finally, when Alanius has transferred his affection from Ismenia
to Selvagia and back to Ismenia, Ismenia hers from Alanius to

Montanus, Montanus his from Ismenia to Selvagia, and even Selvagia, through Ismenia's deceit, hers from Ismenia to Alanius, Selvagia summarizes: 'And it was the strangest thing in the world to heare how *Alanius* sighing saide, Ah my *Ismenia*; and how *Ismenia* saide, Ah my *Montanus*; and how *Montanus* said, Ah my *Selvagia*; and how *Selvagia* saide, Ah my *Alanius*' (p. 42). The relatively light tone of the story is captured in the charming song 'Foolish love' (p. 47). This treatment of the theme provides a happy contrast with the sighs and tears of Syrenus, but it does not upset the unity of impression.

There is only one example of inconstancy in Felismena's story, but it was sufficiently striking for Shakespeare to dub his representation of Don Felix, Proteus.

Both these stories end abruptly, leaving the reader in the same bewilderment and suspense as the constant lovers, Selvagia and Felismena.

The death of Celia in Felismena's tale prepares the way for the darker atmosphere and apparently more hopeless conclusion of Belisa's love-story. Perhaps Belisa deserves greater suffering because she is guilty of a certain kind of inconstancy in the division of her love between Arsenius and Arsileus.

Montemayor has also shown his narrative art by varying his stories of love not only in atmosphere but also in setting: Selvagia is a shepherdess, Felismena a great lady, and Belisa a village maiden.

At this point, in Book IV, he pauses to extol constancy and beauty in women, and to discuss the nature of love. Through its wealth of associations with the highest flights of Renaissance Neoplatonic theories of love this book provides an essential background of ideal conduct in love against which the actual behaviour of the all-too-human lovers may be measured, and in its original form is quite short enough for the reader still to be able to keep clear the narrative threads of the first three books and to maintain his interest in the fates of the lovers.

In the last three books Montemayor in various ways solves the problems of the lovers who appeared in the first three books, but to keep up the interest he introduces new characters whose stories expand themes only lightly touched upon earlier. Diana's late appearance leads us to dwell upon the dilemma of divided loyalties, the hideous spectre of jealousy, and the vagaries of fortune.

The story of Danteus and Duarda further illustrates the theme of divided loyalties, and the story of Amarillis and Filemon the theme of jealousy.

A continuation is, of course, promised, but it is not necessary to the completeness of impression of the book. The problem of Diana and Syrenus can only be stated; it cannot by natural means be brought to a happy conclusion. It may be argued that it was Montemayor's intention to show that love is not natural, just as it is not governed by reason. Certainly his recurrent use of deceit, disguise, and magic, both in the complication and resolution of the plots, is notable.

That Montemayor was capable of holding attention without recourse to the tricks of fairy-tales is obvious from his powers of characterization. His men (except perhaps for the page Fabius) are shadowy, but his women are distinct and lively individuals.

Montemayor's heroines are made real and interesting not by their perfections, but by his delighted and sympathetic recognition of their feminine flaws, and by their possession of a certain hard-headed practicality. From her first appearance Selvagia's realistic insistence that all things may change contrasts favourably with Syrenus's and Sylvanus's idealistic and extravagant complaints. Every woman feelingly responds to her denunciation of the impossible demands that men make of the women upon whom they condescend to bestow their love. But perhaps even more engaging than Selvagia's practical wisdom is the very excusable malice she displays in her triumph over Ismenia, particularly in her comments upon and answer to Ismenia's letter (pp. 39–40). Ismenia herself invites our sympathetic interest by her dismay at the loss of Alanius's love, her age-old expedient to regain it, and the predictable result of this.

Felismena's character is deeper and richer than Shakespeare's representation of it in Julia, and Rosina is even more firmly sketched than Lucetta. Felismena combines the youthful fire and spirit of Julia with the sense of humour and capacity for feeling of Viola. Just as Selvagia becomes more real because she can see something ridiculous in the tangle of their loves, so too Felismena is more human because she can laugh reminiscently at the accidents that befell her on her way to Court, as well as relive the sufferings of her love for Don Felix and the pain she felt for him in his rejection by Celia.

Belisa, too, becomes more than the picture of a sleeping beauty as we see her succumbing to the flattery of Arsenius's love and gifts, then carefully manœuvring Arsileus into a declaration of his love.

Inevitably Diana, who makes no personal appearance until the fifth book, seems the most stiffly ideal of Montemayor's heroines, but as soon as she enters the scene we are assured of her essential femininity by her dog-in-the-manger jealousy of Sylvanus's new love for Selvagia. We admire the self-control with which she hides her emotions, but sympathize with their cause:

> This did *Diana* speake with a gracious smile, although she laughed not so much in minde at these things, nor with so good a hart as they thought. For though she once loved *Syrenus* more then her owne life, and despised *Sylvanus*, as nothing so much, yet it greeved her more, that *Sylvanus* had forgotten her for the love of another, whose sight he now enjoyed every day with great contentment of his newe love, then that *Syrenus* had freed himselfe out of her love, whom nowe no new affection mooved (p. 218).

It is the loving insight into feminine nature which Montemayor reveals in touches such as this that constantly engages our interest.

Montemayor's ability to capture the subtle notes of the conversation of lovers can be seen throughout in such passages as the reported conversations of Syrenus and Diana, Belisa's wooing of Arsileus, and the quarrels of Amarillis and Filemon, and of Danteus and Duarda.

The main charm of Gil Polo's *Enamoured Diana* lies in the poetry, and in his allegorical and thematic presentation of his ideas of love. His narratives are sufficiently interesting, and his characters, drawn mainly from hints in Montemayor, adequate, but above all it is the atmosphere of joyous fulfilment of love which makes his work appealing.

IV. Diana *in England*

The only complete translation of the three *Diana*s into English is that of Bartholomew Yong, finished in May 1583, but not published until 1598. In 1596 Thomas Wilson translated Montemayor's work, dedicating it to the Earl of Southampton, but of this only the first book survives, in a manuscript presented by Wilson to Fulke Greville between the years 1614 and 1620 (after

Greville became Chancellor of the Exchequer and before he was created Lord Brooke), with a promise of more to come: 'S͏ͬ, when the rest of these my chyldish exercises can be found, yo͏ͬ Honor only, shall have the vse of them, for that I know yow will well esteeme of them, because that your most noble and never enough honored frend S͏ͬ Phillipp Siddney did very much affect and imitate the excellent Author there of.'[1]

In 1652 we find some of the tales from Gil Polo's *Enamoured Diana* appearing in R.C.'s *The Troublesome and hard adventures in love*, which purports to be a translation from Cervantes. The structure is similar to Gil Polo's work, in the method of telling the stories, in drawing all the lovers to Felicia's palace, and in the final discourse of love and celebration of the marriages. Two of the stories come directly from Gil Polo: that of Marcelio and Alcida, and that of Ismenia and Lexander (Montanus in Gil Polo).[2] R.C. acknowledges Montemayor's invention of Felicia, but since he excuses himself from describing her and her palace in almost exactly the terms which Gil Polo uses, there is no reason to suppose that he drew directly on Montemayor.

In 1737 there appeared, bound together with Lope de Vega's *The Pilgrim*, an anonymous translation of *Diana. A Pastoral Novel. From the Spanish of George de Montemayor*. The translator claims attention for his labour not by any reference to Sidney, but on the basis of the fame of *Diana* in France and Spain. The texts of Montemayor and Gil Polo have been tailored to 149 duodecimo pages, a curtailment which the translator defends by saying that this 'Retrenchment' is 'only of such Parts as are purely in the *Spanish* Taste, and would be neither beautiful nor intelligible in any other Language'.[3] Most of the poetry has gone, and that which remains is a mere paraphrase or *précis* of the original in eighteenth-century dress. For example, Diana's 124-line song 'O Eies, that see not him, who look'd on yow' is reduced to five quatrains headed 'This SONNET may be sung to the Tune of *The Bonny*

---

[1] British Museum Add. MS. 18638, ff. 4ᵛ–5ʳ. This manuscript has been printed by Sir H. Thomas, *Revue Hispanique*, l (1920), 367–418.

[2] See also Dale Randall, '*The Troublesome and Hard Adventures in Love*: An English Addition to the Bibliography of *Diana*', *Bulletin of Hispanic Studies*, xxxviii (1961), 154–8. The same author's book *The Golden Tapestry* (Durham, North Carolina, 1963) devotes pp. 68–83 to a discussion of *Diana* and its reception and influence in England.

[3] *Diana. A Pastoral Novel*, 1737, 'The Preface to the Reader', pp. 135–6.

Broom.[1] Book IV has lost the description of the palace, Orpheus's Song, and the story of Abindaraez; and the whole of *Enamoured Diana* is represented by the story of Alcida and the death of Delius squeezed into the end of Book VII. The translator has altered some names, but not consistently, which becomes confusing. However, anyone dissatisfied with this treatment of Gil Polo could by 1739 have bought the Spanish text of *Diana Enamorada* published in London by T. Woodward.

There are other occasional translations from *Diana*, such as Googe's *Eglogs* (in Eglog VII he follows Montemayor so closely that it can more properly be called translation than adaptation), Sidney's two translations in *Certaine Sonnets*, and Southey's specimen translation of 'Cabellos, quánta mudança'.[2] Yong's mention of Edward Paston's efforts as being the best of all 'that ever yet I heard translate these Bookes' (p. 6) implies that there were several translations in existence in 1598, but not even Paston's 'leaves' survive.

It should also be remembered that the influence and reputation of *Diana* in England were not dependent on English translations alone. Some, such as Sidney, were acquainted with it in the original; others, such as William Drummond of Hawthornden, read it in French,[3] of which there were several versions available from an early date—Edward Banister possessed that of Colin and Chapuis in 1582. Anybody interested in languages would learn from John Eliot's *Ortho-epia Gallica* (1593) that the best Spanish poets were '*Boscan, Grenade, Garcilasso* and *Montmaior*', but would be discouraged from searching for a translation,[4] and in trying to learn the language the student of Spanish would find the first and by far the largest group in Minsheu's Spanish grammar of illustrative 'Wordes, Phrases, Sentences, and Proverbes' drawn from *Diana*,[5] and would certainly recognize the importance of a book which took precedence over such popular works as *Celestina, Lazaro de Tormes*, and Marcus Aurelius.

Perhaps the most important source of all of *Diana*'s fame and influence in sixteenth-century England was Sidney's use of it as an

---

[1] *Diana. A Pastoral Novel*, 1737, pp. 144–5.

[2] *Letters written during a short residence in Spain and Portugal*, Bristol, 1797, pp. 89–91.

[3] B. H. Newdigate, *Michael Drayton and his Circle*, 1941, p. 174.

[4] Pp. 31–32.

[5] *A Dictionarie in Spanish and English . . . by Ric. Percival Gent. Now enlarged . . .* by John Minsheu, 1599, part 2, pp. 75–78.

inspiration and model for his *Arcadia*. His debt was widely recognized and frequently acknowledged, both explicitly and by imitation of *Diana* in Arcadian prose fiction. In 1599 John Hoskins stated the three main sources of the *Arcadia*: 'For the web, as it were, of his story, he followed three: Heliodorus in Greek, Sannazarius' *Arcadia* in Italian, and *Diana* [by] de Montemayor in Spanish.'[1] In 1598 the pointed terms in which Yong recommends 'this particular subject of DIANA' (p. 3) to Lady Rich, Sidney's Stella, are an unmistakable acknowledgement of the connexion, which Wilson elaborates in his dedication of the first book of *Diana* to Fulke Greville, Sidney's closest friend:

> Sr Phillipp Siddney did very much affect and imitate the excellent Author there of, whoe might well tearme his booke Diana (as the Sister of Apollo, \&/ the twinn borne wth him) as his Arcadia (wch by yor noble vertue the world so hapily enioyes) might well have had the name of Phoebus, for never was our age lightned with two Starres of such high and eminent witt, as are the bookes of these two excelling Authors, wch doe resemble one an other as the Sonne & the Moone doth, but with this contrariety, that as ye Moone takes her light from the Sonne: soe heere this Sonne taking some light from this Moone grewe much more resplendent, then that, from whence it had it.[2]

In 1607 Markham, in the first part of *The English Arcadia*, excuses his imitation of Sidney by pointing out 'were our age but blest with his living breath, he would himselfe confesse the honie hee drew both from *Heliodorus*, and *Diana*',[3] and in 1613, in the second part of *The English Arcadia*, he re-emphasizes Sidney's knowledge of and debt to these works.[3]

In 1644, in the *Areopagitica*, the two books, Sidney's *Arcadia* and Montemayor's *Diana*, come together to Milton's mind when he is considering 'all that is delightfull to man',[4] and he describes village ballads as 'the Countrymans *Arcadia's* and his *Monte Mayors*'.[5] Even in 1649, when he is bent on attacking Charles for his use of Pamela's prayer, thoughts of the *Arcadia* lead him naturally to *Diana*: 'For he certainly whose mind could serve him to seek a Christian prayer out of a Pagan Legend, and assume it

---

[1] *Directions for Speech and Style*, ed. H. H. Hudson, Princeton University Press. 1935, p. 41.
[2] British Museum Add. MS. 18638, ff. 4^v–5^r.
[3] 'To the Reader.'
[4] *Complete Prose Works*, Yale University Press, 1959, ii. 523.
[5] Op. cit. ii. 525.

for his own, might gather up the rest God knows from whence; one perhaps out of the French *Astræa*, another out of the Spanish *Diana*; *Amadis* and *Palmerin* could hardly scape him.'[1]

The details of Sidney's well-attested debt to *Diana* have been examined by T. P. Harrison and H. Genouy.[2] The parallels cited and borrowings alleged by these scholars are numerous, but they vary considerably in importance and conclusiveness, some being so common to romance that they can scarcely be considered as showing the direct influence of *Diana*. However, taken all together the evidence amassed is impressive.[3] But despite the work of these scholars in support of the sixteenth- and seventeenth-century testimony of the influence of *Diana* on Sidney, it still sometimes happens that readers overlook or ignore the debt; two influential critics even go so far as to deny that the *Arcadia* is pastoral,[4] while yet another suggests that Sidney found nothing in *Diana* that he could not just as well have learnt from Sannazaro.[5] I believe, however, that both the *Old* and *New Arcadia*s, different though they are in structure, scope, and intention, are essentially pastoral, in that both are fundamentally concerned with the examination and celebration of love in an ideal world, which is the distinguishing characteristic of pastoral romance. Furthermore, it is unlikely that Sidney could have arrived at the large design and sophisticated manner of the *Old Arcadia*, far less have conceived the tightly knit complexity and grand inclusiveness of the *New*

---

[1] *Complete Prose Works*, Yale University Press, 1959, iii. 366-7.

[2] T. P. Harrison, 'A Source of Sidney's "Arcadia" ', *University of Texas Studies in English*, vi (Dec. 1926), 53-71; H. Genouy, *L'"Arcadia' de Sidney dans ses rapports avec l'"Arcadia' de Sannazaro et la 'Diana' de Montemayor*, Montpellier, 1928, especially pp. 112-17.

[3] Most recently W. R. Davis ('A Map of Arcadia: Sidney's Romance in Its Tradition', *Sidney's Arcadia*, New Haven and London, 1965, pp. 1-179) has used *Diana* in support of his contention that the *Arcadia* is a pastoral romance and not a heroic poem, but I find myself in considerable disagreement with his opinions about both works. K. Myrick's discussions of the *Arcadia* and incidental references to *Diana* (*Sir Philip Sidney as a Literary Craftsman*, 2nd ed., University of Nebraska Press, 1965) are much more sensible, and it is a pity that Davis did not read John Buxton's chapter on the *Arcadia* in *Elizabethan Taste* (1963) before he set out to argue that romance and heroic poem are mutually exclusive.

[4] E. M. W. Tillyard, *The English Epic and its Background*, 1954, p. 296; J. F. Danby, *Poets on Fortune's Hill*, 1952, pp. 47-48.

[5] C. S. Lewis, *English Literature in the Sixteenth Century*, Oxford, 1954, p. 333. Recently D. Kalstone has made excellent use of Sannazaro in interpreting Sidney's Arcadian poetry, in *Sidney's Poetry: Contexts and Interpretations*, Cambridge, Mass., 1965.

Arcadia, directly from Sannazaro's slender and relatively simple romance, even with the help of Heliodorus, had he not known the intermediary philosophic, narrative, and dramatic enrichment of the form provided by the *Dianas*.

In structure, the *Old Arcadia* is more similar to Gil Polo's work than to Montemayor's, not only in the division into five books, but also in the didactic opening of each book, and in the grouping and function of the poems. The third Eclogues, in particular, recall Gil Polo's Books IV and V, in the mingling of nuptial rejoicings with the sadness of Philisides in the *Old Arcadia*, and the misfortunes of Narcisus and Turianus in *Enamoured Diana*. However, Sidney's decision to tighten the structure of his earlier work by presenting it as a five-act tragi-comedy would hardly have been prompted by anything in Gil Polo, but might have been suggested to him by his appreciation of Montemayor's talent for creating realistic characters and allowing them to reveal themselves dramatically. In the *Old Arcadia* Sidney's ambiguous attitude towards the nature and value of love and marriage, his perception of possible discrepancies between actual and ideal behaviour, his irony, and his comedy[1] are also all much more closely akin to Montemayor's manner than to Gil Polo's, although here the tone of Sidney's laughter is different from that of Montemayor's.

When in 1584 Sidney began the radical revision of his pastoral romance cast in the mould of a tragi-comedy into a heroical-pastoral poem in prose in the manner of the romances, he re-read not only Heliodorus but also Montemayor.[2] As S. L. Wolff has shown,[3] many of the structural changes in the *New Arcadia* probably derive from Sidney's enthusiasm for Greek romance, but in at least one alteration in narrative technique Sidney could also have learnt much from Montemayor. In the *New Arcadia* far more of the action of the main and subsidiary stories is narrated by the characters, rather than by the author as in the *Old Arcadia*.

---

[1] These aspects of Sidney's earlier work have recently been interestingly studied by R. A. Lanham, 'The Old Arcadia', *Sidney's Arcadia*, New Haven and London, 1965, pp. 181–405.

[2] Sidney cites Heliodorus as well as Xenophon as an example of a maker of 'an absolute heroical poem' in prose (*An Apology for Poetry*, ed. G. Shepherd, 1965, p. 103), and at about the same period Vauquelin de la Fresnaye couples *Diana* with Heliodorus in support of the theory 'En prose tu pourras poëtiser aussi :' (*L'Art Poétique*, ed. G. Pellissier, Paris, 1885, pp. 78–79. This work was first published in 1605, but was begun *c.* 1574).

[3] *The Greek Romances in Elizabethan Prose Fiction*, New York, 1912.

In this respect the *New Arcadia* is more closely akin than the *Old Arcadia* to *Diana*, for the unification of action and place by what Myrick calls a dramatic method of narration[1] is a prominent feature of Montemayor's technique.

Another striking difference between the *Old Arcadia* and the *New* is the prominence given to heroic or chivalric material in the latter. For this innovation Sidney could have found hints in Montemayor (in, for example, the martial prowess of Felismena), but the amount of space devoted to chivalric material is far beyond what had been suggested as possible by Montemayor, and is perhaps the chief factor which distinguishes the *Arcadia* from those more purely pastoral romances of which *Diana* is the best representative.

But in another and less obvious respect I believe Sidney to have been deeply indebted to *Diana* for a profound alteration that he made in his *New Arcadia*; that is, in his decision to make Neoplatonic philosophic ideals an important dimension of his romance. That this was his intention, and that he was influenced by Montemayor, can be seen in an evident and much-quoted borrowing from *Diana*, the opening description of Strephon and Klaius, and their lament for Urania.[2] What the total effect of the Strephon/Klaius/Urania story would have been in the completed *New Arcadia* cannot of course be known, but we may conjecture that it might have served some of the functions of Montemayor's devotion of his central Book IV to Neoplatonic theories of love, which provide an essential backdrop for his lively narratives of lovers. It is notable that Sidney also has chosen a strikingly prominent position for this story with its strong Neoplatonic overtones: not the centre of the work as in Montemayor, but the beginning.

A further revision of the *Old Arcadia* which was carried out by the Countess of Pembroke in the 1593 edition, very probably in accordance with Sidney's wishes, that is, the excision of Musidorus's intended rape of Pamela and Pyrocles's seduction of Philoclea, is also more in line with Montemayor's treatment of love than the earlier episodes had been.

---

[1] *Sir Philip Sidney as a Literary Craftsman*, 2nd ed., University of Nebraska Press, 1965, pp. 134–6.

[2] This episode has recently been studied by K. Duncan-Jones ('Sidney's Urania', *Review of English Studies*, n.s. xvii (1966), 123–32), but although she notes that it is copied from Montemayor, and explores in some detail its Neoplatonic implications, she does not make a connexion between these two facts.

The more moralistic and Neoplatonic cast of Sidney's revised *Arcadia* does not force him to abandon his humour, but the style of his comedy draws much closer to Montemayor's. In both the *New Arcadia* and *Diana* the absurdities and extravagances of lovers are presented with sympathetic amusement which does not interfere with the readers' recognition of the essential exemplary virtue of the heroes and heroines, whereas the unbridled passions of the *Old Arcadia* invite a corrective laughter antipathetic to the lovers' heroic stature. Only Montemayor among all the authors who influenced Sidney in his *Arcadia* could have helped him to achieve this subtlety of presentation which is so important to his revised idea of his work as a heroic poem.

Sidney is also indebted to *Diana* in his versification, although Genouy maintains that it is Sannazaro whom Sidney has imitated in most of his poems, rather than Montemayor.[1] Of Sannazaro's twelve eclogues, eight are in *terza rima* (of which one also has internal rhyme and three are *rime sdrucciole*), one is a sestina, one a double sestina, and two use the stanza form abCabCcdeeDfF. In support of his contention, Genouy notes that Sidney uses *terza rima* in six poems, and in one ('Dorus, tell me, where is thy wonted motion')[2] he uses internal rhyme, and points out that the form of Sidney's double sestina[3] is exactly the same as that of Sannazaro's Eclogue 4. Genouy might also have noted that in 'Dorus, tell me' Sidney uses *rime sdrucciole*. But examples of sestina, double sestina, *terza rima*, *rime sdrucciole*, and internal rhyme can all be found in Montemayor and Gil Polo (and are reproduced by Yong). All three of Sidney's sestinas are of the strict form, as are those of the other authors, and all three envoys have 135 in the middle, 246 at the ends of the lines, as do Sannazaro's double sestina, Montemayor's 'Waters that fall from top of these steepe Hils', and Gil Polo's 'The faire, the fresh, the red, and rosie morning'. Genouy's argument that Sidney is indebted to Sannazaro rather than to Montemayor is very weak.

The most striking point about Sidney's versification in the *Arcadia* is its variety, a quality possessed in far greater abundance by Montemayor and Gil Polo than by Sannazaro. (It should, how-

---

[1] L'*"Arcadia' de Sidney dans ses rapports avec l'"Arcadia' de Sannazaro et la 'Diana' de Montemayor*, Montpellier, 1928, p. 175.

[2] *The Poems of Sir Philip Sidney*, ed. W. A. Ringler, Jr., Oxford, 1962, p. 47.

[3] Ibid., p. 111.

ever, be remembered that Sidney's great variety in his metrical experiments does not come only from the influence of these three authors. He was indebted also to Virgil, Horace, Ovid, Petrarch, and Tottel's *Songes and Sonettes*).[1] Like Montemayor and Gil Polo, but unlike Sannazaro, Sidney uses the sonnet form, quatrains, *ottava rima*, and even the very common Spanish five-line stanza.[2] If more positive proof is needed that Sidney is indebted in his versification to the *Diana*s, it can be found in the marriage song 'Let mother earth now decke her selfe in flowers',[3] which is directly imitated from Gil Polo's 'Let now each meade with flowers be depainted'. Both Yong in his translation and Sidney in his imitation use a slight modification of Gil Polo's stanza form (ABABbcCdD from ABBAacCdD (Ferreres, p. 206)), which they probably arrived at independently.

Although the influence of the *Diana*s can be perceived at each stage of the development of Sidney's *Arcadia*, his eventual achievement as it was published in 1590 and 1593 (and so very frequently thereafter) is no more a copy of *Diana* than it is of Sannazaro's *Arcadia* or Heliodorus's *Æthiopian History*, but I think one must agree with his contemporaries' opinion that he could hardly have conceived or executed his grand design without the help of these three predecessors.

Apart from Sidney, Lodge and Greene are probably the only writers of original pastoral fiction in Elizabethan England who are today read with any expectation of pleasure.

Greene shows little direct debt to *Diana*, although R. Pruvost sees some similarity between Montemayor and Greene's *Ciceronis Amor* (1589) in the manner of building the plot on a succession of ill-fated love stories.[4]

It is generally agreed that Lodge's *Rosalynde* (1590) draws the story of the old knight and the three sons from the fourteenth-century tale *Gamelyn*, but this is in no way a story of love, the only hint of romance coming at the very end, where we are told that Gamelyn married a good and fair wife. *Rosalynde*, on the other hand, is not primarily a story of adventure, but of love in a pastoral setting. In both these modifications, it seems probable that Lodge

---

[1] See Ringler's above-cited edition of Sidney's *Poems*, p. xxxvi, and J. Thompson, *The Founding of English Metre*, 1961, pp. 139–55.

[2] e.g. *Poems*, ed. cit., p. 72.   [3] Ibid., p. 91.

[4] *Robert Greene et ses romans*, Paris, 1938, pp. 341–2.

owes something to *Diana*. When Rosalynde and Alinda enter the forest of Arden, the pastoral atmosphere is established by a description of the fountain at which they rest and eat, 'compassed with a grove of cypress trees, so cunningly and curiously planted, as if some goddess had entreated nature in that place to make her an arbour'.[1] A few pages later, at the end of their day's journey, Rosalynde and Alinda come into 'a fair valley', and see and hear Montanus and Coridon conversing and singing in another 'glorious arbour', built around 'a fount so crystalline and clear', where the ground is 'diapered with Flora's riches'.[2] These descriptions recall several passages in *Diana*: the 'faire valley, in the mids of which ran a swift brooke' (p. 108), where the nymphs and shepherds find Belisa; the fountain in the 'faire broade court, set round about with high Cypres trees' (p. 133) in the Temple of Diana; Gil Polo's '*faire fountaine*', fully described on p. 323; and all the other clear and crystalline fountains throughout both *Diana*s. Also the manner in which Rosalynde and Alinda 'stole privily behind the thicket', in order to hear Montanus and Coridon debate in song and discover their identity,[3] recalls similar episodes in *Diana*.[4]

Lodge borrowed little directly from the love-plots of *Diana*, though Bullough thinks that his love story is 'of the kind found in Montemayor',[5] and suggests that Montanus's wooing of Rosalynde on behalf of Phoebe is a deliberate reversal of Felismena's wooing of Celia on behalf of Felix.[6] Lodge may certainly have taken hints for the structure of his tale from *Diana*: in Felismena he could find a great lady disguised first as a page and then as a shepherdess, in Alcida (who becomes Felismena's sister-in-law; similarly Alinda is related by marriage to Rosalynde through marrying Rosader's reformed brother Saladyne) a great lady disguised as a shepherdess; the whole work could have given him the hint for multiple love stories.

Two of Lodge's major themes are also to be found in Montemayor. One is the inconstant, whimsical, cross-grained nature of Fortune, and the connexion between Fortune and Love. This theme in Lodge has been thoroughly illustrated by G. Bullough,[7]

---

[1] Ed. W. W. Greg, 1907, p. 35.
[2] Ibid., p. 39.
[3] Ibid., p. 40.   [4] e.g. pp. 58, 199, 230, 257, 277, 316.
[5] *Narrative and Dramatic Sources of Shakespeare*, 1958, ii. 145.
[6] Ibid., ii. 277.
[7] Ibid., ii. 151–2.

and is of such frequent recurrence in *Diana* that it scarcely needs illustration (see, for example, such poems as 'Mine eies, once have I seene you' (p. 29), 'My life (yoong Shepherdesse)' (p. 50), 'My painefull yeeres' (p. 89), 'My passion (Love)' (p. 105), 'O Vainest hopes' (p. 191), 'Now Love, and fortune' (p. 206)).

The other major theme common to both is summarized by Lodge in 'that virtue is not measured by birth but by action',[1] a philosophy which Montemayor shows he shares in the argument about the nature of nobility between Felicia and Syrenus in Book IV. This question is inevitably raised by a contemplation of the two worlds of shepherd and courtier, and in both Montemayor and Lodge is linked to the question 'can shepherds love?'[2]

However far Greene and Lodge are indebted to *Diana* for material and inspiration, they certainly owe their great predecessor thanks for paving the way for their own successes in this field by showing that pastoral romance could have a popular appeal.

Lesser writers of pastoral fiction were inevitably influenced by their vastly successful predecessors, Sidney and Greene. Among these is John Dickenson, the owner of a small but pleasing talent, who endears himself to anyone who has wrestled with the weightier representatives of the genre by the motto in the title of *The Shepheardes Complaint* (1596), 'Brevissima, gratissima'. This brief story in prose with verse interspersed is very similar in atmosphere to the works of Montemayor and Gil Polo.

Another work of mixed parentage, Robert Parry's *Moderatus, the blacke knight* (1595), combines the popular romance with the poetic and philosophic refinements of pastoral. The group of poems in Chapter 5 is reminiscent of Gil Polo, and the debate in Chapter 7 on the proposition 'Whether outward Beautie, or inward Bountie deserveth most praise, or is of greatest force to procure love' recalls the discussions in Montemayor Book IV and those between Alcida and Diana in Gil Polo Book I. The complications of the love affairs are also very much in the same style as those of *Diana*.

The two parts of Markham's *The English Arcadia* (1607, 1613), although he is 'alluding his beginning from Sir Philip Sidneyes ending',[3] are much closer both in manner and matter to *Diana* than to the *Arcadia*. The opening of the first part, where the two

[1] Ed. W. W. Greg, 1907, p. 165.
[2] *Rosalynde*, ed. cit., p. 48; *Diana*, p. 137.   [3] Title of *The First Part*.

shepherds Credulo and Carino meet and lament the cruel beauty of Cinthia, is a direct parallel with the opening of Montemayor. The story of Mellidora and Diatassan, which is begun in the first part and brought to a happy conclusion in the second part, is little but a retelling of the story of Diana and Syrenus. In the first part there is some attempt to follow Sidney's mingling of the heroic with the pastoral, but in the second part the heroic element is submerged in a tale of love, Nymphs, and Shepherds. The book ends in the manner of Gil Polo: when all the love affairs are straightened out, the company adjourns for 'Eglogs, Maskes, Wrastlings, and all manner of pastorall delights'.[1]

A closer imitation of Sidney is to be found in Lady Mary Wroth's *Urania* (1621), but here again Sidney's debt to Montemayor is acknowledged in renewed borrowings. The wise and grave Lady Mellissea in Book II is the counterpart of Felicia, and several resolutions of plot are dependent on the water with the power to make the unfortunate forget their love.

The direct influence of *Diana* on English prose fiction wanes as the seventeenth century progresses, but it is not totally forgotten. John Reynolds, in *The flower of fidelitie* (1650), has obviously been inspired by *Diana*. The theme of the book is that 'All men are subject to Love',[2] the discovery of Florina mourning in her deserted castle recalls the discovery of Belisa in Montemayor Book III, the description of Excellina's tomb and epitaph is copied from that of Lady Katerine's in Montemayor Book IV, and Reynolds's debt is made quite plain in the description of 'a sumptuous Palace . . . the glorious sight whereof (repleating their senses with astonishment) made them conjecture it to be that admired Palace of renowned *Felicia* (so much dignified by the Pens of civil and prophane Poets)'.[3]

John Crowne's *Pandion and Amphigenia* (1665) closely resembles Montemayor's *Diana* in construction, in the device of meeting characters who then recount the story of their love.

Indirectly *Diana* continued to influence English prose fiction in the seventeenth century through translations of foreign works indebted to it, such as Tofte's *Honours academie*, from Nicolas de Montreux's *Bergeries de Juliette*, the translations of Honoré d'Urfé's *Astrée*, and of Sorel's anti-romance *Le Berger extravagant*.

The earliest evidence of the influence of *Diana* on English

[1] P. Q4ʳ.   [2] 'The Preface.'   [3] P. C3ʳ.

drama is to be found in a reference to a play (now lost) in the Revels Accounts for the period November 1584 to February 1584/5, 'The history of felix & philiomena. shewed and enacted before her highnes by her *maiesties* servaunt*es* on the Sondaie next after newe yeares daye at nighte at Grenew*i*che',[1] which was presumably based on Book II of Montemayor. The unknown author was perhaps led to draw on *Diana* because of Sidney's interest in it.

The Court was at this time also being entertained by Lyly's plays (*Campaspe* was performed at Court on 1 January and *Sapho and Phao* on 3 March 1584). G. K. Hunter stresses the central importance of love in Lyly's pastorals, and shows that pastoral was not only in itself attractive to the Court, but also a valuable device to the playwright, in that 'to write about the emotions of courtiers in terms of shepherds and sheep made it possible to deal with subjects which would otherwise have been taboo'.[2] Both in his concentration on love and in his muffling 'under pastorall names and style' 'divers histories of accidents, that have truly happened' (*Diana*, p. 10) Lyly is akin to Montemayor. G. K. Hunter also points out that Lyly could have found a precedent for his disguise-plots in *Diana*.[3] There are in the plays passages reminiscent of *Diana*. In *Endimion* Eumenides's fear of fortune when he thinks of union with Semele[4] is like Arsileus's misgivings when reunited with Belisa (pp. 210-11). In *Loves Metamorphosis* the discussions in II. i. and IV. i. are akin to those on the same subject in Montemayor Book IV and Gil Polo Book I; Cupid's answer to the woeful lovers in IV. i. 'To make them love were a revenge to gentle for *Cupid*: to make you hate, a recompence too smal for lovers'[5] may glance at Felicia's solution of Syrenus's problem. E. G. Mathews[6] has argued that Gil Polo's sonnet 'Probaron en el campo' (Ferreres, p. 256), or Yong's version of it 'Diana, Love, and my faire Shepherdesse' (p. 416), could just as well as Desportes's imitation 'Un jour, l'aveugle Amour' have given the hint for 'Cupid and my Campaspe' to Lyly. But despite these similar preoccupations and possible echoes,

[1] *Documents relating to the Office of the Revels*, ed. A. Feuillerat, 1908, p. 365.

[2] *John Lyly. The Humanist as Courtier*, 1962, p. 130.   [3] Ibid., p. 127.

[4] *The Complete Works of John Lyly*, ed. R. Warwick Bond, 1902, iii. 49.

[5] Ibid. iii. 319.

[6] 'Gil Polo, Desportes, and Lyly's "Cupid and my Campaspe" ', *MLN*, lvi (1941), 606-7.

the atmosphere of Lyly's plays is very different from that of *Diana*. Lyly's presentation of the problems of love is more academic and less romantic than Montemayor's or even Gil Polo's. Unlike Montemayor, he seems more interested in conducting a debate than in observing the conduct of lovers, and unlike Gil Polo, he does not seem convinced of the ultimate good of love. Nevertheless Lyly was undoubtedly influenced in his choice of subject and manner of treatment by the prevailing taste for the analysis of love in a pastoral setting, a taste which Montemayor had himself both exploited and helped to develop.

Though Lyly's direct knowledge of *Diana* is disputable, Shakespeare's is not. His most obvious debt to Montemayor is in the Julia–Proteus story of *The Two Gentlemen of Verona*. Since in this story Shakespeare follows Montemayor closely, and since elsewhere he shows an acquaintance with other parts of *Diana*, there is no reason to suppose that he was indebted to the lost play of *Felix and Philiomena* rather than to Montemayor. The chief points of resemblance between the two plots are summarized thus by R. Warwick Bond:

the use by Don Felix of Felismena's maid as intermediary, and the coyness exhibited by the heroine in receiving his letter; the breach of their intimacy by his dispatch to Court; the pursuit of him thither by Felismena in male dress at some risk to her reputation; her lodging on arrival at an inn and hearing by the host's means the serenading of Celia (Silvia) by Don Felix; her taking service as a page (Valerius) with the latter, and being sent by him to forward his new suit; the conversation between her and Celia about Don Felix' former love, and Celia's unfavourable reception of his addresses; and the heroine's final recognition by, reproach of, and reunion with Felix effected later in a forest after a scene of combat. Also Launce is in some sort represented by Felix' page Fabius, however conventional the latter.[1]

This summary does not do justice to the close similarity between I. ii and IV. iv and the parallel passages in *Diana*. Shakespeare, in devising the character of Lucetta, borrows Rosina's lively repartee, her pert familiarity, and her knowledge of psychology. The device of pretending to let the letter drop, used by Rosina to give Felismena the opportunity to read the letter without backing down from her original position, is copied by Lucetta. Felismena's excuse for reading the letter (pretending that it must be a missive

[1] *The Two Gentlemen of Verona*, The Arden Shakespeare, 1906, pp. xvii–xviii.

from one of Rosina's lovers) is also used by Julia, when she accuses Lucetta:

Some love of yours hath writ to you in rhyme.[1]

Felismena's dependence on Rosina to carry her answer to Felix is not used by Shakespeare, but he represents this dependence by substituting Lucetta for Felismena's 'approoved friend' who helped her provide the means of dressing as a boy to seek Felix.

In iv. iv Julia's words in soliloquy after Proteus has charged her with the ring for Silvia and just before Silvia enters

And now am I, unhappy messenger,
To plead for that which I would not obtain,
To carry that which I would have refused,
To praise his faith which I would have dispraised.
I am my master's true-confirmed love;
But cannot be true servant to my master,
Unless I prove false traitor to myself.[2]

echo Felismena's thoughts on her way to Celia's house 'imagining by the way the wofull estate, whereunto my haplesse love had brought me; since I was forced to make warre against mine owne selfe, and to be the intercessour of a thing so contrarie to mine owne content' (p. 97).

As Celia originally rejects Felix's addresses because of his former devotion to Felismena, so Silvia reproaches Proteus for his faithlessness rather than pleading the prior engagement of her affections by Valentine as a reason for rejecting Proteus.

Both supposed pages nearly give away their identities in muttered comments and double meanings:

Jul. She thanks you.
Sil. What say'st thou?
Jul. I thank you, madam, that you tender her.
Poor gentlewoman! my master wrongs her much.
Sil. Dost thou know her?
Jul. Almost as well as I do know myself:[3]

Doest thou then know *Felismena* (said *Celia*) . . . ? I know her (saide I) although not so well as it was needfull for me, to have prevented so many mishaps, (and this I spake softly to my selfe) (p. 98).

---

[1] i. ii. 79. All references to *The Two Gentlemen of Verona* are to R. Warwick Bond's edition for the Arden Shakespeare.
[2] iv. iv. 104-10.   [3] iv. iv. 143-8.

In response to questions, both Julia and Felismena paint pitiful
pictures of their own loss of beauty because of their sorrow at the
desertion of their lovers.

The most obvious difference between the two plots is that Celia
falls in love with Felismena, and dies when her love is not re-
ciprocated, whereas Silvia already loves Valentine, and remains
constant in her love.

J. C. Dunlop's acidulous comment, that Shakespeare departs
from Montemayor's story 'in a manner (as usual with him) that
rather injures than improves the story',[1] is perhaps of some interest. He notes particularly that whereas Felix, by 'his spirit,
generosity, and honour' manages to 'preserve the esteem and
interest of the reader', Proteus is merely an 'unprincipled villain'.[2]
His objections have some validity, but of course Shakespeare
was not primarily trying to write a story of devoted love, but to
represent a dramatic clash between the rival claims of friendship
and love. Yet in reading the two one is conscious that Montemayor more successfully fulfils his intentions than does Shakespeare. *Diana* is, after all, a mature masterpiece : *The Two Gentlemen
of Verona* the early work of a genius.

G. Bullough ends his introduction to the sources of *The Two
Gentlemen of Verona* by saying that 'Montemayor's *Diana* became
his text-book of amorous entanglements and sentiment as Lyly's
comedies were for a time his handbook to witty converse and
artificial balance of character',[3] but, presumably because of the
scope of his work, he finds little room to substantiate this claim
for *Diana*. Whatever his reasons, it seems strange that Mr. Bullough in his introduction to the sources of *A Midsummer Night's
Dream* should find time to note that Shakespeare, in devising the
character of Hippolyta, would recall the Amazonian qualities of
Felismena, and that the love-juice has an analogue in Felicia's
potions, but that all he should say of the 'amorous entanglements' is that 'The humorous attitude to [the young lovers] and
their passion links *A Dream* with *Love's Labour's Lost* and the
early scenes of *Romeo and Juliet* rather than with *Two Gentlemen of
Verona*.[4]

[1] *History of Prose Fiction*, revised by H. Wilson, 1896, ii. 369.
[2] Ibid. ii. 370.
[3] *Narrative and Dramatic Sources of Shakespeare*, 1957, i. 211.
[4] Ibid. i. 367.

Although Mr. Bullough does not see a connexion between *The Two Gentlemen of Verona* and *A Midsummer Night's Dream*, other critics, such as John Vyvyan[1] and G. B. Harrison (who makes the remarkable statement that '*Two Gentlemen of Verona* had told of the cross-wooing of two pairs of lovers whose affections had become mixed'),[2] have felt a similarity between the plots of the two plays, without apparently having the knowledge of *Diana* that would provide the link: the main plot of *The Two Gentlemen of Verona* is drawn from Montemayor Book II, the main plot of *A Midsummer Night's Dream* is drawn from Montemayor Book I.[3]

Selvagia's story provides as complicated a tangle of affections as one could ever hope to find. Ismenia and Alanius are in love. Through Ismenia's jesting trick, Selvagia falls in love with Alanius, who then falls in love with her. Ismenia encourages another of her lovers, Montanus, and then falls in love with him. Alanius returns his affections to Ismenia. Montanus then falls in love with Selvagia. Thus Selvagia loves Alanius who loves Ismenia who loves Montanus who loves Selvagia. Shakespeare does not attempt to reproduce all these tangles, but there is at least at one point an exact correspondence in the state of the parties. Montanus and Ismenia are in love, and Alanius, deserting Selvagia, woos Ismenia. The position at the beginning of *A Midsummer Night's Dream* is identical: Lysander and Hermia are in love, and Demetrius, deserting Helena, woos Hermia.

Montemayor emphasizes the comedy of the situation, and his light handling of the story provides Shakespeare with a precedent for his humorous attitude towards his lovers. Puck's 'Lord, what fools these mortals be!'[4] expresses much the same reaction to the whole ridiculous tangle as the song 'Foolish love' (p. 47).

Shakespeare echoes the barbed correspondence and conversations between Selvagia and Ismenia in the quarrel between Hermia and Helena. He may also have found a hint for the old friendship between his heroines (which gives their quarrel both

---

[1] *Shakespeare and Platonic Beauty*, 1961, pp. 77–78.

[2] Shakespeare, *The Complete Works*, New York, 1952, p. 514.

[3] This claim was fairly fully explored by R. Tobler, 'Shakespeare's Sommernachtstraum und Montemayor's Diana', *Shakespeare Jahrbuch*, xxxiv (1898), 358–66, and re-emphasized by T. P. Harrison, 'Shakespeare and Montemayor's "Diana"', *University of Texas Studies in English*, vi (Dec. 1926), 72–120.

[4] III. ii. 115. All references to *A Midsummer Night's Dream* are to H. Cuningham's edition for the Arden Shakespeare, 2nd ed., 1922.

zest and poignancy) in the loving greetings between Selvagia and
Ismenia which Gil Polo describes: 'there was great courtesie
between them and many embracings, joyfull to see each other
there after so long a time' (p. 364). In both play and story all
the lovers provide striking examples of the utter selfishness of
love in their complete disregard for anyone else's feelings.

The situation of the four lovers confronting one another in
a wood, and the manner of their arriving there, is borrowed from
Selvagia's amusing description of how each lover followed his or
her beloved to the forest (pp. 42–43), and we find a similar
attraction working upon Demetrius and Helena:

> in love unto Demetrius,
> I told him of your stealth unto this wood.
> He followed you, for love I followed him.[1]

The juice which unties the lovers' knots perhaps owes something to Felicia's 'herbes and wordes, which were of great vertue'
(p. 375), as well as to the water by means of which Sylvanus,
Selvagia, and Felix awake to a happy love. It is interesting that the
herb which in *A Midsummer Night's Dream* remedies the ills
brought about by 'love-in-idleness' is called 'Dian's bud'. Here,
as in Montemayor and Gil Polo, the goddess Diana is seen as
devoted not primarily to chastity, but to finding a happy solution
to lovers' problems.

In at least four other ways *A Midsummer Night's Dream* is
reminiscent in preoccupations and themes of *Diana*. Both, obviously, are concerned with love: in both the signs and perquisites
of lovers are described;[2] in both a description of love is found.[3]

Both are concerned with the problem of constancy and inconstancy in love. The importance of this theme in *Diana* needs
no further illustration,[4] and the following passages give some idea
of its recurrence in *A Midsummer Night's Dream*: Demetrius is 'this
spotted and inconstant man';[5] Hermia, with ironic playfulness,
swears

> By all the vows that ever men have broke,
> In number more than ever women spoke.[6]

---

[1] III. ii. 309–11.

[2] e.g. *A Midsummer Night's Dream*, I. i. 128–55; *Diana*, passim, e.g. 'The authors of
subjections', pp. 135–7.

[3] e.g. *A Midsummer Night's Dream*, I. i. 234–41; *Diana*, pp. 251–53.

[4] See above, pp. xxviii–xxix. [5] I. i. 110. [6] I. i. 175–6.

with equal irony Lysander pledges

> And then end life when I end loyalty![1]

To Oberon's reproach

> Of thy misprision must perforce ensue
> Some true love turned, and not a false turned true.[2]

Puck cynically answers

> Then fate o'errules, that, one man holding troth,
> A million fail, confounding oath on oath.[3]

and Shakespeare, rather strangely, chooses to use the word 'constancy' to describe the intention and effect of the whole tale:

> But all the story of the night told over,
> And all their minds transfigured so together,
> More witnesseth than fancy's images,
> And grows to something of strange constancy.[4]

The connexion (or lack of it) between love and reason is debated in prose and verse in Montemayor Book IV and Gil Polo Book I, with comments on the madness of love. This debate is echoed in *A Midsummer Night's Dream* by Lysander:

> The will of man is by his reason swayed,
> And reason says you are the worthier maid.
> Things growing are not ripe until their season:
> So I, being young, till now ripe not to reason;
> And touching now the point of human skill,
> Reason becomes the marshal to my will,
> And leads me to your eyes; where I o'erlook
> Love's stories, written in love's richest book.[5]

by Bottom:

to say the truth, reason and love keep little company together nowadays; the more the pity, that some honest neighbours will not make them friends.[6]

by Puck:

> Lord, what fools these mortals be![7]

---

[1] II. ii. 63.   [2] III. ii. 90–91.   [3] III. ii. 92–93.
[4] v. i. 23–26.   [5] II. ii. 115–22.   [6] III. i. 145–8.   [7] III. ii. 115.

and by Theseus:

> Lovers and madmen have such seething brains,
> Such shaping fantasies, that apprehend
> More than cool reason ever comprehends.[1]

Shakespeare's fairy world also owes something to *Diana*. In the sources usually quoted for Oberon, Titania, and Puck, Shakespeare would not have found the beauty of their habitat. Is this not reminiscent of the pastoral world? A striking parallel is the importance of water in both, with the fountains, streams, rivers, and seas of *Diana*, and such meeting places of Oberon and Titania as 'By fountain clear'[2] and

> By paved fountain or by rushy brook,
> Or in the beached margent of the sea.[3]

That the pastoral world was in his mind (although he has magically transmuted it) Shakespeare reveals in Titania's accusation of Oberon:

> but I know
> When thou hast stolen away from fairyland,
> And in the shape of Corin sat all day,
> Playing on pipes of corn, and versing love
> To amorous Phillida.[4]

And in the quarrels of Oberon and Titania we see that the fairy world is infected with a disease of love given great prominence in *Diana*: jealousy.

In *Twelfth Night* Shakespeare uses a part of the Felix–Felismena story (the wooed lady falling in love with the page messenger) that he had discarded in *The Two Gentlemen of Verona*. The question of his indebtedness to *Diana* is, however, complicated by the vast popularity and wide diffusion of the story originated (I believe) by the Siennese play *Gl'Ingannati*, published in 1537. Bandello's story[5] is taken from this play, and Montemayor is indebted to Bandello (a fact obscured for R. Warwick Bond in the Arden edition of *The Two Gentlemen of Verona* by his belief in Ticknor's 1542 'ghost' edition of *Diana*). In England, Riche's story of 'Apolonius and Silla' is inspired by Belleforest's French version of Bandello. There are many other plays and stories, in several

---

[1] v. i. 4–6.   [2] II. i. 29.   [3] II. i. 84–85.
[4] II. i. 64–68.   [5] *Novelle*, 1554, ii. 36.

languages, of the same basic plot. When confronted with such a
bewildering multiplicity of possible sources, even the best informed and most dogged of scholars is forced to an inconclusive
conclusion: '*Twelfth Night* became a highly original treatment of
material probably taken in the main from *Apolonius and Silla* and
Gl'Ingannati, with details from Bandello and other parallel stories
and plays.'[1]

That *Diana* is one of these parallel stories is hinted at in the
coincidence of the use of the name Sebastian in both *The Two
Gentlemen of Verona* and *Twelfth Night* (Julia as a page, and Viola's
brother). This name does not occur in any of the versions of the
story that I have seen, and I take its repetition as an indication that
Shakespeare had the latter part of *The Two Gentlemen of Verona* in
mind when he was writing *Twelfth Night*. The flattery of the rival's
beauty by the disguised heroine is a feature common to Montemayor and Shakespeare, but is not found (so T. P. Harrison con-
tends)[2] in other versions. The sentiment, poetry, and chastity of
Twelfth Night also bring it closer to *Diana* than to other possible
sources. As Paul Reyher rather exuberantly claims, 'the characters,
the intensity of feeling, the tone, the inspiration are those of
Diana'.[3]

There is no question about the major source of the most fully
pastoral of Shakespeare's plays, *As You Like It*; the extent of
Lodge's indebtedness in *Rosalynde* to *Diana* I have already at-
tempted to explore. However, keensighted critics have discerned
indications that *Diana* had not been forgotten by Shakespeare
when he was writing *As You Like It*. Paul Reyher[4] finds a direct
reference in Rosalind's words

> I will weep for nothing, like Diana in the fountain.[5]

to the description of Diana lamenting her marriage (p. 199),
and in support of his contention it might be noted that no actual
fountain of Diana with water flowing from her eyes in sixteenth-

[1] G. Bullough, *Narrative and Dramatic Sources of Shakespeare*, 1958, ii. 278.
[2] 'Shakespeare and Montemayor's "Diana" ', *University of Texas Studies in English*,
vi (Dec. 1926), 109.
[3] '*The Two Gentlemen* et *Twelfth Night*: leurs sources communes', *Revue de l'enseignement des langues vivantes*, 1924, p. 448.
[4] 'A. de Vigny, Shakespeare, and George de Montemayor', ibid., 1920, pp. 1–7.
[5] IV. i. 140–1. All references to *As You Like It* are to J. W. Holme's edition for the
Arden Shakespeare, 2nd ed., 1920.

century England is known, that the picture of the shepherdess Diana is a very striking one, and that her repining a fate which she had consented to, or at least not fought against, might well provoke the more robust spirit of Rosalind to a reproach of weeping for nothing.

In a stimulating essay, Miss M. M. Lascelles,[1] using *Diana* for principal illustration, analyses several important characteristics of pastoral romance which throw light on Shakespeare's pastoral comedy. Three of these are of particular relevance to *As You Like It*. The first is the power of magic, which operates in *Diana* benevolently through Felicia, malevolently through Alfeus. So in *As You Like It*, when about to resolve the love dilemmas, Rosalind claims to be a magician. Next, in *Diana* we find in Felicia a benevolent oracular power, who becomes a symbol of a second chance, drawing all things to a happy conclusion. Miss Lascelles suggests that the character of Hymen serves a similar function in *As You Like It*. A third characteristic, evidently present in both *Diana* and *As You Like It*, is found in the theme of loss and recovery.

There are correspondences between the world of Shakespearian comedy and the world of *Diana* more striking than any borrowings of material. In both we find a compelling vision of the attraction of the pastoral idea. In both love and lovers are supreme. In both (and this is by no means generally true of the pastoral convention) we are considerably more interested in the heroines than in the heroes. In both we confidently expect a happy outcome to the trials of love. In both a major virtue of love, which brings the reward of happiness, is constancy. So great is the power of this virtue, that a lover's constancy may redeem the inconstancy or lack of faith of the beloved (e.g. Felismena, Ismenia, Marcelius; Julia, Mariana, Imogen).

In their confidence in the power of constancy Shakespeare, Montemayor, and Gil Polo stand united against the more cynical attitude of Lyly. In several other ways also the kinship between Shakespeare and Montemayor, in particular, is pointed up by a contrast with Lyly. Shakespeare, like Montemayor but unlike Lyly, gives the impression of an interested involvement with his characters. Shakespeare's comedies sparkle as brilliantly with wit

---

[1] 'Shakespeare's Pastoral Comedy', *More Talking of Shakespeare*, ed. J. Garrett, 1959, pp. 70–86.

as Lyly's, but Shakespeare's polish is never hard; like Monte-mayor, Shakespeare views the vagaries of his lovers with a thoroughly sympathetic laughter. As G. K. Hunter suggests, Lyly falls short of Shakespeare in that even when he 'is committed to showing the development of individual love he does so without involving us in the history of an emotion';[1] whereas (like Shake-speare) Montemayor amply demonstrates in the stories of Selvagia, Felismena, and Belisa his ability to trace, with wit and emotional truth, the development of love.

Although Montemayor's genius, even within the limitations of what he is setting out to do, does not approach the comprehensive-ness of Shakespeare's, I know of no single work that sheds greater light on Shakespeare's world of romantic comedy than *Diana*.[2]

Beaumont and Fletcher's familiarity with *Diana* is evident from the mention of Felicia and Duarta in *The Wild-Goose Chase*,[3] but a later passage suggests that they did not expect most of their audience to catch the reference.[4] One might expect to find con-siderable influence of *Diana* on playwrights well acquainted with Spanish, who delighted in complicated love-plots in both comedy and tragedy, but there is surprisingly little. In *Philaster*, Bellario provides an example of a woman dressed as a page in order secretly to serve her beloved, but neither in the circumstances of her story nor in her character is Euphrasia (Bellario) akin to Felismena. It is more possible that Felismena may have provided a hint for Clara, the Martial Maid of *Love's Cure*.

Dyce quotes Weber's opinion that the plot of *Monsieur Thomas* is drawn from Boccaccio's story of Titus and Gisippus,[5] but Fletcher did not find in Boccaccio the situation of father and son falling in love with the same woman, for which idea he may be indebted to Belisa's story in Montemayor Book III.

The plays of Beaumont and Fletcher, particularly the Fletcherian

[1] *John Lyly. The Humanist as Courtier*, 1962, p. 312.

[2] Shakespeare's later romances, pastoral though they are, seem to me so far to transcend the genre that close comparisons are difficult. However, reading *Diana* is perhaps one of the more pleasurable ways of gaining an understanding of the form which Shakespeare was transfiguring. For an interesting discussion of the pastoral aspects of *The Tempest* see Frank Kermode's introduction to the New Arden Shakespeare edition, reprinted with corrections, 1961.

[3] *Works*, ed. A. Glover and A. R. Waller, 1905-12, iv. 339-40.

[4] Ibid. iv. 353.

[5] *Works*, ed. A. Dyce, 1843-6, vii. 307.

comedies, are far removed from the spirit of *Diana* by their frequent eroticism, cynicism, and immorality. As J. H. Wilson points out,[1] even an avowedly chaste heroine, such as Florimel in *The Maid in the Mill*, sounds far from innocent. Such women would certainly not find entry into Diana's Temple.[2]

That *Diana* was still read by playwrights in the mid-seventeenth century is attested by borrowings in Sir William Lower's *The Enchanted Lovers: A Pastoral*, and by mentions in Davenant's *The Distresses* (v. i) and Killigrew's *Bellamira her Dream* (Part I, III. i), but the main influence of *Diana* on English drama after Shakespeare is seen in the development of the heroic romance, which is akin to the long prose romances which had themselves developed from *Diana*, Sidney's *Arcadia*, Barclay's *Argenis*, and d'Urfé's *Astrée*. A. Harbage points out the connexion in his book on Davenant,[3] and also in his book on Killigrew, where he says 'The heroic romance owed many of its sentimental subtleties, its fine-spun disquisitions on love and honor, its strange codes of etiquette, to the pastoral romance; and English readers had not only their native pastorals, but the *Astrée* of d'Urfé, translated in 1620, and the famous father of its kind, Montemayor's *Diana*, translated in 1598'.[4]

Diana exerted a very early influence on English poetry through Barnabe Googe's *Eglogs, epytaphes, & sonettes* (1563). Eglog V is an adaptation of the story of Felix, Felismena, and Celia, and Eglog VII is a versification of the opening pages of *Diana*.[5] Googe's knowledge of *Diana* is also reflected in some of the sonettes and in 'Cupido Conquered'. The praise of the country at the expense of the court, in 'To M. Henrye Cobham, of the most blessed state of Lyfe', may partly be prompted by Syrenus's comments at the beginning of *Diana*, and the poem 'The rushing rivers that do run', which Ellis prints as 'not the least favourable effusion of Googe's genius',[6] is a fairly close translation of

---

[1] *The Influence of Beaumont and Fletcher on Restoration Drama*, Columbus, Ohio, 1928, pp. 108–9.

[2] Ben Jonson's plays reveal even less influence of *Diana* than those of Beaumont and Fletcher, despite the fact that he owned Yong's translation. See *Works*, ed. C. H. Herford and P. Simpson, 1925–52, i, appendix iv, 264.

[3] Philadelphia, 1935, p. 242.

[4] *Thomas Killigrew, Cavalier Dramatist*, Philadelphia, 1930, pp. 149–50.

[5] See T. P. Harrison, 'Googe's "Eglogs" and Montemayor's "Diana" ', *University of Texas Studies in English*, v (Oct. 1925), 68–78.

[6] *Specimens of the Early English Poets*, 1845, ii. 144.

Sylvanus's song in *Diana* 'To heare me wearied is the cleerest river' (pp. 54–55).

Turberville's 'discourse of the friendly affections of Tymetes to Pyndara his ladie'[1] also shows the considerable influence of *Diana*. The main argument closely parallels the story of Syrenus and Diana. Tymetes loves Pyndara; eventually she returns his love, but marries another, less worthy. The central episode is a parting, at which the lovers exchange letters, and in which Pyndara tells Tymetes not to trust himself to the winds and seas, and herself vows constancy (cf. *Diana*, pp. 14–15, 60–74). Later there is given the lament of 'The forsaken Lover' 'that his Ladie is matched with an other'[2] (cf. the opening of *Diana*).

Some of the poems not obviously connected with the story of Tymetes and Pyndara also seem to take their inspiration from the arguments and spirit of *Diana*. For example, the following exchange

Maister Googe his Sonet of the paines of Love

> Twoo lynes shall tell the griefe
> that I by love sustaine:
> I burne, I flame, I faint, I freeze,
> of hell I feele the paine.

Turberviles aunswere and distich to the same.

> Twoo lynes shall teach you how
> to purchase ease anewe:
> Let reason rule where love did raigne,
> and ydle thoughts eschewe.[3]

recalls the poetic dialogue 'The authours of subjections' (pp. 135–37).

It is possible that Googe first brought *Diana* to the attention of Spenser.[4] Echoes of *Diana* have been discovered in the Calidore–Pastorella episode, in the Epithalamion, and, through the influence of Googe, in *The Shepheardes Calender*,[5] but they do not

---

[1] *Epitaphes, epigrams, songs, and sonets*, 1567, reprinted J. P. Collier, 1867.

[2] Ibid., pp. 209–10.

[3] Ibid., p. 14.

[4] For the probability that Spenser knew Googe see F. F. Covington, 'Biographical Notes on Spenser', *Modern Philology*, xxii (1924), 65–66.

[5] *The Works: a variorum edition*, ed. E. Greenlaw, etc., Baltimore, 1936–58, vi. 371–81; vii. 407, 594–5; viii. 485, 492, 494, 652–3. More interesting than such

amount to anything considerable. It would be more surprising that Spenser should have ignored so important and well known an example of pastoral literature than that he should have read it and occasionally echoed it. Spenser's genius is such that what he borrows he transmutes to poetry unmistakably his own, but a lesser poet, William Browne of Tavistock, writing in the Spenserian vein,[1] is more evidently dependent on his sources, among them *Diana*. Certain incidents of *Britannia's Pastorals*, such as Marina's drinking the water of the spring of Oblivion to make her forget Celandine (Book I), and her abandonment by her ravisher on a desert shore where she finds a poem cut in the rock (Book II) (cf. the story of Alcida) can be directly traced to *Diana*. As to the structure of the poem, W. W. Greg attributes the 'marked tendency towards the accumulation of unexplained incidents' 'to the influence of the Spanish romances, especially of the *Diana*'.[2] F. W. Moorman speaks of Browne's 'local interest' and 'love for the home and scenery of his childhood' as 'something new, not only in the history of the Pastoral, but of poetry in general',[3] but surely Montemayor's loving celebration of his home in Book VII of *Diana* at least establishes a precedent.

One would expect to discover some influence of *Diana* on narrative poets who enjoyed the pastoral mood, but it is more surprising to find that Montemayor's work impressed Donne,[4] much of whose secular poetry would seem violently discordant with the chaste and courtly tone of *Diana*. It is not, however, the pastoral atmosphere of *Diana* which appealed to Donne, but Montemayor's exploration of the themes of constancy and change, and of jealousy. The quotation 'antes muerto que mudado' ('Rather dead then changed be' (p. 13)) incorporated into the portrait of Donne chosen as the frontispiece to the 1635 edition of his poems, is a striking and appropriate recognition of the kinship

---

possible echoes is the two authors' analogous treatment of chastity. T. P. Roche Jr.'s analysis of Spenser's handling of Britomart, Amoret, and Belphoebe, Venus, and Diana (*The Kindly Flame*, Princeton, 1964, pp. 51–149), although he does not mention *Diana*, suggests some fascinating parallels with Montemayor, probably arising from both authors' use of Renaissance Neoplatonic mythologizing. See Commentary, note to **131.** 8.

[1] *Poems*, ed. G. Goodwin, 2 vols., 1894.

[2] *Pastoral Poetry and Pastoral Drama*, 1906, p. 138.

[3] *William Browne. His Britannia's Pastorals*, Strassburg, 1897, p. 130.

[4] See also J. A. Muñoz Rojas, 'Apuntes para un estudio de las relaciones literarias de Donne con España', *Homenaje a Walter Starkie*, Barcelona, 1948, 225–42.

between the two authors. The poem in which Montemayor's influence is most apparent is Elegie XII, 'His parting from her'.[1] Situation, tone, and matter are all strongly reminiscent of the story of Diana and Syrenus's love as it is told in Books I and II of Montemayor. Donne's recognition of the baleful influence of Fortune is a reflection of Diana's fears in 'O Eies, that see not him' (pp. 21–23), and the final lines

> The Poles shall move to teach me ere I start;
> And when I change my Love, I'll change my heart;
> Nay, if I wax but cold in my desire,
> Think, heaven hath motion lost, and the world, fire:
> Much more I could, but many words have made
> That, oft, suspected which men would perswade;
> Take therefore all in this: I love so true,
> As I will never look for less in you.[2]

might almost be a paraphrase of Diana's protestations to Syrenus in the heyday of their love.

Further proof that Donne's liking and knowledge of Montemayor was more than ordinary is found in his reference to a gloss on 'Ven muerte tan escondida' in Montemayor's *Cancionero*[3] when writing to Sir Robert Ker, 20 March 1614: 'I begin to be past hope of dying; and I feel that a little rag of Monte Mayor, which I read last time I was in your chamber, hath wrought prophetically upon me, which is, that Death came so fast towards me that the over-joy of that recovered me.'[4]

The importance of the influence exerted by *Diana* on the pastoral romance, drama, and poetry of the latter sixteenth century was fully recognized by the editor of the most charming of the Elizabethan poetical miscellanies, *Englands Helicon*, in which appear twenty-six poems from *Diana*, one translated by Sidney, and twenty-five by Yong.[5] Whatever one may think of Yong's poetical merits, his emergence as the major contributor to the anthology should be seen not as a reflection on the critical judgement of the editor, but as a fitting tribute to the outstanding position of *Diana*.

---

[1] *The Poems of John Donne*, ed. H. J. C. Grierson, 1912, i. 100–4.
[2] Ibid. i. 104.   [3] Ed. Angel González Palencia, Madrid, 1932, pp. 396–7.
[4] *The Life and Letters*, collected by E. Gosse, 1899, ii. 15.
[5] The first 'Pastorall Dialogue' in the second part of John Playford's *Select Musicall Ayres and Dialogues*, 1653, is a setting of one of these: 'I prethee keep my sheep [kine] for me'.

v. *Life of Bartholomew Yong*

Bartholomew Yong was born on 24 August (St. Bartholomew's day) 1560, the son of Gregory Yong, grocer, originally 'of the county of York', but then and until the time of his death resident in the parish of St. Peter's upon Cornhill, London.[1] Gregory was twice married, and Bartholomew was the eldest of a large family. Mr. Harrison has shown that Gregory Yong was the younger brother of the recusant Dr. John Yong, 'who under Queen Mary had been Master of Pembroke Hall, Cambridge, Regius Professor of Divinity, and Vice-Chancellor of the University'.[2] Bartholomew must surely have met his unfortunate uncle when on 13 June 1574 the Privy Council, accepting the bonds of Roger Hool and Gregory Yong for his good behaviour, directed that Dr. Yong, then prisoner in the Marshalsea, 'might enjoye sume libertie within that Citee or in sume place there about till All-halloutide, or suche tyme as they shall see lawfull cause to the contrarie'.[3] Dr. Yong is said to have died in Wisbech castle in October 1580.

In that very year is to be found the first reference to Bartholomew Yong since his birth. In a letter from Paris on 17 June 1580 Sir Henry Cobham writes to Walsingham:

Two young men are come hither who left Spain about the beginning of May, one called Richard Parker, the other Bartholomew Yonge, sons of Gregory Yonge, grocer, of London, and of his wife's first husband. Bartholomew Yonge is the nephew of Dr Yonge imprisoned for papistry, and was sent by him into Spain on purpose to have gone into Italy upon the doctor's direction. He had conference with the Duchess of Feria,[4] being recommended by a privy token from his uncle.

---

[1] The fullest information concerning B. Yong's life and family is to be found in an article by T. P. Harrison, 'Bartholomew Yong, Translator', *MLR*, xxi (1926), 129–39.

[2] Op. cit., p. 131.   [3] *Acts of the Privy Council*, 13 June 1574.

[4] Jane Dormer, Duchess of Feria, 1538–1612, was brought up by her grandmother, sister to Father Sebastian Newdigate, the Carthusian martyr. Her mother, Mary Sidney, eldest sister of Sir Henry Sidney, died when Jane was four. When her grandfather, Sir William Sidney, was tutor and governor to Prince Edward, Jane spent some time with the young prince, her contemporary, who was very fond of her. Jane served Queen Mary, and did not marry the Duke of Feria till just after the Queen's death (date of marriage 29 December 1558); at that time the Duke 'was yet resident as ambassador and viceregent of his king [Philip]' (p. 105). See Henry Clifford, *The Life of Jane Dormer*, ed. Stevenson, 1887.

and adds in a postscript:

The said two Englishmen are gone by Rouen into England.[1]

Richard Parker was the son of Gregory's second wife by her first husband. When Bartholomew arrived with him in Paris he had been two years in Spain—without ever hearing of *Diana*![2] It would be fascinating to know what business Dr. Yong wished to transact with the Duchess of Feria, for which he had employed his eighteen-year-old nephew, and which had taken two years. It is possible that he wanted her help as an intermediary, for 'In suits or pretences that any of our countrymen had in the court of Spain, very forward was she, if they sought it, with her best means to assist them, to write in their favour to the Lords of the Council, and to send some friend or servant with them to further their business'.[3]

On his return to England Bartholomew entered the New Inn, from which he was admitted to the Middle Temple on 19 May 1582.[4] He tells us in his preface to *Diana* that he took part in the dramatic entertainments in the Inns of Court; Mr. Harrison reminds us of the fame of these, and that the first known performance of *Twelfth Night* was given at the Middle Temple in February 1601.[5]

It was at the Middle Temple that Bartholomew met Edward Banister of Idesworth, Hants (admitted 7 February 1561),[6] a recusant[7] and patron of the arts, who suggested to him the translation of *Diana*.[8] The closeness of their friendship is attested by

---

[1] *Calendar of State Papers (Foreign) 1579–80*, pp. 308–9, but the postscript is here corrected from 'It is said' to 'The said' from the original document, MS. France IV. 93.   [2] See below, p. 5.

[3] Henry Clifford, *The Life of Jane Dormer*, ed. Stevenson, 1887, p. 178.

[4] *Middle Temple Records*, i. 250.

[5] Op. cit., p. 133.   [6] *Middle Temple Records*, i. 131.

[7] There are references to Banister's recusancy in *Calendar of State Papers (Domestic) 1581–90* (3 Nov. 1586) and *1598–1601* (18 Dec. 1599 and 10 May 1600). See also W. R. Trimble, *The Catholic Laity in Elizabethan England 1558–1601*, Cambridge, Mass., 1964, in which work are also mentioned Banister's friend Arden Waferer and his cousin John Drury (see below, p. lx). He married Mary Southwell, sister of the poet and martyr.

[8] See below, p. 5. Banister may have introduced Yong to Sir Philip Sidney, but not until after Yong had completed his translation of *Diana*. The first thirteen leaves of British Museum Add. MS. 28253 contain verses collected by Banister, including a copy of 'Ring out your bells' given to him by Sidney on 10 December 1584 at Putney. (See Ringler's edition of Sidney's *Poems*, Oxford, 1962, p. 555.) The small collection does not include any of Yong's poems.

Banister's will,[1] which Yong in part wrote out for him in March 1601:

And be it remembred, that the first leafe of this mye laste will, is written bye mye lovinge ffriende, Mr. Bartellmewe Yonge, which he wrote for me in mye sicknes: And the laste leafe, is myne owne hande, when I finished mye Will, since mye sicknes. And soe this will is written bye bothe our handes.[2]

In the event of various previously named beneficiaries dying without issue, Banister's lands 'called Banister's Courte' go 'to my Coosin Thomas Awdlye, my coosin John Drurye, and to Mr. Bartholomewe Yonge . . . to be bestowed for the benefite of mye Soule'. Finally, Banister makes

mye Overseers of this mye laste will and Testamente, mye welbeloved ffriends, mr Arden Waifarer, Counsell of the Lawe, mye coosin John Darcye, mye Coosin Thomas Awdlye, my coosen John drurye, and mr Bartellmewe Yonge, And I geve eache of them fower Angells a peece to make them ringes of golde, for mye remembrance, and to be Assistantes, and ffriends to mye wife & children.[3]

Yong was fortunate in having as his friend a man who not only was interested in various branches of the arts, but also had the means to indulge his tastes, as we see from his will:

Item I geve unto Edwarde Banister mye sonne, all mye Bookes, all mye Instrumentes of Musicke, all mye paynted Tables, paynted clothes, and pictures, all mye marble stones, stones of white marble, Touche, Porferye, Serpentyne, and all maner of other stones, and carvynges in woode, and thinges of glasse, and all other mye Conceiptes of pleasure, to be had unto Idsworthe, and there to be kepte, for my Remembrance, and in noe case to be solde, But to remayne to mye sonne Edwarde Banister, when he coometh to his full age, and to keepe howse, to use at his pleasure, and to garnishe his howse, at Idsworth withall.

Very properly, books have pride of place among his 'Conceiptes of pleasure'. Yong must sorely have missed such a friend when he died in 1606.[4]

---

[1] P.C.C. 88 Stafforde.

[2] The document which is kept as the original of Banister's will in Somerset House is merely a seventeenth-century copy, so does not provide a specimen of Yong's handwriting and signature.

[3] John Darcy of Lincoln's Inn and John Drury of the Middle Temple figure in land transactions with Yong. See Close Rolls C54/1537, C54/2046.

[4] Will proved 24 November 1606.

Poto El amor en yugo

LA
MOROSOPHIE
de Guillaume de la
Perriere To-
loſaïn,
Contenant Cent Emblemes
moraux, illuſtrez de Cent
Tetraſtiques Latins, re-
duitz en autant de Qua-
trains Françoys.

A LYON,
Par Macé Bonhomme, &
A Toloſe par Iean Perrin.
1553
Auec Priuilege pour dix ans.

It is not unlikely that Banister also directed Yong's attention to Guazzo's *Civile Conversation*,[1] and to Boccaccio's *Amorous Fiammetta*, the translation of which appeared in 1587, 'done into English by B. Giovano del M. Temp.'[2] The Italianate form of Yong's name is, of course, a play on Giovanni Boccaccio. Both these translations are in a more polished and sophisticated style than that of *Diana*, which, together with their earlier date of publication, seems to indicate that Yong felt he had passed the apprentice stage as a translator. Yong's diffidence about publishing his translation of *Diana*, which he considered primarily as a linguistic exercise, is understandable, but modern readers will probably think his earlier plain style more suitable for such a long work than the elaborate artifice of *Fiammetta*. The only other knowledge we have of Yong's reading stresses his fondness for foreign literature. The references to Provençal poets which he inserts into *Florisias Song* (p. 407) indicate that he read either Nostredame's *Lives* or an annotated edition of Petrarch's *Triumph of Love*. His sense of humour is shown by his ownership of Guillaume de La Perrière's *Morosophie* (1553), of which the title-page, bearing Yong's signature, is pasted into Douce's copy of *Diana*, now in the Bodleian Library.[3] The handwritten quotation on this title-page of the tag 'Boto el amor en yugo', with which Yong ends his translation of *Diana* (see below p. 418, and note), gives authenticity to the signature.

Yong's name appears several times in the Close and Patent Rolls of Indentures recording land transactions, but the only one of major interest is that recorded on 7 April 1595[4] in which Yong is making over to Thomas Southwell, Robert Awdeley, John Darcy, John Drury, and Anthony Ashe 'the mannor or lordshippe of Chivers hall al*ia*s Pasfeild Chivers' situated in the 'parishes of high Ongar Blakemore Norton and Writtle or elsewhere in the said Countie of Essex'.

This land apparently belonged to Yong's father, as can be seen from the clause granting 'all the reversion of the said mannor or

---

[1] *The civile Conversation of M. Stephen Guazzo, written first in Italian, divided into foure bookes, the first three translated out of French by G. Pettie . . . the fourth . . . now translated out of Italian into English by Barth. Young, of the middle Temple, Gent.* (1586). Reprinted in the Tudor Translation series with an Introduction by Sir E. Sullivan (1925).

[2] There are two modern editions of this work, one for the Navarre Society by E. Hutton (1926), and one by K. H. Josling (1929).

[3] See illustration, p. lxi.   [4] Close Roll C54/1537.

lordshippe and other the premisses after the decease of Gregorie
Yonge Citizen and Grocer of London Father of the said Bartholomewe Yonge', and the whole transaction is dependent on

this condition That if the said Bartholomewe Yonge his heyres executors admynistrators or assignes or any of them do and shall at any tyme
hereafter in and upon any thirtith daye of any moneth of October
content and paie or cause to be contented and paied or lawfully tender
or offer to content and paye to the said Thomas Southwell Robert
Awdeley John Darcy John Drury and Anthony Ashe their heyres
executors admynistrators or assignes or to any of them any peece or
peeces of golde or silver of the valewe of five shillinges or more at or
upon the Fontstone of the Temple Church in or nere the Suburbes of
London or at the place where the same Fontstone nowe standeth or
heretofore stood That then and at all tymes from and after such payment so made or lawfully tendred or offred to be made as aforesaid
not onely this present bargaine and sale and all other the contentes of
these presentes shall utterly cease be void and of none effect.

Furthermore it appears that Yong was still in possession of this
land in 1598, since he dates the dedication of the *Diana* from
'High Onger in Essex'.

The members of the faculty of the College of Law of the University of Saskatchewan most generously gave their assistance in
interpreting this transaction, and wrote on my behalf to Professor
A. K. R. Kiralfy, who commented

This form of transaction obviously could be used as a mortgage, but
the redemption price, five shillings, seems a bit small as a serious loan
on a whole manor, even in those days. Possibly it is an attempt to
cheat creditors. The Act of 1570 (13 Eliz. I, c. 5) avoids any alienation
without consideration or for a 'feigned consideration' (s. 2), intended
to defeat creditors. On the other hand it preserves alienation 'bona fide
and upon good consideration' when the transferees have no notice of
any fraud. The reference in the Yonge deed to 'a competent and convenient sum of lawful English money' may be meant to satisfy this
section. It is curious that Yonge may redeem *at any time*, whereas the
classic common law mortgage usually set a date six months or a year
ahead.

Perhaps all that can certainly be said is that in 1595 Yong
was pressed for money. It seems that he had a habit of living

beyond his income, for his father, writing his Will in 1604,[1] says

my mynde is that none of my Children shall have part or portion out of anie my goodes for that I have alreadie advanced them and bestowed on them what I thinke sufficient and especiallie my sonne Bartholomew as by assurance to him made of lande and otherwise /also/ by a wryting under my hand and seale testifying the payment of divers /somes/ to him amounting to as full or rather a more greater portion then I have given and bestowed amongst all the rest of my said children.

This particular financial embarrassment caused trouble after Yong's death to the administrator of his estate.[2]

When in London, Yong lived in Shire Lane, a street with a lively reputation,[3] now (perhaps fortunately) destroyed. He died intestate, and the administration of his estate was granted by decree to his nephew, Alexander Holman, merchant,[4] the third son of his sister Jane.[5] The last reference to Bartholomew Yong in the Close Rolls records Holman's bid to retrieve Chivers Hall.[6] On 27 April 1613 a group of men testify as witnesses that on the previous 30 October Alexander Holman went to the Temple Church with 5s. 6d. to reclaim the land according to the terms of the 1595 bargain and sale. Two of the witnesses, John English, a blacksmith, and Gregory Maptyne, Gentleman, 'at the request of the said Alexander Holman went to the Chamber of the said John Darcy one of the said feoffees in Lincolnes Inne and tolde hym that the said Alexander Holman was in the Temple Church ready to tender and pay unto hym five shillings or more according to the /said/ proviso but he refused to come and receive the same'. Holman waited in the Temple Church clutching his 5s. 6d. from three until five in the afternoon, 'during all which tyme there came not any person or persons with any authoritie to

---

[1] P.C.C. 70 Wingfield.   [2] See below.

[3] 'Shire Lane (vulgarly SHEER LANE), TEMPLE BAR. In James I's time, as appears from a list of houses, taverns, etc., in Fleet Street and the Strand, it was known by the name of Shire Lane, *alias* Rogue Lane.' It seems to have been, however, a respectable street with many literary associations, until sometime in the eighteenth century, when it became 'utterly abominable'. Its name was changed in July 1845, and it finally disappeared to make way for the New Law Courts. (H. B. Wheatley and P. Cunningham, *London Past and Present*, 1891, iii. 240.)

[4] Somerset House, *Admins.* Oct. 1612.

[5] Jane and George Holman and their children are mentioned in Gregory Yong's will.

[6] Close Roll C54/2176.

receive the same', so he obtained the right of re-entry to Chivers Hall for nothing.

Bartholomew had died the previous September, and was buried from Shire Lane at St. Dunstan's in the West on 28 September 1612.[1] His life, but for the trip to Spain, was uneventful. For a few years in his twenties he tried his hand, successfully, at translation; a little later his interest was caught by amateur dramatics; but most of his time he spent in the society of a few good friends.

VI. *Yong as Translator*

Yong's reputation as a translator has suffered from the condemnation of his poetry by A. H. Bullen, in his edition of *Englands Helicon*.[2] More scholars seem to have noticed and been influenced by this criticism than by Greg's assertion that Yong's *Diana* is a 'notable exception' to the generally 'negligible' translations of pastoral romance, and that 'the whole forms a not unworthy Tudor translation'.[3] Ticknor was less cautious in his praise, calling Yong's work 'excellent', and speaking enthusiastically of his 'happy versions of the poetry'.[4]

There are times when Yong is stiff, clumsy, or obscure, even in his prose, but on the whole his translation is lively, faithful, yet far from slavish.

Yong's chief tendency, which he shares with most other Englishers of foreign works, is towards expansion. This tendency takes several different forms, and varies in its effects. The most obvious method is simple duplication, a precautionary measure which is noted as an English habit in a translation as early as the eleventh-century version of *Apollonius of Tyre*.[5] So an extreme care to capture the precise sense leads to such duplication as 'with great affection and desire' (10. 17–18) for 'con gran desseo' (Estrada, p. 7, l. 18); 'the great felicitie and content' (11. 2–3) for 'el gran contentamiento' (Estrada, p. 9, ll. 13–14); 'the onely care and interest' (11. 8) for 'en solo el interesse' (Estrada, p. 9, l. 19);

---

[1] St. Dunstan's in the West *Parish Register Bap. Mar. Bur. 1558–1614*, MS. 10, 343, f. 268ʳ. Anthony à Wood's information, that Yong died in 1621 at Ashurst in Kent, is wrong.

[2] Revised ed. 1899, pp. ix–x.

[3] *Pastoral Poetry and Pastoral Drama*, 1906, p. 141.

[4] *History of Spanish Literature*, 1849, iii. 38, note.

[5] Ed. P. Goolden, 1958, pp. xxiv–xxv.

'to staie or mitigate the furie of her immoderate love' (244. 18–19) for 'a detener la furia de su amor' (Ferreres, p. 15, l. 16). The last example shows Yong seeking not only to duplicate but also to interpret the meaning of his text. This example also shows another common method of expansion, addition of an adjective, the effect of which is usually interpretative.

Although sometimes Yong's added adjectives (such as 'his cristalline streames' (11. 2) for 'sus aguas' (Estrada, p. 9, l. 12) or 'a thicke hedge' (11. 37–38) for 'una haya' (Estrada, p. 10, l. 21) contribute little, they more often show his own interpretation of the Spanish author's intentions. So 'poniendo en olvido' (Estrada, p. 7, l. 16) becomes 'burying him . . . in unjust oblivion' (10. 15–16); 'enemiga de mi descanso' (Estrada, p. 11, l. 7) becomes 'cruell enemie to my quiet rest' (12. 8); 'las palabras del pastor Sylvano' (Estrada, p. 19, ll. 26–27) becomes 'This straunge kinde of the Shepherd *Sylvanus* his greeting' (17. 38–39); 'la choça' (Estrada, p. 135, l. 20) becomes 'her melancholie cell' (111. 20); 'sus amores' (Estrada, p. 110, l. 32) becomes 'his injurious love' (91. 28–29); 'el amor' (Estrada, p. 226, l. 29) becomes 'my irremooveable and infinite love' (188. 6); 'nascida del amor de Bartofano' (Ferreres, p. 55, ll. 19–20) becomes 'sprung up of *Sartofanos* vile and filthie love' (273. 19–20). Sometimes his additions provide the explanation for the Spanish author's comment, as when 'un desastrado marido' (Ferreres, p. 199, l. 27) becomes 'a jealous, perverse, and unfortunate husband' (373. 2). Sometimes they provide a glimpse of Yong's own feelings, as when 'el coraçón' (Estrada, p. 12, l. 4) becomes 'her secret hart' (12. 20); 'la muerte' (Estrada, p. 248, l. 16) becomes 'imperious death' (204. 15); 'vuestras almas' (Ferreres, p. 49, l. 30) becomes 'your invincible soules' (268. 37); 'una harpa' (Estrada, p. 107, l. 16) becomes 'a silver-sounding Harpe' (89. 18–19). (Yong was so impressed by the last that he introduced it again, rendering 'estos versos' (Estrada, p. 147, l. 30) as 'this Sonnet to the tune of his silver-sounding Harpe' (120. 19–20)). One of the most strikingly successful of Yong's interpretative adjectives is his rendering of 'Por reyr una hora' (Estrada, p. 48, l. 16) as 'For laughing but one little hower' (39. 10–11). Yong has further emphasized the contrast between the thoughtless merriment intended by the Ismenia–Selvagia episode and its painful results by his own expanded and inserted comments: Ismenia says that her friends dressed her as a woman 'to make some sport and to laugh', (35. 40), and Selvagia regrets that Ismenia's plan was devised by chance and 'onely for merriment' (36. 24).

Yong's desire to make the Spanish author's meaning more explicit seems also to be the reason for even fuller expansion of certain passages. At times this expansion interprets emotion or cause of action, as when 'por su señora Diana' (Estrada, p. 18, l. 19) becomes 'for the love of his cruell *Mistresse Diana*' (17. 1); 'no tuve más poder en mí' (Estrada, p. 42, ll. 32–33) becomes 'I lost the power of my conquered soule' (34. 27); 'cosa de que no poco sobresalto recebí' (Estrada, p. 154, ll. 13–14) becomes 'whose sudden sight engendred a forcible passion of joy and feare in my amazed soule' (125. 11–12); 'Sylvano, ¿qué es dél? ¿A dónde está?' (Estrada, p. 228, ll. 4–5) becomes '*Sylvanus* mine onely life and joy, O *Sylvanus* is he, whom I love. O what is become of my *Sylvanus*? Where is my *Sylvanus*?' (188.39–189.1). At other times Yong enjoys being explicit where the Spanish author is general, as when 'Mas nunca orden tanto adornó hermosura' (Estrada, p. 132, ll. 21–22) becomes 'But never did frizeling and adorned periwigge of any Lady in stately court beautify in such sort' (109. 5–6); 'las mesas fueron puestas' (Estrada, p. 166, ll. 16–17) becomes 'where fine white clothes being spred on the tables, and furnished with daintie cates' (134. 13–14).

That Yong is not slavishly literal can be seen in his idiomatic and lively interpretation of the more restrained Spanish prose. So 'no sabía quien le avía dicho' (Estrada, p. 114, l. 23) becomes 'whosoever it was that buzzed it into her eares' (95. 2–3), and 'muy bien hablado, avisado y entendido' (Ferreres, p. 92, l. 15) becomes 'one that could tell a smooth tale, and with great wisedome and discretion bring his purpose to good effect' (301. 21–22). This freedom can clearly be seen in contrast to some of Wilson's more literal renderings. Wilson renders 'templarme este descontento' (Estrada, p. 12, ll. 11–12) as 'to temper this discontentm^t'[1] but in Yong it becomes 'to tune me this jarring string' (12. 26). Whereas Wilson is satisfied to follow the Spanish 'a sufrir desventuras' (Estrada, p. 10, l. 16) with 'to suffer disadventures'[2] Yong brings out the submerged metaphor in his version 'to suffer Fortunes unworthie disgraces' (11. 32–33). Wilson renders a Spanish figure of speech literally, so that 'me estava llamando a la puerta' (Estrada, p. 23, ll. 15–16) is 'stoode calling mee att the gate',[3] while Yong, albeit

---

[1] British Museum Add. MS. 18638, f. 10ᵛ.   [2] Ibid., f. 8ᵛ.   [3] Ibid., f. 23ʳ.

apologetically, looks for an English equivalent: 'was knocking (as it were) at my doore' (20. 25). Yong emphasizes a more colourful Spanish passage by personification and alliteration, so that 'la primavera, con las alegres nuevas del verano' (Estrada, p. 9, ll. 22–23) becomes 'cheereful spring-tyde (the merry messenger of sommer)' (11. 11–12), but Wilson merely translates 'the springe with his cheareful dewes of the Newyeare'.[1]

Yong's desire to make his prose a little more poetic does not always seem necessary or successful. Perhaps 'she was addressing her resplendant tresses' (19. 2–3) for 'se peinava' (Estrada, p. 21, l. 16) is acceptable, but 'now gan the duskie welkin to waxe cleere, and hastie morning was come' (37. 10–11) for 'La mañana se vino' (Estrada, p. 46, l. 4) is surely excessive. Yong's own insertions of poetic similes are no more interesting or original, for example 'like to the dying swanne neere to this river' (236. 2), and 'as the sun doth the chiefest stars in brightnes' (127. 3–4). It is probably the same urge towards what he thinks poetic that leads Yong to mythologize, so that 'amor' (Estrada, p. 17, l. 9) becomes '*Cupid*' (16. 9), 'el sol' (Estrada, p. 178, l. 17) becomes '*Titan* in his cheefest glorie' (143. 10–11), and 'lo mucho que desto siento' (Estrada, p. 69, l. 6) becomes 'the *Chaos* of griefe wherin I am overwhelmed' (56. 33).

A more interesting stylistic urge is seen in Yong's striving for a euphuistic harmony and balance, usually by repetition of a word or construction, or by alliteration. So 'los tiempos y el coraçón de Diana se mudaron' (Estrada, p. 7, ll. 14–15) becomes 'time, and *Dianas* hart with time were chaunged' (10. 13–14); 'los malos o buenos successos de la fortuna' (Estrada, p. 10, ll. 4–5) becomes 'the prosperous and preposterous successe of fortune' (11. 17–18); 'riéndose de los amores que tú con ella avías tenido' (Estrada, p. 225, ll. 11–12) becomes 'laughing at thy love, and making a sport of thy teares and sighes' (187. 8–9). Sometimes this urge leads Yong to expand a phrase out of all recognition, as when 'el coraçón, de grandíssimo amor' (Estrada, p. 261, ll. 24–25) becomes 'mine eies with teares, my eares with hearing denials, my thoughts with a bitter taste of sorrow' (214. 8–9). Sometimes he will insert balanced or alliterative phrases of his own which are in keeping with the general tenor of the passage he is supposed to be

---

[1] British Museum Add. MS. 18638, f. 8ʳ; 'dewes' is presumably an uncorrected error for 'newes'.

translating, for example 'speake not of his dittie, but of his deeds' (235. 21-22), and 'the substance of my sighs, and the object of my thoughts' (239. 38).

Most of Yong's own additions to the text show the impulses that have already been discussed, particularly his desire to interpret causes of emotion and action more fully, and make the Spanish author's meaning more explicit. The two following passages (with Yong's additions italicized) exemplify these impulses and the methods he uses to fulfil them: so

la pastora ya huya de velle, muriéndose no mucho antes quando no le vía, estuvo por perder el seso de enojo y determinó de estorvar esta buena fortuna de Montano. (Estrada, p. 51, ll. 8-12)

is expanded to

the Shepherdesse did now shun his sight (who not long since before died for the want thereof) *despite, wroth, and jealousie at once so fiercely assailed him*, that his impatience had almost bereft him of his wits, if presently he had not determined to hinder Montanus his good fortune, *or in the pursuite thereof to have lost his deerest life*. (41. 27-33)

and

que por esconderse de mí se había puesto en hábito de pastora
(Ferreres, p. 58, ll. 5-7)

is expanded to

that she had taken upon her the habite of a Shepherdesse; *with as strong a resolution* to hide her-selfe from me, *as strange to live unknowne in those disguised weedes*. (275. 26-28)

Yong's most striking achievement as a translator of poetry lies in his ability to handle a wide variety of metres, some of them of considerable complexity. Although he is not uniformly successful in his attempts to reproduce difficult metres, he shows that he has an ear and care for rhythm in sonnets, both Petrarchian and Shakespearian, sestinas, both single and double, *ottava rima, terza rima, rime sdrucciole*, quatrains, quintains, various six- and eight-line stanzas, and complex lyric measures. His worst fault is a tendency to sacrifice the sense to the metre, particularly in the early part of the translation, before he has warmed to his task (cf. 'Although my quiet' (p. 47), *Arsenius his letter* (p. 114), and most disastrously, the *rime sdrucciole* of 'Syrenus, what thought'st thou' (p. 26)). But his total failures are remarkably few, and his interest in the challenge of the metres is evident in the care with which he follows the mixed forms of such a poem as 'If teares cannot with tendernesse relent thee' (p. 224), and the lyric stanza of *Provençall Rythmes* (p. 254). But Yong is not always content merely to imitate, but exercises his invention rather than copy a metre he has already achieved (for example, the second group of *Provençall Rythmes* (p. 413)), and sometimes shows in one poem (such as 'Now that the sunne' (p. 277)) first his independence from his original, then, when the problem of internal rhyme catches his attention, his capacity to imitate.

Yong's metrical skill and inventiveness is perhaps best shown in his handling of the considerable number of short poems in quatrains (see particularly the groups of poems pp. 47–51, pp. 283–5, and pp. 381–9). The Spanish metre in these poems is regularly octosyllabic. Yong renders some of the poems in iambic tetrameter (e.g. 'If to be lov'd' (p. 385), and 'Since thou to me wert so unkinde' (p. 386)), but the number of variations he introduces elsewhere is astonishing. He expands four (pp. 121, 285, 381, 383) to decasyllabic lines; he renders one (p. 49) in truncated trochaic tetrameter and one (p. 382) in common measure; he combines common measure in the odd stanzas with octosyllabic lines in the even stanzas in one (p. 232) and with decasyllabic lines in the even stanzas in two (pp. 50, 385); he combines octosyllabic odd stanzas with decasyllabic even stanzas (p. 90), and decasyllabic odd stanzas with octosyllabic even stanzas (in the longest poem of this type 'Poore Melibee' (p. 408)), and finds still further variations for the poems 'Weepe not' (p. 50) and 'End now my life' (p. 284).

Although Yong's poetical merits are not confined to metrical care and ingenuity, it is true that his most successful efforts are largely dependent on his good sense of rhythm. This is noticeable in the refrain of his best-known poem 'Let now each meade' (p. 378), 'Ring forth faire Nymphes, your joyfull songs for gladnes', in the tuneful refrain of an otherwise poor poem (p. 21) 'Sweet shadowed river bankes tell me where my Syrenus is', and in the first line and refrain of 'Poore Melibee of love and hope forgot' (p. 408). It is his sense of rhythm and ability to handle the long line which make his rendering of the charming little song 'Foolish love' (p. 47) so effective, particularly in the lilt of the first line, where he has changed the repetition of the Spanish 'Amor loco ¡ay, amor loco!' (Estrada, p. 57) to 'Foolish love, ah foolish lover'.

His sense of rhythm is again evident in a comparison of his translation of 'Love is not blinde' (p. 251, cf. Ferreres, p. 25) with the anonymous translation (p. 441). In the first four lines particularly, Yong's version is smooth and flowing, the other lame. In the fifth and sixth lines Yong shows how effectively he can introduce a pause in one line and point it up by the flow of the next:

> Madnes to say, that flames are *Cupids* pride,
> For my desire his fier doth containe.

In the poem which answers this, Yong shows another of his talents, the choice of a strikingly appropriate word, in his rendering of 'Quien libre está, no viva descuidado' (Ferreres, p. 28) as 'He that in freedome jets it proud and brave' (253. 18). Yong also makes effective use of parallelism, repetition, and alliteration, for example 16. 25–28, where there is no repetition of the phrase 'Love's not a thing' in the Spanish (Estrada, p. 18, ll. 6–9), and his turning of the Spanish 'La hermosa, rubicunda y fresca aurora' (Ferreres, p. 181, l. 9) to 'The faire, the fresh, the red, and rosie morning' (358. 26). His use of repetition and balance to give force and energy to an idea can be seen in his translation

> Lovers, with pride enjoy your full content,
> To see your selves in favour and in grace,
> For I doe joy to see my torments spent,
> And joy to see them in oblivions place:
> I joy to see my captive hart so free,
> I joy to see my selfe in libertie. (360. 27–32)

of Gil Polo's original

> Goze el amador contento
> de verse favorescido;
> yo con libre pensamiento
> de ver ya puesto en olvido
> todo el passado tormento. (Ferreres, p. 184)

Although Yong can by no means rank with poets who make of a translation an original work of genius, he is nevertheless capable of coining an apt image, of making a colourless passage lively, and of elaborating a theme independently and appropriately.

It is Yong, not Montemayor, who sees Delius as 'A sluggish drone', unworthily devouring the honey of 'that sweete and pleasant flower' Diana (57. 31–33, cf. Estrada, p. 70, ll. 24–27), and Yong, living in a London no less rainy but less well paved than today, who sees Gil Polo's

> espesa niebla
> con la tiniebla
> escura y triste   (Ferreres, p. 253, ll. 7–9)

as

> The cloudes as darke as any pitch,
> And thicke as lothsome mud in ditch. (413. 25–26)

Where Gil Polo rather pedantically delivers unembroidered advice, Yong enforces that advice by visualizing the fatuous expression of enamoured shepherds:

> Porque los casos de amores
> tienen tan triste ventura,
> que es mejor a los pastores
> gozar libertad segura
> que aguardar vanos favores.
> (Ferreres, p. 186, ll. 6–10)

> For cruell Love with Fortune doth agree,
>   And tickle Fortune like to *Cupid* wavers:
> Then (jolly Shepherdes) I would counsell yee
>   Not to gape after Loves, and Fortunes favours:
>   And if ye meane a sweete life to procure,
>   Freedome imbrace, and captive Love abjure. (362. 13–18)

Florisias Song (p. 398), where Yong has again expanded octosyllabic quintains to decasyllabic six-line stanzas, provides many examples of similar added liveliness and emphasis.

Yong's success as a translator of poetry is not limited to single lines or passages, and short poems. His ear, his feeling for words, and a certain delighted energy sustain the appeal of the *terza rima* of 'Now Love, and fortune' (p. 206), Montanus's sestina (p. 358), the *Provençall Rythmes* (pp. 254, 413), and the marriage Caroll (p. 378). If it is remembered that he was writing at a point in English literary history when versification was only just finding its feet, and that he himself was not yet twenty-three years old, his achievement must be recognized as considerable.

VII. *Textual Introduction*

There has been only one edition of Yong's translation of the three parts of *Diana*, in 1598, of which at least twenty-eight copies are still in existence. Of this edition, I have examined the seven copies described below, fully collating CTr¹, BM¹, Bodl, and Sus, and partially collating CTr², CUL, and BM².

[CTr¹] Trinity College, Cambridge. Capell F. 11.

> A clean large copy, in excellent condition. The copy text of the present edition.

[CTr²] Trinity College, Cambridge. Munby b. 2.

> Lacks sig. 2M2; text defective at other points. In an extremely battered and scribbled condition.

[CUL] University Library, Cambridge. Hisp. 4.59.2.

> Lacks fly-leaf.

[BM¹] British Museum. 85 k. 13.

> A fine clean copy.

[BM²] British Museum. C59 i. 19.

> Lacks sigs. O5–P1 incl. Title-page mounted, fly-leaf backed.

[Bodl] Bodleian Library, Oxford. Douce M. 740.

[Sus] From the library of the Duke of Sussex, now in my possession.

The title-page of the 1598 edition is reproduced on p. 1; the collation and contents are as follows:

2°, a⁴ A–2R⁶ 2S⁸ [$3(−a3,+2S4) signed. $1 are signed with numeral], 252 leaves, pp. *8* 1–375 *376* 377–496 [= 504] [Errors and corrections in pagination vary from copy to copy]

Contents : a1 : title (verso blank); a2 : Dedication; a3 : Preface; on a3ᵛ : [triangular tailpiece: face in centre, ornamental leaves around, 100×100×110 mm.]; a4 : Dedicatory epistle and sonnet by Montemayor; a4ᵛ : Dedicatory sonnets; A1 : 'The Argument'; A1–O2ᵛ : 'Diana of George of Montemayor' in seven books; O3–2I2 : Perez's addition 'The Second Part of Diana' in eight books; 2I2ᵛ : Head title, and Dedication of 'Enamoured Diana' by Gaspar Gil Polo; 2I3–2S8ᵛ : 'Enamoured Diana' in five books. [The fourth and fifth books are called 'the third Part of Diana'.]

Diana was entered in the *Stationers' Register* on 9 September 1598 to George Bishop (the G.B. of the title-page) in the following terms:

Entred for his Copie under Mr Newberys hand and the hands of the reste of the wardens A booke Called the Diana of George of Monte Mayor Deuided into three p*a*rtes Done out of Spanishe into Englishe by Bartholmewe Younge gent Prouided that if at any tyme hereafter the said booke shall come in question the said \Mr/ Bushopp to answer it vjd.[1]

George Bishop was an eminent bookseller and printer in London, where he was in business from 1562–1611. He was Warden of the Company of Stationers for two terms (1577–8 and 1583–4) and Master for five terms (1589–90, 1592–3, 1599–1600, 1602–3, and 1607–8). He was also an alderman of the City of London, and held shares in several major publishing ventures.[2] It is not surprising that Bishop should sponsor such an expensive publication as *Diana*, but the proviso is puzzling. It is possible that it has something to do with the reputation of the printer, Edmund Bollifant, who seems to have had a fairly short (1584–1602) but stormy career, being twice in prison for acts of piracy, in 1586 and 1595.[3] Bishop was not concerned in Yong's two earlier publications.

Bishop's edition of *Diana* well illustrates McKerrow's dictum that it is always necessary to remember that the unit of printing is the forme.[4] He points out that it is possible to have a corrected forme without having a corrected sheet, and that it is 'quite unscientific to speak of a more or less corrected *copy* of a book', since 'it cannot be supposed that the binder, when gathering the sheets for binding, would trouble himself as to whether they represented the final corrections or not; he would take them as they happened to come.'[5] In the copies of *Diana* I have examined there are twenty press-variant formes, which are listed below.

When speaking of a 'corrected' forme, it should be remembered that the corrections are not always comprehensive. For example,

[1] *Stationers' Company Records Liber C and D Entry Book of Copies 1595–1640*, f. 41ᵛ (Bodleian Library MSS. film 445). See also E. Arber, *A Transcript of the Stationers' Registers: 1554–1640*, 1875–94, iii. 126.
[2] R. B. McKerrow, *A Dictionary of Printers and Booksellers in England, Scotland and Ireland, . . . 1557–1640*, 1910, p. 35.
[3] Ibid., p. 41.
[4] *An Introduction to Bibliography*, 1928, pp. 209–13.   [5] Ibid., p. 209.

on 2K5^v all copies err in reading 'acccustomed'; on H5 'bee d- scended' is corrected in six copies out of seven, but the substantive error of 'It' for 'Ill' on H2^v was not caught until the 'Faultes escaped', and the error on H5 'surmonnteth' slipped past altogether.

The forme 2I3.4(i) provides an example of two stages of correction. At 2I3^v l. 5, CTr$^{1-2}$, CUL, BM$^{1-2}$ err in reading 'blame me.'; Bodl, Sus are corrected to 'blame me'. CTr$^{1-2}$, CUL, BM$^{1-2}$, Sus are wrongly paginated 2, 3 (for 378, 379); Bodl is correctly paginated.

In view of Yong's remark that 'all the last Terme that it was in the Presse (having matters of greater consequence in charge) I could not intende the correction:' most of the corrections during printing must have been made by the printer and compositors, though Yong's comments at the end of his Preface show that he had at least checked, and was perhaps responsible for, the errors corrected in the 'Faultes escaped'.

Of the seven copies examined, CTr$^{1-2}$ and BM^1 contain the largest number of corrected formes (16), Sus by far the fewest (7). Since CTr^2 is incomplete, and BM^1 contains a higher proportion of errors affecting the text than CTr^1, CTr^1 has been selected as the copy text. The alterations in the text recorded in the critical apparatus are largely editorial. In all of these the letter Y has been used to denote all those copies of Bishop's edition of *Diana* examined, and described above; e.g. 21. 34 *hap sway Ed.*] *haps way Y*. Where the copy text errs in varying from the other copies, each copy is denoted as in the descriptive list above; e.g. 190. 37 discourteous *CTr^2 CUL BM$^{1-2}$ Sus*: discourous *CTr^1 Bodl.*

The following 'Faultes escaped' have been silently corrected in the text:

19. 22	debt	*corrected from*	doubt
64. 10	See	,,	She
92. 11	ash colour velvet hose	,,	ash colour hose
96. 11	be not divided	,,	be divided
112. 31	nurse	,,	curse
123. 27	brake with	,,	brake hart with
136. 4	Ill	,,	It
150. 16	Vique	,,	Vigue
156. 29	temerous	,,	timerous

210. 12	such beautie	*corrected from*	each beautie
218. 27	away	,,	alway
219. 23	hap	,,	pap
224. 25	And she	,,	She
229. 34	heades	,,	handes

In the present edition, in accordance with modern typographical practice, i has been modernized to j, u to v, vv to w. Contractions are silently expanded. Ornamental capitals, swash letters, different sizes of type, and all ligatures are ignored.

The decision not to modernize the text any further springs from a conviction that punctuation is a method of 'conveying meaning which is not expressed lexically'[1] (and by no means always a crude method), and that in sixteenth-century prose particularly the punctuation is intimately linked with the idiom and rhetoric, and as such cannot satisfactorily be altered without also embarking on wholesale retranslation (as in 'translations' of Chaucer). Vivian Salmon's analysis of Clapham's practices provides a most useful introduction to the more mechanically grammatical aspects of the punctuation of Yong's *Diana*;[2] the more elusive and subjective semantic values can best be recognized by considering an example.

But tell me, what is the reason, that you are so inconstant, that in a moment you throwe a Shepherde downe from the top of his good hap, to the deepest bottome of miserie: knowest thou whereunto I attribute it? To nothing else but to your owne simplicitie: bicause you have no perfect understanding to conceive the good, nor knowe the value of

---

[1] V. Salmon, 'Early Seventeenth-Century Punctuation as a Guide to Sentence Structure', *Review of English Studies*, N.S. xiii (1962), 348.

[2] Ibid. xiii. 347–60. I have found very little on punctuation in English in the places where one might expect to find guidance (see also Moxon's *Mechanick Exercises on the Whole Art of Printing*, ed. H. Davis and H. Carter, 1962, pp. 215–16, note). Lily's *Brevissima Institutio* (edn. of 1573) has a little section on punctuation, where he says that one of the functions of the comma is for drawing breath, but provides little help on grammatical functions. This section is not in the accompanying English translation (edn. of 1572). Publicius Jacobus's *Ars Oratoriæ* (Venice, 1485) does, however, give some practical guidance on the grammatical functions of punctuation marks ('De modo punctandi', E2r–v). A later work, Charles Butler's *The English Grammar* (published 1633, but this is towards the end of Butler's long life devoted to teaching) gives six pages to punctuation. Butler states that points serve 'for ðe better understanding of Woords' and distinguishes between the four primary simple points both by perfect and imperfect sense of the sentence, and by length of pause.

that, you have in your handes. You meddle with love and are uncapable to judge what it meanes; how doe you, then, knowe to behave
your selves in it.   (p. 31)

The colon 'miserie: knowest' nicely conveys that Syrenus already
knew the answer (and was intent upon giving it) when he began
'But tell me, what is the reason,'. This meaning is not conveyed
by the modernized 'miserie? Knowest'. The choice of a colon
rather than a comma after 'simplicitie' is a subjective judgement
that is not possible within modern grammatical rules, yet it is
a valuable indication that the reader is invited to dwell on the
notion of simplicity in women before proceeding to consider its
causes. In the last sentence the intimate connexion between statement and question which is achieved by the semicolon could only
satisfactorily be rendered in modern English by some complete
re-statement such as 'How can you possibly know how to behave
yourselves in love when you merely dabble in it while lacking the
mental capacity to understand what it means?' But of course this
reversal of the parts of the sentence destroys the logical structure
of the passage as a whole.

Two other possible modernizations of the text were also considered: the introduction of quotation marks, and modernized
spelling. The first was dismissed on the grounds that to provide
quotation marks without also altering the punctuation of direct
speech would have been more jarring and confusing than helpful.
Consider, for example, the following exchanges:

How came they to thy handes, saide *Syrenus*? The next day following
(saide *Sylvanus*) in that very place I founde the paper wherein they were
written.   (p. 19)

Unhappy women are these, saide *Selvagia*, that are so ill intreated by
your wordes: But more unfortunate are those men, saide *Sylvanus*, that
are worse handled by your deedes.   (p. 30)

The old spelling is preserved mainly for the sake of consistency.
Where an unfamiliar spelling might present a momentary diffi-
culty, the modern form is given in the Commentary.

With these considerations then in mind, all care in the present
edition has been devoted to trying to present the text as Yong
would have wished it had he himself had more time to 'intende
the correction' in 1598. Because of Yong's 'verie darke and enterlined' copy, which he was so loth to write out again, there are in

the original edition many misprints and errors besides those listed in the 'Faultes escaped' or corrected at press. I have endeavoured to correct these, taking the type of corrections made by Yong and the compositors as a guide. Nevertheless, I still feel it necessary to echo Yong's defence, that only 'the greatest faults' are corrected, 'the lesse being of no moment purposely omitted'.

Press-variant Formes

C1.6(i) (45. 29–46. 35, 57. 32–59. 5)
  Corrected CTr¹⁻² CUL BM¹⁻² Bodl; uncorrected Sus.
  C1ᵛ 45. 31 *be exprest*] *beexprest*
  C6 58. 27 sung] song
    59. 5 *despite*] *despit*

[D1.6(i) Correctly paginated 38, 47 CUL BM¹⁻² Bodl; wrongly paginated 50, 59 CTr¹⁻² Sus.]

D3.4(i) (66. 25–68. 36)
  Corrected CTr¹⁻² BM¹⁻² Bodl; uncorrected CUL Sus.
  D4 67. 32 *more then I would,*] *more, then I would*

F3.4(i) (100. 38–104. 3)
  Corrected CTr¹ BM¹; uncorrected CTr² CUL BM² Bodl Sus.
  F3ᵛ 102. 17 me alive] m alive

G3.4(i) (120. 24–123. 7)
  Corrected CTr¹⁻² CUL BM² Bodl Sus; uncorrected BM¹.
  G3ᵛ 121. 6 *joy but*] *joy, but*
  G4 121. 28 *In least*] *Is least*
    122. 18 too meane to] to meane too
    122. 27 (my kineswomen] my (kineswomen

H2.5(i) (135. 1–136. 6, 141. 27–143. 8)
  Corrected CTr¹⁻² CUL BM¹⁻² Bodl; uncorrected Sus.
  H5 142. 3 be descended] bee d- scended

K2.5(o) (166. 13–167. 34, 176. 33–178. 15)
  Corrected CTr¹⁻² CUL BM¹⁻² Bodl; uncorrected Sus.
  K5ᵛ 177. 30 while] whille

L3.4(i) 189. 5–192. 5)
  Corrected CTr² CUL BM¹⁻² Sus; uncorrected CTr¹ Bodl.
  [L3ᵛ RT *fifth*] *ſifth*]
  L4 190. 37 discourteous] discourous

N1.6(i) (219. 25–221. 10, 232. 30–234. 15)
  Corrected CTr$^{1-2}$ CUL BM^2 Bodl Sus; uncorrected BM^1.
N6   233. 13 famous] famons

2I3.4(i) (245. 18–247. 36)
  First stage: Corrected Bodl Sus; uncorrected CTr$^{1-2}$ CUL BM$^{1-2}$.
2I3^v 245. 22 *blame me*] *blame me.*
  Second stage: Corrected Bodl; uncorrected CTr$^{1-2}$ CUL BM$^{1-2}$ Sus.
  [Pagination 378, 379] 2, 3]

[2I1].6(o) ([Perez], 253. 31–255. 9)
  Corrected CTr$^{1-2}$ CUL BM^2 Bodl Sus; uncorrected BM^1.
2I6^v 254. 11 this] his

2K2.5(o) (257. 29–259. l. 12, 268. 2–269. 23)
  Corrected CTr$^{1-2}$ CUL BM$^{1-2}$ Bodl; uncorrected Sus.
2K2 259. 2 sigh,] sight
2K5^v 268. 33 misfortune!] misfortune.

2K2.5(i) (259. 13–260. 32, 266. 20–268. 2)
  Corrected CTr$^{1-2}$ CUL BM$^{1-2}$ Bodl; uncorrected Sus.
2K2^v 260. 13 by] yb
2K5 267. 16 governe it, but that] governe that, but it
  267. 23 heard] heatd

2M1.6(o) (289. 20–290. 35, 307. 36–309. 21)
  Corrected CTr^2 CUL BM$^{1-2}$ Sus; uncorrected CTr^1 Bodl.
2M1 290. 25–26 comming; but this is not the first fault that (faire *Diana*) thou must pardon me] comming, thou (faire *Diana*) must pardon me; but this is not the first fault that
  290. 34 morning] morning,

2M3.4(o) (295. 12–296. 27, 299. 31–301. 15)
  Corrected CTr^1 BM^1; uncorrected CTr^2 CUL BM^2 Bodl Sus.
2M3 296. 18 W^2*Hen*] W^2 *en* CTr^2 CUL BM^2 Sus, W^2*e n* Bodl.

2N3.4(o) (315. 31–317. 8, 319. 28–321. 5)
  Corrected CTr$^{1-2}$ CUL BM$^{1-2}$ Bodl; uncorrected Sus.
2N3 316. 22 stinged: but] stinged but

2P2.5(o) (348. 7–349. 14, 357. 33–359. 8)
  Corrected CTr$^{1-2}$ BM^1; uncorrected CUL BM^2 Bodl Sus.
2P2 348. 24 *proclame,*] *proclame*

2P3.4(i) (351. 29–354. 28)
  Corrected CTr$^{1-2}$ CUL BM^1; uncorrected BM^2 Bodl Sus.

2P3v 352. 8 *brest.*] *brest,*
2P4 353. 8 *Marcelius,*] *Marcelius*
353. 25 *Polydorus*] *Polydora*
353. 34 in habit] inhabit
353. 40 name] naue

2Q1.6(i) (362. 33–364. 16, 375. 26–377. 8)
Corrected CTr¹⁻² CUL BM¹⁻² Bodl; uncorrected Sus.
2Q6 377. 1 hart] hatt

2S1.8(i) (398. 25–399. 32, 415. 29–417. 10)
Corrected CTr¹⁻² CUL BM² Bodl Sus; uncorrected BM¹.
2S1v 398. 29 *exceeding*] *exbeeding*

ADDITIONAL NOTE

In the present edition the practice in regard to italic and roman punctuation marks is to use roman characters in a body of roman type, and italic colons, semicolons, question and exclamation marks in a body of italic type. Roman characters are used following words in roman type that occur in a body of italic type (e.g. pp. 53–54). This is in accordance with Bollifant's practice, with the following exceptions: Bollifant does not use italic semicolons or exclamation marks; his use of italic and roman colons is inconsistent (the two are hard to distinguish); and usually, though not consistently, he uses italic question marks and colons following an italicized word in a body of roman type.

DIANA

OF GEORGE OF MONTEMAYOR:

Tranflated out of Spanifh into
Englifh by BARTHOLOMEW
YONG of the Middle
Temple Gentleman.

At London,
Printed by Edm. Bollifant,
Impenfis G. B.

1598

TO THE RIGHT HONORABLE
and my very good Lady
the Lady RICH.

RIGHT HONORABLE, such are the apparant defects of arte and judgement in this new pourtraied DIANA, that their 5 discoverie must needes make me blush and abase the worke, unlesse with undeserved favour erected upon the high and shining pillar of your Honorable protection, they may seeme to the beholder lesse, or none at all. The glorie wherof as with reason it can no waies be thought woorthie, but by boldly adventuring 10 upon the apparant demonstration of your magnificent minde, wherein all noble vertues have their proper seate, and on that singular desire, knowledge and delight, wherewith your Ladiship entertaineth, embraceth and affecteth honest endevours, learned languages, and this particular subject of DIANA, warranted by 15 all vertue and modestie, as COLLIN in his French dedicatorie to the Illustrous Prince LEWIS of LORRAINE at large setteth downe and commendeth: so now presenting it to so soveraigne a light, and relying on a gracious acceptance, what can be added more to the full content, desire and perfection of DIANA, and of her 20 unwoorthie Interpreter (that hath in English attire exposed her to the view of strangers) then for their comfort and defence to be armed with the Honorable titles and countenance of so high and excellent a Patronesse? But as certaine yeares past (my Honorable good Lady) in a publike shewe at the Middle Temple, where 25 your Honorable presence with many noble Lordes and faire Ladies graced and beautified those sportes, it befell to my lot in that woorthie assemblie, unwoorthily to performe the part of a French Oratour by a deducted speech in the same toong, and that amongst so many good conceits and such generall skill in toongs, 30 all the while I was rehearsing it, there was not any, whose mature judgement and censure in that language I feared and suspected more then your Ladiships, whose attentive eare and eie daunted

my imagination with the apprehension of my disabilitie, and
your Ladiships perfect knowledge in the same: Now once againe
in this translation out of Spanish (which language also with the
present matter being so well knowen to your Ladiship) whose
reprehension and severe sentence of all others may I more justly 5
feare, then that which (Honorable Madame) at election you may
herein duely give, or with favour take away. But as then by your
gracious aspect and milde countenance I flattered my selfe with
your favourable applause of the first; So now to prevent the
second, I have no other meanes, then the humble insinuation of it 10
to your most Honorable name and clemencie, most humbly
beseeching the same to pardon all those faultes, which to your
learned and judicious view shall occurre. Since then for pledge of
the dutifull and zealous desire I have to serve your Ladiship, the
great disproportion of your most noble estate to the qualitie of 15
my poore condition, can affoorde nothing else but this small
present, my praier shall alwaies importune the heavens for the
happie increase of your high and woorthie degree, and for the
full accomplishment of your most Honorable and vertuous
desires.   20

From High Onger in Essex the
28. of Novemb.
1598.

Your Honors most
humbly devoted,   25
BARTHOL. YONG.

The Preface to divers learned Gentlemen, and other my loving friendes.

ABout nineteene yeeres past (curteous Gentlemen) comming out of Spaine into my native countrey, and having spent welny three yeeres in some serious studies and certaine affaires, 5 with no meanes or occasion to exercise the Spanish toong (by discontinuance whereof it had almost shaken hands with me) it was my good hap to fall into the companie and acquaintance of my especiall good friend *Edward Banister* of Idesworth in the Countie of Southampton Esquier; who perceiving my remissenes 10 in the saide language, perswaded and encouraged me earnestly, by some good translation to recal it to her former place: And to that intent he gave me the first and second Part of *Diana* of *Montemayor* in Spanish, which Booke (although I had beene two yeeres in Spaine) till then I never saw nor heard of; whose friendly 15 care and desire to prevent so great a losse, and to preserve such an ornament in me, I confesse was the chiefe and principall cause (and therefore the onely credit) of this translation, whereby I recovered that toong againe that lay (as it were) smothered in the cinders of oblivion. The second cause of this my labour, was the 20 delight I passed in discurring most of those townes and places in it with a pleasant recordation of my pen, which mine eies so often with joy and sorrow had beheld. The third, the resolved then intent I had never (howsoever now it hath escaped my hands) to put it in Print, in proofe whereof it hath lyen by me finished 25 *Horaces* ten and six yeeres more. For till then I never tried my unproper vaine in making an English verse: how well or ill then the hard and strange kinde of Spanish is turned, I leave to your favourable censure and pardon: The low and pastorall stile hereof, *Montemayor* in his Epistle to the L. of Villanova excuseth, 30 entreating of Shepherds, though indeed they were but shadowes of great and honorable personages, and of their marriages, that not many yeeres agoe lived in the Court of Spaine, whose

posteritie to this day live in noble estate. But touching the Bookes
following, you must understand that *George* of *Montemayor* a
Gentleman sprung out of the noble house of *Montemayor* in
Portugal, after he had ended his first Part of *Diana*, which he
distributed into seven Bookes, intending to set forth the second 5
Part, and before his departure into Italie (where I heard he died)
imparted his purpose, and the subject of his intended second Part,
to *Alonso Perez*, who answering his intent, wrote the second
Part of *Diana*, contayning eight Bookes, promising in the end
thereof to continue it with a third Part, which yet he hath not 10
done, although I heare he hath a purpose to do it. But *Gaspar Gil
Polo* a Valentian Gentleman, who in my opinion excelleth for fine
conceit (whether before or after that *Alonso Perez* second Part
came forth) made another Part of *Diana*, naming it the first Part
of Enamoured *Diana*; the which being divided into five Bookes, 15
he intituleth to follow in due sequence the first seven Bookes of
Diana of *George* of *Montemayor*. And in the ende of that first Part
of Enamoured *Diana*, he likewise maketh a reference to another
Part which he promised to set foorth; the which and that of *Alonso
Perez*, if ever they come to light, I leave to some finer wit and 20
better judgement to English, my selfe having done too much by
launching so far into the maine, unlesse (happily) in your favourable judgements it may finde a friendly and temperate construction. Having compared the French copies with the Spanish
originall, I judge the first Part to be exquisite; the other two 25
corruptly done with a confusion of verse into Prose, and leaving
out in many places divers hard sentences, and some leaves in the
end of the third Part, wherefore they are but blind guides by any
to be imitated. Well might I have excused these paines, if onely
Edward Paston Esquier (who heere and there for his owne pleasure 30
(as I understand) hath aptly turned out of Spanish into English
some leaves that liked him best) had also made an absolute and
complete translation of all the Parts of *Diana*; the which, for his
travell in that Countrey, and great knowledge in that language,
accompanied with other learned and good parts in him, had of 35
all others, that ever yet I heard translate these Bookes, prooved
the rarest and worthiest to be embraced. The faults escaped in

the Printing, the copie being verie darke and enterlined, and I
loth to write it out againe, I pray you Gentlemen pardon, since
all the last Terme that it was in the Presse (having matters of
greater consequence in charge) I could not intende the correction:
advertising you by the way that the greatest faults are at the ende 5
of the Booke set downe, the lesse being of no moment purposely
omitted. Fare ye well and continue me in your woonted love and
favours.

Yours in all friendly offices,
B. Y.   10

THE EPISTLE

To the Illustrous and noble Lord *Don*
Juan de Castella de Villa Nova,
Baron of Bicorb and Quesa,
of GEORGE *of*   5
Montemayor.

ALthough this custome were not very auncient, most noble
L. for Authours to dedicate their workes to personages of
honour and renowne, by whome they were protected and defended;
notwithstanding your rare and high deserts (as well for your 10
noble and ancient house from whence you are descended, as also
for the resplendant valour and vertue of your person) might with
greater reason then I can expresse, incite me to performe more
then this obliged dutie. And admit the base stile of the worke,
and the Authours small woorth, in reason ought not so far extend 15
as to dedicate it to your Lordship: yet excluded from all other
remedies, I presumed onely on this, that it was somewhat accounted of. For precious stones are not so highly valued for the name
they have (for they may be false and counterfeite) as for his
estimate in whose handes they are: I humbly beseech your good 20
Lordship to entertaine this booke under your Hon. ampare and
correction, as to the Authour heereof (being but a stranger) you
have done no lesse, since his poore abilitie is not able to serve
your Lordship in any other thing: whose wished life and noble
estate our Lord increase for many yeeres.   25

To the same Lord.

Mæcenas was to *Maro* of great fame
  A singular good Lord and loving frend,
And *Alexander* did enjoy that same
  Rare wit of *Homer*, death though him did end: 30
And so the *Villanovas* generous name
  The *Lusitan* poore Authour doth defend,
    Making a base and wanting wit t'aspire
    Unto the clouds, and yet a great deale higher.

Don Gaspar Romani to the Authour.

If Lady LAURAS memorie unstained
  PETRARC in endlesse verse hath left renowned:
  And if with Laurell HOMER hath beene crowned
For writing of the wars the Greekes obtained: 5
If Kings t'advaunce the glorie they have gained
  In life time, when fierce MARS in battell frowned,
  Procure it should not be in LETHE drowned,
But after death by historie maintained:
More justly then shouldst thou be celebrated   10
  (O excellent DIANA) for the fairest
  Of all the faire ones, that the world hath brought foorth:
Since all those wits, whose pens were estimated
  To write the best, in glorie thou impairest,
  And from them all the Laurell crowne hast sought foorth. 15

Don Hieronymo Sant-Perez, to George of Montemayor.

Parnasse, O sacred mount and full of glorie,
  The Poets muse, delight of their desires:
Me thinkes thou art too comfortlesse and sorie,   20
  Compar'd with this, whose famous name aspires.

In deede I am, since that the Muses left me,
  And with their gracious Quire from hence descended
To mount this Hill, whose Greatnes hath bereft me
  Of all my fame, and glorie that is ended.   25

Thrise happie his Diana, since her flower
  In top of this High Hill was set so lately,
That all the world might view it every hower,
  Where she doth live most soveraigne and stately:

    In all the world most celebrate and graced,   30
    Being no lesse excelse, then highly placed.

The Argument of the first Seven Bookes.

IN the fieldes of the auncient and principall citie of *Leon* in Spaine, lying along the bankes of the river *Ezla*, lived a Shepherdesse called *Diana*, whose beautie was most soveraigne above all others in her time. She loved, and was deerely beloved againe 5 of a Shepherd called *Syrenus*, in whose mutuall love was as great chastitie and vertue as might be. At the same time another Shepherd called *Sylvanus* loved her also more then himselfe, but so abhorred of the Shepherdesse, that there was not any thing in the world, which she hated more. But it fell out, that as *Syrenus* 10 was constrained to be out of the kingdom about certaine affaires, which could by no means be excused, nor left undone, and the Shepherdesse remaining at home very sad for his absence, time, and *Dianas* hart with time were chaunged, who then was married to another Shepherd called *Delius*, burying him, whom she had 15 but of late so greatly loved, in unjust oblivion. Who, after a whole yeere of his absence comming home againe with great affection and desire to see his beloved Shepherdesse, knew before he came, that she was already married. And from hence the first booke begins: and in the others following, they shall finde divers 20 histories of accidents, that have truly happened, though they goe muffled under pastorall names and style.

The first Booke of Diana *of* George *of* Montemayor.

DOwne from the hils of *Leon* came forgotten *Syrenus*, whom love, fortune, and time did so entreate, that by the least 25 greefe, that he suffered in his sorrowfull life, he looked for no lesse then to loose the same. The unfortunate Shepherd did not now bewaile the harme, which her absence did threaten him, and the feare of her forgetfulnes did not greatly trouble his minde, bicause he sawe all the prophecies of his suspicion 30 so greatly to his prejudice accomplished, that now he thought he had no more misfortunes to menace him. But the Shepherd

comming to those greene and pleasant meades, which the great
river *Ezla* watreth with his cristalline streames, the great
felicitie and content came to his wandring thoughtes, which
sometimes he had enjoyed there, being then so absolute a Lord
of his owne liberty, as now subject to one, who had wrongfully 5
enterred him in darke oblivion. He went musing of that happie
time, when in those medowes, and on those faire banks he fed his
flocks, applying then his minde in the onely care and interest he
had to feede them well: and spending the rest of his howers in
the onely delight, that he tooke in the sweete smell of those 10
golden flowers, at that time especially, when cheerefull spring-tyde
(the merry messenger of sommer) is spread over the face of the
whole earth: sometimes taking his rebecke, which he ever caried
very neate in a scrip, and sometimes his bagpipe, to the tune of
which he made most sweete ditties, which of all the Shepherdesses 15
of those hamlets thereabouts made him most highly commended.
The Shepherd busied not his thoughts in the consideration of the
prosperous and preposterous successe of fortune, nor in the
mutabilitie and course of times, neither did the painfull diligence
and aspiring minde of the ambitious Courtier trouble his quiet 20
rest: nor the presumption and coye disdaine of the proude and
nice Ladie (celebrated onely by the appassionate vowes and
opinions of her amorous sutours) once occurre to his imaginations. And as little did the swelling pride, and small care of the
hawtie private man offend his quiet minde. In the field was he 25
borne, bred, and brought up: in the field he fed his flockes, and
so out of the limits of the field his thoughts did never range,
untill cruell love tooke possession of his libertie, which to those
he is commonly woont to doe, who thinke themselves freest
from his tyrannie. The sad Shepherd therefore came softly on his 30
pace, his eies turned into fountaines, the fresh hew of his face
chaunged, and his hart so tempered to suffer Fortunes unworthie
disgraces, that if she would have given him any content, she
must have sought him a new hart to receive it. The weedes that
he did weare, was a long gray coate, as rugged as his haps, 35
carrying a sheepehooke in his right hand, and a scrip hanging on
his left arme. He laide himselfe downe at the foote of a thicke
hedge, and began to cast foorth his eyes along those faire river
banks, untill their beames came to that place, where first they
beheld the beautie, grace, and rare vertues of the Shepherdesse 40

Diana, she, in whom skilfull nature had consummated all perfections, which in every part of her dainty body she had equally
bestowed. Then did his hart imagine that, which before it divined
of, That sometimes he should finde himselfe put amongst sorrowfull memories. And then could not the wofull Shepherd stop 5
his teares from gushing out, nor smother his sighes which came
smoking out of his brest, but lifting up his eies to heaven began
thus to lament. Ah memorie (cruell enemie to my quiet rest)
were not thou better occupied to make me forget present corsies,
then to put before mine eies passed contents? What saiest thou 10
memorie? That in this medow I beheld my Lady *Diana*, that in
the same I began to feele that, which I shal never leave of to
lament, That neere to that cleere fountaine (set about with high
and greene Sicamours) with many teares she solemnly sware to
me, that there was not the deerest thing in the world, no, not the 15
will of her parents, the perswasion of her brethren, nor the im-
portunities of her allies, that were able to remoove her from her
setled thoughts? And when she spake these words, there fell out
of those faire eies teares like orientall pearles, which seemed to
testifie that, which remained in her secret hart, commanding me, 20
upon paine to be accounted of her a man but of a base and abject
minde, if I did not beleeve that, which so often times she had told
me. But stay yet a little Memorie, since now thou hast put before
me the foundations of my mishap (and such they were, that the
joy, which I then passed, was but the beginning of the greefe 25
which now I suffer) forget not to tune me this jarring string, to
put before mine eies by one and one, the troubles, the turmoiles,
the feares, the suspects, the jealousies, the mistrusts, and cares,
which leave not him, that most truly loves. Ah memorie, memorie,
how sure am I of this answere at thy hands, that the greatest 30
paine, that I passed in these considerations, was but little in
respect of that content, which in lieu of them I received. Thou
hast great reason memorie, and the worse for me that it is so
great: and lying and lamenting in this sort, he tooke a paper out
of his bosome, wherein he had a few greene silken strings and 35
haire tyed up together, and laying them open before him upon
the greene grasse, with abundance of teares he tooke out his
Rebecke, not halfe so jocund as it was woont to be, at what
time he was in *Dianas* favour, and began to sing that which
followeth.
                                                                        40

HAire in change what libertie,
Since I sawe you, have I seene?
How unseemely hath this greene
Bene a signe of hope to me?
Once I thought no Shepherd might   5
In these fieldes be found (O haire)
(Though I did it with some feare)
Worthy to come neere your sight.
Haire, how many times and tydes
Did my faire Diana *spie,*   10
If I ware or left you by
And a thousand toyes besides.
And how oft in weeping sort
(Of deceitfull teares O springs)
Was she jealous of the things,   15
Which I spake or did in sport?
Those faire eies which wrought my woe,
(Golden haire) tell me what fault
In beleeving them I caught,
When they did assure me soe?   20
Saw you not how she did greeve,
Spilling daily many a teare,
Unto her till I did sweare,
That I did her words beleeve?
Who more beautie ever knew   25
In a subject of such change,
Or more sorrowes, or more strange
In a love so perfect true?
On the sand her did I see
Sitting by yon river bright,   30
Where her finger this did wright
Rather dead then changed be.
See how love beares us in hand,
Making us beleeve the wordes,
That a womans wit affordes,   35
And recorded in the sand.

Syrenus had not so soone made an end of his sorrowful song, if
that his teares had not bene at hand, for such an one was he, from
whom fortune had cut off all the waies and meanes of his remedie.

Sorrowing thus, his Rebecke fell out of his hand, and taking up the golden haire he put them in their place againe, saying, O pledges of the fairest and most disloyall Shepherdesse that humane eies may behold, how with your owne safetie have you beguiled me? Woe is me, that I cannot choose but see you, my whole 5 greefe consisting in having seene you. And pulling his hande out of his scrip, he found a letter, that *Diana* in time of his prosperitie had sent him, which when he beheld, with a burning sigh, that came from his very hart, he saide. O letter, letter burned maist thou be by his handes, who may best doe what he list: and woe be 10 to him that now shall reade thee: But who may doe it? And opening it, he sawe that it said thus.

Dianas letter to Syrenus.

HOw ill I should brooke thy words (my *Syrenus*) who would not thinke, but that love made thee utter them? Thou 15 saiest I love thee not so much as I ought to doe, I knowe not whereby thou perceivest it, and conceive not, how I should love thee more. Behold, it is now no time not to beleeve me, bicause thou seest, that the love, which I beare thee, compels me to beleeve that, which from thy very thoughts and affection thou 20 dost tell me. I imagine oftentimes, that as thou supposest, that I love thee not (by loving thee more then my selfe) so must thou thinke, that thou lovest me by hating me. Behold *Syrenus*, how time hath dealt better with thee then thou didst imagine at the beginning of our loves (with safetie yet of mine honour) which 25 owes thee all that it may: wherein is not any thing, that I would not doe for thy sake, beseeching thee, as much as I may, not to trouble thy minde with jealousie and suspicions, bicause thou knowest, how few escape out of their hands with safetie of life, which God give thee with all the content that I wish thee.   30

Is this a letter saide *Syrenus*, sighing, to make one thinke, that oblivion could enter into that hart, from whence such wordes came foorth? And are these wordes to be passed so slightly out of memorie? And that she then spake them, and now forget me? O sorrowfull man, with what great content did I reade this letter 35 when my Mistresse had sent it me, and how many times in the same hower did I reade it over againe? But for every pleasure then, with seven folde paine I am now apaide: and fortune could doe no lesse with me, then to make me fall from one extreme to another: For it had ill beseemed her with partiall hand to exempt me from that, which to all others she is commonly wont to doe.

About this time from the hill beneath, that led from the village to the greene medowe, *Syrenus* might perceive a Shepherd comm- ing downe pace by pace, and staying awhile at every step, sometimes looking up to heaven, and sometimes casting his eies upon the greene medow and faire river bankes, which from aloft he might easily view and discover (the thing which more augmented his sorrow) seeing the place, where the beginning and roote of his mishap did first growe. *Syrenus* knew him by and by, and looking towardes the place from whence he came, saide. Unfortunate Shepherd (though not halfe so much as I am) that art a corrivall with me in *Dianas* love, to what end have thy bootelesse suites served thee, and the disdaine that this cruell Shepherdesse hath done thee, but to put them all on my score? But if thou hadst knowen that the finall summe of all thy paines should have bene like to mine, what greater favour hadst thou found at fortunes hands, by preserving thee still in this haplesse estate of life, then by throwing me headlong downe from it, when I did lest suspect it? But now despised *Sylvanus* tooke out his bagpipe, and playing on it a little, with great sorrow and greefe did sing these verses following.

I Am a lover, but was never loved,
 Well have I lov'd, and will, though hated ever,
Troubles I passe, but never any mooved,
Sighes have I given, and yet she heard me never:
I would complaine, and she would never heare me,
And flie from love, but it is ever neere me:
Oblivion onely blamelesse doth beset me,
For that remembreth never to forget me.

For every ill one semblant I doe beare still,
To day not sad, nor yesterday contented,
To looke behinde, or go before I feare still,
All things to passe alike I have consented:
I am besides my selfe like him that daunceth,
And mooves his feete at every sound that chaunceth:
And so all like a senselesse foole disdaines me,
But this is nothing to the greefe that paines me.

The night to certaine lovers is a trouble,
When in the day some good they are attending:
And other some doe hope to gaine some double
Pleasure by night, and wish the day were ending:
With that, that greeveth some, some others ease them,   5
And all do follow that, that best doth please them:
But for the day with teares I am a crying,
Which being come, for night I am a dying.

Of Cupid to complaine who ever crave it,
In waves he writes and to the windes he crieth: 10
Or seeketh helpe of him, that never gave it:
For he at last thy paines and thee defieth.
Come but to him some good advise to lend thee,
To thousand od conceits he will commend thee.
What thing is then this love? It is a science,   15
That sets both proofe and study at defiance.

My Mistresse *loved her* Syrenus *deerely,*
And scorned me, whose loves yet I avouched,
Left to my greefe, for good I held it cleerely,
Though narrowly my life and soule it touched: 20
Had I but had a heaven as he once shining,
Love would I blame, if it had bene declining.
But love did take no good from me he sent me,
For how can love take that he never lent me.

Love's not a thing, that any may procure it,   25
Love's not a thing, that may be bought for treasure;
Love's not a thing, that comes when any lure it,
Love's not a thing, that may be found at pleasure:
For if it be not borne with thee, refraine it
To thinke, thou must be borne anew to gaine it: 30
Then since that love shuns force, and doth disclame it,
The scorned lover hath no cause to blame it.

Syrenus was not idle when *Sylvanus* was singing these verses, for
with his sighes he answered the last accents of his wordes, and
with his teares did solemnize that, which he conceived by them. 35
The disdained Shepherd after he had ended his song, began to
revolve in his minde the small regarde he had of himselfe, and

how for the love of his cruell *Mistresse Diana*, he had neglected all
his busines and flockes: and yet he reckoned all this but small. He
considered, that his service was without hope of recompence,
a great occasion to make him, that hath but small firmnesse,
easily cut off the way of his love. But his constancie was so great, 5
that being put in the middes of all the causes, which he had to
forget her, who never thought of him, with his owne safetie he
came so easily out of them, and so cleerely without prejudice to
the sincere love, which he bare his Shepherdesse, that (without
any feare) he never committed any ignorance, that might turne to 10
the hurt or hinderance of his faith. But when he sawe *Syrenus* at
the fountaine, he woondred to see him so sad, not that he was
ignorant of the cause of his sorrow, but bicause he thought that
if he had tasted but the lest favour, that *Syrenus* had sometimes
received at *Dianas* handes, such a contentment had bene ynough 15
for him all his life time. He came unto him and imbraced him,
and with many teares on both sides they sat them downe upon the
greene grasse, *Sylvanus* beginning to speake in this sort. God forbid (*Syrenus*) that for the cause of my mishap, or at the lest for the
small remedie thereof, I should take delight or revenge in thine, 20
which though at mine owne pleasure I might well doe, yet the
great love which I beare to my Mistresse *Diana*, woulde never
consent thereunto, nor suffer me to goe against that, which with
such good will and liking she had sometimes favoured: if thy
sorrowes greeve me not, let me never have end of mine; and in 25
such sort, that as soone as *Diana* was about to marry, if it killed
not my hart with thinking, that her marriage and thy death should
have bene both at one time, let me never enjoy any other estate
and condition of life then now I doe. Canst thou then thinke
(*Syrenus*) that I would wish thee ill, bicause *Diana* loved thee? 30
And that the favours that she did thee, were the occasions to
make me hate thee? What man, my faith was never so basely
poysed, but that it was ever so serviceable to my Mistresse
humour, not onely in loving thee, but in loving and honouring
all that ever she loved. And yet thou hast no cause to thanke me 35
for this care and compassion of thy greefe, for I am so dissolved
into cares, that for mine owne good I would be sorie, how much
more then for other mens harmes. This straunge kinde of the
Shepherd *Sylvanus* his greeting caused no small admiration in
Syrenus, and made him for a while in suspence with himselfe, 40

woondring at his great sufferance, and at the strange qualitie of his love, that he did beare to his Shepherdesse. But remembring himselfe at last, he said. Hast thou (*Sylvanus*) happily, bene borne for an example of patience to those, who know not how to suffer the adversities, that fortune puts before their eies? Or may it be, 5 that nature hath given thee so strong a minde, that it is not ynough for thee to suffer thine owne, but thou wilt needes helpe others to support theirs? I see thee so conformable to the hard condition of thy fortune, that, promising thee no helpe of remedie, thou doest aske no other, then that it hath already given thee. 10 I tell thee (*Sylvanus*) that time shewes well by thee, how every day it discovers novelties and straunge conceites beyonde the compasse of mans imagination. O how much more then ought this unfortunate Shepherd to emulate thee, by seeing thee suffer thy greefes with such content, which thou mightest rather have done 15 to him, when thou sawest him so happily enjoy his merry times. Hast thou not seene how greatly she favoured me, and with what sweete and gracious wordes she manifested her love unto me? Didst thou not see, how she could never goe with her flockes to the river, or take her lambes out of the folde, or in the heate of the 20 day drive her sheepe into the shades of these Sicamours without my companie? But for all this, I wish I may never see the remedie of my greefe, if I ever expected or desired any thing at *Dianas* hands that was repugnant to her honour, or if any such thing did ever passe my thought. For such was her beautie, her brave minde, 25 her vertue, and such unspotted puritie in her love to me againe, that they admitted no thought into my minde, which in prejudice of her goodnes and chastitie I might have imagined. I beleeve it well (saide *Sylvanus* sighing) for I can say as much by my selfe, and thinke moreover that there was never any, that 30 casting his eies on *Dianas* peerelesse beautie, durst desire any other thing, then to see her, and to converse with her. Although I knowe not, whether such rare and excellent beautie might in some mens thoughts (not subject to such a continent affection as ours) cause an excessive desire: and especially, if they had seene 35 her, as I did one day sitting with thee neere to yon little brooke, when she was kembing her golden haire, and thou holding the glasse unto her, wherein now and then she beheld her divine figure, though neither of you both did (perhaps) knowe that I espied you from those high bushes, neere to the two great okes, 40

keeping (yet) in minde the verses, that thou sungest upon the
holding of the glasse, whiles she was addressing her resplendant
tresses. How came they to thy handes, saide *Syrenus*? The next
day following (saide *Sylvanus*) in that very place I founde the paper
wherein they were written, and reading them, committed them 5
to memorie: And then came *Diana* thither weeping for the losse
of them, and asking me, if I had found them, which was no small
joy and contentment to me, to see my Mistresse powre foorth
those teares, which I might speedily remedie. And this I remember was the first hower, that ever I had a gentle and curteous 10
word of her mouth (how greatly in the meane time stood I neede
of favours) when she saide unto me, that I might highly pleasure
her, to helpe her to that, which so earnestly she sought for: which
wordes, like holy relikes, I kept in my minde; for in a whole
yeere after I tooke no regarde of all the woes and greefes that 15
I passed, for joy of that one onely word, which had in it but
a small apparance of joy and happinesse. Now as thou lovest
thy life (saide *Syrenus*) rehearse those verses, which, thou saidst,
I did sing, since thou hast them so well by hart. I am content,
saide *Sylvanus*: and these they were. 20

> *FOr a favour of such woorth*
> *In no debt I doe remaine,*
> *Since with selfe same coyne againe*
> (Mistresse) *thou art paide right foorth.*
> *For if I enjoy with free* 25
> *Pleasure, seeing before me*
> *Face and eies, where Cupid stands:*
> *So thou seeing in my hands,*
> *That which in thine eies I see.*

> *Let not this to thee seeme ill,* 30
> *That of thy beautie divine*
> *Thou see'st but the figure shine,*
> *And I natures perfect skill:*
> *Yet a thought, that's free and set*
> *Never yet in Cupids net,* 35
> *Better then the bond beholdes,*
> *Though the one the lively mouldes,*
> *Th'other but the counterfet.*

When *Syrenus* had heard the song out, he saide to *Sylvanus*.
I wish that love, gentle Shepherd, with hope of impossible felicitie
may remedie my greefes, if there be any thing in the worlde, that
I would sooner choose to passe away my sorrowfull life with,
then in thy sweete and gracious companie, and if it greeves me 5
not now to the hart, that *Diana* is so cruell unto thee, that she
hath not (which well she might have done) once thanked thee,
nor showen thee a favourable and gratefull countenance for all
thy long and loyall service, and for so true love that thou hast
shewed therein. I could with a little content me (saide *Sylvanus* 10
sighing) if my angrie fortune would perswade *Diana* to give me
some hope, which she might well affoord without staine to her
honour, or breach of faith to thee. But so hard harted is she, that
not onely when I crave it, she denies it me, and flies from me
when I come in her sight, but to comfort me with any small 15
signe or token, whereby I might imagine or hope hereafter to
enjoy it, she would never yet consent. Whereupon I saide many
times to my selfe. It may fall out that this stonie harted and fierce
Tygresse may one day conceive some displeasure against *Syrenus*,
for revenge whereof, and to despite him, she will perhaps shew 20
me some fained favour; for so disgraced and comfortlesse a man
as I am would be glad but with fained favours to content him,
and to imbrace them as true ones. And when thou wentst out of
this countrie, then I infallibly perswaded my selfe, that the remedie
of my greefe was knocking (as it were) at my doore, and that 25
oblivion was the certainest thing to be expected after absence, and
especially in a womans hart. But after when I saw her teares, her
little rest and staying in the village, her delight in seeking out
solitarie places, and her continual sighes, when I say I beheld all
these things, God knowes with what impatience and greefe of 30
minde I felt them. For though I knewe, that time was an approoved phisition of sorrow, which absence is commonly woont
to procure, yet I desired not, that my Mistresse might passe one
hower of greefe, although I hoped to get thereby two thousand
of content. A few daies after thy departure I saw her at the foote 35
of yonder hill, leaning against an oke, and staying her tender
brest upon her sheepehooke, where she stood in that sort a good
while before she espied me, who, though afterwards she lifted up
her eies, yet her teares that issued out so fast, did also hinder her
(I thinke) that she could not well perceive me. She should then be 40

musing on her solitarie and sorrowfull life, and on the greefe that
by thy absence she conceived: But a little after that, not without
many teares (accompanied with as many painfull sighes) she tooke
out her bagpipe which she caried in a fine scrip, and began to play
on it so sweetely, that the hils, and dales, the rivers, the enamoured 5
birdes, and the rockie mountaines of that thicke wood were amazed
and ravished with her sweete musicke. And leaving her bagpipe,
to the tune that she had plaied, she began to sing this song following.

O *Eies, that see not him, who look'd on yow*
  When that they were the mirrours of his sight,   10
What can you now behold to your content?
Greene flowrie meade where often I did vew,
And staid for my sweete friend with great delight,
The ill, which I doe feele with me lament.
Heer did he tell me how his thoughts were bent,   15
And (wretch) I lent an eare;
But angry more then whelplesse Beare
Presumptuous him I call'd, and undiscreete:
And he layde at my feete,
Where yet (poore man) me thinkes I see him lye: 20
And now I wish that I
Might see him so, as then I did: O happy time were this,
Sweete *shadowed river bankes tell me where my* Syrenus *is.*

Yon is the river banke, this is the meade,
From thence the hedge appeeres and shadowed lay,   25
Wherein my flockes did feede the savourie grasse:
Behold the sweete noys'd spring, where I did leade
My sheepe to drinke in heate of all the day,
When heere my sweetest friend the time did passe:
Under that hedge of lively greene he was;   30
And there behold the place,
Where first I saw his sweetest face
And where he sawe me, happy was that day,
Had not my ill hap sway
To end such happy times, O spring,   35
O hedge, and every thing

34 *hap sway* Ed.] *haps way* Y.

Is heere, but he, for whom I paine continually, and misse,
Sweete shadowed river bankes tell me where my Syrenus is.

Heere have I yet his picture that deceaves me,
Since that I see my Shepherd when I view it,
(Though it were better from my soule absented)   5
When I desire to see the man, that leaves me
(Which fond deceipt time showes, and makes me rue it)
To yonder spring I goe, where I consented
To hang it on yon Sallow, then contented
I sit by it, and after   10
(Fond love) I looke into the water,
And see us both, then am I so content heere,
As when his life he spent heere:
This bare devise a while my life sustaineth;
But when no more it faineth,   15
My hart surcharg'd with anguish, and cries out, but yet amisse,
Sweete shadowed river bankes tell me where my Syrenus is.

Speaking to it no wordes it is replying,
And then (me thinkes) revenge of me it taketh,
Bicause sometime an answere I despised.   20
But (wofull soule) I say unto it crying,
Syrenus speake, since now thy presence maketh
Aboade, where never once my thoughts surmized:
Say, in my soule art thou not onely prized?
But not a word it saieth,   25
And as before me there it staieth,
To speake, my soule doth pray it (in conclusion)
O what a brave delusion,
To aske a simple picture toong or sences?
O time, in what offences   30
Of vainest hope is my poore soule so subject unto his?
Sweete shadowed river bankes tell me where my Syrenus is.

I never can go homeward with my sheepe,
When to the west the sunne begins to gyre,
Nor to the foldes returne from our towne,   35
But every where I see, and (seeing) weepe
The sheepe cote of my joy and sweete desire

Broken, decaied, and throwen unto the ground:
Carelesse of lambes and sheepe, there sit I downe
A little while, untill
The herdesmen feeding on the hill,
Cry out to me, saying, O Shepherdesse   5
What doe thy thoughts possesse,
And let thy sheepe goe feeding in the graine?
Our eies doe see it plaine:
For them the tender grasse in pleasant vales doth growe ywisse,
Sweete shadowed river bankes tell me where my Syrenus *is.*   10

Yet in thine owne opinion greater reason
(Syrenus) *it had bene, thus to have started*
With more constraint, and force then I did see yet,
But whom doe I accuse of guiltlesse treason?
For what could make him stay and not have parted,   15
If fate and fortune thereto did agree yet?
No fault of thine it was, nor could it be yet
In my beleefe, have ended
Thou wouldst in ought, or have offended
Our love so plaine and simple, as to leave it   20
Nor will I once conceave it,
Though many shewes and signes thereof there were yet:
O no, the fates did sweare it,
With cloudes of sorrow to obscure my heaven of joy and blisse,
Sweete shadowed river bankes tell me where my Syrenus *is.*   25

My song take heede thou goest where I betake thee,
Yet shalt thou not forsake me:
For it may be that fortune will with such a humour place thee,
That may terme thee importunate and by that meanes disgrace thee.

After *Sylvanus* had made an ende of *Dianas* amorous song, he 30
saide to *Syrenus*, who in hearing the loving verses that his Shepherdesse had sung after his departure, was almost besides his
wits. When faire *Diana* was singing this song, it was seene by my
teares if I felt not those at my hart, which for thy sake she powred
out: but making as though I had not heard, nor seene any thing, 35
by dissembling the matter the best I could, (which I could scarce
doe) I came to the place where she was. *Syrenus* interrupting him
at these wordes, saide. Stay a little *Sylvanus*, (I pray thee) and tell

me what hart was able to chaunge, that felt such passions?
O constancie, O firmnesse, how seldome and how small a time
doe you sojourne in a womans hart? That the more subject she
is to love and to imbrace you, the more ready she is to leave and
forget you. And surely I was of this opinion, that this imperfec- 5
tion was incident to all women, but to my Mistresse *Diana*, in
whom I ever thought that nature had not omitted to frame every
good and perfect thing. But *Sylvanus* after this prosecuting his
historie, saide unto him. When I came neere to the place where
Diana was, I sawe her fixing her faire eies in the cleere fountaine, 10
where using her accustomed maner, she began to say. O woefull
eies, how sooner shall you want teares to water my cheekes, then
continuall occasions to powre you out? O my *Syrenus*, I would to
God, before the winter with his blustring stormes despoyles the
greene medow of fresh and fragrant flowers, the pleasant vallies of 15
fine and tender grasse, and the shadowed trees of their greene
leaves, that these eies may behold againe thy presence so much
desired of my loving soule, as mine is eschewed and (perhaps)
hated of thine: With this she lifted up her divine countenance,
and by chance espied me, and going about to dissemble her 20
sorrowfull complaint, she coulde not so cunningly doe it, but that
her teares made it too manifest, by stopping the passage of her
dissimulation. She rose up at my comming, and saide. Sit downe
heere *Sylvanus*, and see how thou art now (to mine owne cost)
sufficiently revenged of me. Now doth this miserable woman pay 25
thee home againe those paines, which thou didst suffer (as thou
saidst) for her sake, if it be true, that she was ever, or yet is the
cause of them. Is it possible *Diana* (saide I againe) that these eares
may heare these wordes? In the end, I perceive, I am not deceived
by saying, that I was borne to discover every day new kindes of 30
torments for thy sake, and thou to requite them with the greatest
rigour in the world. Dost thou now therefore doubt, that thou
art the cause of my greefe? If thou art not, who (dost thou
imagine) can deserve so great love as this: or what hart in the
world (but thine) had not before this bene mollified and made 35
pitifull by so many teares? And to these I added many other
wordes, which now I doe not so well remember. But the cruell
enemie of my rest cut off my wordes, saying. If thy toong,
Sylvanus, fondly presumeth to speake to me againe of these matters, and not to entertaine the time with talke of my *Syrenus*, I will 40

(at thine owne pleasure) leave thee to enjoy the delight of this faire fountaine, where we now sit. For knowest thou not, that every thing that intreates not of the goodnes of my Shepherd is both hatefull and hurtfull to my eares? And that she, that loveth well, thinketh that time but ill imploied, which is not spent in hearing of her love? Whereupon, fearing least my wordes might have bene an occasion to have made me loose that great content and happines, that I had by her sweete sight and presence, I sealed them up with silence, and was a good while without speaking a worde, onely delighting my selfe with the felicitie I had, by contemplating her soveraine beautie, untill night with greater haste then I desired, came on, when both of us then were constrained to goe homewards with our flockes to our village. Then *Syrenus* giving a great sigh, saide. Thou hast tolde me strange things, *Sylvanus*, and all (wretched man) for the increase of my harmes, since I have tried too soone the small constancie that is in a womans hart, which for the love that I beare to them all (for her sake) in very trueth greeves me not a little. For I would not, Shepherd, heereafter heare it spoken, that in a moulde, where nature hath conjoined such store of peregrine beautie, and mature discretion, there should be a mixture of such unworthy inconstancie as she hath used towards me. And that, which comes neerest to my hart, is, that time shall make her understand, how ill she hath dealt with me, which cannot be, but to the prejudice of her owne content and rest. But how lives she, and with what contentment after her marriage? Some tell me, saide *Sylvanus*, that she brookes it but ill, and no marvell, for that *Delius* her husband though he be (as thou knowest) enriched with fortunes giftes, is but poore in those of nature and good education: For, thou knowest, how lowtish of spirit and body he is, and namely for those things, which we Shepherds take a pride in, as in piping, singing, wrestling, darting of our sheepehookes, and dauncing with the wenches on Sunday, it seemes that *Delius* was borne for no more, but onely to beholde them. But now good Shepherd, said *Syrenus*, take out thy Kit, and I will take my Bagpipe, for there is no greefe that is not with musicke relented and passed away, and no sorrow, which is not with the same againe increased. And so both the Shepherdes tuning, and playing on their instruments with great grace and sweetnesse began to sing that which followeth.

Sylvanus.

SYrenus, *what thought'st thou when I was viewing thee*
  From yonder hedge, and in great greefe suspending me
    To see with what affliction thou wert ruing thee?
There doe I leave my flocke, that is attending me: 5
  For while the cleerest sunne goeth not declining it,
    Well may I be with thee, by recommending me
Thine ill (my Shepherd) for that (by defining it)
  Is passed with lesse cost, then by concealing it:
    And sorrow (in the end) departs resigning it.   10
My greefe I would recount thee, but revealing it,
  It doth increase, and more, by thus recording me
    How in most vaine laments I am appealing it:
My life I see (O greefe) long time's affoording me
  With dying hart, and have not to revive me it,   15
    And an unwonted ill I see aboording me,
From whom I hop'd a meane, she doth deprive me it:
  But (sooth) I hop'd it never, for bewraying it,
    With reason she might gainsay to contrive me it.
My passions did sollicite her, essaying yet   20
  With no importune meanes, but seemely grounding them,
    And cruell love went hindering and dismaying it.
My pensive thoughts were carefully rebounding them
  On every side, to flie the worst, restraining them,
    And in unlawfull motions not confounding them.   25
They prai'd Diane, *in ils, that were not fayning them,*
  To give a meane (but never to repell it thee)
    And that a wretch might so be entertaining them.
But if to give it me, I should refell it thee,
  What wouldst thou doe (O greefe) that thus adjuring it,   30
    Faine would I hide mine ill, and never tell it thee.
But after (my Syrenus) *thus procuring it,*
  A Shepherdesse *I doe invoke (the fairest one)*
    And th'end goes thus, unto my cost enduring it.

Syrenus.   35

Sylvanus *mine, a love, of all the rarest one,*
  A beautie blinding, presently disclosing it,
    A wit, and in discretion the waryest one,

37 *beautie blinding,* Ed.] *beautie, blinding* Y.

A sweete discourse, that to the eare opposing it,
 The hardest rocks entendereth in subduing them.
 What shall a haplesse lover feele in loosing it?
My little sheepe I see, and thinke in viewing them,
 How often times I have beheld her feeding them, 5
 And with her owne to foulde them, not eschewing them.
How often have I met her drive, and speeding them
 Unto the river, in the heate, where resting her
 With great care she was telling yet, and heeding them.
After, if that she was alone, devesting her, 10
 Thou shouldst have seene the bright sunne beames envying her
 Resplendant hayre, to kembe them manifesting her.
But on the sudden meeting, and espying her,
 (My deerest friend Sylvane) how oft incended was
 Her fairest face, with orient blushing dying her? 15
And with what grace, how mildly reprehended was
 My staying long, which she did aske, correcting me?
 Which if I greev'd, with blandishments amended was.
How many daies have I found her expecting me
 At this cleere fountaine, when that I was seeking her 20
 Along that thickest hedge, to greefe subjecting me?
All paines and troubles what so ere (in meeting her)
 Of sheepe, or lambes, we straightway were forgetting them,
 When she sawe me, or when that I was greeting her.
Some other times (Sylvane) we tun'd (in setting them) 25
 Our Bagpipe and the Rebeck, which we plaied on,
 And then my verses sung we, nothing letting them.
After with bowe and arrowes we estraied on,
 Sometimes with nets, and she never refraining me,
 And came not home without some chase we praied on. 30
Thus fortune went by these meanes entertaining me:
 Reserving for some greater ill, and tendring me,
 Which hath no end, but by deathes end restraining me.

Sylvanus.

Syrenus, that most cruell love, engendring me 35
 Such greefe, stints not, nor hindreth the perswading me
 Of so much ill: I die therein remembring me.
Diane I sawe, but straight my joy was fading me,
 When to my onely sight she was opposing her:

And (to my greefe) I saw long life invading me.
How many tymes have I found her, in losing her,
   How often lost, in finding and espying her?
   And I my death and service not disclosing her.
My life I lost, when meeting I was eying her   5
   Faire lovely eies, which, full of anger, cruelly
   She turn'd to me, when that my speech was plying her:
But her faire haire, where Cupides in their fuell lye,
   When she undid and kemb'd, unseene, then leaving me,
   My ils return'd most sensibly, which rue well I.   10
But pitilesse Diana *then perceiving me,*
   Turn'd like a cruell serpent, that in winding it,
   Assailes the lion: thus my life bereaving me.
One time false hope (deceitfully but blinding it)
   My hart maintain'd, even for my comfort choosing it,   15
   But afterwardes in such an error finding it,
   It mocked hope, and then it vanisht loosing it.

Not long after that the Shepherdes had made an ende of their sorrowfull songs, they espied a shepherdesse comming out of the thicket neere to the river, playing on a Bagpipe, and singing with 20 as sweete a grace and delicate voice, as with no lesse sorrow and greefe, which by her countenance and gesture she so lively expressed, that it darkened a great part of her excellent beautie: Whereupon *Syrenus*, who had not of a long time fed in those vallies, asked *Sylvanus* what she was, who answered: This is 25 a faire Shepherdesse, that hath fed but a fewe daies since in these medowes, complaining greatly of love, and (as some say) with good cause, though others say, that she hath bene a long time mocked by the discoverie of a deceite: Why, saide *Syrenus*, lies it then in her to perceive it, and to deliver her selfe from it? It 30 doth, saide *Sylvanus*, for I thinke there is no woman, though never so much in love, whose wits and senses the force and passion of love can so much blinde, that may not perceive whether she be beloved againe or not. I am of a contrarie opinion, saide *Syrenus*. Of a contrarie, saide *Sylvanus*? Why, thou shalt not flatter thy 35 selfe so much, for, the affiance which thou hadst in *Dianas* wordes, hath cost thee deere, and yet I blame thee not, considering that as there is none, whom her beautie overcomes not, so is there not any, whom her wordes deceive not. How knowest thou that,

since she never deceived thee by word nor deede. It is true, saide
Sylvanus, that I was ever (if so I may terme it) undeceived by her,
but I durst swear (by that which hath hitherto fallen out) that
she never meant any deceit to me, but only to deceive thee. But
let us leave this, and harken to this Shepherdesse, that is a great
friend to *Diana*, who is well worthy for the commendable report
of her wisedome and good graces to be harkened unto. But now
was the faire Shepherdesse comming towards the fountaine, and
began to sing this Sonnet following.

A Sonnet.

Mine eies, once have I seene you more contented,
And my poore hart, more joyfull I have knowne thee:
Woe to the cause, whose greefes have overgrowne thee,
And yet whose sight your comforts once presented.
But as this cruell fortune hath invented
(Sweete joy) to roote thee up, where she had sowen thee,
So now (Selvagia) she hath overthrowen thee:
Thy pleasures scarce begun, she hath tormented.
Let me to time or to his changing take me,
Let me with motions out of order leade me,
Then I shall see how free my hart is to me.
Then will I trust in hopes that not forsake me,
When I have staide her wheeles that overtread me,
And beaten downe the fates that doe undoe me.

After that the Shepherdesse had made an end of her song, she
came directly to the fountaine where the Shepherdes were, and
while she was a comming, *Sylvanus*, smiling, saide. Marke but
those wordes, and the burning sigh wherewith she ended her
song, what witnesses they are of her inward love and greefe.
Thereof I have no doubt, saide *Syrenus*, for I woulde to God I
could so speedily remedie her sorrowe, as I beleeve (to my great
greefe) all that she hath by dolefull song uttered. And talking
thus together, *Selvagia* was by this time come, and knowing the
Shepherds, curteously saluted them, saying. What doe you in this
greene and pleasant medow, despised Shepherds? Thou saiest not
amisse, faire *Selvagia*, by asking us what we doe, saide *Sylvanus*,

---

3 durst swear (by *Ed.*] durst (by *Y.*   30 *Syrenus Ed.*] *Syrenns Y.*

for we doe so little in respect of that we shoulde doe, that
we can never conclude and bring any thing to passe, that in our
loves we desire to have. Marvell not thereat, saide *Selvagia*, for
there are certaine things, that before they ende, they that desire
them, are ended. True, saide *Sylvanus*, if a man puts his rest in 5
a womans disposition, for she will first ende his life, before she
will ende or determine to give him any favour, that he is still
hoping to receive at her handes. Unhappy women are these,
saide *Selvagia*, that are so ill intreated by your wordes: But more
unfortunate are those men, saide *Sylvanus*, that are worse handled 10
by your deedes. Can there be a thing more base and of lesse
account, then that you are so ready for the lightest thing in the
worlde to forget them, to whom you have borne the greatest
love? For, absent your selves but a day from him whom you love
well, and then shall he neede to commence his suite new againe. 15
Two things I gather, saide *Selvagia*, by thy speech, which make
me wonder not a little. The one, to see thy toong goe so much
awrie, and contrarie to that which I ever conjectured, and knew
by thy behaviour and conditions. For I thought, when I heard
thee talke of thy love, that in the same thou wert a Phœnix, and 20
that none of the best lovers to this day came ever neere to the
extreme that thou hadst, by loving a Shepherdesse, whom I
knowe, a cause sufficient ynough not to speake ill of women, if
thy malice were not greater then thy love. The second, that thou
speakest of a thing thou understandest not; for to blame forget- 25
fulnes, who never had any triall thereof, must rather be attributed
to follie and want of discretion, then to any thing else. For if
Diana did never remember thee, how canst thou complaine of her
oblivion? I thinke to answere, saide *Sylvanus*, both these pointes,
if I shall not wearie thine eares with hearing me. To the first, 30
saying, That I wish I may never enjoy any more content then
now I have, if any (by the greatest example that he is able to alleage me) can with wordes set downe the force and power, that
this thanklesse and disloyall Shepherdesse, whom thou knowest,
and I would I knew not, hath over my subjected soule. But the 35
greater the love is I beare her, the more it greeves me, that there
is any thing in her that may be reprehended. For heere is *Syrenus*,
who was favoured more of *Diana*, then any lover in the world of
his Mistresse, and yet she hath now forgotten him, as thou faire
Shepherdesse, and all we doe know. To the other point, where 40

thou saiest, that I have no reason to speake ill of that, whereof
I never had experience, I say, that the Phisition may judge of that
greefe, which he himselfe never had: and will further satisfie
thee, *Selvagia*, with this opinion of me, that I beare no hate to
women, nor (in very trueth) wish them ill, for there is nothing in 5
the world, which I would desire to serve with more reverence and
affection. But in requitall of my zealous love, I am but ill intreated, and with such intolerable disdaine, which made me speake
so much by her, who takes a pride and a glorie in giving me such
cause of greefe. *Syrenus*, who had held his peace all this while, 10
said to *Selvagia*: If thou would'st but listen to me, faire Shepherdesse, blamelesse thou wouldest hold my rivall, or (to speake
more properly) my deere friend *Sylvanus*. But tell me, what is the
reason, that you are so inconstant, that in a moment you throwe
a Shepherde downe from the top of his good hap, to the deepest 15
bottome of miserie: knowest thou whereunto I attribute it? To
nothing else but to your owne simplicitie: bicause you have no
perfect understanding to conceive the good, nor knowe the value
of that, you have in your handes. You meddle with love and are
uncapable to judge what it meanes; how doe you, then, knowe to 20
behave your selves in it. I tell thee, *Syrenus*, saide *Selvagia*, that the
cause why Shepherdesses forget their lovers, is no other, but
bicause they are forgotten of them againe. These are things,
which love doth make and undoe, things which time and place
alters and buries in silence, but not for the want of womens due 25
knowledge in them, of whom there have bene an infinite number
in the world, who might have taught men to live, and to love, if
love were a thing that might be taught or learned: But yet for all
this, there is not (I thinke) any baser estate of life then a womans;
for if they speake you faire, you thinke them by and by to die for 30
your love; if they speake not to you, you thinke them proude and
fantasticall; if their behaviour be not to your liking, you thinke
them hypocrites. They have no kind of pastaunce, which you
thinke not to exceede: if they holde their peace, you say they are
fooles: if they speake, you say they are so troublesome, that none 35
will abide to heare them: if they love you the most in the world,
you thinke they goe about to deceive you: if they forget you,
and flie the occasions of bringing their good names in question,
you say they are inconstant, and never firme in one minde and

11 *Selvagia Ed.*] *Selvaggia* Y.

purpose: So that the good or ill woman can doe no more to please
your mindes, then never to exceede the limits of your desires and
dispositions. If every one faire *Selvagia*, saide *Syrenus*, were indued
with this finenesse of wit and grave understanding as thou art,
they woulde never give us occasions to make us complaine of their 5
small regarde in their love. But bicause we may knowe what
reason thou hast to finde thy selfe so much aggreeved with it, so
may God give thee comfort needefull for such an ill, as thou
wouldest vouchsafe to tell us the substance of thy love, and all the
occurrents which have hitherto befallen thee therein. For (it 10
seemes) thou canst tell us more of ours, then we are able to informe thee, to see, if his effects, which thou hast passed, will give
thee leave to speake so freely as thou dost: for by thy wordes
thou seemest to have more experience in them, then any woman
that ever I knewe. If I were not the most tried woman in them, 15
saide *Selvagia*, I am (at the lest) the worst intreated by them, as any
ever was, and such an one, who with greater reason then the rest
may complaine of loves franticke effects (a thing sufficient to
make one speake ynough in it.) And bicause by that which is
past, thou maiest knowe that which I now suffer, to be a divellish 20
kinde of passion, commit your misfortunes a while to silence, and
I will tel you greater then ever you heard before.

IN the mightie and invincible kingdome of Portugall run two
great rivers, which wearied with watring the greater part of
our Spaine, not far from one another enter into the maine Ocean. 25
Betweene both which are situated many olde and ancient townes,
by reason of the great fertilitie of the soile, which hath not the
like in the whole world. The inhabitants lives of this province
are so much sequestred and estranged from things, that may
disturbe the minde, that there is not any (but when *Venus* by the 30
mightie handes of her blinde sonne meanes to shew her power)
who troubles his minde more, then to sustaine a quiet life, by
maintaining a meane and competent living with those things,
which for their poore estates are requisite. The mens endevours
are naturally disposed to spend their life time in sufficient con- 35
tent, and the womens beauties to take it from him, who liveth
most assured of his libertie. There are many houses in the
shadowed forrestes, and pleasant vales, the which being nourished
by the silver deaw of soveraine heaven, and tilled by their in-

habitants, favourable sommer forgetteth not to offer up into their
handes the fruites of their owne travels, and provision for the
necessitie of their lives. I lived in a village neere to great *Duerus*
one of these two rivers, where *Minerva* hath a most stately temple
built unto her, the which in certaine times of the yeere is visited of 5
all, or most of the Shepherdesses, that live in that province: who,
with the faire Nymphes thereabouts, begin, a day before the holy
feast, with sweete songs and hymnes to celebrate it, and the
Shepherdes likewise to solemnize the same with challenges of
running, leaping, wrestling, and pitching the barre, appointing 10
severall rewardes and giftes for them, that beare the bell away,
sometimes a garland of greene Ivie, sometimes a fine Bagpipe,
Flute, or Sheepehooke of knottie Ashe, and other guerdons which
Shepherdes make most account of. But the festivall time being
come, I with other Shepherdesses my friendes and acquaintance, 15
leaving of our servile and worke-day apparell, and putting on the
best we had, went the day before to that place, determining to
watch all that night in the temple, as other yeeres before we were
wont to doe. Being therfore in companie of my friendes, we sawe
comming in at the doore a Bevie of faire Shepherdesses, attended 20
on by jolly Shepherdes, who leaving them within, and having
done their due orisons, went out againe to the pleasant valley:
for the order of that province was, that no Shepherd might enter
into the temple, but to doe his devotion, and then presently to goe
foorth againe, untill the next day, when all came in together to 25
participate the ceremonies and sacrifices, which were made there.
The reason was, bicause the Shepherdesses and Nymphes might
sit alone, and without trouble or occasion to thinke of any other
matter, then devoutly to celebrate the feast, and to make merry
with one another, according to the ancient accustomed manner. 30
And the Shepherdes to remaine amongst themselves without the
temple in a faire greene meade hard by, where by the brightnesse
of nocturnall *Diana* they might disport themselves. But the foresaid Shepherdesses being come into the sumptuous temple (after
they had saide a fewe prayers, and presented their offerings upon 35
the altar) they placed themselves downe by us. And it was my ill
hap, that one of them sat next unto me, to make me infortunate
as long as her memorie did importune me. The Shepherdesses
came in muffled, for their faces were covered with white vailes
tied up above their hats, which were artificially made of fine 40

strawe, and so curiously wrought with many workes of the same, that it excelled the glittering golde in shew. But as I was eying her, that sat next unto me, I perceived how she did seldome cast off her eies from beholding me againe; and when I looked on her, I might see her cast them downe, fayning as though she would see me, but in such sort, that I might not perceive it. I did not meanely desire to knowe what she was, bicause, if she had spoken to me, I might not upon ignorance have made a fault by not knowing her againe, who all the while that I sat thinking of some other matter, did never cast her eies off me, but viewed me so much, that a thousand times I was about to speake unto her, being suddenly enamoured of those faire eies, which of all her face were onely discovered and open. But she seeing me sitting in this perplexitie, pulled out the fairest, and most dainty hand, that ever I did see, and taking mine into it, did with a sweete and amorous eie a little while behold me: whereupon being now so striken in love, as toong cannot expresse, I saide unto her. It is not onely this hand, most faire and gracious Shepherdesse, that is alwaies ready to serve thee, but also her hart and thoughts, to whom it appertaineth. *Ismenia* (for so she was called, that was the cause of my disquiet and molested thoughts) having now complotted in her minde to mocke me (as you shall heare) answered me softly, that none might heare her, in this manner, saying. I am so much thine, sweete Shepherdesse, that, as such an one, I boldly presumed to doe that which I did, praying thee not to be offended with me, for no sooner I viewed thy faire and amiable face, but presently I lost the power of my conquered soule: I was so glad to heare these wordes, that comming neerer unto her, with a smile I answered her thus. How can it be, gentle Shepherdesse, that thy selfe being so passing faire, shouldest fal in love with her, who wants it so much, to make her have the name of such an one, and more, with a woman as I am. It is that love (faire Shepherdesse) saide she againe, that seldome endes, surviving all destinies, and which is neither subject to change of time, nor fortune. If the condition of my estate (saide I againe) could prompt me so fit an answere, as thy wise and discreete wordes doe inforce, the desire which I have to serve thee, should not let me from manifesting the same by most loving termes, but in these few ones beleeve me (faire Shepherdesse) that the resolution which I have to be thine, not death it selfe can determine, nor take away. After these

wordes, our mutuall imbracings were so many, and our loving
speeches to one another so often redoubled, and of my part so
true and unfained, that we regarded not the Shepherdesses songs,
nor beheld the daunces, nor other sportes that were made in the
temple. And now by this time was I earnest with *Ismenia* to tell 5
me her name, and to put off her muffler, both which not onely she
cunningly excused, but very suttly turned her talke to another
matter. But midnight being now past, and I having the greatest
desire in the worlde to see her face, and to knowe her name, and
of what village she was, began to complaine of her, and to tell 10
her, that it was not possible that the love, which by her wordes
she protested to beare me, was so great, since having tolde her my
name, she concealed hers from me: and that loving her as I did,
it was impossible for me to live, unlesse I knewe whom I loved,
or from whence I might heare newes from my love againe, and 15
many other things I tolde her in so good earnest, that the same,
and my teares helped to moove false *Ismenias* hart: who rising up
and taking me by the hand, to carry me aside into some secret
place, where none might heare her, began to say these wordes
unto me, making as though they came out from the bottome of 20
her hart. Faire Shepherdesse, borne onely for the unrest and
torment of a soule, that hitherto hath lived as exempt and free as
possible might be, who can choose, but tell thee that thou re-
quirest at my handes, having now made thee the sole Mistresse of
my libertie? Unhappie me, that the chaunge of my habit hath 25
deceived thee, although the deceit redoundes to mine owne
harme: The muffler, which thou intreatest me to pull off, behold,
to please thee, I take away, but to tell thee my name makes not
much to thy purpose, when as heereafter (though I would not)
thou shalt see me oftener then thou maiest well suffer. And speak- 30
ing these wordes, and pulling off her muffler, mine eies behelde
a face, whose countenance, though it was somewhat manlike, yet
was the favour and beautie of it so singular, that it made me to
woonder. But *Ismenia* prosecuting her speech, saide. And bicause
thou maist knowe (faire Shepherdesse) the summe of this paine 35
which thy beautie hath made me feele, and that the wordes which
have passed betweene us but in sport, are true, knowe, that I am
a man, and not a woman, as thou takest me to be: These Shepherdesses, which thou seest heere in my companie (my kinswomen
and familiar acquaintance) to make some sport and to laugh, 40

apparelled me in this sort; for otherwise I could not have staied in
the temple, by reason of the olde custome so strictly observed
heere. When I heard these wordes, and perceived as I said before,
not those effeminate lookes in her face, nor that demure modestie
in her eies, which maidens for the most part are woont to have, 5
I verily beleeved that all was true that she tolde me, and then was
so far besides my selfe, that I knew not what to answere her. Yet
mine eies did still contemplate that most perfect beautie, and
marked those words, which with so great dissimulation she had
tolde me: for never could any make a false and fained tale seeme 10
more apparant and true as that craftie and cruell Shepherdesse did.
Then I felt my selfe so intangled in her love, and so well content
to heare that she was enamoured of me againe, as (gentle Shepherdes) I am not able to declare. And though I had not till then
any experience of love passions (a cause sufficient not to make me 15
expresse them) yet forcing my selfe the best I could, in this sort
I saide unto her. Faire Shepherdesse, that hast (to make me live
without libertie, or for some other respect, which fortune best
knowes) taken upon thee the habit of her, who for thy love hath
entirely vowed her affections to thee, thine owne had sufficed to 20
overcome me, without making me yeelde with mine owne weapons.
But who can flie from that, which fortune hath allotted her?
Thrise happy might I have thought my selfe, if on purpose thou
hadst done that, which by chaunce, and onely for merriment
thou hast devised. For, if by changing thy naturall habit, it had 25
bene onely to have seene me, and to unfolde to me thy amorous
desires, I would then have attributed it to mine owne desertes, and
(no doubt) to thy great affection, but seeing that the intent was of
an other consequence, although the effect hath resulted to this
thou seest, it contents me not so greatly (I must needes confesse) 30
being done in such sort as I have saide. And let not this desire
amaze nor greeve thee; for there is no greater signe of a perfect
lover, then to desire to be beloved of him, to whom she hath
wholy offered up her libertie. Whereupon by that thou hast
heard me utter, thou maiest gather, how thy sight hath blinded 35
my understanding, and made me become such an one as I am,
beseeching thee to use the power thou hast over me, in such sort,
that I may entertaine this opinion, to thinke my selfe happie and
fortunate to the end of our love, the which for my part (while life
doth last) shall not die in my faithfull and loving brest. Deceitfull 40

Ismenia was so skilfull to frame a suttle answere to my simple
wordes, and to faine speeches so fit for the subject of our talke,
that none coulde escape the cunning deceit, whereinto I fell,
unlesse fortune by the threed of wisedome had unwound her
out of so intricate a laberinth. And in this sort we were together 5
untill morning came on, talking of that, which she may imagine,
that hath passed the like disordered occurrents in love. She tolde
me her name was *Alanius*, her countrie village *Gallia*, three miles
from our towne, where we appointed to meete, and see one
another many times together. But now gan the duskie welkin to 10
waxe cleere, and hastie morning was come, when both of us
with many imbracings, teares, and sighes were constrained to
depart from one another. She went from me, and I, turning my
head backe to beholde her, and to see if she looked backe at me
againe, perceived how she went away smiling to her selfe, whereof 15
(thinking that mine eies did but deceive me) I made no regarde at
all. Away she went with the companie that came with her, and
I with more then I brought, since in my troubled minde I carried
backe with me the eies and Idea of fained *Alanius*, the wordes, by
the which she had opened to me her malicious and ridiculous love, 20
the imbracings, that I received of her, and the cruell greefe, which
untill that time I had never prooved before. And now you must
knowe (good Shepherdes) that this false and suttle *Ismenia* had
a cosin called *Alanius*, whom she loved more then her selfe, for in
countenance and eies, and in every other part and lineaments, she 25
resembled him so much, that if they had not bene of different sexe,
none could have judged the one from the other. And the love
which she did beare him, was so great, that when I asked her her
name in the temple, and seeing that she must needes tell me some
Shepherdes name or other, the first that came to her minde and 30
mouth, was that of *Alanius*. *For there is no greater certaintie, then that
the toong in a sudden matter doth ever concurre with the hart.* And her
the Shepherd loved well, but yet not so much as she did him. But
now when the Shepherdesses were come out of the temple, to goe
home to their villages, *Ismenia* went to her kinsman *Alanius*, who, 35
to shew her all the curtesie, that in so great and mutual love was
requisite, leaving the yongsters companie of his towne, accompanied her all alone: whereat *Ismenia* was not a little proude and
joyfull: who to entertaine the time with some talke by the way,
tolde him all that had passed betweene us, not omitting any thing, 40

and not without great sport and laughter of them both, telling
him also, that I went away with firme beleefe, that she was a man,
and greatly enamoured of her. When *Alanius* heard these novelties, he dissembled the matter the best he coulde, saying, that it
was a pleasant and pretie jest. And picking all out of her, that had 5
passed betweene us, so that (he thought) there was nothing left
untold, they came to their towne. But eight daies after (which
I thought were eight thousand yeeres) the traitour *Alanius* (for so
I may with greater reason call him, then he had afterward to cast
me off) came to our towne, and stood attending me in such 10
a place, where I could not choose but see him, as I was going
with other maides to the fountaine not far from the towne: whom
when I espied, I was rapt out of minde for extreme and sudden
joy, thinking he was the very same, that in the habit of a Shepherdesse had spoken to me in the temple; whereupon I made him 15
some secret signes to come to the fountaine, whither I was going,
who knowing my meaning, performed foorthwith my minde.
Thither he came, and there we were talking together as long as
time woulde give us leave, and the love (of my side at the lest)
was so strongly confirmed betweene us, that though the deceit had 20
bene discovered (as not many daies after it was knowne) it was
yet of so great force and vertue, that it coulde never make me
alienate my minde and affection from him. And I also beleeved,
that *Alanius* loved me well, and that especially from that time he
was greatly enamoured of me, though afterwardes in effect he 25
did not so well declare it: so that for certaine daies together our
love happily continued, and was handled with the greatest secrecie
that might be, which was not yet so great, but that subtile *Ismenia*
in the end perceived it: who (seeing her selfe to be the onely
cause thereof, and most in fault) not onely by deceiving me, but 30
by ministring occasion to *Alanius* of discovering himselfe, and by
that which passed, to fall in love with me, and to forget her (as
indeede he did) for very greefe was almost out of her wits, but
that with this poore hope she comforted her selfe againe, that, if
I knew the trueth, I would immediately forget and cast him off, 35
wherein she was not a little deceived: for as he afterwardes loved
me more and more, so by his severall beauties and singular deserts,
I was more obliged to love and honour him. But *Ismenia* purposing
to open the deceite, which by her owne follie and suttletie she had
framed, wrote me this letter following.   40

Ismenias letter to Selvagia.

IF we are bound to love those well (*Selvagia*) that love us, there is nothing in the world, which I ought to esteeme deerer then thy selfe; but if to hate them that are the cause, why we are forgotten and despised, I leave it to thine owne discretion. I would 5 put thee in some fault, for casting thine eies upon my *Alanius*, but (wretched woman) what shall I doe, that am the organ of mine owne mishap. O *Selvagia*, to my greefe I sawe thee, and well could I excuse that which I passed with thee, but in the end such fonde prankes have seldome good successe. For laughing but one little 10 hower with my *Alanius*, and telling him what had passed betweene us, I must now weepe and lament all my life time, if my greefe (at the lest) may not moove thee to some remorse of pitie. I beseech thee (by all I may) that the discoverie of this deceite may suffice, and so worke with thee, to make thee forget my *Alanius*, and 15 restore this haplesse Shepherdesse to that, which (being not a little) thou art able to doe, if love will permit thee to graunt me this favour, which I request at thy hands.

When I had read this letter, and imparted it to *Alanius*, he then at large unfolded unto me the maner of her deceit, but not one 20 word of the love, that was betweene them both, whereof I made no great reckoning; for I was so assured of that which he seemed to beare me, that I woulde never beleeve that any passed or future thoughts might have bene an occasion to have made him afterwardes forget me. But bicause *Ismenia* might not by my silence 25 thinke me discurteous, I answered her letter thus.

Selvagias letter to Ismenia.

I Knowe not faire *Ismenia*, whether I may justly accuse thee, or give thee thankes for disposing my minde and affection in this sort, nor can resolve with my selfe whether of these two I should 30 doe, untill the successe of my love doe counsell me heerein. On the one side I am sorie for thy ill hap; on the other, I see that thou wentst foorth (as it were) to meete and imbrace it. *Selvagia* was free when thou didst delude her in the temple, and is now subject to his will, into whose handes thou wouldst needes deliver her. 35 Thou praiest me to leave off the love, that I beare *Alanius*, with that which thou thy selfe wouldst doe in this behalfe, I may easily

answere thee. Yet one thing makes me very sad, that thou art
greeved for that, for which thou hast no just cause of complaint,
which to the patient therof giveth the greatest paine in the world.
I do often consider and thinke of those faire eies, with which thou
didst behold me, and of that sweete face, which (after many im- 5
portunate requestes) thou didst shew me, and it greeves me
Ismenia, that such faire things, and so like to my *Alanius*, should
suffer any sorrow and discontentment at all. Behold then what
remedie is left for thy greefe: that for the bountie, which thou
hast used towardes me, by giving me the most precious gemme 10
thou hadst, I kisse thy faire and daintie hands; which curtesie of
thine being so great, God graunt that by some meanes or other
I may be able to requite. If thou seest my *Alanius* there, tell him
(I pray thee) what reason he hath to love me, for he knoweth
already, how much he hath to forget thee. And God give thee the 15
content thou desirest, which may not be to the cost of that which
I have, by seeing my affection so happily and well imploied.

    Ismenia could not reade this letter to the end, for in the middest
of it her sighes and teares, which she powred out, were so many,
that she thought at that very time to have lost her life. She 20
laboured (as much as she could) to make *Alanius* forsake me, and
devised so many meanes for the same purpose, as he, to shun
those places and occasions, whereby he thought he might see her.
Not that he meant her any harme thereby, but bicause he thought
(by doing so) in some part he requited the great love that I bare 25
him. All the daies that he lived in this minde, there escaped not
any, wherein I sawe him not; for he passed evermore that way,
feeding his flockes, which from our towne did leade to his. He
accounted no travels nor troubles too great, which he did for my
sake, and especially, if he thought I regarded them. Day by day 30
Ismenia inquired after him, and never ceased to seeke him out,
who being sometimes tolde by others, and sometimes knowing
her selfe, that he was in our towne, had no patience at all to suffer
such a corsive at her hart. And yet for all this, there was not anything, that contented and pacified her troubled minde more, 35
then when she could get some little time to speake with him. *But as*
necessitie is so ingenious and politike, that it seekes out remedies, where
mans wit can scarce imagine any, despised *Ismenia* adventured to
helpe her selfe by one, which I woulde to God had never entred
into her thought, by faining that she extremely loved another 40

Shepherd called *Montanus*, who a long time had loved and served her before. And as she purposed, so she put it in practise, to trie if by this sudden change she might draw *Alanius* to that which so much she desired. *For there is not any thing, which a man thinks he hath most sure, though making but a small account thereof, but that the* 5 *losse of it (if on a sudden he loose it) doth not a little greeve him.* But now when *Montanus* perceived that faire *Ismenia* his love and Mistresse had at last mollified her long obdurate hart, and now thought good to requite the great love that he had so long time borne her, Shepherdes, you may well imagine, what content he felt. For so 10 great was his joy, so obsequious his services to her, and so many troubles that he passed for her sake, that they were an occasion (with the disfavours and contempt that *Alanius* had shewen her) to make that fained love proove true, which but in jest she began to beare him. So that *Ismenia* yeelded her hart wholy to *Montanus* 15 with such firmnesse, that there was not any in the world, whom she loved more then him, nor whom she desired lesse to see then my *Alanius*: the which (as soone as she could) she gave him to understand, thinking that as by these meanes she was sufficiently revenged of his forgetfulnesse, she had likewise busied my head 20 with the cruell thought therof. The love that *Alanius* did beare me (although it greeved him to the hart to see *Ismenia* love that Shepherd, whom in all his life time he could never abide) was yet so great, that he never seemed to make any shew of his secret greefe. But certaine daies passing on, and thinking with himselfe, 25 that he onely was the cause of his enemies good hap, and of those singular favours, that *Ismenia* shewed him, and that the Shep-herdesse did now shun his sight (who not long since before died for the want thereof) despite, wroth, and jealousie at once so fiercely assailed him, that his impatience had almost bereft him of 30 his wits, if presently he had not determined to hinder *Montanus* his good fortune, or in the pursuite thereof to have lost his deerest life. For performance whereof, he began to looke on *Ismenia* againe, and not to come so openly in my sight, as he was wont to doe, nor to be so often out of his towne, least *Ismenia* might have 35 knowen it. The love betweene her and *Montanus* went not on so forwardes, as that betweene me and my *Alanius* backwardes, though not of my part (when nothing, but death, was able to divorce my minde from him) but of his, in whom I never thought to see such a sudden change: For so extremely he burned with 40

choler and rancour against *Montanus*, and so deepely envied his
good fortune, that (he thought) he could not execute nor asswage
that anger, but by renewing the olde love, that he bare to *Ismenia*;
for furtherance whereof, his comming to our towne was a great
impediment, whose absence from me as it engendred forgetful- 5
nesse in him, so the presence of his *Ismenia*, rekindled his hart with
a straunger kinde of love then before: whereupon he returned
againe to his first thoughts: And I (poore soule) remained all
alone deceived and scorned in mine owne affection. But all the
service that he bestowed on *Ismenia*, the tokens and letters that 10
he sent her, and the pitifull complaints that he made unto her, or
any thing els that he was able to doe, could never moove her
setled minde, nor make her forget the lest part of that love, which
she bare *Montanus*. I being therefore lost for the love of *Alanius*,
Alanius dying for *Ismenia*, and *Ismenia* for *Montanus*, it fell out, that 15
my father had a certaine occasion of busines about the buttals of
certaine pastures with *Phylenus* father to *Montanus*, by reason
whereof both of them came often to our towne, and in such
a time, that *Montanus* (whether it was for the superfluous favours,
that *Ismenia* bestowed on him (which to men of a base minde 20
is a cloying) or whether he was too jealous of the renewed and
earnest suites of *Alanius*) waxed very colde in his love to *Ismenia*.
In the end when he espied me driving my sheepe to the folde,
and with a curious eie looking on me, he began presently to be
enamoured of me, so that (by the effects which he daily shewed) it 25
was not possible for me to beare greater affection to *Alanius*, nor
Alanius to *Ismenia*, nor *Ismenia* to *Montanus*, nor *Montanus* to love
me more, then in very trueth he did. Beholde what a strange
cousinage of love: If *Ismenia* went by chaunce to the fielde,
Alanius went after her; if *Montanus* went to his flockes, *Ismenia* 30
after him; if I went to the hils with my sheepe, *Montanus* after me;
if I knew that *Alanius* was in the wood, where he was wont to
feede his flocks, thither I hied me after him. And it was the
strangest thing in the world to heare how *Alanius* sighing saide,
Ah my *Ismenia*; and how *Ismenia* saide, Ah my *Montanus*; and how 35
Montanus said, Ah my *Selvagia*; and how *Selvagia* saide, Ah my
Alanius. It fell out afterwardes on a day, that we fower met
together in a forrest that lay betweene all our townes, and the
reason was, bicause *Ismenia* went to visite certaine Shepherdesses
of her acquaintance, which dwelt thereabouts, which when *Alanius* 40

knew, being forced, and driven on by his fleeting thoughts, he
went after to seeke her out, and found her neere to a fine spring
kembing her golden haire. I being tolde by a certaine Shepherd
(my neighbour) that *Alanius* was gone to the forrest of the valley
(for so it was called) tooke out before me a few goates, that were 5
shut up in a little yarde neere to our house, (bicause I would not
goe without some errant) and went after him, where my desire
guided me; whom by chaunce I found weeping and complaining
of his ill fortune, and the Shepherdesse laughing and jesting at his
bootlesse teares, and sighes. When *Ismenia* espied me, she was not 10
a little glad of my companie, and began to be merry with me,
although I had no cause to be so with her, to whom I rather
objected the small reason, and lesse regarde of modestie and
discretion she had, to greeve my hart with that uncivill part and
bad deceit; whereof she so wisely excused her selfe, that whereas 15
I thought she would have made me some amendes for all my
greefe and sorrow, by her wise and well ordered reasons, she gave
me to understand, that I was rather bound to her, in that if she
had mocked me, I had (saide she) satisfied my selfe as well, and
requited her againe, not onely by taking *Alanius* her cosin from 20
her, whom she loved more then her selfe, but also by enticing
Montanus to my love, from that he was wont to shew her. By this
time came *Montanus*, who was tolde by a Shepherdesse (a friend of
mine) called *Solisa*, that I was gone to the forrest of the valley
with my goates. And when all the fower discontented and dis- 25
cordant lovers met there together, it cannot be imagined what we
all felt: for every one looked upon another that would not have
bene viewed of those eies againe. I asked my *Alanius* the cause of
his forgetfulnes, he sued for mercie at craftie *Ismenias* handes; she
accused and complained of the colde love of *Montanus*; he of 30
Selvagias cruelty. Being therefore in this sort (as you have heard)
every one tormented for them, who loved them not againe,
Alanius to the tune of his Fiddle by this dolefull song began to
complaine of *Ismenias* crueltie.

N O *more (O cruell Nymph) now hast thou prayed*   35
      Ynough in thy revenge, proove not thine ire
On him that yeeldes, the fault is now apayed
Unto my cost: now mollifie thy dire

38 *dire Hardnes, Ed.] dire, Hardnes, Y.*

Hardnes, and brest of thine so much obdured:
And now raise up (though lately it hath erred)
A poore repenting soule, that in the obscured
Darknes of thy oblivion lies enterred.
 For it fals not in that, that doth commend thee,   5
 That such a Swaine as I may once offend thee.

If that the little sheepe with speede is flying
From angrie Shepherd (with his wordes affraied)
And runneth here and there with fearfull crying,
And with great greefe is from the flocke estraied: 10
But when it now perceives that none doth follow,
And all alone, so far estraying, mourneth,
Knowing what danger it is in, with hollow
And fainting bleates, then fearefull it returneth
 Unto the flocke, meaning no more to leave it,   15
 Should it not be a just thing to receive it?

Lift up these eies (Ismenia) which so stately
To view me, thou hast lifted up before me:
That libertie, which was mine owne but lately,
Give me againe, and to the same restore me: 20
And that milde hart, so full of love and pittie,
Which thou didst yeeld to me, and ever owe me.
Behold (my Nymph) I was not then so witty
To knowe that sincere love, that thou didst shew me:
 Now wofull man full well I knowe and rue it,   25
 Although it was too late before I knew it.

How could it be (my enemie) say, tell me,
How thou (in greater fault and errour being
Then ever I was thought) should'st thus repell me?
And with new league and cruell title seeing   30
Thy faith so pure and woorthy to be changed.
And what is that Ismenia, that doth binde it
To love, whereas the same is most estranged,
And where it is impossible to finde it?
 But pardon me, if herein I abuse thee,   35
 Since that the cause thou gav'st me doth excuse me.

18 *before me:* Ed.] *before me* Y.

But tell me now what honour hast thou gained,
Avenging such a fault by thee committed;
And thereunto by thy occasion trained:
What have I done, that I have not acquitted?
Or what excesse, that is not amply paied, 5
Or suffer more, that I have not endured?
What cruell minde, what angry brest displaied,
With savage hart, to fiercenes so adjured,
　　Would not such mortall greefe make milde and tender,
　　But that, which my fell Shepherdesse doth render? 10

Now as I have perceived well thy reasons,
Which thou hast had, or hast yet to forget me,
The paines, the greefes, the guiltes of forced treasons,
That I have done, wherein thou first didst set me:
The passions, and thine eares, and eies refusing 15
To heare, and see me, meaning to undoe me:
Cam'st thou to know, or be but once perusing
Th'unsought occasions, which thou gav'st unto me,
　　Thou should'st not have wherewith to more torment me,
　　Nor I to pay the fault my rashnes lent me. 20

Thus did my *Alanius* end his sweet song, wherewith I would my life had also ended, and not without great cause, since my mishap could not be more extreme, then to see him (whom I loved more then my selfe) before mine eies to pine so much for the love of another, and so strangely to forsake me. But as I was not alone in 25 these misfortunes, I did dissemble them for that time (as well as I could) as also bicause faire *Ismenia*, casting her eies upon her *Montanus*, began to sing that which followeth.

HOw fond am I to hope for any rest
　In endlesse plaints, vaine sighes, and bootlesse teares? 30
The present now at hand to be exprest,
Yet few to these, that, with ten thousand feares,
I have powr'd out unto thy cruell eares.
And if at any time my life did tend
To other loves in earnest or in jest, 35
This love by that I never could offend,
　　Bicause I did but then begin to proove,
　　And learne, how well Montanus *I could love.*

Then did I learne to love, my selfe I taught
To love, by him, who lov'd me not againe:
For I suspected that I should be brought
Unto thy love (Montanus) *when in vaine*
I loved him, that did my love disdaine: 5
I try'de (I say) my free and carelesse hart
Of love to taste some sorrow, that it sought:
And let that Shepherd with his love depart,
    That loves with thee, for all his paine and greeʃe
    Is but in vaine, when vaine is his releefe. 10

Let none accuse me then, if I disdaine
Alanius loves, whose loves are but a showe,
For I could never love, nor entertaine
Any but thee, for whom I will bestowe
My deerest life, since heavens will have it soe. 15
And if at any time I fein'd to like,
I lik'd (I say) but how I did I knowe,
For never any Shepherd els could strike
    My hart indeede, but thou, to whom I give
    My faith kept for thee since I first did live. 20

Let burning sighes go forth and still increase,
Let both mine eies become two springs of teares,
Let accidents, repugnant to mine ease
Arise, for thoughts, which now my minde forsweares,
Shall never hurt that love which now it beares: 25
Let sorrow goe, and ill which way they will,
And now let joies returne which way they please,
For where they are, there will I hover still,
    Since that no harme my purpose may reclame,
    Nor cruell death it selfe, although it came. 30

Ismenia by this song had revenged me of cruell and disloyall *Alanius*, (if in the love (at the lest) which I did beare him, any desire of revenge could befall,) but *Montanus* staied not long from requiting *Ismenia* againe, who casting his eie upon me, sung this song as followeth. 35

*F*Oolish love, ah foolish lover,
   I for thee, thou for another.

I am a foole, and seeme no lesse,
For thee who will not be?
For he's a foole I doe confesse,   5
That is not one for thee:
And yet this doth not well agree,
      To be a foolish lover,
Or foole for her, that is a foole for loving of another.

Now seeing thee, thou seest not mee,   10
And diest for my foe,
Eate me with sauce (that loveth thee)
Of him thou lovest soe:
So shalt thou make me (to my woe)
      To be a foolish lover,   15
And such a foole for loving thee as thou art for another.

When he had made an ende of the last verses, notwithstanding
the present agonie and sorrow, that we al suffered, we could not
choose but laugh hartily to see how *Montanus* would have me
deceive my taste by looking on him, with the sauce and appetite of   20
Alanius, whom I loved, as if it might have fallen in the compasse of my thought, to suffer it to be deceived by the apparance
of an other thing. But now with greater firmnesse then the rest,
I began to tune and play on my Bagpipe, and to sing a song to it,
as you shall heare; for by the same I thought to shew how more   25
constantly then any of the rest there, I had persevered in my love
to *Alanius*.

*A*Lthough *my quiet it doth let,*
   Rather then blame discredit me,
(For God forbid that I forget)   30
Let me with wrong forgotten be.

Not onely where oblivion raineth,
There is no love, nor can be none,
Nay, where there is suspicion,
There is no love, but such as faineth;   35

Great harme it is to love, where set
In bootlesse hopes, the minde they free,
But God defend that I forget,
Forgotten though a jest it bee.

If that I love, why then love I,　　　　　　　5
To sport or leave to love at all?
For what more honor can befall,
Then die for that, for which I die:
To live therefore and to forget,
Is such a shamefull life I see,　　　　　　　10
That I had rather love one yet,
Forgotten though to death I bee.

When I had made an ende of my song, the Shepherdes teares
(but those especially of faire *Ismenia*) were so many, that of force
they made me participate some of her greefe, which thing I might 15
well have left undone, for no fault could justly have bene attributed to my great mishap, as to all those that were there, it was
sufficiently knowen. After this every one of us went to their
owne towne, bicause it was not meete for us to be out of them at
such inconvenient and late howers. And the next day, my father 20
(without telling me the cause why) caried me out of our towne,
and brought me to yours, placing me there in the house of *Albania*
mine aunt, and his sister, whom you knowe well, where I have
remained a few daies since my comming hither, not knowing the
cause of my sudden exile, but have heard of late, that *Montanus* 25
hath married *Ismenia*, and that *Alanius* was about to marrie a sister
of hers called *Sylvia*: whereupon to conclude, I wish that he may
live (since it was not my good fortune to have him) as joyfull
a life with his new spouse, that nothing may want to the full
accomplishment of their content and happinesse: For, the love, 30
which I beare him will suffer me no lesse, then to wish him all
the felicitie of this life.

When *Selvagia* had made an end of her sorrowfull tale, she
began to weepe so bitterly, that both the Shepherdes (being
a kinde of friendly dutie, wherein they had no small experience) 35
began also to helpe her with their teares, and after having spent
a little time in this sort, *Syrenus* saide unto her. Great is thy greefe
(faire *Selvagia*) and yet I judge thy patience and discretion greater.

Take example by other mens harmes, looke into their paines, consider their woes, if thou wilt the better support thine owne: And bicause it growes now towardes night, let us be jogging towardes our towne, and to morrow passe away the heate of the day neere to this cleere fountaine, where we will all three meete. 5 Let it be as thou saiest (said *Selvagia*) but bicause betweene this and the towne there is a pretie way, let every one of us (to passe it away with some thing) sing a song befitting the condition and qualitie of his love. The Shepherdes answered, if she would begin, they would follow, which *Selvagia* did, all three going on 10 softly towardes the towne.

> *SHepherd, who can passe such wrong*
> *   And a life in woes so deepe?*
> *Which to live is to too long,*
> *   As it is too short to weepe.*   15
>
> *Greevous sighes in vaine I waste,*
> *   Leesing my affiance, and*
> *I perceive my hope at last*
> *   With a candle in the hand.*
>
> *What time then to hope among*   20
> *   Bitter hopes, that ever sleepe?*
> *When this life is to too long,*
> *   As it is too short to weepe.*
>
> *This greefe which I feele so rife,*
> *   (Wretch) I doe deserve as hire,*   25
> *Since I came to put my life*
> *   In the handes of my desire.*
>
> *Then cease not my plaints so strong,*
> *   For (though life her course doth keepe)*
> *It is not to live so long,*   30
> *   As it is too short to weepe.*

With a burning sigh that came from her afflicted soule, *Selvagia* ended her song, saying, How unfortunate (alas) am I that see my selfe buried in jealousie and despaire, which cannot in the end but bring my life to no other passe, then to that which is infallibly 35

expected of them. After this, forgotten *Syrenus* to the tune of his
Rebecke began to sing this song following.

*W*Eepe not my dolefull eies,
    But if you weepe, thinke (at the lest)
They tolde no trueth but lies,   5
    And then it may be you may rest.

Since that imagination
    Doth cause so much in every state,
    Thinke that she loves thee as of late,
And thou shalt have lesse passion.   10

And if you will (mine eies)
    Have ease, imagine then the best,
And that they told you lies:
    And so perhaps you may have rest.

Thinke that she loves as well,   15
    As ever she did heretofore:
    But this sad men cannot restore,
To thinke what once befell:

Then mournfull eies, where lies
    Your helpe? Yet thinke of some at lest,   20
If not, weepe still mine eies,
    Or make an end, and you shall rest.

After that sorrowfull *Syrenus* with many teares had made an end
of his song, despised *Sylvanus* began his thus.

*M*Y life (*yoong Shepherdesse*) *for thee*   25
   Of needes to death must post;
But yet my greefe must stay with mee
    After my life is lost.

The greevous ill, by death that cured is
    Continually hath remedie at hand: 30
But not that torment, that is like to this,
    That in slowe time, and fortunes meanes doth stand.

And if this sorrow cannot be
  Ended with life (as most)
What then doth this thing profit me,
  A sorrow wonne or lost?

Yet all is one to me, as now I trie   5
  A flattring hope, or that that had not bene yet.
For if to day for want of it I die,
  Next day I doe no lesse for having seene it.

Faine would I die, to end and free
  This greefe, that kils me most   10
If that it might be lost with me,
  Or die when life is lost.

And in this sort the two Shepherdes went homewardes in companie of *Selvagia*, departing from one another with accorde to
meete the next day following at the same place.   15

The end of the first booke of Diana.

The second Booke of Diana of George
of Montemayor.   20

NOw did the Shepherdes, which fed their sheepe in the fieldes
of *Ezla*, begin to shew themselves, every one with his
flockes along the bankes of those cristalline waters (each Shepherde knowing, and choosing out the best place before the Sun
did rise, the better to passe away the burning heate of the day) 25
when the faire Shepherdesse *Selvagia* came down from the hil,
which from her towne did leade to a thick wood, driving her
gentle sheepe and lambes before her: who, after she had put them
amongst the lowe shrubs, which grew very thicke thereabouts,
and seeing them busie in knobbing the yoong and tender boughes, 30
to stanch their hunger, went directly to the fountaine of the Sicamours, where the day before, in companie of the two Shepherds,

she had passed away the noone-tide heate: and seeing the place so agreeable to melancholie, and contemplation of her sorrowes, she thought it not amisse to take the opportunitie of the time, and place, and to sit downe by the fountaine, whose waters seemed with her swelling teares to increase: where, after she had a great while busied her selfe in divers and sundrie thoughts, she began thus to say. May it be possible *Alanius*, that thou art the man, whose eies I never saw dried up from teares in presence of mine? And he, who, falling downe so many times at my feete, with loving and pitifull wordes, craved mercie and clemencie at my handes, the which (to my great harme and greefe) I so gently bestowed on thee? Tell me Shepherd (the falsest that lives on earth) is it true that thou lovedst me, to cloy thy minde with my favours, and so soone to be wearie of the love that thou didst beare me? Thou mightest imagine, that it was no lesse in my power, to forget and despise thee, as thou hast forgotten me. For it is the part of those, that handle not their matters of love so well as they shoulde, to thinke that their Mistresses may play the like partes with them, as they have done before; though some use it for a remedie and policie to make their love encrease the more. And others, that jealousie (the occasion whereof most commonly they faine) may so captivate their Mistresses mindes, that (as they make them beleeve) they are not able to settle their affection in any other place: whereupon most of them come by little and little to manifest all that they fained before, whereby more cleerely they discover their disloyaltie. All which extremes at last result to the greefe and prejudice of us poore soules, who (not considering how the endes of such things commonly fall out) doe so deepely sinke into that kinde of assured affection, that we never leave of to love you, nor you to requite us with ingratitude and inconstancie, as thou dost that love (disloyall *Alanius*) which I have borne, and doe still beare thee. So that which of these thou hast bene, I cannot conjecture. But wonder not *Selvagia*, that thou understandest so little in matters of disdaine, that art so well practised in loves affaires. Thou didst ever beare an honest and vertuous pretence by thy wordes, whereby I never looked for lesse by thy deedes, which made me thinke, that that love, (whereby thou mad'st me beleeve, that thy desire extended to wish no more of me, then pure love againe) should never have an end: for if any further drift

13 minde *Catchword*: minde, *Text.*

had bene in thy desires, I woulde never have suspected firmnesse in thy love. O wretched woman, how soone have I begun to know thy intentions, and yet how late to prevent my harmes? Come thou to me my pretie Bagpipe, and with thee will I passe the time away: for had I spent it onely in thy exercise and delight, it 5 had bene better for me: and after she had plaied a while on it, she began to sing this *Sextine* following.

Waters that fall from top of these steepe Hils,
　With such a noyse into these lowe deepe Vales,
Why thinke you not of those, which from my Soule   10
Continually distill my wearied Eies?
And what's the cause of them? Unluckie Time,
In which hard fortune robbed all my Joy.
Love gave me hope of such a golden Joy,
That ther's no Shepherdesse in all these Hils,   15
That had such cause to praise a happy Time:
But after he did put me in these Vales
Of swelling teares, that fall from both mine Eies:
Not to behold such greefe as kils my Soule.
Such is the paine, that wounds a loving Soule,   20
That in the end I know what thing is Joy:
O where shall I then turne my wearied Eies?
If that the medowes, woods, the plaines, and Hils,
The pleasant groves, and fountaines of the Vales,
Still to my thoughts present so sweete a Time?   25
Who would have thought that such a happy Time
Should be so fierce a torment to my Soule?
Or cruell fortune banish me the Vale,
Wherein all things were objects of my Joy?
Untill the hungrie woolfe, which to the Hill   30
Ascending up, was pleasant to mine Eies.
But fortune now, what may my drenched Eies
Behold, which saw their Shepherd many a Time
Driving his lambes before him downe this Hill?
Whose name for ay shall rest within my Soule.   35
O fortune foe unto my former Joy,
How doe I languish in this irkesome Vale?
But when so pleasant and so fresh a Vale
Is not delightfull to my wearied Eies,

And where I cannot finde content and Joy:
And hope not now to have it any Time,
See what extremes environ then my Soule:
O that he came againe. O that sweete Hill:
O highest Hils, *and fresh and pleasant* Vale,   5
Where once my Soule *did rest and both these* Eies,
Tell me shall I in Time *have so much* Joy?

About this time *Sylvanus* was with his flockes in a thicket of
Mirtle trees neere to the fountaine, musing and imagining divers
things in his minde: but when he heard *Selvagias* voice, awaked as 10
it were out of a slumber, he gave attentive eare to the verses, that
she did sing. But as this Shepherd was cruelly intreated of love,
and contemned of *Diana*, so his passions made him wander a
thousand times out of his wits, as that he now spake ill of love,
and by and by praised it, sometimes merrie, and other times more 15
pensive and sad, then the most sorrowfull man in the world, to
day speaking ill of women, to morrow extolling them above all
mortall creatures. And thus did this sorrowfull Shepherd leade
a life, which as to all, so especially to those that are free from love
would be tedious and difficult to describe. But having heard 20
Selvagias sweete verses, and obtained leave of his sad thoughts, he
tooke his Kit, and to the tune thereof began to sing that which
followeth.

*T*O *heare me wearied is the cleerest river,*
  Tedious I am to every vale and mountaine: 25
And now to heare (O love, my sorrowes giver)
My plaining, wearied is each cristall fountaine.
  The Sicamour, the Oke, and Elme are wearie,
  Spring, Sommer, Autumne, and the winter season
  Hearing my cries, are sworne not to be merry.   30
  With teares I melt these rocks: and yet all reason
Of pitie (Tigresse) thou dost still deny me,
When trees, and stones for greefe are dying by me.

A bondslave of a freeman thou hast made me,
And of a man of reason, cleane contrarie: 35
With life, and death, by turnes thou dost invade me,
And to tormenting greefe my soule dost carrie.

Of affable, and one that liv'd so gayly,
Made me thou hast to frowards disdaining:
Of one, that did converse with all men daily,
Made me thou hast their company refraining.
Eies had I once, now blinded with desire: 5
I was a man of flesh, but now of fire.

What's this my hart, thy torments dost thou double?
Tell me mine eies, and are you still a weeping?
My soule, sufficeth not my passed trouble?
My teares, and are ye yet in rivers steeping?   10
   My wandring wits, and are you not molested
   More then ynough with such incessant sorrow?
   And are ye not my senses also wrested
   From your right course, resting not even nor morrow?
How know I then, weepe, see, or feele this hower,   15
When torments waste their force and severall power?

Who made my Shepherdesses tresses twistall
Of fine Arabian gold, not gilt-like shining:
Her face of cleerest and of chosen christall,
Her rubie lips, two rowes of pearle combining: 20
   Her dymond eies, like to those stars above all,
   Her necke, that whitest Allablaster stayneth,
   Her passing wit, inforcing us to love all:
   Her stately minde, that all our loves disdaineth.
Why made shee not her hart of melting matter,   25
Then of such marble stone so hard to batter?

One day I do conforme me to my fortune,
And to my griefe, that faire Diana *causeth:*
Next day mine yll doth vex me, and importune
My soule with thoughts of griefe that seldome pauseth: 30
   Cruell and fierce and inhumane I call her,
   And so there is no order in my sorrow:
   For afterwards in phrases I install her,
   What now I say, I do deny to morrow.
And all is thus leading a life in anguish,   35
Which soone mine eies may see by death to languish.

When faire *Selvagia* knew the Shepherd *Sylvanus* by his voice, she went to him, and saluting one another with curteous and loving words, they sat them downe under the shadow of a thicke and leafie mirtle, in the mids of a little medow, which for the diversitie of fine golden flowers wherewith it was spotted, more then their sorrowfull thoughts could desire, was most pleasant to the wandring eie. And *Sylvanus* began to speake in this sort. The diversitie of so many unaccustomed mishaps, that daily harme us woefull and true lovers cannot be (faire *Selvagia*) without griefe and compassion of minde considered. But amongst them all, there is none (me thinks) that ought to be so much feared as that, which he suffers, who hath once seene himselfe in a good and joyfull estate: the which by experience (as yesterday thou didst tell me) I never came yet to know: for the life (which I passe) is so far from rest, and delivered up to sorrowfull imaginations, that a thousand times in vaine I seeke out new inventions and means to deceive and alter my tast. For remedy wherof, I do sometimes think, That I am deerely beloved of my mistresse, which thought (without opening any further passage to this fiction) I retaine as long as I can in my mind: but when I consider afterwards the truth of my estate, I am so confounded with my selfe, as I am not able to expresse it, and then (against my will) am voide of all patience: since then a bare imagination is not such a thing, that may be suffered, behold what the truth is able to do? I would to God (*Sylvanus*) I were free (said *Selvagia*) from this franticke passion that I might speake the better in it, as in such a case it were most needfull. For thou canst not know any greater signe of love, whether it be little or much, or of passion, whether it be small or great, then by hearing her tell it, that feeles it: for a passion extremely felt can never be well manifested by her toong that suffers it. So that I (being subject to my mishap, and sorrowfull for that disgrace, which *Alanius* doth me) am not with words able to expresse the *Chaos* of griefe wherin I am overwhelmed. Wherefore I leave it to thy consideration and judgement, as to things wherin I may put an assured confidence and trust. I know not *Selvagia*, what to say (replied *Sylvanus* sighing) nor what remedies we may hope for of our harms, dost thou (perhaps) know any? How should I not know (said *Selvagia*) And wottest thou what it is? To leave of to love. And this maiest thou do thy selfe (said *Sylvanus*.) As fortune and time shall ordaine (saide

Selvagia.) Then I tell thee (said *Sylvanus* marvelling much) that thou needest not trouble thy selfe so much by complayning of thy griefe, bicause that love, which is subject to time and fortune, cannot be so extreme, to give one any trouble or paine that suffers it. And canst thou deny (said *Selvagia* againe) that it is not possible 5 to have an end in thy love, either by death or absence, or by being favoured in some other place, where thy sutes and services may be more esteemed, and better recompenced? I will not make my selfe (saide *Sylvanus*) such an hypocrite in love, that I will not graunt, what thou saiest may be possible, but not in me. For woe 10 betide that lover, that (though he see such fortune fall to others) would have so little constancie in his love, to thinke that any thing (contrary to his faith) may befall unto him. I am a woman (said *Selvagia*) and thou shalt see by me if I love not as much as any may. And yet this offendes not my love to thinke, that there 15 may be an end of every thing, be they never so firme and strong, since it is the propertie of time and fortune with their usuall changes to alter all things, as they have ever done. And thinke not Shepherd, that any oblivious thought of his love, that hath so injuriously forgotten me, makes me speake this, but that, which 20 I have seene by experience in these passions. And talking thus together they heard a Shepherd singing, as he came along the medow before them, whom they knew by and by to be the forgotten *Syrenus*, who, to the tune of his Rebecke came singing this Sonnet.   25

> *G*Oe now my thoughts, where one day you were going,
>   *When neither fortune, nor my love did lower:*
>   *Now shall you see that changed day and hower,*
> *Your joies decaied, and uncouth sorrowes growing?*
> *And in the glasse, where I was oft bestowing*   30
>   *Mine eies, and in that sweete and pleasant flower,*
>   *A sluggish drone unwoorthely devower*
> *That honie, which for me sometimes was flowing.*
> *And you shall see to whom I did surrender*
>   *My subject life, that causelesse did despise it:*   35
>   *And though this ill no remedy can borrow,*
> *Yet tell her, that my minde did once ingender*
>   *A feare of that, which after to mine eyes yet*
>   *She makes more plaine, to end my life in sorrow.*

After *Syrenus* had made an end of his Sonnet, he sawe faire
Selvagia, and *Sylvanus* comming towards him, whereof he was not
a little glad, and after some curteous salutations between them,
they determined to go to the fountaine of the Sicamours, where
they had beene the day before, but before they were come thither, 5
Sylvanus said, Hearke, do you not heare certaine voices singing?
Yes (said *Selvagia*) and me thinks of more then one. Where might
it be (said *Syrenus*.) In the meadowe of the Laurell trees, said
Sylvanus, in the mids whereof the spring, that comes out of this cleere
fountaine so pleasantly runneth : It shall not be amisse for us to go 10
thither, but so softly, that they that are singing, may not perceive
or heare us, lest we breake off their sweete musicke. Let us go,
said *Selvagia* : and so step by step, they went towards the place,
where they heard that singing, and hiding themselves behind
certaine trees neere unto the brook, they saw three Nymphes 15
sitting upon the golden flowers, of such excellent beauty that (it
seemed) nature had made a manifest proofe of that, she was able
to do. They were apparelled with upper garments of white silk,
wrought all above with fringe of gold, their haire, (which in
brightnes obscured the sunnie beames) was tied about their 20
heads with fillets of orientall pearle, whose curled lockes upon
their christalline foreheads made a fine periwig; just in the mids
wherof hung downe an Eagle of gold, holding betweene her
talants a rich and pretious Diamond. All three with marvellous
good consent so sweetly plaied on their instruments, where- 25
unto they joyned their Angelicall voices, that it seemed no lesse
then celestiall musicke, and the first thing they sung, was this
fancie.

> *C*Ontents of love,
> *That come with so great paine,*   30
> *If that you come, why go you hence againe?*
>
> *Not fully come,*
> *But you begin to starte:*
> *Never with perfect some*
> *To nestle in a woefull heart.*   35
> *And will you now so soone depart,*
> *And leave me in such paine?*
> *Then hence delights, and see me not againe.*

From you I flye,
(Since you denie my sight)
To make me know thereby
The losse, if that I loose you quite.
Then (since you do me such despite)   5
Depart not griefe and paine,
For when you goe, you soone returne againe.

After they had ended their song, one of them called *Doria* said.
Are these (*Cynthia*) the river bankes, where the Shepherd *Syrenus*
went up and downe, tormented and lost for the love of the faire 10
Shepherdesse *Diana*? I without doubt (said the other) they must
be these, for neere unto a fountaine not far from this medow, it
was told me, they tooke of each other their last farewell, which is
(I assure thee) worthie to be celebrated with eternall memorie, for
the amorous and loving speeches, that passed betweene them. 15
When *Syrenus* heard this, he was almost out of his wits, to see
how the three Nymphes had knowledge of his mishaps. But
Cynthia, proceeding, said. And among these river banks are many
other faire Shepherdesses, and enamoured Shepherds, where love
hath shewed his mightie power and effects, and some cleane 20
contrary to that they hoped for. This is a thing (said *Polydora*, for
so was the third called) not greatly to be marvelled at, bicause
there is no successe in love, (be it never so preposterous) which
may cause wonder in those that have passed his disordinate
effects. But tell me *Cynthia*, how knewest thou of this farewell? 25
I knew it thus (said *Cynthia*) for at that time when they tooke it,
neere to the foresaid fountaine, *Celius*, who behind an Oke was
listening to them, heard it, and committing it to memorie, did
truly put it in verse, as it passed betweene them. Therfore if thou
wilt heare it, I thinke, I can sing it to the tune of my lute. Faire 30
Cynthia (answered *Polydora*) so may thy destinies and fortune
favour thee, as thy beauty and good graces are no lesse delightfull
unto us, then the hearing of so sweete a song shall be (wherein is
matter so woorthie to be knowen) if thou wilt deyne to pleasure us
with the recitall of it. *Cynthia* then taking her harpe, began to sing 35
as followeth.

The song of the Nymph.

NEere to the river bankes, with greene
    And pleasant trees on every side,
Where freest mindes would most have beene,
That never felt brave Cupids pride,   5
    To passe the day and tedious how'rs
    Amongst those painted meades and flow'rs,

A certaine Shepheard full of woe
(Syrenus call'd) his flockes did feede,
Not sorowfull in outward showe,   10
But troubled with such greefe indeede,
    As cruell love is wont t'impart
    Unto a painfull loving hart.

This Shepherd every day did die
For love he to Diana bare,   15
A Shepherdesse so fine perdie,
So lively yoong and passing faire,
    Excelling more in beautious feature,
    Then any other humane creature.

Who had not any thing, of all   20
She had, but was extreme in her,
For meanely wise none might her call,
Nor meanely faire, for he did erre,
    If so he did: but should devise
    Her name of passing faire and wise.   25

Favours on him she did bestowe,
Which if she had not, then (be sure)
He might have suffred all that woe,
Which afterwards he did endure
    When he was gone, with lesser paine,   30
    And at his comming home againe.

7 flow'rs, Ed.] flow'rs. Y.

For when in deede the hart is free
From suffring paine or torments smart,
If wisedome doth not oversee,
And beareth not the greater part,
    The smallest greefe and care of minde   5
    Doth make it captive to their kinde.

Neere to a river swift and great
(That famous Ezla had to name)
The carefull Shepherd did repeate
The feares he had by absence blame,   10
    Which he suspect, where he did keepe
    And feede his gentle lambes and sheepe.

And now sometimes he did behold
His Shepherdesse, that thereabout
Was on the mountaines of that old   15
And ancient Leon, seeking out
    From place to place the pastures best,
    Her lambes to feede, her selfe to rest.

And sometimes musing, as he lay,
(When on those hils she was not seene)   20
Was thinking of that happy day,
When Cupid gave him such a Queene
    Of beautie, and such cause of joy,
    Wherein his minde he did imploy.

Yet saide (poore man) when he did see   25
Himselfe so sunke in sorrowes pit,
The good that love hath given mee
I onely doe imagine it:
    Bicause this neerest harme and trouble
    Hereafter I should suffer double.   30

The Sunne, for that it did decline,
The carelesse man did not offend
With firie beames, which scarce did shine,
But that which did of love depend,
    And in his hart did kindle fire   35
    Of greater flames and hot desire.

Him did his passions all invite,
The greene leaves blowne with gentle winde,
Cristalline streames with their delite,
And Nightingales were not behinde,
    To helpe him in this loving verse,   5
    Which to himselfe he did rehearse.

Syrenus *his song.*

A Farewell they departure call,
     That loves delight did never knowe,
But that that endes with life and all,   10
I terme a greefe and endlesse woe.

God graunt therefore that all that space
My lingring life I might sustaine,
Untill I see againe the place
Where my true hart doth still remaine.   15

For onely thinking to depart,
The thought doth make me so afraid,
That it must kill my trembling hart
With force of such great greefe apaid.

Syrenus *did these verses sing,*   20
And on his Rebecke sweetely play,
So far from joy or joyfull thing,
And from contentment any way:
    That he could not pronounce his minde
    For weeping, which was left behinde.   25

And now bicause he would not be
In fault, (if that his greefe and paine
The accents and the verse, which he
Pronounc't, did hinder or restraine)
    That which his willing minde did let,   30
    His hart to end did not forget.

But after that the Shepherd had
With moornefull voice these verses soong,
He sawe Diana *come so sad,*
And yet so faire, so fresh and yong,
    That where she cast her starlike eies,   5
    With colours brave the meades she dies.

Her face as faire and fresh as flower,
And yet so sorrowfull againe,
That none could judge at that same hower,
Whether her greefe and inward paine,   10
    Or her brave beautie did surpasse?
    In her so faire, and sad (alas.)

Thus comming many a time she staide,
Casting unto the ground her eies,
So comfortlesse and so dismade,   15
And sometimes up into the skies,
    That there they hung with greefe in steede
    Of two bright stars, like stars in deede.

Saying with greater greefe of minde
(Then humane thought can once conceave)   20
Since such annoy in joy I finde:
From this day (love) well maist thou leave
    Thy joies unto thy selfe to keepe,
    And me, to feede no more but sheepe.

The cause of all her greefe and woe,   25
Which she by absence wrong did feare,
There did she very cleerely showe,
And if she wasted many a teare,
    Aske but those blasing eies, which still
    With passions did Syrenus *kill.*   30

If that her love had ever peere,
Her goodnes there hid not the same:
And if that absence cost her deere,
Or feared her before it came,
    This song above each other thing   35
    Can tell, which she with teares did sing.

Song with a song

Dianas *song.*

O *Love thou gav'st me not the joy,*
 That in sweete presence I did finde,
But that in absence the annoy
Should seeme more greevous to my minde.   5

Thou givest ease, thou givest rest,
But not to give content but guile,
And that the suffrance in my brest,
Might be but idle for a while.

See loves inventions, never scant   10
In presence to affoord releefe,
Bicause in absence I should want
Defence against my mortall greefe.

Now faire Diana *being come*
Unto the place, where she did spie   1
Her love, she would have spoken some
Few wordes, but greefe did them denie:
    And wofull man, he nothing spake,
    Though he did oft a semblant make.

How much they had betweene them both   2
To talke, their eies made manifest,
Declaring that, which very loth
Lay in their secret harts and brest,
    With that milde countenance and show,
    With which they spake not long agoe.   2

They both together downe did sit
Under a flowrie Myrtle tree,
One by the hand the other yet
Did take, for overcome was he
    By her, and she by him againe,   3
    Both in their mutuall passions slaine.

For that great pleasure and delight
Of seeing one an other there,
And greefe, to leese that happie sight,
So wrought their harts with joy and feare,
   That to each other neither could   5
   Utter a word, though faine they would.

Some other times they met againe
Upon this banke with other passions,
Which meetings they did entertaine
And celebrate with other fashions: 10
   Not, as in times then gone and past,
   For of this sort, this was the last.

A strange effect of mighty love,
To see two love in such degree,
That greater torments they did prove,   15
When either did each other see,
   Then when they were remooved quite
   From joying in each others sight.

Syrenus *seeing now the howre,*
When greefe of parting was to come,   20
He had no patience nor no powre
To speake, but straight was striken dumbe:
   Nor of his teares he could get leave
   To utter what he did conceave.

His Shepherdesse he did behold,   25
His Shepherdesse beheld againe
The man, whose hart with feare was cold,
Speaking to her with cruell paine:
   Indeede his Greefe for him did speake,
   For he could not whose hart did breake.   30

Alas Diana, *who would have said,*
When I was in most heavie case,
Or who would have imagined,
But that, when I did view thy face,
   My very soule then most opprest,   35
   Should by that sight have found some rest.

In any time who would have thought,
That any thing (sweete Mistresse*) might*
A greater greefe or paine have brought
Unto my soule with more despight,
    Then thy sweete presence and thy sight,   5
    (My soveraine joy and chiefe delight)

Who would have thought, but that againe
Those eies, when that they viewed me,
Should have dissolv'd, and burst in twaine
The knot of all my miserie: 10
    Which my mishaps (so long assured)
    By any way might have procured.

Faire Mistresse *then behold my state,*
And how mishap my soule doth chace,
For if I died but of late   15
With great desire to see thy face,
    Now doe I die by seeing thee:
    Present and not thou killest me.

And thinke not that this passion drawes
To want of loving thee, for none   20
Hath bene so firme, but now bicause
I come unto this meade with mone
    To take my leave, where I before
    To see thee came, but now no more.

My soule I would have given faine   25
This day, which thou hast conquer'd soe,
Not to have seene thee in this plaine
(Although no other life I knowe)
    Onely to misse (I care not how)
    The greefe of this departure now.   30

And give me leave (faire Shepherdesse*)*
To thinke, that thou canst not deny it,
But thou dost feele my heavinesse
In that degree, as I doe trie it:
    For in thy presence t'is not such   35
    A matter to presume so much.

If then, Diana, *it be so,*
Tell me, how can I now depart?
How dost thou suffer me to go
When each doth carry others hart?
  Or how doe I come hither yet,   5
  To take my farewell without let?

O my faire Shepherdesse againe
No reason can I yeeld thee why,
Nor how of thee I should complaine,
As thou shalt have continually   10
  Absent, when I am gone from thee
  O, never to remember me.

I knowe right well it is not thow,
That mak'st me to depart, and lesse,
My purest faith constraines me now,   15
(For needes I must the same confesse)
  And if I should but tell and show it,
  Who doth the same, I doe not know it.

Thus full of paine and bitter teares,
And sighing, which he never spar'd,   20
The Shepherd to her loving eares
Did speake these words which you have heard.
  And hearing them, in minde she kept
  Them, and full bitterly she wept.

To answere him she went about   25
A thousand times, but could not doe it,
For still her greefe did put her out,
And so she could not frame her to it.
  But then for her, her love so stable
  An answere shapt (her toong unable.)   30

My friend in such a time I am,
Where I shall speake more then I would,
That though mine ill, which lately came,
Cannot be uttered (as it should:)
  Yet (Shepherd) would I thinke it good,   35
  To hold my peace if that I could.

But woe is me, that this great ill
I come to tell, and publish it
In such a time against my will,
That it availes not any whit
   Thy journey to delay a while,   5
   Nor these my torments to beguile.

Why goest thou hence (O Shepherd) tell:
Why wilt thou now forsake me heere?
So full of greefe alone to dwell,
Where time, and place, and all the deere,   10
   And sweetest joyes of this our love
   Shall never from my minde remoove.

What shall I feele (unhappy wight)
Comming unto this pleasant greene,
When I shall say (Farewell sweete sight)   15
Heere have I my Syrenus seene;
   Heere did we sit, heere did we play,
   Discoursing with him day by day.

Behold if that it will not bee
A daily sorrow, when these bankes   20
I doe beholde, and cannot see
Thy selfe, where goodly trees in rankes
   And in their barke my name to stand
   Carved so finely by thy hand.

And see if any greefe or dole   25
Is like to this, when I behold
The place so sorrowfull and sole,
Where deere Syrenus with a cold
   And trembling feare thou didst protest
   Thy greefe to me within thy brest.   30

If then thy hart (so cruell now)
Is mollified by falling teares,
How melts it not for greefe, and how
Consumes it not with many feares,
   At this occasion (so unjust)   35
   To leave my comfort in the dust?

Then Shepherd weepe not, for in vaine
Thy plentious teares and sighes are spent,
For he that doth lament the paine,
In whom it lieth to prevent,
   I thinke he is not sound of wit,   5
   If such a folly he commit.

But my Syrenus *pardon me,*
If my sharpe wordes thine eares offend,
And give me leave to speake with thee
In this faire meade, where (cruell frend)   10
   Thou leav'st me not one little how'r
   With my poore selfe, nor in my pow'r.

For I will not, (nor yet in jest)
Shepherd from thee my selfe absent,
Then goe not, wilt thou? say at lest,   15
And to these eies, that ever lent
   Such helpe to thee, some pitie keepe,
   And sorrow now to see them weepe.

Syrenus *answered her againe,*
Alas thou canst not choose but knowe   20
By all these teares I spend in vaine,
If that I doe desire to goe;
   But thou commaundest me to stay,
   And my hard hap to goe away.

Thy matchlesse beautie when I see,   25
(Mistresse) then am I ever bound
Willing at thy commaund to be:
But wofull Shepherd when I found
   My hap to beare so great a sway,
   Of force I must the same obay.   30

Then my departure forced is,
But by no fault that I did make,
And credit me (sweete Nymph) in this,
That all the world I would forsake,
   In these faire meades with thee to wende,   35
   Where now I see my joyes doe ende.

My Master that great Shepherd is
He, that doth make me to depart,
Whom I may see, and wish that his
Exempted thoughtes and freest hart
   Brave love may punish with such paine,   5
   As at this parting I sustaine.

I would to God, my going hence
(Onely to pleasure thee this day)
By shewing of my just pretence,
Lay in my power any way: 10
   As Mistresse in thy fairest handes
   My life and death at mercie standes.

But credit me, it is in vaine,
(To that which ever I doe trie,
And that thou think'st as much againe)   15
That never in my handes did lie
   Ought in the world, that might but give
   Any content to make me live.

Another course well might I take,
And leave my flocke to stray about,   20
I might my Shepherd to forsake
And seeke some other Master out:
   But if the end I marke and see,
   This with our love doth not agree.

For if I doe forsake my flocke,   25
Which unto me he did commend,
And take in hand some other stocke
Of cattell or of sheepe to tend,
   Tell me, how can I come unseene
   Without thy harme upon this greene?   30

And if the force of this great flame
My willing presence heere detaines,
It is a signe, that I doe frame
My thoughts on thee, and so it staines
   Thy honour, which to saile is sent,   35
   Onely (sweete life) for my content.

And if (they say) I doe imploy
(Faire Shepherdesse) my love on thee,
And that againe I doe enjoy
Thy love so frankly given me,
  Thee they condemne, thou dost sustaine   5
  The onely losse, and I no gaine.

The Shepherdesse at this same season
This answer with great greefe did make,
O Shepherd tell me now, what reason
Thou hast my presence to forsake?   10
  Since that in love there is no sound
  Of any reason to be found.

A signe it is (not good to use)
By daily proofe we see the same,
That he that can so well excuse   15
His absence from his loving dame,
  If he were gone out of her sight,
  He would account the same but light.

Ah greefe, since going now away,
I knowe not what will chaunce to thee,   20
And forced if I am to stay
Nor then what shall become of me?
  Nor there if thou wilt thinke (my deere)
  That one did see another heere.

I knowe not if I am deceav'd,   25
By having laide before thine eies
This painfull greefe that hath bereav'd
Me of my joy, where now it dies,
  But that which to my harme must be,
  I knowe shall be most sure in me.   30

Thou greev'st not at my little ease,
Go Shepherd then, take shipping now,
With brittle barke the Ocean seas,
In steede of these greene fieldes goe plow:
  Since of my teares these seas (alas)   35
  So quickly thou dost overpasse.

4 *given me, Ed.] given me. Y.*

The heavens from stormes thy barke defend,
From rockes, from wrecke, and swallowing sand,
And that thou maist (my sweetest frend)
Safely arrive in wished land:
  And fortune better deale with thee,   5
  Then at this time thou dost with me.

Alas for very greefe I die,
Seeing mine eies to take their leave
Of all their sweete contents, whereby
This greefe, and teares doe so bereave   10
  My toong of speech, that faine I would
  Speake more unto thee if I could.

And Shepherd I doe wish besides,
That these two eies (which weepe in vaine)
Before that death my life devides,   15
May see thee heere yet once againe:
  And though their harme thou dost procure,
  They wish thee yet all good be sure.

He answered her, my Mistresse deere,
A mischeefe never comes alone: 20
A mortall greefe doth not appeere
Without more companie, and one
  That is more mightie then the rest,
  And this it is that wounds my brest.

For though I see I must depart   25
From my sweete life, (since from thy sight)
Not halfe so much it greeves my hart,
As seeing thee in such a plight
  For my departure, and sustaine
  Such greefe indeede and cruell paine.   30

But if those eies I doe forget,
(The mirrours of my happinesse)
I wish that God above may let
Me not this wished life possesse,
  Or if my thoughtes imploied be   35
  (Sweete life) on any but on thee.

And if that any beautie else
Shall make new motions in my minde,
(Though it be never so excelse)
Or in the same content I finde,
   For one small howre of such content,   5
   I wish eternall punishment.

And if my firmest faith for strange
And forren love, that may befall,
Or my sincerest love I change,
I wish that fortune may recall   10
   Me to a life most desperate,
   Throwing me downe from this estate.

O sweetest Mistresse of my hart,
Prescribe no time for my retourne:
For it doth kill me to depart,   15
And I shall never cease to mourne,
   And passe the greatest greefe and paine,
   Untill these eies see thee againe.

She answered him, (my deere Syrenus)
If that I shall in any day   20
(Though now our destinies doe weane us)
Forget thee, then I wish the May
   And freshest flowers in this meade
   May die, when on them I doe treade.

And if on any man alive,   25
But onely thee (my love) I thinke,
I wish, that, (when my sheepe I drive
Unto the river streames to drinke)
   Comming unto them, at my sight,
   The waters may be dry'd up quite.   30

Shepherd, receive this little string
Made of my haire for thy sweete sake,
Bicause by seeing of the thing,
Thou maist remember thou did'st take
   Possession of my loving hart,   35
   And them, with which thou doest depart.

And this ring with thee thou shalt beare,
With hand in hand, as thou dost see,
Which for my sake I pray thee weare,
That though our bodies parted bee,
  Nothing shall part, not death alone,   5
  Two soules united both in one.

He saide with thee what shall I leave,
Naught have I but this Sheepehooke heere:
The which I pray thee to receive,
And Rebecke, to the which (my deere)   10
  Thou saw'st me sing in this greene meade,
  And play and many a daunce to leade.

To sound of which (my Shepherdesse)
A thousand songs to thee I soong,
Singing of thy great worthinesse   15
(Too high for my base song and toong)
  And of our loves and of my passions,
  And of my sweetest lamentations.

Each one imbrac't the other fast,
And this (I thinke) the first time was,   20
And (as I gesse) it was the last,
Bicause those times did change and passe:
  And love with time did change and varie
  From that, which once they both did carie.

For though Diana *felt great paine*   25
For absence of her lover deere,
Yet in the same she found againe
A remedie, as did appeere,
  For after he the seas did passe,
  She to another married was.   30

Faire *Cynthia* having made an end of her sweete song, *Doria* and
Polydora wondred that a Shepherdesse could be the cause, that
love kindled such burning flames, and marveiled no lesse how
time had cured her greefe, which seemed at their farewell to be
remedilesse. But unfortunate *Syrenus* all the while the Nymph with   35
her sweete song did manifest his old cares and sighes, forgot not

to breath them out so thicke, that *Sylvanus*, and *Selvagia* could not
by any meanes comfort him: for he was now no lesse pensive
then at the very time, when he passed them, marvelling much how
she knew of these particulars which passed betweene him and
Diana. And *Sylvanus* and *Selvagia* were no lesse astonished at the 5
passing sweete grace, wherewith *Cynthia* both song and plaied
the same.

But now the faire Nymphes, tooke up their instruments, and
went walking up and downe the greene meadow, lest of all
suspecting that, which happened unto them: for having gone but 10
a little way from the place, where the Shepherdes were secretly
abiding, three monstrous and foule Savages came out of a thicket
of high broome and bushes on the right hande of the woode,
armed with corselets and morions of tygres skins, and so ugly to
behold, that to the fearefull Nymphes it was a strange and terrible 15
sight. The braces of their corselets were at the endes armed with
gasping mouthes of serpents, out of the which their armes
shewed monstrously great, and full of haire, and their morions
that encompassed their grisely foreheads, with dreadfull heads of
lyons, being naked in every other part of their body, but that it 20
was covered all over with long and thicke haire, and bearing in
their rude hands clubs, armed with iron and sharpe steeled
points. At their neckes their bowes and arrowes, and likewise their
shields, which were broad shels of monstrous Tortuses were
hanging downe behinde them: who with an incredible swiftnes 25
ranne upon the fearefull Nymphes, saying. Now is the time come
(ingrate and scornefull Nymphes) that by our strength and wils
you shall be forced to do that, which our milde love and longe
suites could never bring to passe, for it is not reason that fortune
should doe such injurie to our captive harts, with so long and 30
great paine to defer our remedies. In fine, we have now in our
hands the guerdon of our sighes and lamentations, which wearied
the birds and beasts of the darke and enchaunted woode, where we
dwell: and the recompence of our burning teares, wherewith we
made the raging and lothsome river, that watreth the dreadfull 35
fieldes and plaines of our territories to swell, and overflowe his
banks: Since then you have no other meanes to save your lives,
but by easing and helping our harmes, be not so wilfull by
resistance, to make our cruell hands take vengeance of that paine,
which so long you have made our afflicted harts to feele. The 40

Nymphes at the sudden sursault of these monsters were so
amazed, that they were not able to answer to these proude and
cruell wordes, but onely with silence and teares. Albeit faire
Doria, who had more courage then the rest, at last did stoutly
answer them thus againe. I never thought that love could bring 5
a lover to so foule an extreme, as with violent hands, and such
unseemly force to sease upon his beloved. It is the manner of
cowards to carie weapons, and fight with silly women, in an open
and desart fielde, where none is able to defend them, but their
vertue, and honest reasons. But of one thing (cruell and vile 10
beasts) you may be ascertained, that your menaces shal not make
us leese one jot of that, which our honours require, and that we
will sooner leave our lives in your barbarous hands, then suffer
our deer chastities by your beastly forces to be violated. It is
needlesse (*Doria*) (saide one of them againe) to harken to their 15
reasons, who had none at all to handle us with so great scorne
and crueltie: whereupon unloosing the string from his bowe, that
hung at his necke, he tooke her by both her faire hands, and
rudely tied them togither, and so did his companions, *Cynthias* and
Polydoras. The two Shepherds and the Shepherdesse *Selvagia*, 20
astonished at the monstrous violence of the Savages, and seeing
what beastialitie they beganne to use to the faire and tender
Nymphes, not able to endure it, resolved to die, or to defende
them from their cruell handes. Wherefore all three taking out
their slings, and filling their scrips with stones, came out of the 25
woode, into the greene medowe, and beganne to throwe them at
the Savages with such courage and dexteritie, as though their
lives had lien in their handes; And thinking to plie them so fast
with stones, that the Nymphes (while the Savages were busie
about their owne defence) might escape, and save their persons 30
from their vile immanitie, they redoubled their force, with the
greatest speede and valour they coulde: Whose driftes the suttle
Savages suspecting, one of them had an eie to the faire prisoners
for running away, while the other two, by winning ground on
their enemies, thought to make a quicke dispatch of them. But the 35
stones came so dangerously and so many, that they had ynough to
defende themselves, so that, as long as they lasted, the Savages
fared very ill. But as the Shepherdes were afterwardes occupied in
stowping downe to take uppe more stones, the Savages came
running in to them so speedily with their massie clubs, that nowe 40

they were without any hope of life, if presently a certaine strange
Shepherdesse (of such singular beautie and comely feature, as
made both the Savages and the rest amazed at her goodly personage) had not come out of the thicke wood neere unto the
fountaine, where they before were singing. She had her bowe 5
hanging on her left arme, and a quiver of arrowes at her shoulder,
in her hand a fine staffe of wilde oke, armed at the end with a long
and well steeled pike. But when she saw the three Nymphes in so
great distresse, and the effray betweene the two Savages and the
Shepherdes, who now looked for nothing more then present 10
death, by putting quickly a sharpe headed arrow into her bowe,
with no meane force and skill she shot it at one of the Savages,
leaving it halfe hidden in his hard brest, whereby the arrow of
love, that pearced his hart lost the force, and the Savage his life.
Neither was she slowe in putting another in her bowe, nor lesse 15
skilfull in shooting it, for with the same she as well ended the
enamoured passions of the second Savage, as of the first. But
setling her selfe to shoote at the third, that was keeping the three
Nymphes, she could not so soone effect it, but that he came running in to her, within the length of his club, and had surely dis- 20
patched her with one blowe, if the faire Shepherdesse, by lifting
up her knottie staffe (as he was discharging upon her) had not
taken it upon the iron point (whereby his club brake in two peeces)
and immediately requited him with another upon the top of his
crowne, wherewith she made him stagger on his knees, and then 25
running a thrust at his face (and with such force and aime it was)
that pearcing his eies, her staffe made speedie passage thorow his
braines, so that the fierce Savage, yelling out a horrible and
lowde grone, fell downe dead to the ground. The Nymphes
seeing themselves delivered from so great violence, and the Shep- 30
herdes and Shepherdesses from expected death, whereunto they
were so neere, and how by the admirable valour and strength of
that Shepherdesse, not onely they, but the Shepherdes had escaped,
they were in a traunce for a while, and could not afterwardes
imagine her to be any humane wight. But the Shepherdesse 35
comming now unto them, began to untie their handes, saying.
They deserved no lesse punishment, then that they have (faire
Nymphes) that with these rude and rough bonds durst presume
to binde such white and delicate hands, whose beauties are fitter
to binde tender and relenting harts. Accursed be such proude 40

monsters, and ill befall to such senselesse and beastly men: but
Ladies, they have their hire, and I my desire, by having done you
this small service, and comming in so good a time with speedie
remedie for such an outrage, although these hardie Shepherdes,
and faire Shepherdesse deserve no lesse thankes for hazarding 5
their lives in your defence, who woulde (no doubt) like my selfe
have thought them well emploied, and themselves well appaied,
if in so good a quarrell, and for such woorthy personages they
had jointly lost them. The Nymphes were no lesse amazed at her
rare beautie and wisedome, then at the courage and force, that she 10
had shewed in their defence, whereupon *Doria* with a gratious
semblant answered her thus againe. Faire Shepherdesse, if thou
art not (as by thy approoved valour and brave minde, thou
seemest to be) the daughter of invincible *Mars*, yet for thy beautie
(which is celestiall) thou must needes be the daughter of lovely 15
Venus and faire *Adonis*; and if of neither of them, it cannot then
otherwise be, but that *Minerva* must be thy mother, since such
great wisedome cannot proceed from any other part, although it is
most true that nature hath endowed thee with the principall of
them all. And since for so strange a curtesie, and good turne that 20
thou hast done us, extraordinarie and great must the services be,
wherewith they must be requited, we hope, that at somtime or
other, occasion may be offered, wherein thou maiest knowe, what
earnest desire and entyre good wils we have, to repaie so singular
and woorthie a favor. But bicause (it seemes) thou art wearie, let 25
us go to the fountaine of the Sicamours, neere to yonder wood,
where thou maist rest and refresh thy selfe. Let us goe ladie (said
the Shepherdesse) not so much to ease my wearied body, as to
talke of other matters, wherin my soules health and the summe of
my content doth chiefely consist. That will we do with all possible 30
diligence (said *Polydora*) since there is not any, whom we should
with greater reason endevor to content then thy selfe. But faire
Cynthia turning to the Shepherdes, said. The debt (faire Shepherdesse, and stout Shepherds) wherein you have perpetually
bound us to you, your selves know well ynough, which though we 35
are never able to acquite, yet we will not cease to wish, that some
occasion may heereafter fall out, wherein we may shewe the earnest
will and affection we have to discharge it, according to our great
desire. These thankes (faire Nymphes) answered *Selvagia*, and
your gentle offers, are more due to these two Shepherds then to 40

me, that could do no more then praie for your safe deliverie. But
is this the Shepherd *Syrenus* (said *Polydora*) so much beloved in
times past, as now forgotten of the faire *Diana*? And is this other,
his corrivall *Sylvanus*? They are the same (saide *Selvagia*.) Then am
I glad (said *Polydora*) that you are such kind of men, whom we 5
may in some part recompence, the great good will you shewed,
and the perill you passed to set us free. *Doria* woondring at that
she had heard, said. And is it true that this is *Syrenus*? I am very
glad that I have founde thee, and that there is an occasion
ministred me to seeke out some remedie (which (I hope) shall not 10
be small) for thy great cares and sorrow. Nor sufficient ynough for
so great griefe, if it be small (saide *Syrenus*.) Let us go to the
fountaine (saide *Polydora*) where we will at large discourse of these
and other matters. To the which when they were come, the
Nymphes, placing the Shepherdesse in the middes of them, sat 15
them downe, and the Shepherds at the Nymphes requests, went
to the next towne to provide some victuals, bicause it was now
somewhat late, and that they all had an appetite to eate. But the
three Nymphes remaining all alone with the unknowne Shepherdesse, faire *Doria* thus began to say unto her. It is no lesse 20
strange to us, to see such an one as thou art (most valiant and faire
Shepherdesse) of such valour and strength in these plaines and
woods, sequestred from all popular concourse, then to thee
(I thinke) to see three Nymphes heere all alone, and without
companie to defend them from the like assaults. But bicause we 25
may knowe what thou art (which is our chiefe desire) we will
inforce that favour with this small desert, by telling thee first
what we are, for the better knowledge wherof, thou shalt understand (couragious Shepherdesse) that this Nymph is called *Polydora*, that *Cynthia*, and my selfe *Doria*, we having our mansion 30
place in *Dianas* wood, where sage *Felicia* keepes her stately court,
whose course of life, and onely exercise, is to cure and remedie the
passions of love. We, going to visit a certaine Nymph her cousin,
that liveth on this side of the *Gallician* hils, came by chance to this
pleasant and shadowed dale, where, seeing the place fit to passe 35
away the heate of the noone day, under the shadowe of these
greene Sicamours and Laurell trees, and emulating the harmonie
of this running spring, which passeth thorow this greene medow,
we tooke our instruments, to see if we could imitate the same.
And our hap (or rather mishap) it was that these Savages long 40

since captivated (as they say) in our loves, by chaunce came
hither, who importuning us many times with their brutish requestes, to graunt them our love, and seeing that by no meanes
we gave them any hope thereof, with violent hands determined to
put their beastly intents in practise; and finding us heere all alone, 5
did that, which (faire Shepherdesse) thou sawest, when so fortunately thou camest to our rescue. The Shepherdesse hearing
what faire *Doria* had told her, with plentious teares gave an
evident testimonie of the inward greefe, which her afflicted hart
felt, and looking upon the Nymphes, she began thus to say.   10

Love is not such a qualitie (faire Nymphes of the chaste Goddesse) that the person, whom it holdeth in captivitie, can have any
regarde of reason, neither is reason a meanes to make an enamoured
hart forsake that way, wherein the cruell destinies will conduct it.
For proofe whereof, experience is at hand: for though you were 15
loved of these cruell Savages, and that the lawes of honest and
pure love doth prohibite all injuries, and whatsoever might offend
you, yet on the other side, that headlong disorder comes, wherewith it workes such strange and sundrie effectes, that the same
men, that should serve and honour you, seeke to spoile and hurt 20
you. And bicause you may knowe, that I am not urged to say this,
as onely induced by that, which now at my comming I have seene
in this vallie, I will tell you that, which I thought to conceale from
all the world, but onely from him, to whom I yeelded up long
since the freedome of my hart, (if ever time and fortune grant 25
mine eies such favour, that they may see him once againe) whereby you shal see how in the schoole of mishaps I have learned to
talke of loves consequences, and of the effectes, which the traitor
works in their sorrowfull harts, that are subject unto him.

You shall therefore knowe (faire Nymphes) that great *Vandalia* 30
is my native countrie, a province not far hence, where I was borne,
in a citie called *Soldina*, my mother called *Delia*, my father *Andronius*,
for linage and possessions the chiefest of all that province. It fell
out that as my mother was married many yeeres, and had no
children, (by reason whereof she lived so sad and malecontent, 35
that she enjoyed not one merry day) with teares and sighes she
daily importuned the heavens, and with a thousand vowes and
devout offerings besought God to grant her the summe of her
desire: whose omnipotencie it pleased, beholding from his im-
periall throne her continuall orisons, to make her barren bodie 40

(the greater part of her age being now spent and gone) to become fruitfull. What infinite joy she conceived thereof, let her judge, that after a long desire of any thing, fortune at last doth put it into her handes. Of which content my father *Andronius* being no lesse partaker, shewed such tokens of inward joy, as are impossible to 5 be expressed. My mother *Delia* was so much given to reading of ancient histories, that, if by reason of sicknes, or any important businesse, she had not bene hindred, she would never (by her will) have passed the time away in any other delight: who (as I said) being now with childe, and finding her selfe on a night ill at ease, 10 intreated my father to reade something unto her, that, her minde being occupied in contemplation thereof, she might the better passe her greefe away. My father, who studied for nothing els but to please her in all he might, began to reade unto her the historie of *Paris*, when the three Ladies referred their proude 15 contention for the golden Apple, to his conclusion and judgement. But as my mother held it for an infallible opinion, that *Paris* had partially given that sentence, (perswaded thereunto by a blinde passion of beautie) so she said, that without all doubt he did not with due reason and wisedome consider the Goddesse of 20 battels; for as martiall and heroicall feates (saide she) excelled all other qualities, so with equitie and justice the Apple should have bene given to her. My father answered, that since the Apple was to be given to the fairest, and that *Venus* was fairer then any of the rest, *Paris* had rightly given his judgement, if that harme 25 had not ensued thereof, which afterwardes did. To this my mother replied, that, though it was written in the Apple, (*That it should be given to the fairest*) it was not to be understood of corporall beautie, but of the intellectuall beautie of the mind. And therfore, since fortitude was a thing that made one most beautiful, and the 30 exercise of arms an exterior act of this vertue, she affirmed, that to the Goddesse of battels this Apple should be given, if *Paris* had judged like a prudent and unappassionate judge. So that (faire Nymphes) they spent a great part of the night in this controversie, both of them alledging the most reasons they could, to confirme 35 their owne purpose. They persisting in this point, sleepe began to overcome her, whom the reasons and arguments of her husband coulde not once moove, so that being very deepe in her disputations, she fell into as deepe a sleepe, to whom (my father being now gone to his chamber) appeered the Goddesse *Venus* with as 40 frowning a countenance, as faire, and saide. I marvell *Delia*, who hath mooved thee to be so contrarie to her, that was never opposite to thee? If thou hadst but called to minde the time, when thou wert so overcome in love for *Andronius*, thou wouldest not have paide me the debt (thou owest me) with so ill coine. But thou shalt not escape free from my due anger; for thou shalt bring forth a sonne and a daughter, whose birth shall cost thee no lesse then thy life, and them their contentment, for uttering so much in disgrace of my honour and beautie: both which shall be as infortunate in their love, as any were ever in all their lives, or to the age wherein with remedylesse sighes they shall breath forth the summe of their ceaselesse sorrowes. And having saide thus, she vanished away: when likewise it seemed to my mother that the Goddesse *Pallas* came to her in a vision, and with a merry countenance, saide thus unto her. With what sufficient rewardes may I be able to requite the due regarde (most happie and discreete *Delia*) which thou hast alleaged in my favour against thy husbands obstinate opinion, except it be by making thee understand, that thou shalt bring foorth a sonne and a daughter the most fortunate in armes that have bene to their times. Having thus said, she vanished out of her sight, and my mother thorow exceeding feare, awaked immediately. Who within a moneth after, at one birth was delivered of me, and of a brother of mine, and died in childebed, leaving my father the most sorrowfull man in the world for her sudden death, for greefe whereof within a little while after, he also died. And bicause you may knowe (faire Nymphes) in what great extremities love hath put me, you must understand, that (being a woman of that qualitie and disposition (as you have heard) I have bene forced by my cruell destinie to leave my naturall habit, and libertie, and the due respect of mine honour, to follow him, who thinkes (perhaps) that I doe but leese it by loving him so extremely. Behold how bootelesse and unseemely it is for a woman to be so dextrous in armes, as if it were her proper nature and kinde, wherewith (faire Nymphes) I had never bene indued, but that by meanes thereof, I should come to doe you this little service against these villaines, which I account no lesse then if fortune had begun to satisfie in part some of those infinite wrongs, that she hath continually done me. The Nymphes were so amazed at her words, that they coulde neither aske nor answere any thing, to that the

faire Shepherdesse tolde them: who prosecuting her historie,
saide. My brother and I were brought up in a Nunnerie, where an
aunt of ours was Abbesse, untill we had accomplished twelve
yeeres of age, at what time we were taken from thence againe, and
my brother was caried to the mightie and invincible *King of* 5
Portugall his Court (whose noble fame and princely liberalitie
was bruted over all the world) where, being growen to yeeres able
to manage armes, he atchieved as valiant, and almost incredible
enterprises by them, as he suffered unfortunate disgraces and foiles
by love. And with all this, he was so highly favoured of that 10
magnificent King, that he would never suffer him to depart from
his Court. Unfortunate I, reserved by my sinister destinies to
greater mishaps, was caried to a grandmother of mine, which
place I would I had never seene, since it was an occasion of such
a sorrowfull life, as never any woman suffered the like. And 15
bicause there is not any thing (faire Nymphes) which I am not
forced to tell you, as well for the great vertue and desertes, which
your excellent beauties doe testifie, as also for that my minde doth
give me, that you shall be no small part and meanes of my comfort; knowe that as I was in my grandmothers house, and almost 20
seventeene yeeres olde, a certaine yoong Gentleman fell in love
with me, who dwelt no further from our house, then the length of
a garden Terrasse, so that he might see me every sommers night,
when I walked in the garden. When as therefore ingratefull *Felix*
had beheld in that place the unfortunate *Felismena* (for this is the 25
name of the wofull woman that tels you her mishaps) he was
extremely enamoured of me, or else did cunningly dissemble it,
I not knowing then whether of these two I might beleeve, but am
now assured, that whosoever beleeves lest, or nothing at all in
these affaires, shall be most at ease. Many daies *Don Felix* spent in 30
endevouring to make me know the paines, which he suffered for
me, and many more did I spende in making the matter strange,
and that he did not suffer them for my sake. And I know not why
love delaied the time so long by forcing me to love him, but
onely that (when he came indeed) he might enter into my hart at 35
once, and with greater force and violence. When he had therefore
by sundrie signes, as by Tylt and Tourneyes, and by prauncing up
and downe upon his proude Jennet before my windowes, made it
manifest, that he was in love with me (for at the first I did not so
well perceive it) he determined in the end to write a letter unto 40

me, and having practised divers times before with a maide of
mine, and at length with many gifts and faire promises, gotten her
good will and furtherance, he gave her the letter to deliver to me:
But to see the meanes that *Rosina* made unto me (for so was she
called) the dutifull services and unwoonted circumstances, before 5
she did deliver it, the othes that she sware unto me, and the subtle
words and serious protestations she used, it was a pleasant thing,
and woorthie the noting. To whom (neverthelesse) with an angrie
countenance I turned againe, saying. If I had not regard of mine
owne estate, and what heereafter might be said, I would make this 10
shamelesse face of thine be knowne ever after for a marke of an
impudent and bolde minion. But bicause it is the first time, let this
suffice that I have saide, and give thee warning to take heede of the
second. Me thinkes I see now the craftie wench, how she helde
her peace, dissembling very cunningly the sorrow, that she con- 15
ceived by my angrie answer: for she fained a counterfaite smiling,
saying. Jesus Mistresse, I gave it you, bicause you might laugh at
it, and not to moove your pacience with it in this sort: for if I had
any thought that it woulde have provoked you to anger, I praie
God he may shew his wrath, as great towards me, as ever he did 20
to the daughter of any mother. And with this she added many
wordes more (as she could do well enough) to pacifie the fained
anger, and ill opinion that I conceived of her, and taking her
letter with her, she departed from me. This having passed thus,
I began to imagine what might ensue thereof, and love (me 25
thought) did put a certaine desire into my minde to see the letter,
though modestie and shame forbad me to aske it of my maide,
especially for the wordes, that had passed betweene us, as you
have heard. And so I continued all that day untill night, in varietie
of many thoughts. But when *Rosina* came to helpe me to bedde, 30
God knowes how desirous I was to have her entreat me againe to
take the letter, but she woulde never speake unto me about it, nor
(as it seemed) did so much as once thinke thereof. Yet to trie, if by
giving her some occasion, I might prevaile, I saide unto her. And
is it so *Rosina*, that *Don Felix* without any regard to mine honour 35
dares write unto me? These are things Mistresse (saide she
demurely to me againe) that are commonly incident to love,
wherfore I beseech you pardon me, for if I had thought to have
angred you with it, I woulde have first pulled out the bals of mine
eies. How cold my hart was at that blow, God knowes, yet did 40

I dissemble the matter, and suffer my selfe to remaine that night onely with my desire, and with occasion of little sleepe. And so it was indeede, for that (me thought) was the longest and most painfull night, that ever I passed. But when with a slower pace (then I desired) the wished day was come, the discreet and subtle 5 *Rosina* came into my chamber to helpe me to make me readie, in dooing whereof, of purpose, she let the letter closely fall, which when I perceived, what is that that fell downe (said I,) let me see it. It is nothing Mistresse, saide she. Come, come, let me see it, (saide I) what, moove me not, or else tell me what it is. Good 10 lord Mistresse (saide she) why will you see it: it is the letter I would have given you yesterday. Nay that it is not (saide I) wherefore shew it me, that I may see if you lie or no. I had no sooner said so, but she put it into my handes, saying: God never give me good, if it be anie other thing; and although I knewe it 15 well indeede, yet I saide, what, this is not the same, for I know that well enough, but it is one of thy lovers letters, I will read it, to see in what neede he standeth of thy favour. And opening it, I founde it conteined this that followeth.

I ever imagined (deere Mistresse) that your discretion and 20 wisedome woulde have taken away the feare I had to write unto you, the same knowing well enough (without any letter at all) how much I love you, but the very same hath so cunningly dissembled, that wherein I hoped the onely remedie of my griefes had been, therein consisted my greatest harme. If according to 25 your wisedome you censure my boldnes, I shall not then (I know) enjoy one hower of life: but if you do consider of it according to loves accustomed effects, then will I not exchange my hope for it. Be not offended I beseech you (good Ladie) with my letter, and blame me not for writing unto you, untill you see by experience, 30 whether I can leave of to write: And take me besides into the possession of that which is yours, since all is mine doth wholly consist in your hands, the which with all reverence and dutifull affection a thousand times I kisse.

When I had now seene my *Don Felix* his letter, whether it was 35 for reading it at such a time, when by the same he shewed, that he loved me more then himselfe, or whether he had disposition and regiment over part of this wearied soule, to imprint that love in it, whereof he wrote unto me, I began to love him too well (and

9 see it, *Ed.*] see, it *Y*.

alas for my harme) since he was the cause of so much sorrow, as
I have passed for his sake. Whereupon asking *Rosina* forgivenes of
what was past (as a thing needfull for that which was to come) and
committing the secrecie of my love to her fidelitie, I read the
letter once againe, pausing a little at every worde, (and a very little 5
indeede it was) bicause I concluded so soone with my selfe, to do
that I did, although in verie truth it lay not otherwise in my
power to do. Wherefore calling for paper and inke, I answered his
letter thus.

Esteeme not so slightly of mine honour, *Don Felix*, as with 10
fained words to thinke to enveagle it, or with thy vaine pretenses
to offend it any waies. I know wel enough what manner of man
thou art, and how great thy desert and presumption is, from
whence thy boldnes doth arise (I gesse,) and not from the force
(which thing thou wouldst faine perswade me) of thy fervent love. 15
And if it be so, (as my suspicion suggesteth) thy labor is as vaine,
as thy imagination presumptuous, by thinking to make me do any
thing contrarie to that, which I owe unto mine honour. Consider
(I beseech thee) how seldome, things, commenced under suttletie
and dissimulation, have good successe; and that it is not the part 20
of a Gentleman, to meane them one way, and speak them another.
Thou praiest me (amongst other things) to admit thee into possession of that, that is mine: but I am of so ill an humour in
matters of this qualitie, that I trust not things experienced, how
much lesse then thy bare wordes, yet neverthelesse, I make no 25
small account of that, which thou hast manifested to me in thy
letter; for it is ynough that I am incredulous, though not unthankfull.

This letter did I send, contrarie to that I should have done,
bicause it was the occasion of all my harmes and greefes: for after 30
this, he began to waxe more bolde by unfolding his thoughts, and
seeking out the meanes to have a parly with me. In the ende (faire
Nymphes) a few daies being spent in his demaunds and my
answers, false love did worke in me after his wonted fashions,
every hower seasing more strongly upon my unfortunate soule. 35
The Tourneies were now renewed, the musicke by night did
never cease, amorous letters and verses were recontinued on both
sides: and thus passed I away almost a whole yeere, at the end
whereof, I felt my selfe so far in his love, that I had no power to
retire, nor stay my selfe from disclosing my thoughts unto him, 40

(the thing which he desired more then his owne life.) But my
adverse fortune afterwardes would, that of these our mutuall
loves (when as now they were most assured) his father had some
intelligence, and whosoever revealed them first, perswaded him so
cunningly, that his father (fearing least he would have married 5
me out of hand) sent him to the great Princesse *Augusta Caesarinas*
court, telling him, it was not meete that a yoong Gentleman, and
of so noble a house as he was, should spende his youth idly at
home, where nothing could be learned, but examples of vice,
whereof the very same idlenes (he said) was the onely Mistresse. 10
He went away so pensive, that his great greefe would not suffer
him to acquaint me with his departure, which when I knew, how
sorrowfull I remained, she may imagine, that hath bene at any
time tormented with like passion. To tell you now the life, that
I led in his absence, my sadnes, sighes, and teares, which every 15
day I powred out of these wearied eies, my toong is far unable:
if then my paines were such, that I cannot now expresse them,
how could I then suffer them? But being in the mids of my mishaps, and in the depth of those woes which the absence of *Don
Felix* caused me to feele, and it seeming to me that my greefe was 20
without remedie, if he were once seene or knowen of the Ladies
in that Court (more beautifull and gracious then my selfe,) by
occasion whereof, as also by absence (a capitall enemie to love)
I might easily be forgotten, I determined to adventure that, which
I thinke never any woman imagined: which was, to apparell my 25
selfe in the habit of a man, and to hye me to the Court to see him,
in whose sight al my hope and content remained: which determination, I no sooner thought of, then I put in practise, love blinding
my eies and minde with an inconsiderate regarde of mine owne
estate and condition. To the execution of which attempt, I wanted 30
no industrie, for, being furnished with the helpe of one of my
approoved friends, and treasouresse of my secrets, who bought
me such apparell, as I willed her, and a good horse for my
journey, I went not onely out of my countrie, but out of my deere
reputation (which (I thinke) I shall never recover againe) and so 35
trotted directly to the Court, passing by the way many accidents,
which (if time would give me leave to tell them) woulde not make
you laugh a little to heare them. Twenty daies I was in going
thither, at the ende of which, being come to the desired place,

22 selfe,) by *Ed.*] selfe.) By *Y.*

I tooke up mine Inne in a streete lest frequented with concurse of people. And the great desire I had to see the destroier of my joy, did not suffer me to thinke of any other thing, but how or where I might see him. To inquire of him of mine host, I durst not, lest my comming might (perhaps) have bene discovered: and to 5 seeke him foorth, I thought it not best, lest some inopinate mishap might have fallen out, whereby I might have bene knowen. Wherefore I passed all that day in these perplexities, while night came on, each hower whereof (me thought) was a whole yeere unto me. But midnight being a little past, mine host called at my 10 chamber doore, and tolde me if I was desirous to heare some brave musicke, I should arise quickly, and open a window towards the street. The which I did by and by, and making no noise at all, I heard how *Don Felix* his Page, called *Fabius* (whom I knew by his voice) saide to others that came with him. Now it is time my 15 Masters, bicause the Lady is in the gallerie over her garden, taking the fresh aire of the coole night. He had no sooner saide so, but they began to winde three Cornets and a Sackbot, with such skill and sweetenesse, that it seemed celestiall musicke. And then began a voice to sing, the sweetest (in my opinion) that ever 20 I heard. And though I was in suspence, by hearing *Fabius* speake, whereby a thousand doubtes and imaginations (repugnant to my rest) occurred in my minde, yet I neglected not to heare what was sung, bicause their operations were not of such force, that they were able to hinder the desire, nor distemper the delight that I conceived 25 by hearing it. That therefore which was sung, were these verses.

> *SWeete Mistresse harken unto me*
> *(If it greeves thee to see me die)*
> *And hearing though it greeveth thee,*
> *To heare me yet, do not denie.*   30
>
> *O grant me then this short content,*
> *For forc'd I am to thee to flie:*
> *My sighes do not make thee relent,*
> *Nor teares thy hart do mollifie.*
>
> *Nothing of mine doth give thee payne,*   35
> *Nor thou think'st of no remedie:*
> *Mistresse how long shall I sustaine*
> *such ill, as still thou dost applie?*

In death there is no helpe, be sure,
  But in thy will, where it doth lie:
For all those illes which death doth cure,
  Alas, they are but light to trie:

My troubles do not trouble thee,   5
  Nor hope to touch thy soule so nie:
O from a will that is so free,
  What should I hope, when I do crie?

How can I mollifie that brave
  And stonie hart, of pittie drie?   10
Yet Mistresse turne those eies (that have
  No peeres) shining like stars in skie:

But turne them not in angrie sort,
  If thou wilt not kill me thereby:
Though yet in anger, or in sport,   15
  Thou killest onely with thine eie.

After they had first with a concent of musicke sung this song, two plaied, the one upon a Lute, the other upon a silver sounding Harpe, being accompanied with the sweete voice of my *Don Felix*: the great joy that I felt in hearing him, cannot be imagined, for 20 (me thought) I heard him nowe, as in that happie and passed time of our loves. But after the deceit of this imagination was discovered, seeing with mine eies, and hearing with mine eares, that this musicke was bestowed upon another and not on me, God knowes what a bitter death it was unto my soule: And with a greevous sigh, that 25 caried almost my life away with it, I asked mine host, if he knew what the Ladie was, for whose sake the musick was made? He answered me, that he could not imagine on whom it was bestowed, bicause in that streete dwelled manie noble and faire Ladies. And when I saw he could not satisfie my request, I bent mine eares 30 againe to heare my *Don Felix*, who now to the tune of a delicate harpe whereon he sweetely plaied, began to sing this Sonnet following.

A Sonnet.

MY painefull yeeres impartiall Love *was spending*
In vaine and booteles hopes my life appaying,   35
  And cruell Fortune *to the world bewraying*
Strange samples of my teares that have no ending.

Time *everie thing to truth at last commending,*
　　Leaves of my steps such markes, that now betraying
　　And all deceitfull trusts shall be decaying,
And none have cause to plaine of his offending.
Shee, *whom I lov'd to my obliged power,*   5
　　That in her sweetest love to me discovers
　　Which never yet I knew (those heavenly pleasures,)
And I do saie, exclaiming every hower,
　　Do not you see, what makes you wise, O Lovers?
　　Love, Fortune, Time, *and my faire* Mystresse *treasures.*

                                                            10

The Sonnet being ended, they paused a while, playing on fower
Lutes togither, and on a paire of Virginals, with such heavenly
melodie, that the whole worlde (I thinke) could not affoord
sweeter musick to the eare, nor delight to any minde, not subject
to the panges of such predominant greefe and sorrow as mine was. 15
But then fower voices passing well tuned and set togither, began
to sing this song following.

A Song.

*T*Hat sweetest harme I doe not blame,
　　First caused by thy fairest eies,   20
But greeve, bicause too late I came,
To know my fault, and to be wise.

I never knew a worser kinde of life,
To live in feare, from boldnesse still to cease:
Nor woorse then this, to live in such a strife,   25
Whether of both, to speake, or holde my peace?

And so the harme I doe not blame,
Caused by thee, or thy faire eies:
But that to see how late I came,
To knowe my fault, and to be wise.   30

I ever more did feare, that I should knowe
Some secret things, and doubtfull in their kinde,
Bicause the surest things doe ever goe
Most contrarie unto my wish and minde.

And yet by knowing of the same,
There is no hurt, But it denies
My remedie, Since late I came,
To knowe my fault, and to be wise.

When this song was ended, they began to sound divers sorts of 5
instruments, and voices most excellently agreeing togither, and
with such sweetnes, that they could not chuse but delight any
very much, who were not so farre from it as I. About dawning of
the day the musicke ended, and I did what I could to espie out my
Don Felix, but the darknes of the night was mine enimie therein. 10
And seeing now that they were gone, I went to bed againe,
where I bewailed my great mishap, knowing that he, whom most
of al I loved, had so unwoorthily forgotten me, whereof his
musicke was too manifest a witnes. And when it was time, I arose,
and without any other consideration went straight to the Princesse 15
her pallace, where (I thought) I might see that, which I so greatly
desired, determining to call my selfe *Valerius*, if any (perhaps) did
aske my name. Comming therefore to a faire broad court before
the pallace gate, I viewed the windowes and galleries, where
I sawe such store of blazing beauties, and gallant Ladies, that 20
I am not able now to recount, nor then to do any more, but
woonder at their graces, their gorgeous attyre, their jewels, their
brave fashions of apparell, and ornaments, wherewith they were
so richly set out. Up and downe this place before the windowes
roade many lords, and brave gentlemen in rich and sumptuous 25
habits, and mounted upon proud Jennets, every one casting his
eie to that part, where his thoughts were secretly placed. God
knowes how greatly I desired to see *Don Felix* there, and that his
injurious love had beene in that famous pallace, bicause I might
then have beene assured, that he shoulde never have got any other 30
guerdon of his sutes and services, but onely to see, and to be
seene, and sometimes to speake to his Mistresse, whom he must
serve before a thousand eies, bicause the privilege of that place
doth not give him any further leave. But it was my ill fortune,
that he had setled his love in that place, where I might not be 35
assured of this poore helpe. Thus as I was standing neere to the
pallace gate, I espied *Fabius*, *Don Felix* his page, comming in
great haste to the pallace, where speaking a word or two with

9 did what *Ed.*] did, what *Y.*

a porter that kept the second entrie, he returned the same waie
he came. I gessed his errant was, to knowe whether it were fit
time for *Don Felix* to come to dispatch certaine busines, that his
father had in the court, and that he could not choose but come
thither out of hand. And being in this supposed joy, which his 5
sight did promise me, I sawe him comming along with a great
traine of followers attending on his person, all of them being
bravely apparelled in a liverie of watchet silke, garded with yellow
velvet, and stitched on either side with threedes of twisted silver,
wearing likewise blew, yellow, and white feathers in their hats. 10
But my Lorde *Don Felix* had on a paire of ash colour velvet hose,
embrodered and drawen foorth with watchet tissue, his dublet
was of white satten, embrodered with knots of golde, and likewise an embrodered jerkin of the same coloured velvet, and his
short cape cloke was of blacke velvet, edged with gold lace, and 15
hung full of buttons of pearle and gold, and lined with razed
watchet satten, by his side he ware at a paire of embrodered
hangers a rapier and dagger, with engraven hilts and pommell of
beaten golde. On his head, a hat, beset full of golden stars, in the
mids of everie which a rich orient pearle was enchased, and his 20
feather was likewise blew, yellow, and white. Mounted he came
upon a faire dapple graie Jennet, with a rich furniture of blew,
embrodered with golde and seede pearle. When I sawe him in this
rich equipage, I was so amazed at his sight, that how extremely my
senses were ravished with sudden joye, I am not able (faire 25
Nymphes) to tell you. Truth it is, that I could not but shed some
teares for joy and greefe, which his sight did make me feele, but
fearing to be noted by the standers by, for that time I dried them
up. But as *Don Felix* (being now come to the pallace gate) was
dismounted, and gone up a paire of staires into the chamber of 30
presence, I went to his men, where they were attending his returne, and seeing *Fabius*, whom I had seene before amongst them,
I tooke him aside, and saide unto him. My friend, I pray you tell
me what Lord this is, which did but even now alight from his
Jennet, for (me thinkes) he is very like one, whom I have seene 35
before in an other farre countrey. *Fabius* then answered me thus.
Art thou such a novice in the court, that thou knowest not *Don
Felix*? I tell thee there is not any Lord, knight, or gentleman
better knowne in it then he. No doubt of that (saide I) but I will
tell thee what a novice I am, and how small a time I have beene in 40

the court, for yesterday was the first, that ever I came to it. Naie
then I cannot blame thee (saide *Fabius*) if thou knowest him not.
Knowe then that this gentleman is called *Don Felix*, borne in
Vandalia, and hath his chiefest house in the ancient cittie of
Soldina, and is remaining in this court about certaine affaires of 5
his fathers and his owne. But I pray you tell me (said I) why he
gives his liveries of these colours? If the cause were not so manifest, I woulde conceale it (saide *Fabius*) but since there is not any
that knowes it not, and canst not come to any in this court, who
cannot tell thee the reason why, I thinke by telling thee it, I do no 10
more then in courtesie I am bound to do. Thou must therefore
understand, that he loves and serves a Ladie heere in this Citie
named *Celia*, and therefore weares and gives for his liverie an
azure blew, which is the colour of the skie, and white and yellow,
which are the colours of his Lady and Mistresse. When I heard 15
these words, imagine (faire Nymphes) in what a plight I was, but
dissembling my mishap and griefe, I answered him. This Ladie
certes is greatly beholding to him, bicause he thinkes not enough,
by wearing her colours, to shew how willing he is to serve her,
unlesse also he beare her name in his liverie: whereupon I gesse, 20
she cannot be but very faire and amiable. She is no lesse indeede
(saide *Fabius*) although the other, whom he loved and served in
our owne countrey, in beautie farre excelled this, and loved and
favoured him more then ever this did. But this mischievous
absence doth violate and dissolve those things, which men thinke 25
to be most strong and firme. At these wordes (faire Nymphes)
was I faine to come to some composition with my teares, which if
I had not stopped from issuing foorth, *Fabius* could not have
chosen, but suspected by the alteration of my countenance that
all was not well with me. And then the Page did aske me, what 30
countrey-man I was, my name, and of what calling and condition
I was: whom I answered, that my countrey, where I was borne
was Vandalia, my name *Valerius*, and till that time served no
Master. Then by this reckoning (saide he) we are both countrey-
men, and may be both fellowes in one house if thou wilt: for *Don* 35
Felix my Master commanded me long since to seeke him out
a Page. Therefore if thou wilt serve him, say so. As for meate,
drinke, and apparell, and a couple of shillings to play away, thou
shalt never want, besides pretie wenches, which are not daintie in
our streete, as faire and amorous as Queenes, of which there is not 40

anie, that will not die for the love of so proper a youth as thou art.
And to tell thee in secret (because perhaps we may be fellowes)
I know where an old Cannons maide is, a gallant fine girle, whom
if thou canst but finde in thy hart to love and serve, as I do, thou
shalt never want at her hands, fine handkerchers, peeces of bacon, 5
and now and then wine of S. *Martyn*. When I heard this, I could
not choose but laugh, to see how naturally the unhappie Page
played his part, by depainting foorth their properties in their
lively colours. And because I thought nothing more commodious
for my rest, and for the enjoying of my desire, then to follow 10
Fabius his counsell, I answered him thus. In truth I determined to
serve none, but now, since fortune hath offered me so good a service, and at such a time, when I am constrained to take this course
of life, I shall not do amisse if I frame my selfe to the service of
some Lord or Gentleman in this Court, but especially of your 15
Master, because he seemes to be a woorthy Gentleman, and such
an one, that makes more reckoning of his servants then an other.
Ha thou knowest him not as well as I (said *Fabius*) for I promise
thee by the faith of a Gentleman (for I am one in deede, for my
father comes of the *Cachopines* of *Laredo*) that my Master *Don* 20
Felix is the best natured Gentleman that ever thou knewest in thy
life, and one who useth his Pages better then any other. And
were it not for those troublesome loves, which makes us runne
up and downe more, and sleepe lesse, then we woulde, there were
not such a Master in the whole worlde againe. In the end (faire 25
Nymphes) *Fabius* spake to his Master *Don Felix* as soone as he
was come foorth in my behalfe, who commanded me the same
night to come to him at his lodging. Thither I went, and he
entertained me for his Page, making the most of me in the worlde,
where, being but a fewe daies with him, I sawe the messages, 30
letters, and gifts that were brought and caried on both sides,
greevous wounds (alas and corsives to my dying hart) which
made my soule to flie sometimes out of my body, and every
hower in hazard to leese my forced patience before every one.
But after one moneth was past, *Don Felix* began to like so well of 35
me, that he disclosed his whole love unto me from the beginning
unto the present estate and forwardnes, that it was then in, committing the charge thereof to my secrecie and helpe, telling me,
that he was favoured of her at the beginning, and that afterwards

14 service *Ed.*] serviee *Y*

she waxed wearie of her loving and accustomed entertainment, the cause whereof was a secret report (whosoever it was that buzzed it into her eares) of the love, that he did beare to a Lady in his owne countrey, and that his present love unto her was but to entertaine the time, while his busines in the Court were 5 dispatched. And there is no doubt (saide *Don Felix* unto me) but that indeede I did once commence that love that she laies to my charge, but God knowes if now there be any thing in the world, that I love and esteeme more deere and precious then her. When I heard him say so, you may imagine (faire Nymphes) what 10 a mortall dagger pierced my wounded heart. But with dissembling the matter the best I coulde, I answered him thus. It were better sir (me thinkes) that the Gentlewoman should complaine with cause, and that it were so indeed, for if the other Ladie, whom you served before, did not deserve to be forgotten of you, you do her 15 (under correction my Lord) the greatest wrong in the world. The love (said *Don Felix* againe) which I beare to my *Celia* will not let me understand it so, but I have done her (me thinkes) the greater injurie, having placed my love first in an other, and not in her. Of these wrongs (saide I to my selfe) I know who beares the 20 woorst away. And (disloyall) he pulling a letter out of his bosome, which he had received the same hower from his Mistresse, reade it unto me, thinking that he did me a great favour thereby, the contents whereof were these.

Celias letter to Don Felix. 25

N Ever any thing, that I suspected touching thy love, hath beene so farre from the truth, that hath not given me occasion to beleeve more often mine owne imagination, then thy innocencie, wherein, if I do thee any wrong, referre it but to the censure of thine owne follie: For well thou mightest have denied, 30 or not declared thy passed love, without giving me occasion to con-demne thee by thine owne confession. Thou saiest I was the cause that made thee forget thy former love: Comfort thy selfe, for there shall not want another to make thee forget thy second. And assure thy selfe of this (Lord *Don Felix*) that there is not any thing more 35 unbeseeming a Gentleman, then to finde an occasion in a Gentle-woman to leese himselfe for her love. I will saie no more, but that in an ill, where there is no remedie, the best is not to seeke out any.

After he had made an end of reading the letter, he said unto me. What thinkest thou *Valerius* of these words? With pardon be it spoken my Lord; That your deedes are shewed by them. Go to, said *Don Felix*, and speake no more of that. Sir, saide I, they must like me wel, if they like you, because none can judge better of their words, that love well, then they themselves. But that which I thinke of the letter is, that this Gentlewoman would have beene the first, and that Fortune had entreated her in such sort, that all others might have envied her estate. But what wouldest thou counsell me saide *Don Felix*? If thy griefe doth suffer any counsell, saide I, that thy thoughts be not divided into this second passion, since there is so much due to the first. *Don Felix* answered me againe sighing, and knocking me gently on the shoulder, saying. How wise art thou *Valerius*, and what good counsell dost thou give me, if I could follow it. Let us now go in to dinner, for when I have dined, I will have thee carie me a letter to my Lady *Celia*, and then thou shalt see, if any other love is not woorthy to be forgotten in lieu of thinking onely of her. These were wordes, that greeved *Felismena* to the hart, but bicause she had him before her eies, whom she loved more then her-selfe, the content, that she had by onely seeing him, was a sufficient remedie of the paine, that the greatest of these stings did make her feele. After *Don Felix* had dined, he called me unto him, and giving me a speciall charge what I should do (because he had imparted his griefe unto me, and put his hope and remedie in my hands) he willed me to carie a letter to *Celia*, which he had alreadie written, and reading it first unto me, it said thus.

Don Felix *his letter to* Celia.

THe thought, that seekes an occasion to forget the thing, which it doth love and desire, suffers it selfe so easily to be knowne, that (without troubling the minde much) it may be quickly discerned. And thinke not (faire Ladie) that I seeke a remedie to excuse you of that, wherewith it pleased you to use me, since I never came to be so much in credit with you, that in lesser things I woulde do it. I have confessed unto you, that indeede I once loved well, because that true love, without dissimulation, doth not suffer any thing to be hid, and you (deere Ladie) make that an occasion to forget me, which should be rather a motive to

love me better. I cannot perswade me, that you make so small an
account of your selfe, to thinke that I can forget you for any thing
that is, or hath ever been, but rather imagine, that you write
cleane contrarie to that, which you have tried by my zealous love,
and faith towards you. Touching all those things, that in pre- 5
judice of my good will towards you, it pleaseth you to imagine,
my innocent thoughts assure me to the contrarie, which shall
suffice, to be ill recompenced, besides, being so ill thought of, as
they are.

After *Don Felix* had read this letter unto me, he asked me if the 10
answer was correspondent to those words that his Ladie *Celia* had
sent him in hers, and if there was any thing therein, that might be
amended. Whereunto I answered thus. I thinke Sir, it is needlesse
to amende this letter, or to make the Gentlewoman amendes, to
whom it is sent, but her, whom you do injurie so much with it. 15
Which under your Lordships pardon I speake, bicause I am so
much affected to the first love in all my life, that there is not any
thing that can make me alter my minde. Thou hast the greatest
reason in the world (said *Don Felix*) if I coulde perswade my selfe
to leave of that, which I have begun: But what wilt thou have me 20
do, since absence hath frozen the former love, and the continuall
presence of a peerelesse beautie rekindled another more hot and
fervent in me. Thus may she thinke her-selfe (saide I againe) unjustly deceived, whom first you loved, because that love, which is
subject to the power of absence, cannot be termed love, and none 25
can perswade me that it hath beene love. These words did I dissemble the best I could, because I felt so sensible griefe, to see
my selfe forgotten of him, who had so great reason to love me,
and whom I did love so much, that I did more, then any would
have thought, to make my selfe still unknowen. But taking the 30
letter and mine errant with me, I went to *Celias* house, imagining
by the way the wofull estate, whereunto my haplesse love had
brought me; since I was forced to make warre against mine owne
selfe, and to be the intercessour of a thing so contrarie to mine
owne content. But comming to *Celias* house, and finding a Page 35
standing at the dore, I asked him if I might speake with his Ladie:
who being informed of me from whence I came, tolde *Celia* how
I would speake with her, commending therewithall my beautie
and person unto her, and telling her besides, that *Don Felix* had
but lately entertained me into his service, which made *Celia* saie 40

unto him. What, doth *Don Felix* so soone disclose his secret loves to a Page, but newly entertained? he hath (belike) some great occasion that mooves him to do it. Bid him com in, and let us know what he would have. In I came, and to the place, where the enimie of my life was, and with great reverence, kissing her hands, 5 I delivered *Don Felix* his letter unto her. *Celia* tooke it, and casting her eies upon me, I might perceive how my sight had made a sudden alteration in her countenance, for she was so farre besides her-selfe, that for a good while she was not able to speake a worde, but remembring her-selfe at last, she saide unto me. What good 10 fortune hath beene so favourable to *Don Felix* to bring thee to this Court, to make thee his Page? Even that, faire Ladie, saide I, which is better then ever I imagined, bicause it hath beene an occasion to make me behold such singular beautie and perfections, as now I see cleerely before mine eies: And if the paines, the 15 teares, the sighes, and the continuall disquiets, that my Lord *Don Felix* hath suffred, have greeved me heeretofore, now that I have seene the source, from whence they flow, and the cause of all his ill, the pittie, that I had on him, is now wholly converted into a certaine kinde of envie. But if it be true (faire Lady) that my 20 comming is welcome unto you, I beseech you by that, which you owe to the great love, which he beares you, that your answer may import no lesse unto him. There is not anie thing (saide *Celia*) that I would not do for thee, though I were determined not to love him at all, who for my sake hath forsaken another. For it is no 25 small point of wisedome for me, to learne by other womens harmes to be more wise, and warie in mine owne. Beleeve not good Lady (saide I) that there is any thing in the worlde, that can make *Don Felix* forget you. And if he hath cast off another for your sake, woonder not thereat, when your beautie and wisedome is so 30 great, and the others so small, that there is no reason to thinke, that he will (though he hath woorthelie forsaken her for your sake) or ever can forget you for any woman else in the worlde. Doest thou then know *Felismena* (said *Celia*) the Lady whom thy Master did once love and serve in his owne countrey? I know her 35 (saide I) although not so well as it was needfull for me, to have prevented so many mishaps, (and this I spake softly to my selfe). For my fathers house was neere to hers, but seeing your great beautie adorned with such perfections and wisedome, *Don Felix* can not be blamed, if he hath forgotten his first love, onely to 40

embrace and honour yours. To this did *Celia* answer merily, and
smiling. Thou hast learned quickly of thy Master to sooth. Not so
faire Ladie, saide I, but to serve you woulde I faine learne: for
flatterie cannot be, where (in the judgement of all) there are so
manifest signes and proofes of this due commendation. *Celia* 5
began in good earnest to aske me what manner of woman *Felismena* was; whom I answered, that touching her beautie, Some
thought her to be very faire, but I was never of that opinion,
bicause she hath many daies since wanted the chiefest thing, that
is requisite for it. What is that said *Celia*? Content of minde, saide 10
I, bicause perfect beautie can never be, where the same is not
adjoyned to it. Thou hast the greatest reason in the world, said
she, but I have seene some Ladies, whose lively hewe sadnes hath
not one whit abated, and others, whose beautie anger hath
encreased, which is a strange thing, me thinkes. Haplesse is that 15
beauty said I, that hath sorrow and anger the preservers and
mistresses of it, but I cannot skill of these impertinent things:
And yet that woman, that must needes be molested with continuall paine and trouble, with greefe and care of minde, and with
other passions to make her looke well, cannot be reckoned 20
among the number of faire women, and for mine owne part, I do
not account her so. Wherein thou hast great reason said she, as in
all things else that thou hast saide, thou hast shewed thy selfe wise
and discreete. Which I have deerely bought, said I againe: But
I beseech you (gracious Lady) to answer this letter, because my 25
Lord *Don Felix* may also have some contentment, by receiving
this first well emploied service at my hands. I am content, saide
Celia, but first thou must tell me if *Felismena* in matters of discretion be wise and well advised? There was never any woman
(saide I againe) more wise then she, bicause she hath beene long 30
since beaten to it by her great mishaps; but she did never advise
her selfe well, for if she had (as she was accounted wise) she had
never come to have bene so contrarie to her selfe. Thou speakest
so wisely in all thy answeres, saide *Celia*, that there is not any, that
woulde not take great delight to heare them: which are not 35
viands (said I) for such a daintie taste, nor reasons for so ingenious and fine a conceit (faire Lady) as you have, but boldly
affirming, that by the same I meane no harme at all. There is not
any thing, saide *Celia*, whereunto thy wit cannot attaine, but
because thou shalt not spende thy time so ill in praising me, as thy 40

Master doth in praying me, I will reade thy letter, and tell thee what thou shalt say unto him from me. Whereupon unfolding it, she began to read it to herselfe, to whose countenance and gestures in reading of the same, which are oftentimes outwarde signes of the inwarde disposition and meaning of the hart, I gave a watch- 5 full eie. And when she had read it, she said unto me. Tell thy Master that he that can so well by wordes expresse what he meanes, cannot choose but meane as well as he saith : And comming neerer unto me, she saide softly in mine eare. And this for the love of thee *Valerius*, and not so much for *Don Felix* thy Master his sake, 10 for I see how much thou lovest and tenderest his estate : And from thence alas (saide I to my selfe) did all my woes arise. Whereupon kissing her hands for the great curtesie and favour she shewed me, I hied me to *Don Felix* with this answer, which was no small joy to him to heare it, and another death to me to report 15 it, saying manie times to my selfe (when I did either bring him home some joyfull tydings, or carrie letters or tokens to her) O thrise unfortunate *Felismena*, that with thine owne weapons art constrained to wounde thy ever-dying hart, and to heape up favours for him, who made so small account of thine. And so did 20 I passe away my life with so many torments of minde, that if by the sight of my *Don Felix* they had not beene tempered, it coulde not have otherwise beene, but that I must needes have lost it. More then two monethes togither did *Celia* hide from me the fervent love she bare me, although not in such sort, but that by 25 certaine apparant signes, I came to the knowledge thereof, which was no small lighting and ease of that griefe, which incessantly haunted my wearied spirites; For as I thought it a strong occasion, and the onely meane to make her utterly forget *Don Felix*, so likewise I imagined, that, perhaps, it might befall to him, as it 30 hath done to many, that the force of ingratitude, and contempt of his love, might have utterly abolished such thoughtes out of his hart. But alas it happened not so to my *Don Felix*, for the more he perceived that his Ladie forgot him, the more was his minde troubled with greater cares and greefe, which made him leade the 35 most sorowfull life that might be, whereof the least part did not fall to my lot. For remedie of whose sighes and pitious lamentations, poore *Felismena* (even by maine force) did get favours from *Celia*, scoring them up (whensoever she sent them by me) in the catalogue of my infinite mishaps. For if by chaunce he sent her 40

anie thing by any of his other servants, it was so slenderly accepted, that he thought it best to send none unto her but my selfe,
perceiving what inconvenience did ensue thereof. But God knowes
how many teares my messages cost me, and so many they were,
that in *Celias* presence I ceased not to powre them foorth, earnestly 5
beseeching her with praiers and petitions, not to entreat him so
ill, who loved her so much, bicause I woulde binde *Don Felix* to
me by the greatest bonde, as never man in like was bounde to
any woman. My teares greeved *Celia* to the hart, as well for that
I shed them in her presence, as also for that she sawe, if I meant 10
to love her, I woulde not (for requitall of hers to me) have sol-
licited her with such diligence, nor pleaded with such pittie, to
get favours for another. And thus I lived in the greatest confusion
that might be, amids a thousand anxieties of minde, for I imagined
with my selfe, that if I made not a shew that I loved her, as she 15
did me, I did put it in hazard, lest *Celia*, for despite of my simplicitie or contempt, woulde have loved *Don Felix* more then
before, and by loving him, that mine coulde not have any good
successe; And if I fained my selfe on the other side, to be in love
with her, it might have beene an occasion, to have made her reject 20
my Lord *Don Felix*, so that with the thought of his love neglected,
and with the force of her contempt, he might have lost his content, and after that, his life, the least of which two mischiefes to
prevent, I woulde have given a thousand lives, if I had them.
Manie daies passed away in this sort, wherein I served him as 25
a thirde betweene both, to the great cost of my contentment, at
the end whereof, the successe of his love went on woorse and
woorse, bicause the Love, that *Celia* did beare me was so great,
that the extreme force of her passion made her leese some part of
that compassion, she should have had of her selfe. And on a day 30
after that I had caried, and recaried many messages and tokens
betweene them, somtimes faining some my selfe from her unto
him, because I could not see him (whom I loved so deerly) so sad
and pensive, with many supplications and earnest praiers I
besought Lady *Celia* with pittie to regard the painfull life, that 35
Don Felix passed for her sake, and to consider, that, by not favouring him, she was repugnant to that, which she owed to her selfe:
which thing I entreated, bicause I sawe him in such a case, that
there was no other thing to be expected of him but death, by
reason of the continuall and great paine, which his greevous 40

thoughts made him feele. But she with swelling teares in her eies, and with many sighes answered me thus. Unfortunate and ac- cursed *Celia*, that nowe in the end dost know, how thou livest deceived with a false opinion of thy great simplicitie (ungratefull *Valerius*) and of thy small discretion. I did not beleeve till now, that thou didst crave favours of me for thy Master, but onely for thy selfe, and to enjoy my sight all that time, that thou diddest spende in suing to me for them. But now I see thou dost aske them in earnest, and that thou art so content to see me use him well, that thou canst not (without doubt) love me at all. O how ill dost thou acquite the love I beare thee, and that, which for thy sake I do nowe forsake? O that time might revenge me of thy proude and foolish minde, since love hath not beene the meanes to do it. For I cannot thinke, that Fortune will be so contrarie unto me, but that she will punish thee for contemning that great good which she meant to bestow on thee. And tell thy Lord *Don Felix* that if he will see me alive, that he see me not at all: And thou vile traitour, cruell enemie to my rest, com no more (I charge thee) before these wearied eies, since their teares were never of force to make thee knowe how much thou art bound unto them. And with this, she suddenly flang out of my sight with so many teares, that mine were not of force to staie her. For in the greatest haste in the worlde she got her into her chamber, where locking the dore after her, it availed me not to call and crie unto her, requesting her with amorous and sweete words to open me the dore, and to take such satisfaction on me, as it pleased her: Nor to tell her many other things, whereby I declared unto her the small reason she had to be so angrie with me, and to shut me out. But with a strange kinde of furie she saide unto me. Come no more, ungratefull and proud *Valerius* in my sight, and speake no more unto me, for thou art not able to make satisfaction for such great disdaine, and I will have no other remedie for the harme, which thou hast done me, but death it selfe, the which with mine owne hands I will take in satisfaction of that, which thou deservest: which words when I heard, I staied no longer, but with a heavie cheere came to my *Don Felix* his lodging, and with more sadnes, then I was able to dissemble, tolde him, that I could not speake with *Celia*, because she was visited of certaine Gentlewomen her kinsewomen. But the next day in the morning, it was bruted over all the citie, that a certaine trance had taken her that night, wherein she gave up the ghost, which stroke all the court with no smal woonder. But that, which *Don Felix* felt by her sudden death, and how neere it greeved his very soule, as I am not able to tell, so can not humane intendement conceive it, for the complaints he made, the teares, the burning sighes, and hart-breake sobbes, 5 were without all measure and number. But I saie nothing of my selfe, when on the one side, the unluckie death of *Celia* touched my soule very neere, the teares of *Don Felix* on the other, did cut my hart in two with greefe: And yet this was nothing to that in-tollerable paine, which afterwardes I felt. For *Don Felix* heard no 10 sooner of her death, but the same night he was missing in his house, that none of his servants, nor any bodie else could tell any newes of him.

Whereupon you may perceive (faire Nymphes) what cruell torments I did then feele, then did I wish a thousand times for 15 death to prevent all those woes and myseries, which afterwards befell unto me: For Fortune (it seemed) was but wearie of those which she had but till then given me. But as all the care and diligence which I emploied in seeking out my *Don Felix*, was but in vaine, so I resolved with my selfe to take this habite upon me 20 as you see, wherein it is more then two yeeres, since I have wandred up and downe, seeking him in manie countryes: but my fortune hath denied me to finde him out, although I am not a little now bounde unto her by conducting me hither at this time, wherein I did you this small peece of service. Which (faire 25 Nymphes) beleeve me, I account (next after his life in whom I have put all my hope) the greatest content, that might have fallen unto me.

When the Nymphes had heard faire *Felismenas* tale, and under-stoode what a great Lady she was, and how love had made her 30 forsake her naturall habite, and taken upon her the weedes and life of a shepherdesse, they were no lesse amazed at her con-stancie and zeale, then at the great power of that cruell tyrant, who absolutely commands so many liberties to his service. And they were mooved besides to no small pittie, to see the teares and 35 burning sighes wherewith the Ladie did solemnize the historie of her love. *Doria* therefore, whose tender soule *Felismenas* greefe did most transpierce, and who was more affected to her, then to any woman, with whom she had ever conversed before, tooke her by the hand, and began to say to her in manner follwing. What 40 can we do (faire Lady) against the blowes of Fortune, what place is there so strong, where one may be safe from the mutabilities of time? What harneys so impenetrable, and steele so well tempered, that may serve for a defence against the violence of this tyrant, whom so unjustly they call *Love*? And what hart (though it be harder then diamond) which an amorous thought can not mollifie and make tender? Certes this beautie, this valour, and this wisedome, deserve not to be forgotten of him, who had but once seene and knowne them: But we live now in such an age, that the deserts of any thing, are the meanes and occasions of not obtaining it. And cruell love is of so strange a condition, that he bestoweth his contents without any good order and rule, and giveth there greatest favours, where they are lest esteemed; but the medicine of so many ils, (whereof this tyrant is the cause) is her discretion and courage that suffers them. But whom doth he leave so free, that these may serve her for a remedie? Or who can command her selfe so much in this passion, that in other womens affaires she is able to give counsell, how much lesse to take it in her owne. Yet for all this, I beseech thee (faire Ladie) to put before thine eies, and consider what thou art, bicause if women of such high renowne and vertue as thou art, are not able to tolerate his adverse effects, how can they suffer them, that are not such. And in the behalfe of these Nymphes and mine owne, I request thee, to go with us to the sage *Felicias* pallace, which is not farre from this place, for that to morrow about this time we may be well there: where (I am assured) thou shalt finde great remedies for thy greefes, as many others have done heeretofore, that have not deserved them as much as thou hast: whose profounde skill and rare experiments (besides many other notable things in her, wherein no man or woman in our times came ever neere her) and her princely bountie doth make her so famous and renowned, that the greatest kings and estates in the worlde are desirous of her companie. I know not faire Nymphes (said *Felismena* againe) who is able to applie a remedie to such an ill, but he that first caused it. But neverthelesse I will fulfill your wils heerein, and since your companie is such an ease and lighting to my paine, it were a fond part to reject that comfort, whereof at this time I stande in so great neede. I woonder said *Cynthia*, that *Don Felix* (al the while thou didst serve him) did not know thee by thy faire face, thy sweete grace, and looking daily on such faire eies. He did so little remember those beauties, saide *Felismena*, which he had once seene in me, (his thoughts being so deeply imprinted on *Celias* which he daily viewed) that he had no power, nor knowledge left to thinke once of mine. And talking thus togither, they heard the Shepherds singing, (that in companie of discreet *Sel-* vagia were comming down the hill) the oldest songs they knew, or that their severall greefes did put into their heads, everie one taking that, which made most for his purpose. And the first that began to sing, was *Sylvanus*, who did sing this song following.

*M*Y *passion* (Love) *thou dost disdaine,*
  But God keepe thee from such a paine.
I am of Love *disdained,*
And Fortunes *wheele doth broose me,*
I care not now to loose me,
And hope not to be gained.
So care to care is chained
    By Fortune *and by* Love *againe:*
    But God keepe thee from such a paine.

In playntes Love *entertained*
My hart (such sport to choose me)
And fortune thus undooes me,
To make me thinke unfained,
That Time a change maintained,
But Both do still my greefes ordaine,
But God keepe thee from such a paine.

Selvagia, who bare no lesse love, or at lest no lesse presumption thereof to her *Alanius*, then *Sylvanus* to faire *Diana*, and who thought her selfe no lesse greeved for the change, that he had made in his love, then *Sylvanus* for the long perseverance in his harme, changing the first verse of this old pastorall round that followeth, she began to sing it, applying it to her purpose in this sort.

*S*Aie *Shepherdesse, what hath deprived thee*
    Of curtesie and joy,
Since that so merrie thou were woont to be?

The deere remembrance of my passed gladnes
In middes of all my present greefe and paine,
Woe to my soule, that feeles it with such sadnes,
If long in such a state it doth remaine:
And since that time hath changed (to be plaine)   5
*   A Shepherd to offend and trouble me,*
*   Merrie and pleasant I could never be.*

Syrenus thought *Selvagias* song sufficient enough to manifest his
greefe, if *Sylvanus* and she had agreed thereunto; who also perswading him to choose out some song, that he had sometimes 10
heard most fit for his purpose, he began to sing this which
followeth.

M Istresse thou hast forgotten me,
*   But more I love and honor thee.*

Haples, I see I am forgot,   15
*   And yet I know no reason why,*
*   To whom thy faith thou dost apply,*
And tak'st from whom thou dost not wot:
Being belov'd, he loves thee not,
*   And Mistresse thou dost not love me,*   20
*   But more I love and honor thee.*

Me thinkes I do behold with pride
*   Those eies (my joyes not long ago)*
*   And for thou wilt not see me so,*
Thy fairest face from me dost hide: 25
And that I saie to thee, beside,
*   Mistresse lift up those eies to me,*
*   For more I love and honor thee.*

The Nymphes with no small delight and content, were harkening to the Shepherds songs, but the infinite sighes and teares 30
which the noble Shepherdesse powred foorth, did not suffer her
to be idle, while the Shepherds were a singing. When they were
come to the fountaine, and had done their due reverence, they
spred a faire white cloth upon the greene grasse, and setting that
meate on it, which they had brought with them from the towne, 35

17 *apply,* Ed.] *apply.* Y.

they sat them downe to eate, whom their thoughts (at lest) would give them leave, and they, (who had not such a priviledge) importuned by them, that were most free, must needes do the like. And after they had refreshed themselves, *Polydora* saide thus. The remedie of your paines disdained Shepherds, (if it be lawfull 5 to call you by that name,) which (to your greefe) fortune hath cast upon you, consisteth in the hands of the grave Lady *Felicia*, to whom nature hath given that divine knowledge, which she hath denied us: And therefore since you see, how greatly it importeth you to go visit her, in the name of these two Nymphes 10 (to whom you have done this day so great service) I request you, not to refuse our companie, bicause by no other meanes you may receive the rewarde of your travell and paine, the which this woorthie Shepherdesse intends to take, who needes it no lesse then your selves. And thou *Syrenus*, whom Fortune hath tossed 15 from a happie and joyfull time, to a life as haplesse and full of sorrowe, despaire not, but cheere up thy selfe, for if thy Mistresse had the remedie of the miserable life, which she leades with *Delius* so neere her, as thou of that, which she makes thee suffer, it would be no small lighting to those churlish wordes, and jealous 20 jarres, which I know she passeth every day with him. There is nothing faire *Polydora* (saide *Syrenus*) that gives me now any greater discontent, then that *Diana* hath revenged herselfe on me so much to her owne cost, for loving one, who hath not any thing in him that deserves such love, and being perforce in his 25 companie, thou seest how much it must greeve her; and as for me, to seeke a remedie for my greefe, I woulde do it, if time and fortune would permit me. But I plainly see, that all the waies of it are stopped up, and know not whither thy selfe and these faire Nymphes will carrie me to seeke it out. But let it be as it will, 30 I will followe you, as *Sylvanus* (I thinke) and *Selvagia* will do no lesse, if they be not of so small understanding, that they conceive not the great favour, that you do to us all. And so they two referring themselves to that, which *Syrenus* had answered, and committing their flockes to their friends (which were not feeding 35 farre from that place) while they came backe again, they went altogither, which way the Nymphes did lead them.

The end of the second booke of Diana.

The third Booke of Diana of George of Montemayor.

WIth great content the faire Nymphes with their companie were going on their way thorow the middes of a thicke wood, and now the sunne being readie to set, they entred into a faire valley, in the mids of which ran a swift brooke, beset on either side with thicke Sallows and Sicamours, amongst the which were many other kindes of lesse trees, which twyning about the greater, and the golden and coloured flowers of the one, woven (as it were) with the greene bowes of the other, represented a goodly sight and delight to the eie. The Nymphes and Shepherds tooke a pathway betweene the brooke and the faire arbours, who had not gone farre, when they came to a large greene meadow, wherein was a very faire great moate of cleere water, from whence the brooke did spring, that with great force ranne thorow the valley. In the middes of that moate was an Iland, wherein grew some greene trees, amongst the which stoode a Sheepe-cote, and about the same a flocke of sheepe went feeding of the greene and tender grasse. The Nymphes thinking this a fit place to passe away the night, which was neere at hand, upon a fine causey of stones most artificiallie (as it seemed) laide in order, they passed all over into the iland, and went directly to the cote which they sawe before them. But *Polydora* going in first (for she was a little before the rest) was scarce entred in when she came foorth as fast againe, and looking towards her companie, did put her finger upon her mouth, in token that they should come softly on and without any noise, which the Nymphes and the Shepherdes perceiving, with the least they could, came into the cote, and looking into it, espied a bed in a corner, not made of any other thing, then of the greene bowes of those Sicamours, that were growing about it, and of the greene grasse, that did growe about the water brinkes. Upon the which they sawe a Shepherdesse lying a sleepe, whose beautie stroke them with no lesse admiration, then if on a sudden they had seene faire *Diana* before their eies. She had on a light skie coloured petticoate, and under that a gorget of so passing fine net-worke, that they might at pleasure behold the delicate proportion of her snow white brest, and comely feature of her even body, for the upper part (being of the same colour with the rest) hung so loose about her, that they might take a perfect view of her fine and daintie waste. Her yellowe haire in brightnes surpassing the sunnie beames, were loose and hanging downe without any order. But never did frizeling and adorned periwigge of any 5 Lady in stately court beautifie in such sort, as the carelesse disorder that these had; and her white legge, being bare by the negligence of her harmelesse sleepe, laie seemely out of her petticoate, but not so much, that the lookers on might perceive any part, but what with modestie they might well beholde. And by 10 manie teares that (sleeping yet) went trickling downe her faire and rosie cheekes, her sleepe (it seemed) shoulde not hinder her sorrowfull imaginations. The Nymphes and Shepherds were so amazed at her beautie, and at her inward sorrow, which by outward signes they well conjectured did trouble her waking soule, 15 that they knew not what to saie, but were forced to shed teares for pittie of those, which they sawe the Shepherdesse powre foorth: who (as with pittie and admiration they were looking on her) turned her on the other side, and with a greevous sigh fetch't from the bottome of her hart, saide thus to her selfe. 20 How unfortunate art thou _Belisa_, that thy greefe consisteth in no other thing, but in that thy life is of so small value, that it is not able to pay those things with extinction thereof, which by thine owne occasion are destroyed and lost? And then with a sudden sursault she awaked in such sort, that the end of her daies (it 25 seemed) was neere at hand: But when she sawe the three Nymphes, and two such faire Shepherdesses with two Shepherds, she was so amazed, that it was a good while before she came to her selfe againe, who at last lifting up her eies to looke on them againe, without stopping her teares, which continually she powred out, 30 or putting silence to her burning sighes, which her afflicted hart sent foorth, began to speake in this sort. Howe great a comfort to so comfortles a soule as mine is should it be, if I were assured, that none by worde nor deede woulde endevour to give me any at al; bicause the great reason, that I have (faire Nymphes) to live 35 enwrapped in such sadnes as I doe, hath put such a kinde of enmitie betweene me and the consolation of my greefe, that if I thought at any time to enjoy it, I would my selfe be the authour of mine owne death: Whereat marvell not faire Nymphes, or that

37 enmitie _Ed._] emnitie _Y._

I woulde seeke to prevent me of this remedie, since there is no
other, that can greeve me more, then this your sudden sight and
comming to this uncouth cote, a place selected out and fit for no
other thing, but to bewaile remedilesse greefes. Wherefore let it be
a warning to those that are attending their torments, to go quickly 5
out of this place, bicause the misfortunes of love have stopped up
the waies in such sort, that they never let any hope of comfort or
remedie enter in. But what hap hath ledde such a faire companie
to this place, where nothing is that yeelds content. What is it
(thinke you) that makes the greene grasse of this iland growe, and 10
the waters (that encompasse it rounde about) to encrease, but my
ceasles teares? What is it, that moves the trees of this faire valley,
but the voice of my piteous outcries, and the violent breath of my
sorrowfull sighes, which, filling the aire, do execute that office for
it, which for it selfe it cannot do? Why do the pretie birdes sing 15
among these springes, when golden Phoebus is in all his force,
but to helpe to lament and bewaile my mishaps? Wherefore is it
that the timerous wilde beastes come foorth to the greene
meadowe, but to heare my continuall plaints? I pray God your
fortune hath not brought you (faire Nymphes) to this place to that 20
end, that mine hath, bicause nature (according to the sorrowfull
life, that I doe passe in it) hath for no other thing (it seemes)
framed it, but for those that are troubled with the incurable
malladies of love, therein to passe away their sorrowfull lives: If
any of you therefore be in this extremitie, let her passe on no 25
farther, if not, let her go quickly from hence againe, least by
staying heere long, she be forced by the nature and qualitie of the
place. The faire Shepherdesse spake these words with so many
teares, that there was not any amongst them, that coulde staie
theirs. They were all amazed to see the spirit, gesture and coun- 30
tenance wherewith she spake them, for they came (as it appeered)
from the verie center of her painfull soule. And she coulde do no
lesse then this, because the sorrowfull successe of her love did
take away all manner of suspicion, that that greefe, which so
extremely she shewed, was either counterfaite or fained. But faire 35
Doria spake thus unto her. What is the cause (faire Shepherdesse)
that hath driven thy beautie to these extremities? What greefe so
strange coulde love make an occasion of so manie teares, accompanied with so sole and solitarie a life, as thou dost leade in this
place? But what do I aske, when seeing thee to complaine of 40

love, thou tellest me more then I am able to aske thee. It was thy
desire, when we came hether, to be assured that none of us would
offer thee any comfort, wherein I cannot blame thee, since it is the
propertie of sorrowfull soules not onely to abhorre comfort, but
to flie from them, by whom they thinke by any meanes to receive 5
it. If I should tell thee (faire Shepherdesse) that I could helpe thy
greefe, what doth it availe, if the same will not give thee leave to
beleeve me? To tell thee, that in thine owne judgement and
discretion thou dost help thy selfe, I know thou hast it not so
free, that thou canst do it: Of one thing yet (good Shepherdesse) 10
thou maist be assured, that there is no meanes in the whole world
to rid thee from this painfull life, which I would not give thee, if
it lay in my power. And if this good will deserveth any thing at
all, I beseech thee for their sakes (that are heere present) and for
mine owne, to tell us the cause of thy greefe, because there are 15
some in this companie, that have as great neede of remedie, and
whom love hath driven to so narrow a streight, that, if Fortune
do not succour them the sooner, I knowe not what will become
of their lives. The Shepherdesse, hearing *Doria* speake these
wordes, came out of her melancholie cell, and taking her by the 20
hand, carried her unto a fountaine in a little greene meadowe not
farre off. Whither the Nymphes and Shepherdes went after them,
and about the same sat them downe altogither, when golden
Phoebus had made an end of his diurnall course, and silver *Diana*
began hers with such brightnes, as if it had beene midday. Where 25
being in such sort as you have heard, the faire Shepherdesse
began to tell this which followeth.

AT that time (faire Nymphes of the chaste Goddesse) when
I was free from love, I heard once a certaine thing, the
experience whereof did afterwardes beguile me, finding it cleane 30
contrarie to that which I heard reported. For it was tolde me, that
there was no kind of greefe, but (by telling it) was some lighting
and ease to her that did suffer it. I finde, that there is not any
thing, that more augments my mishap, then to call it to memorie,
and tell it her, that is free from the like. For if I thought other- 35
wise, I durst not (beleeve me) recount unto you the historie of
my annoies. But because it is true, that the telling of it to you shall
be no cause of comfort to my balefull soule (which are the two

causes most abhorred of me,) give eare, and you shall heare the
most strange and haples accidents, that ever fell in love.

Not farre from this valley towards that part, where the sunne
doth set, there is a village in the middes of a forrest neere to two
rivers, which with their currants do water and give life to the 5
greene trees, whose shadowed bowes are so delightfull, and thicke
togither, that one house may hardly be discerned from another.
Everie one of them hath their limits rounde about them, where the
gardens in sommer time are decked with fragrant flowers, besides
the aboundance of pleasant orchards, which are there naturally 10
brought foorth, though helped by the industrie of them, which in
great Spaine are called (Freemen) by reason of the antiquity of
their houses and linage. In this place was the unfortunate *Belisa*
borne, for this name I tooke from the funt, where I would to God
I had left and lost my life. Heere lived also a certaine Shepherd, 15
one of the chiefest for birth and riches, that was in all that
countrey, called *Arsenius*, and married to the fairest Shepherdesse
in all her time, but untimely death (because her destinies woulde
have it so, or else for avoyding some other inconvenience that
her beautie might have caused) did within a fewe yeeres after she 20
was married, cut asunder her vital thred. The greefe that *Arsenius*
felt for the death of his beloved *Florida*, was so extreme, that he
was almost in danger of loosing his life: the which yet he preserved by the comfort of a sonne she left behinde her called
Arsileus, whose beautie and comely feature so farre excelled 25
others, that they matched the gifts so highly commended (and
descended to him) from *Florida* his mother. And yet did *Arsenius*
for the losse of her, leade the most sorrowfull and desolate life,
that might be. But seeing his Sonne in sufficient yeeres to set him
to some vertuous exercise, knowing, *That idlenes in boyes was the* 30
nurse of vices, and an enimie to vertue, he determined to sende him
to the famous Academie of *Salamanca*, with intent to have him
learne those sciences, which make men mount uppe to higher
degrees then men, and so sent him thither indeede. But fifteene
yeeres being nowe past since the death of his mother, it fell out 35
that I going on a daie with others of our neighbours daughters
to the market, kept in a prettie towne not farre from ours, unfortunate *Arsenius* (to his owne harme, and (alas) to mine, and to
the prejudice of his haplesse sonne) by chance espied me. This
sight kindled an extreme kinde of love in him, as it appeered 40

afterwardes by the strange effects he shewed: for he endevoured to
make me know it sometimes in the fielde, as I was going to carrie
the Shepherds their dinner; sometimes againe, as I was going to
the river to rince my clothes; and sometimes for water to the
fountaine, where he never missed, of purpose to meete me. But 5
I, (that was till then but a novice in matters of love, although by
heare-saie I understoode some of his disordinate effects) sometimes dissembled the matter, as though I understoode not his
meaning, and sometimes made but a mocke of them, and was
angry to see him so importunate and earnest. But my wordes 10
were not able to defende my selfe from his continuall suites, nor
the great love he bare me, suffered him to leave of to woe me
more and more: And in this sort I passed away more then fower
yeeres, in which space he left not of his fond attempt, nor I to
resolve with my selfe to give him the lest favour in the worlde. 15
About this time came his haplesse sonne *Arsileus* from his studie,
who amongst other sciences, that he had studied, was so bravely
seene in Poetrie and Musicke, that he excelled all others in his
time. His father tooke such exceeding joy in him, that he could
never be out of his sight, and not without great reason, bicause 20
Arsileus was such an one indeed that he deserved to be beloved,
not onely of his father whom nature constrained to love as his
sonne, but of every one else in the worlde: And so in our towne
he was so much esteemed and regarded of the cheefest and vulgar
sort, that they talked amongst themselves of no other thing, then 25
of the great wisedome, graces, gentilitie, and many other good
parts more, which beautified the flourishing prime of his youth.
Arsenius was so secret to his sonne, that by no meanes he would
let him understand any thing touching his love, whom although
Arsileus had seene on a day very sad, yet he durst not aske him 30
the cause of his heavines, but rather thought, those passions to be
the reliques of that sorrow, which yet for the untimely death of
his faire mother, remained in his fathers brest. But *Arsenius*
greatly desiring to sende me a letter, and to get it in such sort
from his sonne, (for he knewe him to be an excellent Poet) that 35
he might not perceive for whom it was, he thought it most fit to
discover the matter, and the summe of his love to a great friend of
his called *Argastus*, a towns-man and our neighbour, praying him
earnestly to request his sonne *Arsileus* (as a thing that he stood
greatly in neede of) to pen him a letter, and to tell him, that it was 40

to be sent a good waie thence to a bonnie Shepherdesse, whom he loved and served. And so he gave him instructions of other things, making most for his purpose, that he was to request him to put in the letter. *Argastus* was so carefull about his friends busines, that *Arsileus* (urged thereunto by his incessant requests) delivered him the letter in as ample sort as he requested it. Which *Arsenius* seeing so fit for his purpose, wrought the meanes, that it came to my hands: the which receiving much against my will, I founde that it saide thus.

Arsenius *his letter.*

FAire Shepherdesse whose hap and fare,
   That such it be, it is Gods will:
Let not such grace and beautie rare
Decay, or be imployed ill.
And whose milde lambes and marked sheepe
Thou maist behold (with merrie cheere)
By flockes increase, where they doe keepe
On tops of these greene hillocks heere.

Harke to a Shepherdes wretched crie,
Unto himselfe so great a foe,
As for thy sweetest sake to die,
He findes he doth it well bestowe:
Turne thy deafe eares unto my smart,
And mollifie thy hard pretences,
And now begin to put thy hart
Into the handes of thy sweete sences.

Turne these two faire and cruell eies
Unto this haplesse Shepherd Swaine:
Thy flocke regarde not, but his cries,
And thinke a little on his paine,
Let that but moove and change thy will:
To thinke thereof, I pray thee deine yet,
And not to remedie mine ill,
But to behold how I susteine it.

How often hast thou come and leade
Unto the field thy flocke and dams,
How many times unto the meade
Hast thou brought forth thy pretie lambes?

That I told not my little ease,
That I became a foole for thee,
But better had I held my peace,
So little it availed me.

That which I feele for thy sweete sake 5
With what wordes shall I now declare?
Or with what knowledge shall I make
My faith but knowen and heavie care?
What humane senses shall suffice
To feele that paine, and that unrest, 10
Which for thy sake Love did devise
To give me (though I tell it best.)

Why dost thou hide thy selfe from me,
Since thou dost knowe it very cleere,
That present when I am with thee, 15
Most absent from thee I appeere:
I, in suspences to enfolde me
Being where thy faire beauties are:
And thou, when that thou dost beholde me,
From seeing me then art thou far. 20

To shewe me likewise thou dost knowe
(To mocke me when thou dost pretend)
Things from thy thought, which ever goe,
And so deceive me in the end.
See then who greater love can give, 25
Or greater grounded love in hand,
That my deceived thought must live
With that thou mak'st it understand.

Behold th'extreme wherein I am,
Seeing my good in doubtfull state, 30
That silly creatures I became,
(Lesse then my selfe) to emulate:
For, for the bird the winde doth beare,
And fish that in the waves doe live,
For their sweete freedome everywhere 35
My understanding I would give.

A change of thousand times I see,
And novels every day doe raine:
Minds change from that they wont to bee,
Oblivions doe revive againe.
In every thing there is great change,   5
The which I never saw in thee,
Whereby thou maist perceive how strange,
And vaine my hope is unto me.

The other day thou didst passe by,
Feeding thy flocke upon the hill: 10
For greefe I sighed somewhat high;
Meaning thereby to thee no ill:
A lambe the head then lift up, that it
Did heare, and did some pitie feele,
And thou didst fling thy sheepehooke at it: 15
See what a hardned hart of steele.

Could'st thou not (armed with such power)
After such long time killing me
Helpe me a day, or but an hower?
If that doth seeme too much to thee,   20
Doe it to see how I may prove
Or how with favours, that ensue,
In better sort intreate this love:
Then after kill my soule anew.

I doe desire to change estate   25
From paine to paine, and not to pleasure:
Nor yet to change from love to hate,
And all in one degree and measure.
And though the ill in substance should
Be but all one and of one sort: 30
Yet in the circumstance I would
That more or lesse it did import.

For that may be of such behoofe,
And Mistresse, so much it may doe
That love may give thee greater proofe,   35
Then it hath giv'n thee hitherto.

And whom an ill and firmest love
Can neither greeve, nor mollifie,
It may be such a greefe may move
Thee, of some greater qualitie.

Unto the meade if thou dost goe,   5
Unto the river or the plaine,
Then am I diligent to knowe,
If thou art gone or come againe.
If angrie, when I follow thee,
Or mocke me, if behinde I stay: 10
See then how feare doth trouble me,
And what extremes I doe essay.

To Sylvia *then thy deerest friend*
I goe (to seeke a poore releefe)
To know if (haply) in the end   15
Thou hast inform'd her of my greefe.
But nothing when of thee she speakes,
Then doe I say, this cruell foe
Unto her good companion breakes
Nothing of me, nor of my woe.   20

Some other times I watch the place,
To heare the singing in the night,
With singular and sweetest grace,
A thousand songs of great delight:
For I doe heare them one by one,   25
And thou seek'st out the worst of all,
And ever from thy mouth heare none
That in love matters doe befall.

I sawe thee yet the other day,
Talking with Maudline, *who in fine*   30
To thee her sorrow did bewray:
O would to God it had bene mine.
I thought thou wouldst not long defer
(Poore soule) to cheere her heavy hart,
But laughing, thou didst answere her.   35
It is a jest, in love's no smart.

Thou left'st her weeping all in vaine,
And I came thither by and by:
Of thy hard hart she did complaine,
And sighing, this I did reply:
No wonder, for this cruell one   5
Delights not onely, that above
All others she loves not alone,
But that all others should not love.

Some other times I thee espie
Talking with other Shepherdesses,   10
All is of feastes and braverie,
Who daunceth best, and like digresses:
That this maide hath a seemely grace,
And he this, or that interest:
But if of love they touch an ace,   15
Then straight thou turn'st it to a jest.

Beware yet, live not too secure,
For in brave love and fortunes art,
There is not any thing lesse sure
Then such a free exempted hart.   20
And it may be with after woe
That cruell love will subject thee,
To one that will intreate thee soe,
(Cruell) as thou intreatest me.

But (if that fall out to thy cost)   25
God graunt the same may never bee,
And first I wish my life were lost,
Rather then such a thing to see.
For this poore hart which in my brest
Is burning in so strange a fire,   30
Feares more thy harme and thy unrest,
Then it respects her owne desire.

With the greatest signes of dolour and of a most afflicted hart
indeede, the Shepherdesse *Belisa* rehearsed *Arsenius* his letter, or
(to say more truely) the letter of his sonne *Arsileus*, staying 35
betweene many verses, and repeating some of them twise, and at

other some lifting up her eies to heaven with such anguish and greefe of minde, that one woulde have thought her hart would have burst in peeces. But prosecuting the sorrowfull historie of her love, she said unto them.

This letter (faire Nymphes) was the beginning of all the harme of the woefull man, that made it, and the end of all the rest and content of the haplesse woman, to whom he wrote it. For when I had read it, by some curious investigation that my surmise found out, I perceived, that it savoured more of his sonne his quicke wit, then of the father his blunt affection. And bicause the time was now at hand, wherin love came to take an account of the small care, I had till then of his invincible power, or bicause in the end I should have some feeling of his poysoned sweete, I perceived my selfe a little more mollified then before, and not so little, but that I gave love place to take possession of my libertie. And that which this tyrant did by me, was the strangest thing that ever hapned in matters of love, for he made me not onely love *Arsileus*, but also his father *Arsenius*. Truth it is, that I loved the father to requite the love he bare me; and the sonne, to yeeld up my entyre libertie into his hands, as from that hower I did indeed give it him. So that I loved the one, not to seeme ungratefull; and the other, because it was not in my power to do any lesse. But when *Arsenius* perceived me to be more gentle then before (which thing he desired so long since) there was not any thing in the world, which he woulde not have done for my content and pleasure: For so many were the presents, the jewels, and manie other gifts he sent me, that it greeved me a little to see my selfe so greatly indebted to him. With every thing he sent me, came so many amorous verses and letters, that I was forced to answer them againe, whereby I shewed him no signes of love to put him in any hope, nor my selfe so coie as I was woont to be. But the love I bare to *Arsileus* tooke every day deeper roote in my hart, and molested my sences in such sort, that it left no quiet place in all my soule. It fell out afterwards, that *Arsenius* and *Arsileus* being in companie on a sommers night with certain of their neighbours, and sitting under a faire great Oke, that stoode in a broade place before our house, *Arsenius* began to commend the skill which his sonne *Arsileus* had in musick and musicall instruments, to give them occasion that were present, to praie him to go fetch a harpe from home, and to plaie and sing there among them,

who sat so neere to our house, that I could not choose, but heare
the musicke. And as he imagined it, so it fell out answerable to his
desire: For *Arsileus*, being earnestly requested by the companie,
sent for a harpe, and sweetely thereon began to plaie and singe.
When I heard *Arsileus*, and with what daintie melodie he plaied, 5
and enticing grace he sung, I was gone almost as farre as might be
in Cupids affects, seeing his father would needes bestowe the
musicke on me, and unwittingly enamour me of the excellent
graces of his woorthie sonne. Wherefore I saide to my selfe.
Thou dost no lesse deceive thy selfe *Arsenius* by procuring thy 10
sonne to sing, that I might heare him, then by sending me a letter
of his owne hande. If thou didst but knowe what will ensue
thereof, thou mightest well from this day admonish all lovers, not
to procure their Mistresses love by other mens gifts and graces,
bicause it commonly fals out that women do sooner fall in love 15
with those that are the instruments and meanes, then with those
that thinke to benefite themselves by them. But nowe by this
time did my *Arsileus*, with a singular sweete grace and voice,
begin to sing this Sonnet to the tune of his silver sounding
Harpe.   20

A Sonnet.

IN *this cleere Sunne with golden beames that shineth,*
   In this most high divine and rare perfection,
In this sweete soule and figure, that refineth
   Our age with joyes, with treasures and affection.   25

   O blinding light and face each harts subjection,
Where beauties store to pities want inclineth:
   Sweete words, but hard condition of rejection;
   Sweete lookes, yet sight that many sorrowes shrineth.

For these sweete Mistresse, I am thus enwrapped,   30
   For these I feare to see mine owne desire,
      And passe the time in thinking of thy treasures.
A case most strange, effects that never happed,
   That seeing thee, I see my greatest pleasures,
      And harmes, when that to see thee I require.   35

After he had made an end of this Sonnet, he began to sing this
song with so marvellous sweete grace and delectable voice, that

he helde all his hearers in a great suspence, and me (poore sorrowfull soule) that loved him more, then ever any coulde be.

TO see thee I lift up my happie eies,
      And having seene thee, cast them downe againe.
For further to proceede the same denies:
Nor other joy but thy love to containe.   5

What greater glory is there then to view thee,
If that he knew the sight that he did see,
For never was there any one that knew thee,
That could be wearie of beholding thee,   10
And though he could not knowe thee any wise
As well as I have knowen thee to my paine,
Yet should he be besides himselfe, if dies
Not at the least, to see thee once againe.

If that my erring pen did others praise   15
It was but tri'd, I see, upon the lest,
For they were all but papers of essaies
Of that, wherewith thou truly wert possest.
And if (before I lov'd thee) with surmise,
My pen hath for some other writ in vaine,   20
It was not for bicause I sawe her eies,
But hop't it should see such a Soveraine.

Nature in framing thee did so excell
      And shew'd so brave a skill and suttle art,
That one of thy perfections served well   25
      Beautie to thousand others to impart.

She that to thee is like in any wise
In least of all I sawe in thee so plaine:
To passe no further she may well suffice,
Nor he, that sees thee but must love containe.   30

Who sees thee as God made thee, and hath seene
An other thing that's faire and of delight,
He thinkes, he sees a thing that would have beene
Thy selfe in any thing, if that it might:

But if he sees thee with such perfect eies,
And (Mistresse) as I sawe thee, then againe
There's no compare (compare for it denies)
Nor glorie, but thy sweete love to containe.

It was not onely this, which *Arsileus* sung that night to the
sounde of his Harpe, but as *Orpheus*, when he demaunded his
Nymph *Euridice*, made the hellish furies gentle with his sweete
song, suspending for a while the paines of the damned ghostes; so
did unfortunate *Arsileus* not onely amaze and mollifie their harts
that were present, but wretched *Belisaes* also, who with great
boldnes from a high garret windowe was harkening unto him:
whose sweete musicke delighted moreover the heaven, the starres,
and the cleere moone, which was then in her force and vigour,
that in what part soever I did then cast mine eies, it admonished
me (me thought) and tolde me, that I loved him more then mine
owne life: whereof it was needlesse for any to put me in minde,
for if I had then beene Lady of all the worlde, I had thought my
selfe too meane to be woorthie of him. And from thence I purposed to hide this affection as little from him as I could. All that
night I laie imagining, by what meanes I might best discover
unto him my griefe, but in such sort, that my vertuous name and
modestie might not suffer any blemish, though death (when this
was wanting) with her appalled feare and danger should not have
hindred mine intent. And yet when that should come, and when we
have the greatest care to avoid the occasions that might hinder it,
even then and most of all they present themselves. The next day
after needs I must go with other countrey maides (my kineswomen
and neighbours) to a thicke wood, in the mids whereof was a cleere
fountaine, whither every other holy day we caried our kine, as well
for that there was good pasture for them, as also for that (the fresh
and hungry evening being come) we might take the milke of the
next day, whereof we made sweete butter, and fresh cheese and
creame. But I and my companie being set round about the fountaine, and our kine liyng in the coole shades of the thick and
branchie trees of that hedge, licking their yong and tender calvelings, that lay by them, one of my friendes amongst the rest, (unacquainted (it seemed) with that love that warred within my soule)
with many requests importuned me (upon paine never to receive
any pleasure at her handes) to entertaine the time and that companie

with some song or other. My many excuses (with telling her besides
that times and occasions were not alwaies one, nor alike) availed me
very little from performing that, which with so great instance she
requested of me : And therefore to the sound of a Bagpipe, whereon
one of them most sweetely plaied, I began to sing these verses.   5

L Ove passed by me with his bowe unarm'd,
  His eies cast downe, milde, gentle, modest gay,
  And (carelesse) left me then behinde unharm'd:
How small a time did I this joye essaie?
  For presently envious Fortune saide,   10
  Staie love, why passest thou so soone awaie?
Foorthwith the blinde boye turn'd to me, and staide
  Angry to see himselfe so checkt with blame,
  For ther's no blame, where his hot fire is laide:
Cupid was blinde, but well he spide his game: 15
  So blinded be he, that he may see none,
  That did so blinde my wit, and sence enflame:
O that I might revenge my selfe of one
  That wisheth harme to all, and will not free
  (With his consent) not one poore hart alone: 20
Straight did the traytour arme his bowe, and he
  with poysoned shaft did pierce my carelesse hart,
  Which in his bowe he put, and aym'd at me:
Fortune unarm'd did take me, for his parte
  Love never plaies, nor workes not any feate,   25
  But on free soules, exempted from his darte:
A hardned hart his arrow brake with heate,
  And brake a never subject freedome, so
  That I did yeeld, and his content was great:
O sole free quiet life that I forgo,   30
  O meadowe seene so oft with freest eies,
  Cursed be Love, his arrowes, and his bowe:
Nowe follow love, and what he doth devise,
  Come from securitie to greatest care,
  And passe from rest, to thousand miseries: 35
See now how that a carefull hart doth fare,
  Which lately was without suspect or thought
  Subject to be to such a tyrants snare.
  O soule with teares undone and brought to nought,

Now learne to suffer, since you learn'd to see,
  But what availes, if this my Fortune wrought?
O wretched eies (if with this terme he be
  Not angry) whom you sawe with free consent,
  Where have you put and plac'd my libertie?   5
O meadowes, groves, and woods of sweete content,
  Which bred so free a hart as I had heere,
  So great an ill why did you not prevent?
Swift running brooke, and river pure and cleere,
  Where once my flocke were wont to drinke their fill,   10
  O every season of the passing yeere,
Why have you put me in a state so ill?
  Since onely I did love you, and these plaines,
  And this most pleasant vale, and greenest hill.
Heere did I mocke a thousand Shepherd swaines: 15
  Who now will laugh at me, when they shall know,
  That nowe I doe begin to feele their paines.
They are not ils of Love, that wound me soe,
  For if they were, then should I passe them all,
  As thousands, who have died in Cupids *woe.*   20
Fortune it is, that turnes, and makes me fall
  From every meane, occasion, path, and way,
  Wherby I might but shew my painfull thrall.
How can the causer of my passion (say)
  Helpe them, if that their paine he never knowes,   25
  But there's no love, where reason beareth sway,
To how much ill is fortune drawing those,
  Whom she makes love? since nothing can restore
  (Sea, earth nor Sunne, moone, stars, nor any showes)
Or give delight, unlesse one love before.   30
  And all is thus, and wretched thus am I,
  Whom time perswades and hinders more and more.
Cease now my verse, since love with angrie eie,
  Beholds, how soone of him I doe complaine,
  And for my harmes doe crave his remedie.   35
Complaine not oft, for feare of his disdaine,
  Now hold your peace, since I seale up my wordes,
  And when you see Loves fell, and angrie vaine,
  Cease, for Loves wroth no remedie affoordes.

22 *meane,* Ed.] *meane* Y.

These verses of the Shepherdesse *Belisa* pleased the Nymphes
and Shepherdes, no lesse then the sweete and sorrowfull note,
wherewith she sung them, who (prosecuting the historie of her
mishap) said: But *Arsileus* was not farre from thence, when
I sung these verses, for having gone foorth that day a hunting, 5
and being in the thickest of the woode to passe away the heate of
the day, it seemed he heard us, and as one, that loved musicke
well, came softly pacing amongst the thickest trees that were
neere unto the fountaine, bicause he might from thence the better
heare us. But our musicke being ended, he came straight to the 10
fountaine, whose sudden sight engendred a forcible passion of
joy and feare in my amazed soule. Which was no great marvell,
bicause an enamoured hart may be as well sursaulted with a sudden joy, as with an unexpected sorrow. He came to us where we
were set, and curteously saluting us, in very good sort, and with 15
a good grace requested pardon of us; That certes (faire Nymphes)
when I begin to thinke of the sweete behaviour, and ripened
wisedome of unfortunate *Arsileus*, I do not thinke that his
sinister fates and fortune were the cause, that death tooke him
away so quickly from my sight, but rather that the worlde was not 20
woorthie to enjoye any longer so singular a youth, on whom
nature had bestowed so many perfections of beautie and enriched
with so many gifts of the minde, as that hee left not his like
behinde him. After hee had saluted us, and leave obtained (which
hee humblie requested of us) to passe away the heate of the daye in 25
our companie, hee cast his eies upon me (which had hee never
done, happie had we both beene) and was (as it appeered afterwardes by divers signes, whereby hee manifested his affection to
me) extremely overcome in my love. Unhappie I, (that needed
not to looke on him to love him, being so much enwrapped in 30
his, by seeing him before, as hee was nowe in mine after hee had
seene me) lifted up mine eies to beholde him at the verie instant
when he addressed his to looke on me, which forcible encounter
both of us would willingly had not befell, bicause that modestie
and shame sharpely rebuked me, and feare left not him without 35
bitter punishment. But he to dissemble his newe greefe, began to
discourse with me in matters cleane different from those, which
he woulde have imparted to me, to some of which I answered
againe, my thoughts and sences being then more careful to see, if

16 Nymphes *Ed.*] Nympes *Y*.

by the alteration of his countenance, or mildenes in his words he
shewed any signes of love, then fully to satisfie his questions. For
then so greatly I desired to heare him sighe, (to confirme me in
my doubtfull hope) that in lieu of such a happines I woulde not
have cared to have passed any greefe whatsoever. And in the 5
end I coulde not wish for more apparant signes of love in him,
then at that present I behelde: for what with his toong he coulde
not, with his eies he manifestly declared unto me the amorous
and secret passions of his hart. And being in these points, the
two Shepherdesses, that were with me, rose up to milke their 10
kine, whom I praied to take the paines to milke mine likewise, for
that I felt my selfe not well at ease. And needlesse it was for me to
entreate them much, and for *Arsileus* to have any fitter occasion
to declare unto me his greefe, wherein I knowe not if he was
deceived, by imagining the occasion why I would be without 15
companie, but am assured, that he was not a little glad to helpe
himselfe by the opportunitie thereof. The Shepherdesses were
busie about milking their kine, which suffered themselves to be
deceived with humane industry by tying their gentle calvelings to
their feete. That *Arsileus* now (newly surprised in love) had 20
yeelded himselfe so much to Cupids bonds, that nothing but
speedie death could give him libertie, I perceived apparantly, in
that fower or five times he began to speake unto me, and every
time in vaine: for the feare he had of my displeasure came ever
betweene him and his speech, and therefore I began to talke to 25
him of another matter, not farre from his intent, bicause he
might not digresse much from it, inducing him thereby to tell
me what it was that so often he went about to speake and could
not utter, saying. Doth this countrey like thee well, *Arsileus*? For
the entertainment and conversation of that, where thou hast 30
lately spent thy time, is, I knowe, farre different from ours, which
therefore cannot so well content thee as that. As of my selfe
(quoth he) I have not so much power, so hath not my understanding (faire Shepherdesse) so much libertie, to answer this
demand. And changing this manner of talke (to shewe him the 35
way with occasion) I said unto him againe: I have heard say,
that in those parts are many faire Shepherdesses, that paragonned
to us, they so farre excell us, that we must seeme but meane in
thy sight that are heere. I might be thought too simple (saide

19 calvelings *Ed.*] cavelings *Y.*

Arsileus) if I woulde confesse this, for though there are as faire
there (as you have heard) yet heere are they which with mine
owne eies I daily see, that so farre surmount them, as the sun doth
the chiefest stars in brightnes. This is the greatest glose in the
world (said I againe) and yet for all this I am not sorrie, that our 5
countrey-women are so farre in your good opinion and liking,
because I am one of them my selfe. Which onely reason (saide he)
if there were no other, were sufficient enough to proove what
I have said. So that by word and worde he came to tell me that,
which I desired to heare, though I would not then make him 10
knowe so much, but rather intreated him to stop up the passage of
his wordes. But fearing least this might have bene an occasion to
qualifie his love (as often times it falleth out, that disgraces and
disfavours in the beginning are the meanes to make any leave of
their true commenced love) I began to tune againe my jarring 15
answere, saying thus unto him. And if thy love be such *Arsileus*,
that it will not suffer thee to leave of to love me, be secret therein,
since it is the manner of those that are wise and judicious (like thy
selfe) to be no lesse in things of meaner consequence. Albeit by
all this, which I have saide unto thee, I would not have thee 20
thinke to profit thy selfe any more, then that I must for ever live
bounde unto thee, if thou wilt follow my counsell in this behalfe.
This did my toong speake, but an other thing did my pitifull eies
affirme, with the which I still looked him in the face, and casting
out a sigh (an assured messenger of my inwarde and sensible 25
passion) which *Arsileus* might have perceived well ynough (if
Love at the least would have given him leave) I held my peace.
In this sort we departed from one another, and many times afterwards he talked with me of these matters, who sent me besides
many letters, and fine Sonnets of his owne making. And as he 30
sung them night by night to the tune of his sweete Harpe, with
amorous teares I oftentimes harkened unto him, so that in the
ende both of us was assured of each others love. But now did
Arsenius his father importune me in such sort, with his messages
and presents, that I knew not what way to take, to defend me 35
from him. And it was the strangest thing in the world to see, how
the love, which increased every day in the sonne, was also augmented in the father, though they were both of different age and
powers: and yet the same (I must needes confesse) made me not
reject him, nor refuse any thing, that he sent me. But living now in 40

all contentment, and seeing my selfe so truly beloved of *Arsileus*, whom I loved so deerely againe, it seemed that fortune would make an end of all my joy with the most haplesse event that was ever seene before. For thus it was, that *Arsileus* and I appointing to meete together on a certaine night (too darke and dismall for me, bicause I never since knew perfectly what day meant) we concluded that he should come into my fathers orchard, and I to my chamber windowe, which opened right upon a Mulberie tree, whereon he might easily get up to be neere unto me, there to talke togither of our matters. Accursed *Belisa* that shalt never conceive to what purpose I brought him to such danger, when as every day, sometimes in the fielde, sometimes at the river side, and sometimes at the wood, when I carried my kine to pasture, and sometimes when I drive my sheepe to the folde, he might at pleasure have talked with me, as he did many daies before. But my hard hap was the cause, that fortune would be paied for the content, which she had lent me till then, with making me live all my life time without it. For now the appointed hower, (which was the ende of his daies, and the beginning of my woes) being come, *Arsileus* came just at the time, and to the very place, where both of us talking together of those things, which they may imagine, that have sometimes loved well, his wretched father *Arsenius*, that accustomed many nights to walke up and downe about our house, to see if he could see me (which if I had so well remembred, for it was so far out of my thoughtes, as if I had never knowen any such matter, I would never have consented to put him in such danger) in the ende happened to come thither that night, and just at that hower when his sonne was in the tree, and so privily, that though he had quickly espied us, we could neither heare, nor see him. And knowing it was I, that was speaking out at the window, but not his sonne, that was in the Mulberie tree, nor imagining who he might be, it was the principall cause of our ill successe. For thereupon he conceived such great wroth and jealousie, that, without any noise at all, he hied him home, where bending a Crossebowe, and putting a poisoned arrow in it, came againe to the place where we were, and aimed so right at his sonne, that the arrow pearcing his tender hart, he fell immediately downe dead from the tree, saying. How little time (my deere *Belisa*) doth fortune lend me to serve thee according to my great good will and desire. Which wordes he could scarce utter, when the accursed father, who by his speech knew that he was the homicide of his owne sonne, with a desperate outcrie saide. Thrise wretched and accursed may I ever be, if thou art my sonne *Arsileus*, who seemest to be no other by thy voice. Where-upon comming unto him, and by the light of the moone, that 5 shone upon his face, knowing him well, and that he had given up the ghost, he saide. Since (cruell *Belisa*) my unfortunate sonne by thy means hath bene slaine, it is not meete that the murdering father survive to lament his untimely death. At which wordes taking out his Woodknife, he thrust it into his hart, and fell 10 downe presently dead! O unhappie chaunce! O strange case, never heard of, nor seene before! O greevous scandale to their eares that shall heare the lamentable discourse of my balefull tragedie? O miserable *Belisa*, may thy guiltie hart thinke of these things, and not take that way, which both father and sonne have 15 taken for thy sake? Alas it shall be great impietie not to mingle thy blood with theirs, who desired so much to serve thee. But when wretched soule I sawe this unluckie accident, without any more adoe, I left my fathers house, and went up and downe, wearying the heavens with importunate complaints, and burning 20 the aire with smokie sighes, untill I came to this place, where accusing cruell fortune and hatefull death, that had in so short time taught me to feele the woundes of their cruell dartes, I have lived sixe monethes, without seeing or speaking to any person, and not desirous of any companie or consolation whatsoever.   25

Faire *Belisa* having made an end of her pitifull tale, began to weepe so bitterly, that every one there was forced with their teares to helpe to bewaile her dire misfortune. And adding further she saide. This is faire Nymphes, the sorrowfull historie (or rather dolefull tragedie) of my haplesse loves, and of their bloodie 30 successe: Behold then if this be such an ill, that fortune or time may cure and remedie? O *Arsileus*, how often did I feare it, with-out thinking of that, which I justly feared. But she that will not beleeve her feare and prevent it, let her not marvell, when she sees that come to passe which she feared, for well I knew, thou 35 couldst not be any long time without meeting me, and that my joy could endure no longer, then when *Arsenius* thy father per-ceived any thing of our loves. I woulde to God it had so fallen out, that the greatest hurt that he could have done me, had bene

23 dartes, *Ed.*] dartes. *Y.*

but to banish thee his sight and our towne. For an ill which is cured with time, may with lesse harme be suffered. O *Arsenius*, the death of thy sonne is no impediment to the greefe, that I also conceive for thine, for the love which thou didst continually beare me, thy vertuous and pure zeale, wherewith thou didst ever love me, thy bountie and cost bestowed on me, the tempestuous and ill nightes, that thou hast passed for my sake, will let me doe no lesse, then lament and bewaile thy disastrous end, for by this time I had bene married unto thee, if thy sweete sonne *Arsileus* had not come to our towne. If I should say, that I did not love thee well, I should deceive the world; for in the end there is no woman, if she knowes she is truly beloved, but will love little or much againe, although otherwise she manifest the same. But now my toong holde thy peace, since thou hast told more then thou wert asked. And pardon me (faire Nymphes) if I have bene tedious in my sorrowfull narration, bicause so great mishaps cannot be comprised in fewe wordes. Whilest the Shepherdesse was telling that which you have heard, *Syrenus*, *Sylvanus*, *Selvagia*, and faire *Felismena*, and the three Nymphes coulde not give eare without some secrete teares, although the Nymphes, as women never touched with love, felt her paine and greefe, but not the circumstances of it. But faire *Doria* seeing the comfortlesse Shepherdesse did not leave of her bitter complaint, began to comfort her in this sort. Let thy teares cease *Belisa*, since thou seest what small remedie thou hast of them, and waigh that two eies are not able to bewaile so great a greefe. But what sorrow can there be, which is not ended, or endes not her that suffers it: and yet I could shew thee the way whereby I could a little lighten thy paine. Wherefore, I pray thee goe with us as well for this respect, as for that it is not meete thou shouldest waste thy life so fondly, for in that place where we carrie thee, thou maist choose out what manner of life thou list, and where none is that may hinder thee of it. This place (answered the Shepherdesse) I thought most fit not onely to lament my woes in, but to end my life in the same, the which (if time doth but intreate me as it hath done hitherto) shall not be very long. But now since this is thy will, I am minded not to gainsay it; and as for mine (faire Nymphes) from this time forward you may use it according to your owne pleasures. They were all glad that she yeelded to goe with them. And bicause the night was passed on more then three howers, and the moone did

shine as cleere as day, they supped there with that provision the
Shepherdes had in their scrips. And after they had supped, every
one chose out her place that did best content her, to passe the
rest of the night away, the which the lovers spent more in teares
and sighes then in sleepe; and the rest that were free, eased 5
themselves of their wearinesse they had the day before.

The end of the third booke

The fourth Booke of Diana of George of Montemayor.

NOw did the morning starre begin to cast foorth her woonted 10
brightnes, and with the comfort of her light the prety
birdes and nightingales were warbling up their sweetest notes to
the skies, when the three Nymphes with their companie departed
from the little Iland, where *Belisa* passed away her sorrowfull
life; whose greefe, though she was a little comforted by the 15
enamoured shepherdes, and cheered up by the rest, did neverthelesse haunt her so much, that she founde no remedie, nor
meanes to rid hir-selfe from it. Both the Shepherds acquainted her
with their passed paines, and the Shepherdesses tolde her the
sorrowfull summe of their loves, to trie if by these meanes they 20
might mitigate her paine a little. But all comfort is in vaine where
the greefe is remedilesse. The disguised Ladie tooke such delight
in *Belisaes* beautie, discretion, and sweete graces, that she coulde
not satisfie her-selfe by asking her still more questions, though
Belisa was almost wearie with answering to them. And the 25
familiaritie betweene them both was so great, that it made the
Shepherds and the Shepherdesse in a manner emulate their conversation. But they came to a thicke woode full of wilde shadowed
trees, where they coulde not chuse, (had they not beene guided by
the Nymphes) but have lost themselves. They therefore led the 30
way before thorow a narrow glade, where they could not enter in
but by one and one. And having gone halfe a league thorow the
thickest thereof, they came into a broade and faire plaine lying
betweene two goodly rivers, both which were brinked on either
side with greene and tall trees. In the middes thereof suddenly 35

appeered unto their sight a stately Pallace, with so high and loftie
turrets, that it filled them full of woonder and delight to behold it.
Before they came to this great pallace, they sawe divers Nymphes
of incomparable beautie comming foorth to meete them: All of
them apparelled with daintie white vailes, curiously woven with
fine threeds of golde and silver, wearing garlands of redolent
flowers upon their yellow haire, which in most comely grace
was hanging downe loose upon their shoulders. After them came
a Lady, which seemed (by the gravitie and majestie of her person)
to be a woman of some great state and authoritie, attyred in
blacke velvet, and leaning (as she came) upon one of her Nymphes
shoulders, the fairest in the companie. When the three Nymphes
were come unto them, with great joy and many imbracings they
were received of the other. But when the Lady came nigh, with
great reverence they kissed her handes, whom she entertained and
wel-commed as joyfully as they could wish. And before the
Nymphes spake one worde of that which had passed, sage *Felicia*
(for so was this honorable Ladie called) saide to *Felismena*. The
great adventure which thou hast done for these three Nymphes,
cannot (faire Shepherdesse) be requited with lesse, then by ever
having me bound unto thee, and to do thee all the favour I may,
which shal not be smal, thy neede being so great: For since
I knowe what thou art (without report of anie) and whether thy
thoughts do leade thee, thou shalt in the ende perceive if I be able
to helpe thee in any thing. Wherefore be of good cheere, for if
I live, thou shalt see and enjoy thy desire, in pursuite whereof
though thou hast passed much paine and travell, there is nothing
(as thou knowest) obtained nor gotten without it. Faire *Felismena*,
marvelling much at *Felicias* wordes, and forgetting not to give
her due thankes for so great curtesies and promises, answered
thus. Since you deigne (sage Ladie) not onely in the end to
remedie my griefes, but to blesse the remnant of my life with
happines and content, whereas there is no desert of my part that
may chalenge any such favour at your gracious hands, do but
consider (good Lady) what is due to your selfe, and then you shall
see how I remaine acquited of this debt, and your selfe sufficiently paied. For so great deserts as thine are (saide *Felicia*) and
for such excellent beautie, as nature hath bestowed on thee, all
that may be done, is little enough. *Felismena* then bowed herselfe
at these wordes to kisse her hands: but *Felicia* embraced her

lovingly, and looking upon the Shepherds and Shepherdesses, saide unto them. Be not dismaied couragious Shepherds, and discreete Shepherdesses, at the continuance of your severall greefes, for I have also no lesse care of their speedie remedies. The Shepherdes and the Shepherdesse kissed her handes, and went in all together to the stately Palace. Before which was a faire broade court, set round about with high Cypres trees, and placed in good order, and interpaved all over with Lozanges of Allablaster and blacke Marble in manner of checkey worke. In the mids whereof stood a fountaine of Jaspar Marble, set upon 10 fower great brasen Lions. And in the mids of the fountaine a Jaspar piller, about the which fower Nymphes (most lively made out of white Marble) had their places. They reached up their armes on high, and in their handes held severall vessels after the Antique Roman manner, out of the which from certaine Lions 15 mouthes, that were painted in them, they powred Cristalline water: The portall of the Palace was of polished Marble, with all the bases and chaptres of the pillers gilded, as likewise the garments of the imagerie that was set in it. All the house seemed to be made of shining Jaspar, with statues and figures of many 20 Roman Emperours and matrones therein engraven, and with other like antiquities. All the windowes were double leafed a peece, and the springs and bars belonging to them of bright silver, and all the gates of stately Cedar. The house was quadrant, and at every Canton was reared up a high and artificiall tower. Comming 25 to the portall, they staied a little to behold the strange workmanship and the imagerie that was so lively graven in it, that it seemed rather a naturall then artificiall worke, or wrought by humane industrie, wherein were two Nymphes of massie silver that stood on the tops of two pillers, and helde up betweene them a polished table 30 of smooth Jeat with golden letters graven in it, that saide thus.

WEll let her life that enters heere be waighed,
And if she hath not chastitie estranged,
And she that loves, or Loves lawes hath essaied,
If for anothers love she hath not changed: 35
And if from former faith she hath not straied,
And kept her first true love, and hath not ranged:
May enter heere into Dianas temple,
Whose soveraigne grace to such appeeres most gentle.

When faire *Felismena* heard this, she saide to the Shepherdesses *Belisa* and *Selvagia*, I thinke we may safely enter into this sumptuous Palace, without breach of the lawes, that this table doth depaint unto us. *Syrenus* answering to that, saide. But faire *Diana* coulde not doe so, bicause she hath not onely gone against them, but against all, that good and honest love commaunds to be observed. Be not angrie with her Shepherd (saide *Felicia*,) for before many daies hence thou shalt wonder that thou wert so much angrie, and laugh at this harde opinion thou hadst of her. And so handes in handes they went into the sage *Felicias* chamber, which was richly hanged with cloth of golde and tissue of inestimable value. And by and by (after they were come in) supper was made ready, where fine white clothes being spred on the tables, and furnished with daintie cates, every one was placed in order: *Felismena* was set next to the sage Lady *Felicia*, and the Nymphes tooke the Shepherdes and Shepherdesses betweene them, whose talke at the boord was full of modest mirth and delight. There were the rich tables of Cedar, and stooles framed out of Ivorie, with cushions of fine needle worke wrought with golde and silver, many cups, goblets, and glasses of divers formes and mettals, were common there, and all of no small price, some of them artificially made of strange glasse, others of fine Cristall, with the feete and handles of pure golde; others, all of golde and silver most richly garnished with precious stones of inestimate value. They were served with such plentie of sundrie daintie dishes, as is almost impossible in order to set downe. After that supper was ended, three Nymphes came into the hall, one of them playing on a Harpe, another on a Lute, and the third on a base Vial de gamba, but with such sweetenesse and melodie, that they that were present, were (as it were) enchaunted and ravished with it. They placed themselves in one side of the hall, and the Shepherdes and Shepherdesses (being lovingly requested by the three Nymphes, and by sage *Felicia*) placed themselves right over against them on the other side, with their Rebeckes and a Bagpipe, whereon *Selvagia* sweetely plaied. And then the Nymphes began to sing this song, and the Shepherdes to answere them in manner following.

The Nymphes.

THe authours of subjections
Fortune and Love, and of most peevish fashions,
 Above the moone affections
 Doe place, and hard rejections,   5
And in the same extremest paines and passions.

The Shepherdes.

Lesse may he vaunt and boast
For joy, whom Love did never yet molest,
 Then he, that loveth most,   10
 And favours ever lost,
Since they that suffer more are ever best.

The Nymphes.

If Loves extremes releeve you,
And did not gainsay reason, as we view them,   15
 Perhaps we would beleeve you:
 But seeing how they greeve you,
Happy are we that can so well eschew them.

The Shepherdes.

The hardest things the stoute   20
And valiant persons ever take in hand:
 And that of greatest doubt
 Brave courage brings about,
For t'is no honour small things to withstande.

The Nymphes.   25

The Lover well doth see,
To fight it out, it is not Loves intent
 With magnanimitie:
 In torments he must be
Of those, that suffring them are most content.   30

The Shepherdes.

If any joy we sought
By any ill of Love which we obtaine,
    Ill cannot be the thought
    Unto the passion brought: 5
But he's more happy that endures more paine.

The Nymphes.

The best estate and fare,
Where he doth see himselfe that loveth best,
    Brings nothing els but care: 10
    And yet doth never spare
With flames to burne the dame and servants brest:
And he that's favour'd most,
Is changed in the twinkling of an eie:
    For with disfavours tost,   1
    And in oblivion lost,
It kils his hart and makes his joyes to die.

The Shepherdes.

To leese a good estate
By falling from it, is a greefe and paine: 2
    Blamelesse is Love, but fate
    It is, and Fortunes hate,
That no exception makes from his disdaine:
Unjust and far unfit
Is death, if Love doth say that we shall live,   2
    If death it promis'd yet,
    No fault he doth commit:
For in the ende his promise he doth give.

The Nymphes.

Fierce Love they doe excuse,   3
That finde themselves entangled with his fetter:
    And blame those that refuse
    Him, but of these to chuse
The blamed mans estate is far the better.

The Shepherdes.

Faire Nymphes, it is denied
The free and bond with one toong to debate,
Live men and those that died,
The loved, and defied,   5
All speake according to their owne estate.

Sage *Felicia* and the Shepherdesse *Felismena* gave attentive eare
unto the musicke, that the Nymphes and Shepherdes made, and
to the sundry opinions, which on both sides they shewed by
singing. And *Felicia* smyling on *Felismena*, saide to her in her 10
eare. Who beleeves not (faire Shepherdesse) but that most of these
words have touched thy soule to the quicke? who with a milde
and sober grace, answered her againe. Such were the words
good Lady, that whose soule they did not touch, the same should
not be touched with such love as mine is. *Felicia* then lifting up 15
her voice a little higher, saide unto her. In these love matters
I note a certaine conclusion, which I finde for the most part true,
That the generous minde and delicate witte by many degrees
excelleth him in affection, that hath not these gifts. Because as
love is a vertue, and vertue doth ever choose her being in the 20
best place, it is cleere, that persons of valour and dignitie, are
more enamoured, and (as they are properly termed) better lovers,
then those of baser condition and estate. The Shepherds and
Shepherdesses hearing what *Felicia* saide, seemed to be somewhat
angry in their mindes, which made *Sylvanus* to thinke, that her 25
words ought not to escape without an answer, who therefore
saide thus unto her. Wherein good Ladie doth a noble minde and
fine witte consist? *Felicia* (who by and by perceived to what purpose the Shepherd demanded this question, because she woulde
not give him anie occasion of discontent) saide. In no other 30
thing but in the proper and sole vertue of him that loves, as to
have a lively and quicke witte, a mature and good judgement,
a thought tending to high and stately things, and in other vertues
which doe arise and flow from them themselves. I am satisfied
saide *Sylvanus*, and so are these Shepherdesses, because we imagined 35
(discreete Lady) that you take valour and vertue to be onely in
noble personages. I speake it to this ende, bicause he is but poore
in the giftes of nature, that goes to seeke them foorth in those

that are gone and past. It pleased not the other Shepherdesse
a little to heare what *Sylvanus* had saide; and the Nymphes did
laugh, to see how the Shepherds did blush at *Felicias* proposition.
Who taking *Felismena* by the hand, brought her into a faire
chamber, where she lay her selfe all alone: And after she had 5
passed the time with her in many discourses, she put her in great
hope of enjoying her desire, and the vertuous end of her love, by
having *Don Felix* to her husband, albeit she saide, that this could
not be done, without passing first some fewe travels and troubles
more: which the Lady made small account of, who in counter- 10
maund of them did encourage and comfort her selfe with the
guerdon that she hoped to gaine by them. *Felicia* tolde her moreover, that during her abode in her pallace, she shoulde put off
her pastorall habits, untill the time came, when she was to weare
them againe. And therefore calling unto her the three Nymphes, 15
in whose companie she came, she commanded them to apparell
her in such garments, as to her noble and high estate were
requisite. The Nymphes were not slow in executing her command, nor *Felismena* disobedient in doing that which *Felicia*
thought convenient for her. They leading her therefore away by 20
the hand, brought her into an inward chamber, at the one side
whereof was a dore, which faire *Doria* opening, they went downe
a paire of alablaster staires into a faire hall, in the middest whereof
was a cesterne of most cleere water, where all the Nymphes did
use to bathe themselves. Where stripping themselves naked with 25
Felismena, they did bathe themselves. And after they had adressed
their golden haire, they went up to one of *Felicias* inward chambers, where the Nymphes having apparelled themselves, they did
also put these garments on *Felismena*: A faire petticoate of carnation printed satten, the upper body of shining cloth of gold, of 30
the same colour, and fringed beneath, and garded with a lace of
beaten golde and small pearle. A gowne of crymosin velvet, with
the sleeves, the bodies and skirts beneath embrodered with knots
of seede pearle, and golde which was curiously wrought with
needle by artificiall and cunning hande. A kirtle of pure white 35
satten full of embrodered flowers and rare works of silver, in the
middes whereof did sticke out faire orientall pearles. And tying
up her haire with a carnation ribbon of silke and silver, they did
put thereon a caule of glittering golde, in every corner whereof
a precious Ruby was set, with a naturall crisped periwigge of her 40

owne haire, matching the brightest golde in colour, which
adorned either side of her cristalline forehead: wherein were put
two jewels curiouslie enchased with tablet Diamonds and Saphires
of infinite value. The border that bound up her caule, was of
chosen flowers of golde, enameled with sundrie lively colours, 5
and beset betweene with Emeraulds and Rubies, in the middes
whereof, just betweene the two periwigs, hung downe a rich
jewell of sparkeling Diamonds upon her snowe white browe, with
three long orientall pearles in forme of acornes, hanging thereat.
The attyre of her head was in forme of two little ships made of 10
Emeraulds, with all the shrouds and tackling of cleere Saphyres.
About her white necke, they put a little chaine of fine golde,
made in manner of a wreathed snake, with an enameled Eagle of
golde in her mouth, which helde betweene both her tallons a Rubie
of infinite price. When the three Nymphes did see her adorned in 15
this sort, they wondred at her excellent beautie, and then brought
her into the hall, where the other Nymphes and Shepherds were.
And whereas they did till then knowe her for none other then
a Shepherdesse, they remained so astonished, that they knewe not
what to saie. *Felicia* commanded her Nymphes after this to carie 20
faire *Felismena* and her company to see the sumptuous and rich
temple, which was presently done, the sage Lady betaking her
selfe to her solitarie chamber. *Polydora* therfore and *Cynthia* taking
Felismena between them, and the other Nymphes the Shepherdes
and Shepherdesses, who for their wisedome, and many other 25
good parts were not a little made of, went out into a great court,
the arches and pillers whereof were of Jaspar marble, and the
bases and chaptres of Allablaster, with many borders and workes
cut out after the Romaine manner, gilded in some places very
curiously, and wrought all over with Moysaical worke: the pillers 30
were supported with Lyons, Ounces and Tygres, so lively cut of
brasse, that they looked as though they would assaile them that
came into that place. In the midst of the court was an eight
square paterne or Obeliske of shining copper, ten cubits high,
upon the top whereof stoode fierce *Mars* armed at all points after 35
the ancient manner, whom the Gentils called the God of battailes.
In this Obeliske with marvellous art and skill were set foorth
the proud squadrons of the Romaines on the one side, and the
Carthaginian campe on the other side. Before the one stoode

23 *Polydora Ed.*] *Pol-lydora Y.*   39 the one stoode *Ed.*] the one one stoode *Y.*

the noble captaine *Hanniball*; and before the other, the invincible
and valiant African *Scipio*, in whom, before he had either age or
experience, nature shewed great tokens of valour and magnanimitie. On the other side stoode *Marcus Furius Camillus* the wise and
valiant captaine fighting in the high capitoll, to set his countrey 5
at libertie, from whence he had himselfe beene late banished.
There stoode *Horatius, Mutius Scævola,* the happie Consull *Marcus
Varro, Cæsar, Pompey* with great *Alexander,* and all they who by
warre had atchieved great enterprises, and woone great fame,
with scrolles and characters in golde, declaring their names and 10
famous deeds, and in what especiall point every one of them had
shewed himselfe most valiant and couragious. And a little above
these stoode an invincible knight armed all over, with a naked
sworde in his hande, and with manie dead mens heads under his
feete, with these words over his head.   15

> *I Am* Cid *th'honour of Spaine,*
> *If that any more could bee*
> *In my workes thou shalt see.*

On the other side stoode another brave knight armed in like
maner, the sight of his bever lifted up with these words also above 20
his head.

> Hernand Gonçales *of* Castile *I am*
> *In number the first Earle, and endlesse praise,*
> *The* Spanish *Scepters honor, since the same*
> *With my brave deedes so highly I did raise,*   25
> *My valour and my manhood golden Fame*
> *Can tell, that sawe it, wherefore she displaies*
> *My high deedes in eternall memorie,*
> *As tels you the Castilian historie.*

Next to him stoode another knight of great force and courage, 30
as by his face they might well judge, armed in bright silver,
which was sowen full of Lyons and castles, who shewed by his
countenance a kinde of fiercenes, making them (almost) afraide
that looked on him; and that which was written above him was
this.   35

Bernard *of* Carpio *I am,*
The Pagans terror, and their smart:
An honour to the Christian name,
Since that my handes advaunc't the same
By valour of my stoutest hart: 5
Fame, just it is not thou conceale
My matchlesse deedes from tender yeeres,
But nothing if thou wilt reveale,
To Ronçes-Vales *I appeale,*
That sometimes was of the twelve Peeres. 10

On the other side stoode a valiant captaine in gilded armour, with six bendes gueles in the middes of his shielde, and on the other side of him many enfolded Auncients, and a captive king in a chaine, whose superscription said thus.

My greatest valours they shall see, 15
Which knewe them not, whereby againe
I onely have deserv'd to bee
Surnamed (The great Capitaine)
And in strange landes, and in our owne
I purchased so great a fame, 20
That my exploites are held and knowne
To be far greater then my name.

Next to this stout captaine stoode a knight all in silver armour, sowen full of starres, and on the other side of him a king with three *Fleure de Lyses Or* in his shielde Azure, before whom he tare 25 certaine papers; the superscription above him was this.

I am Fonseca *whose brave historie*
Europe doth knowe, and doth so much commend,
(Whose life though ended) yet my memorie
Enroll'd by living fame shall never end. 30
My soveraigne King I served, and did beare
My countrey love, and not in fained showe,
I never did leave of for servile feare
To keepe that holy lawe, which every where
The servant doth unto his master owe. 35

13 of him *Ed.*] on him *Y.*   24 on the . . . of him *Ed.*] of the . . . on him *Y.*

In another quadrant of the Obeliske stoode an armed knight, his armour sowen full of little golden shieldes, who by the valour of his personage seemed to be descended from some noble and high blood: casting his eies amongst manie other Lords and knights of his ancient lynage, the subscription beneath his feete 5 was this.

> Don Luys *of* Villanova *I am named,*
> *And from the great Marquesse of* Tranz *descended,*
> *My valour and renowne (with praise proclamed*
> *In Italie, Fraunce, Spaine) is far extended.*   10
> Bicorb, *an ancient house my state is framed,*
> *That fortune to a hart hath now commended*
> *So high, sans peere, and that so much surmounteth,*
> *As to commaund a world, it smally counteth.*

After they had particularly behelde the paterne, and all the 15 knights and valiant champions placed in it, they went into a rich hall, the seeling whereof was all of yvorie, woonderfully wrought and carved, the wals of allablaster, and many ancient histories so lively cut out and graven in them, that one would verily have thought, that *Lucretia* killed her selfe indeede, and subtill *Medea* 20 undid her webbe in the Iland of Ithaca; and that the famous Romaine Lady yeelded to the fatall sister, bicause she would not offende her honour with the sight of the horrible monster; and that the loving wife of *Mauseolus* was making great lamentation, thinking to what end the sepulcher of her husband was counted 25 for one of the seven wonders of the world: And many other histories and examples of chaste Ladies worthie to be eternized with immortall fame thorow out the whole world, bicause it seemed not sufficient ynough for some of them, to give manifest examples by their unspotted life, but for others, by their untimely 30 and cruell death great testimonie of their pure and undefiled thoughts, amongst the which the Spanish *Coronella* was one, who did rather commit her body to consuming flames, then suffer her chaste minde to be overcome with the motion and delight of a dishonest thought. After they had viewed all the figures well, 35 and the varietie of the histories round about the wals of the hall, they went into another square court, which for the riches thereof,

13 *surmounteth Ed.*] *surmonnteth Y.*

seemed to their judgements so much to excell all that they had
seene, as the substance doth the shadowe; for all the wals of it
were covered over with fine golde, and the pavements of precious
stones. Round about this Quadrant stood the figures of many
Ladies of Spaine, and of other nations, and above them all, the 5
Goddesse *Diana* curiously cut out of mettall of Corynth, with
short garmentes like a hunter, adorned with much pearle and
precious stones of great value, who had her bowe in her hande,
and her golden quiver hanging downe by her side, environed
rounde about with a troupe of Nymphes fairer then *Titan* in his 10
cheefest glorie. The Shepherdes and the Shepherdesses were so
amazed at the sight of these things, that they knew not what to
say, bicause the riches of the house were so infinite, the figures so
lively, the workmanship of the Quadrant so excellent, and the
proportion of the Ladies that were retracted there, with so great 15
art, that they thought it impossible to imagine a more perfect and
absolute, or a more sumptuous building in the whole world then
that was. On the one side of the Quadrant stood fower Laurell
trees of gold, so bravely enameled with greene leaves, that in
gardens there were none more fresh or lively, and neere to them 20
a little fountaine made all of beaten silver, in the middes whereof
was likewise a Nymph of beaten gold, which at her faire breastes
thorow nybles of Rubies spouted out water cleerer then Cristall:
and neere to this fountaine did *Orpheus* the famous musition sit,
enchaunted with the age that he was in, when his *Euridice* was 25
requested of importunate *Aristeus*: He had on a cote of cloth of
silver, interseamed and imbrodered with flowers of seede pearle,
his sleeves broad about the shoulders, and falling very narrow to
his elbowes, from whence his armes came out naked. He had on
a paire of hose of cloth of silver to the knee, and made after the 30
olde fashion of Thrace, wrought full of little golden Harpes and
Citherens, his golden bush of haire, which hung downe curled
and long, was tied about with a faire Laurell wreath. But when he
perceived the Nymphes comming towardes him, he began most
sweetely to touch a fine Harpe, which he had in his handes, with 35
the divine melodie whereof the strangers were so much ravished,
that they forgot all that they had seene, in respect of this new
delight. *Felismena* sate her downe upon a faire lowe bed in the
Quadrant, which for the most was covered all over with purple
damaske, finely wrought and fringed with golde, and the Nymphes 40

and Shepherdesses about her, the Shepherdes leaning upon the silver fountaine. In this sort therefore they were harkening to worthy *Orpheus,* as if he had bin singing amongst the *Cyconians* when *Cyparisus* was turned into a Cypres tree, and *Atis* into a Pine tree. Enamoured *Orpheus* then began to sing so sweetely to the tune of his Harpe, that with the heavenly musicke thereof he suspended their amazed senses. And turning his sweete face to *Felismena,* he began to sing these verses following.

Orpheus his song.

*H*Arke Felismena *to the sweetest song* 1
Of Orpheus, *whose love hath bene so high,*
Suspend thy greefe (Selvagia) *somewhat long,*
Whilst now I sing, that once for love did die:
Forget (Belisa) *now thy woefull wrong,*
And to my voice sweete Nymphes your eares apply: 1
    That lost his eies, to beauties blaze then turning,
    And Shepherdes, cease a while your amorous mourning.

I will not speake (for God forbid the same)
Of that most heavie process of mine ils,
Nor when I so did sing, that I did tame 2
Wilde beastes and birdes, and mooved trees and hils:
Nor when I did suspend th'infernall flame,
Nor when I sawe Pluto, *nor that, that kils*
    My soule with greefe, when I lookt backe to see,
    If that Euridice *did follow me.* 2

But I will sing with pure and sweetest voice
Of those perfections, and that grace display,
That wisedome, wit and beautie of such choice,
Of those who doe illustrate Spaine this day.
Then see her (Nymphes) *whose beautie doth rejoice* 3
Us all: her great Diana, *and her gay*
    And goodly traine, on whom both Gods and men
    Cannot ynough imploy their toongs and pen.

Lift up your eies this Lady to beholde,
That heere is sitting in this highest chaire, 3
With scepter neere to her and crowne of golde,
And angrie fortune by her on the staire:

This is the star that Spaines light did enfolde,
Whose absence now her glory doth impaire:
   Her name is Lady Mary *that hath beene*
   Of Hungarie, Boeme, *and of* Austrie *Queene.*

The next that sits to her, is Lady Jane   5
Princesse of Portugall *and of* Castille
The Infant, *and from whom fortune had tane*
The crowne and scepter by her turning wheele:
And unto whom death was so inhumane,
That in her selfe great wonder she doth feele,   10
   To see how soone she did stretch forth her hands
   On her, that was the light of Lusitans.

Behold (faire Nymphes) that Lady Mary *great*
And soveraigne Infant *of her* Portugall:
Whose grace and beautie hath this day a seate,   15
Where humane thought could never reach at all:
Behold, though cruell fortune there doth threat:
Her wisedome yet doth count of her but small:
   For time, and death, and destinie cannot
   Conquere her goodnes, vertues, and her lot.   20

Those two that are by her on either side,
Whose beauties Titans *brightnesse doe offend:*
Their sleeves of gold, their gownes of damaske tide
With pearle, and where faire Emera[u]ldes *depend:*
Their curled golden lockes, waving so wide   25
Upon their shoulders, loose that doe descend:
   *Daughters they are of th'*Infant Lusitane:
   Duarta *the valiant, and great* Cristiane.

Those two great Dutchesses of worthy fame,
For beauties prize in either of our Spaines   30
Which there you see to life set out in frame,
With grace, and features, that all others staines
Of Sessa *and* Najare *each hath her name:*
Whose companie Diana *not disdaines*
   For their exceeding beautie, and desartes,   35
   Discretion, wisedome, and all other partes.

Behold a golden Phoenix *all alone*:
A rare perfection never seene before,
Wisedome, as like was not in any one,
Beautie, and grace, where never could be more.
She that puls fortune from her vaunting throne,   5
And hath her subject to her will and lore:
    Great Lady Leonore Manuell *hath to name,*
    The Lusitane *light that doth the world inflame.*

The Lady Luise Carillo, *that in Spaine*
Hath made Mendoças *blood of such renowne:*   10
Whose beautie, and brave grace hath in a chaine
Cupid *himselfe, for love of her cast downe:*
She's waiting still upon our Goddesse *traine:*
For chastitie worthie to weare a crowne.
    Of faire and honest an example heere,   15
    And of them all a mirrour bright and cleere.

Behold a sweete perfection and a rare,
Of her, whom fame her selfe doth greatly feare:
Behold a passing beautie, sans compare,
Founded in grace and wisedome every wheare: 20
That both with reason binde to love and care.
For in her doth the lest part beautie beare.
    Lady Eufrase *of* Guzman *is her name,*
    Worthy to be eternized with fame.

That matchlesse beautie sweete and peregrine,   25
Not seene in any, but in her alone,
Which every wit and soule doth so refine
With holy love, as like was never none:
Apparelled with Crimson, that doth shine
With flowres of gold, and pearle that there are sowne.   30
    The Lady Mary Aragon *her name:*
    The world doth know, and heaven doth knowe the same.

Her doe you knowe to whome Diane *her face*
Doth turne, and points her to us with her hand,
Who matcheth her in wisedome and in grace,   35
And equall is with others in this land

In wit, and hath in beautie highest place:
Apt to conduct and leade a martiall band.
    T'is Lady Isabell Manriq *of* Padille,
    Who Mars *doth conquer and with wonder fill.*

The Ladies Mary Manuell *and* Jone   5
Osorius, *are those two, which you doe see,*
Whose grace, and beautie, as the like not knowne,
Even Love *himselfe with love doth wound and slee.*
And this our Goddesse doth not joy alone,
To see two such with her, but also wee.   10
    Since then no toong their worthinesse may praise,
    Reason, and fame to heaven the same shall raise.

And those two sisters of such worthy name,
Either of them a second never had.
Their grace, and beautie fils the world with fame: 15
·*This day their golden beames doth each one glad:*
Me thinkes I see them in their perfect frame,
To which more beautie nature could not adde.
    The Lady Bettrice Sarmient *is one,*
    With Castro *her faire sister so well knowne.*   20

That cleerest sunne, which heere you see doth shine,
And heere and there her golden beames doth cast,
She, that doth laugh at lovers that doe pine
In love, and at the teares, that they doe wast,
And at Loves *powre: whose countenance divine*   25
Saies more then I, though praising her so fast,
    T'is Lady Jane Carate, *in whom we see*
    Surpassing grace and beauties praise to bee.

The Lady Anne Osorius, *that brave dame,*
And Castro *next to her possesse their place,*   30
For peerelesse beautie honoured with fame,
For goodly giftes, for modestie, and grace:
But her hard hap (alas) was much to blame,
So cruelly her glory to deface:
    Bicause her fortune equall might not bee   35
    Unto her wisedome, beautie, and degree.

That matchlesse beautie that's adorned so
With honestie, and grace so soveraine,
Which was with reason chosen to bestowe
Her honour in the Temple of Diana,
Not conquer'd, but still conqu'ring high and lowe: 5
Her name (O Nymphes) is Lady Juliana,
    Neece to that greatest Duke and Conestable,
    Speake fame of her, for I am far unable.

Behold the beautie (on the other part)
Of many faire and brave Valencian *Dames,*   10
Whom with my pen, but more yet with my hart,
I will procure to celebrate their names?
Heere Fount of Helicone, *vouchsafe thy art,*
And heere Minerva *helpe me in these blames;*
    To tell what those brave Ladies be, whose sight   15
    Onely to them all eies and harts invite.

See heere fowre blasing stars that brightly shine,
Of whom Fame *brutes their name in every ground,*
That from three famous kingdomes drawe their line,
And from Cardonas *ancient house come downe,*   20
On th'one side Dukes most excellent decline,
And from the other scepter, throne, and crowne:
    Daughters unto Segorbe, *whose golden fame*
    From Atlas *unto* Maurus *soundes their name.*

The light of all the world, the flowre of Spaine,   25
The end of perfect beautie, and of grace,
A royall hart, that ever doth maintaine
Valour, and bountie, in a vertuous race:
That looke so modest, and so sweete againe,
Adorned with so faire and milde a face,   30
    Gives Lady Anne *of* Aragon *such fame,*
    That Love himselfe is captive to her name.

Her sister Lady Bettrice, *that you see,*
Is next (if that you can behold such light)
Whom none can praise, for this is onely shee,   35
Whom none can praise according to her right:

23 Segorbe *Ed.*] Sogorbe *Y.*

That Painter *that did make her, so must bee*
Her praiser, and her giftes he must recite:
  For where all humane wit cannot attaine,
  My poore conceite doth labour there in vaine.

The Lady Frances *of great* Aragon   5
Shew you I would, but she is alwaies hid:
Her sweetest beauties leaves not any one
With life, for so her starlike eies forbid
Our mortall sight to view the same alone:
In life and death, her vertues ever did   10
  Subject each hart to love, and admiration:
  As fame can tell in every forrain nation.

Now Lady Magdalene *you may reveale,*
Sister unto those three which I have showne,
Behold her well, and see how she doth steale   15
Her gazers harts, and subject lives to none.
Her peerelesse beautie threats, and in a chaine
Leades little Cupid, *turn'd into a stone:*
  None see her, but they die, and none there ar
  But she doth conquer without armes or war.   20

Those two bright stars, that heere and there doe vaunt
Their shining beames, that dim the starrie skie,
And making that illustrous house of Gaunt
In all the world with high renowne to flie.
This day their wisedome, and their beauties daunt   25
Each humane thought, and every mortall eie.
  For who sees Magdeline *and* Marguerite,
  That doth not die (for love) at such a sight?

But will you see the thing, that hath undone
All wits, and made them all to wonder so?   30
Behold a Nymph more faire then orient sunne,
Or lovely rose, or lilly hard by Po;
This Phœnix *name, that through the world doth runne,*
Is Lady Caterine Milane, *for so*
  Valencia *cals her, and the world doth say,*   35
  She is as faire, and wise, as lives this day.

Lift up your eies (faire Nymphes) and now behold
The Lady Mary Pexon çannoguere,
How by the river banks her locks of gold
She kembes, adorning of her shining heare,
Whose beautie, wisedome, and brave giftes are told   5
For rarest in our Europe every wheare.
   Behold her eies, her faire and Cristalline face,
   Her sweete demeanour and her heavenly grace.

Those two behold, the rest that doe excell
In perfect wisedome, and in quicke conceate: 10
And for brave beautie beare away the bell,
A paire sans peere, whose starlike eies doe threate
Despaire and death, to those that view them well:
For there sits Cupid in his proper seate.
   Their blessed names doe with their nature fit,   15
   Faire Bettrice Vique and Bettrice Fenollit.

What time Diana went to sport and play,
With her most soveraine face, and more divine,
A morning star arose in moneth of May,
Like to that Star, that neere the Moone doth shine: 20
Which when she sawe so glorious every way,
A famous place to her she did assigne:
   Her beauties tell you, if her name you seeke,
   That she's the peerelesse Lady Anna Vique.

Faire Nymphes, behold the Lady Theodore   25
Carroz, that is great Lady and the Queene
Of such brave beautie, never seene before,
Wisedome, and grace, as like was never seene:
Each thing of hers enamours more and more.
The bravest mens deserts have never beene   30
   Such, as they durst attempt, or ever sought,
   By them to place in her an amorous thought.

See (Shepherdes) Lady Angelas brave grace,
Of Borja, looking on Diana bright;
And how to her the Goddesse turnes her face,   35
To view those eies, that all eies doe invite,

24 Vique *Ed.*] Vigue *Y.*

And mightie Love himselfe weeping apace,
And how the Nymph derides his conquer'd might:
And laughes to see the cruell Tyrant lying,
Wrapped in chaines, to her for mercy crying.

Of that most famous stocke of çannoguere   5
A flowre sprung out, so perfect and so pure,
That living yet but yong, she neede not feare
Any that may her beauties blaze obscure:
Her mothers heire she is, for she doth beare
The praise, which she did with her giftes procure.   10
So hath Lady Hieronyma, *you see,*
In grace, and wit obtain'd the high'st degree.

Now in a wonder (Nimphes) *will you remaine?*
And see what fortune gave to her alone,
How wisedome, beautie, and the goodly traine   15
Of vertues, make in her the chiefest throne?
Lady Veronica Marrades *see againe,*
For onely by her figure it is knowne
That she hath all, and nothing wants to serve her,
Unlesse it be, that none can well deserve her.   20

The Lady Luise Penaroje *we see*
In more then humane beautie and in grace,
In every thing most excellent is shee;
All beauties els she staines, and gaines apace.
Love dies for her, and he will not agree,   25
That any should behold so sweete a face:
Who sees it dies, unlesse he see'it againe,
And seene it, then his sight augments his paine.

Now see I (Nymphes) *that you are seeing her,*
On whom my thoughts continually devise;   30
And yours perforce from her can never stirre,
Cupid she robs, and in her love he dies:
See how her beauties make the world to erre?
See, but beware such light blinde not your eies.
The Lady Jane Cardona, *that faire star,*   35
It is to whom loves powres subjected ar.

That beautie, which exceedeth humane thought,
Which you doe see, if that you can behold it,
She, whose estate was blest, esteeming nought
Of fortune, time, or chaunce, that could enfold it.
She, to the world that such rare giftes hath brought: 5
She, that's my Muse, and Parnasus, *untold yet,*
    Lady Jone Anne *of* Catalane, *The end*
    She is of all, that e're I did commend.

Neere unto her there is a great extreme
In purest vertue, high and sublimate,   10
In comely grace, the fairest in this Realme,
Her golden haire, her necke most delicate;
Each gracious eie a firie pointed beame,
A noble wit, and name of heavens estate:
    The Lady Angela Fernando *named:*   15
    Whom nature to her name like gifts hath framed.

Next to her sits the Lady Marian,
Who hath not in the world her paragon,
Neere to her sister, fairer then the swan
In cristall streames, or fine Vermillion.   20
Proud is our age of both of them, that can
In tender yeeres have no comparison
    For wisedome; for so much they may presume,
    As thousand toongs can tell, or golden plume.

The two fine sisters Borjas *which you see,*   25
Hyppolita *and* Isabell *so faire,*
With grace and giftes, that so adorned bee,
That Phebus *brightest beames they doe impaire.*
And see how many lives, that once were free,
*Their beauties conquers (*Cupids *onely snare)*   30
    Behold their haire, their countenance, and eies,
    This gold, that sweete, and those like stars in skies.

Behold the Lady Mary Cannoguere,
Who now is Lady of faire Catarosse,
Whose beautie, and sweete grace doth every where   35
Conquer each hart with unrepaired losse:

34 Catarosse *Ed.*] Catarasse *Y.*

Fame on her wings th'row-out the world doth beare
Her vertues rare, that shine like gold to drosse.
　　Since each one then that sees her, must commend her,
　　Who then can praise her well, and not offend her?

The Lady Isabell Borja here doth stand　　　　　　　5
Perfect and absolute in every thing:
Behold her face, her fine and dainty hand,
Over whose head the nightingales doe sing.
Our age she honours, and th'Hiberian land:
Of grace, and vertue she's the onely spring:　　　　10
　　And those, to whom nature did beautie give,
　　She staines, as fairest that did ever live.

She, that her haire hath hanging downe, and spred
Abroad, and tide with golden thred behinde:
And that faire face, that hath so often led　　　　15
So many harts to bondage of the minde:
Her Ivorie necke, her eies in beautie bred,
Faire, modest, gray, not looking out of kinde:
　　Her famous name is Lady Juliana,
　　That honours heere the Temple of Diana.　　　　20

She, whom you there doe see, whom nature made
So curiously, as never like before,
Since that her beautie never seem'd to fade,
Nor that a faire one can desire more:
Whose great deserts, and wit, doth still perswade　　25
Fame, to the world her praises to restore:
　　Is called Lady Mencia Fenollit,
　　To whom Love yeelds himselfe and doth submit.

The song of renowned *Orpheus* was so pleasant in *Felismenas*
eares, and in all theirs, that heard it, that it held them in such　30
a suspence, as if they had passed by no other thing but that,
which they had before their eies. Who now having particularly
viewed the rich chamber of estate with every thing in it that was
woorth the seeing (as all was) the Nymphes went foorth by a certaine dore into the great hall, and by an other out of the hall into　35
a faire garden, the beautie whereof stroke no lesse admiration into

their mindes, then the strange things which they had seene before:
for amongst the fruitfull trees, and sweete flowers, were many
sepulchers and tombes erected of divers Nymphes and Ladies,
which with great puritie had kept their chastitie (due to the
Goddesse thereof) inviolate and unstained. Some of the tombes 5
were adorned with coronets of knottie Ivie; others with chapplets
of sweete Myrtles; and some with garlands of greene Laurell.
There were also manie Allablaster fountaines in the garden,
some of Jaspar marble, and some of other mettall seated under
vines, which with artificiall arches and wreathes aloft did spred 10
foorth their branches depressed with clusters of coloured grapes.
The Myrrhe trees grew in manner of fower walles, with embattle-
ments and pinnacles on the tops of them, and on the sides above
them were certaine Terrasses and walkes, reared up, whereon (as
over all the garden besides) did growe many sweete flowers of 1
sundry colours, as white Jesmins, Woodbyne, and many more
delightfull to the insatiable eie. In the middes of the garden stoode
a Jeat-stone upon fower brazen pillers, and in the mids of it
a tombe framed out of Jaspar, which fower Nymphes that were
wrought out of white Allablaster did hold up with their handes, 20
and about it stoode manie Tapers of Virgine waxe burning in
massie candlestickes of bright silver, that were made in artificiall
manner. About this tombe stoode certaine Lordes and Knights,
some fashioned out of stone, and mettall, other som out of Jaspar
marble, and other matter. Which figures shewed such great 25
sorrow by their countenances, that they filled *Felismenas* hart,
and all theirs that were looking on the tombe, with no lesse
greefe, then admiration. But viewing it narrowly, they sawe in
a table of shining golde, which at the foote of the sepulchre, a
dead and pale matrone held betweene her hands, this Epitaphe 30
subscribed.

> HEere *Lady* Katherine *entombed lies,*
> *Of Aragon and Sarmient, whose fame*
> *Doth mount with praise unto the loftie skies:*
> *And sounds from North to South, her woorthy name.* 35
> *Death kil'd her, to revenge the sacrifice*
> *Of those she killed, when she was a dame:*
>   *Her body's heere, her soule in heaven with pleasure:*
>   *The world unwoorthy to possesse such treasure.*

After they had read this Epitaphe, they sawe an Eagle of blacke
marble, with displaied wings on the top of the tombe, with
a golden table betweene her tallons, with these verses in it.

> *E*Ven as (O death) the Planets should remaine
>   Without Apollo and Diana bright,   5
> The ground without mankinde, and beasts againe,
> The Marriner without the North-starre light;
> The fielde without faire flowers, grasse, or graine,
> The mornings showe without the dewe of night:
>   Vertue and beautie so remaine and die   10
>   Without the dame that in this tombe doth lie.

When they had read both these Epitaphs, and *Belisa* had understoode by them what the Nymph was, that was buried therein,
and how much Spaine lost by leesing her, calling therewithall to
minde the untimely death of her deere *Arsileus*, she could not, 15
but with teares breath out these sorrowfull wordes. O death, how
far am I from thinking, that thou maiest comfort me with other
womens harmes? The small time, that the world enjoyed the
great beautie and wisedome, wherewith they tell me this Nymph
was endowed, doth not a little greeve me, bicause as she was not 20
her-selfe in love, so did not any deserve, she should be so. For
had she beene, I would then account her for so happie a woman
by dying, as my selfe unfortunate, by seeing how small reckoning
thou makest of me (cruell death) since taking from me all my
good, and the onely joy of my life, thou dost not leave me heere, 25
but onely to feele the never-ceasing paine of this heavie want. O
my *Arsileus*, O rare wisedome in such yoong yeeres? O the most
faithfull lover that ever was, and the finest wit that the heavens
could ever infuse into so brave an ornament of nature. What
eies may without inundations of teares behold thy sorrowfull 30
absence? And what hard hart suffer thy untimely and disastrous
end? O *Arsenius*, *Arsenius*, how smal a time wert thou unable to
endure the violent death of thy unfortunate sonne, having more
occasion to suffer it, then my selfe? Why didst thou make me
(cruell *Arsenius*) participate of two deathes? Of both which to 35
prevent the least that did greeve me, I would have given a
thousand lives. Farewell (happie Nymphe) the light and honour
of the royall house of Aragon : God give thy soule eternall glory,

and deliver mine from so many woes and afflictions, wherinto it
is so deepely sunke. After that *Belisa* had spoken these wordes,
and after they had seene many tombes more, very richly erected,
they went out by a backe dore in the garden, into a greene
meadowe, where they found the sage Ladie *Felicia* recreating her-
selfe alone, and walking up and downe, who seeing them comming towards her, received them all with a joyfull countenance.
And whilest it was time to go to supper, they went to a pleasant
walke in a grove of Sicamours harde by, where the Nymphes of the
sumptuous temple were woont many times to go and disport
themselves: where sitting downe in a little plat of greene grasse,
that was encompassed round about with leavie Sicamours, they
began to discourse one with another of that, which did best
please their fancies. The Lady *Felicia* called the Shepheard *Syrenus*,
and *Felismena* to her. The Nymph *Doria* sat her downe with
Sylvanus in one place of the greene meadowe, and the Shepherdesses
Selvagia and *Belisa* went by themselves, with the most beautifull
Nymphes *Cynthia* and *Polydora* into another, so that (though they
were not farre asunder) yet they might talke togither well enough,
and not trouble one another. But *Syrenus* desiring that their talke
and conversation might be conformable to the time, place, and
person with whom he talked, began to saie in this manner. I thinke
it not (sage Lady) much beyond the purpose, to demand a certaine question, to the perfect knowledge whereof, as I could
never yet attaine; so do I not meanely desire by your Ladiships
wisedome to be resolved therein: and this it is. They do all
affirme (that would seeme to know something) *That true Love
doth spring of reason*: which if it be so, what is the reason, that there
is not a more temerous and unruly thing in the worlde then love,
and which is lest of all governed by it? As this Question (answered
Felicia) is more then a simple Shepherdes conceit, so is it necessarie, that she that must answer it, ought to have more then
a sillie womans wit: But to satisfie thy minde with that little skill
I have, I am of a contrarie opinion, affirming that Love, though it
hath Reason for his mother, is not therefore limited or governed
by it. But it is rather to be supposed, that after reason of knowledge and understanding hath engendred it, it will suffer it selfe
to be governed but fewe times by it. And it is so unruly, that it
resultes oftentimes to the hurt and prejudice of the lover: since
true lovers for the most part fall to hate and neglect themselves,

which is not onely contrarie to reason, but also to the lawe of nature. And this is the cause why they paint him blinde, and void of all reason. And as his mother *Venus* hath most faire eies, so doth he also desire the fairest. They paint him naked, because good love can neither be dissembled with reason, nor hidden 5 with prudence. They paint him with wings, because he swiftly enters into the lovers soule: and the more perfect he is, with more swiftnes and alienation of himselfe, he goeth to seeke the person of the beloved, for which cause *Euripides* saide; That the lover did live in the body of the beloved. They paint him also shooting his 10 arrowes out of his bowe, because he aymes right at the hart, as at his proper white: And also, because the wound of love is like that, which an arrow or dart maketh, narrow at the entrance, and deepe in his inward soule that loveth. This is an inscrutable, and almost incurable wounde, and very slowe in healing: So 15 that thou must not marvell *Syrenus*, that perfect love (though it be the sonne of reason) is not governed by it, bicause there is nothing, after it is borne, that doth lesse conforme it selfe to the originall of his birth, then this doth. Some saie there is no other difference betweene vertuous and vicious love, but that the one 20 is governed by reason, and the other not: but they are deceived; because excesse and force is no lesse proper to dishonest, then to honest love, which is rather a qualitie incident to everie kinde of love, saving the one doth make vertue the greater by it, and the other doth the more encrease vice. Who can denie, but that in 25 true and honest love excessive and strange effects are oftentimes founde? Aske it of many, who for the onely love of God made no account of themselves, and cared not to leese their lives for it, although knowing the reward they looked for, did not worke so much in their minds. And how many againe (enflamed with the 30 love of vertue) have gone about to cast away themselves, and to end their lives, to get thereby a glorious and surviving name? A thing truely, which ordinarie reason doth not permit, which doth rather guide every effect in such sort, that the life may honestly preserve it selfe. But what diversitie of examples could 35 I bring thee (*Syrenus*) of many, who onely for the love of their friendes have lost their lives, and every thing that with life is lost. But let us leave this love, and come againe to that which nature hath bred betweene man and woman: wherein thou must know, that if the love, which the lover beares to the mistresse of 40

his affections, (although burning in unbridled desire) doth arise
of reason, and of true knowledge and judgement, as by her onely
vertues he doth judge her woorthy to be beloved, That this kinde
of love (in my opinion,) (and yet I am not deceived) is neither
unlawfull nor dishonest, bicause all love being of this qualitie, 5
doth tende to no other end but to love the person beloved for her
owne sake, without hoping for any other guerdon or effect of
his true, and sincere love. So that this is as much as (me thinkes)
may be saide in answer of thy question, which thou hast put me.
Syrenus then saide unto her. I am resolved (sage Lady) of that 1
which I desired to understande; and also beleeve, that by your
gracious wisedome which is great, and bountie which is no lesse,
I shall be thorowly instructed of whatsoever I woulde desire to
know, although some finer capacitie then mine were more requisite to conceive these deepe reasons, so perfectly alledged by 1
your learned assertions.

Sylvanus, that was talking with *Polydora*, saide: It is strange
(faire Nymph) to see what a sorrowfull hart (that is subject to the
traunces of impatient love) doth suffer, because the lest ill, that it
causeth in us, is the deprivation of our judgement, the losse of our 2
memorie, and the surcharging of our imaginations with his onelie
objects, making every one to alienate himselfe from himselfe,
and to impropriate himselfe in the person of his beloved. What
shall that wofull man then do, who sees himselfe so great an
enimie to pleasure, such a friende to solitarines, so full of pas- 2
sions, environed with feares, troubled in his spirits, martyred in
his wits, sustained by hope, wearied with thoughts, afflicted with
griefes, haunted with jealousies, and continually worne with sobs,
sighes, sorrowes, and woes, which he never wanteth? And that,
which makes me more to marvel, is, that the mind doth not pro- 3
cure, (this love being so untolerable and extreme in crueltie) nor
hath any desire at all to part from it, but doth rather account it her
enimie, that gives it any counsell to that effect. All this is true
(saide *Polydora*) but I know well that Lovers for the most part
have more words, then passions. This is a signe (saide *Sylvanus*) 3
that thou canst not conceive them (faire Nymph) because thou
canst not beleeve them, nor that thou hast beene ever touched
with this pleasing ill. And I wish thou maist not, the which none
can beleeve, nor knowe the multitude of woes proceeding from
it, but onlie she that doth participate of his bitter effects. Why? 4

dost thou thinke (faire Nymph) when the lover that findes himselfe continually confused, his reason obscured, his memorie gone,
his fancies and sences wearied by excessive love, that his toong
can then remaine so free, that it may faine passions, and shew
another thing by words, then that he feeles by deedes? Ah
deceive not thy selfe with these wordes, which I know are cleane
contrary to thy thought. Beholde heere am I, in whom there is
nothing, that can be governed by reason; neither can he have it,
that is so much without his libertie as I am, because all corporall
subjections do suffer the will (at the least) to be free, but the
bondage of love is such, that the first thing it takes in hand, is to
constraine one, to make a profession of it. And wilt thou Shepherdesse then beleeve, that he doth form complaints, and faine
sighes, that sees himselfe handled in this sort? It seemes well thou
art free from love, as I did but even now tell thee. I know *Sylvanus*
(saide *Polydora* againe) that lovers are full of troubles, and afflicted
in mind all the while they do not obtaine their desires. Thou
speakest in a thing (saide *Sylvanus*) wherein it seemes thou hast no
experience, bicause their love, whose paines cease after the accomplishment of their desires, proceedeth not from reason, but
from a base and dishonest appetite.

Selvagia, Belisa, and faire *Cynthia* were talking togither, what the
reason was that in absence, love did for the most part waxe colde.
Belisa coulde not beleeve, that for any thing in the worlde she
might entertaine such disloyaltie in her hart, saying: That since
she did beare her *Arsileus* (being now dead, and too well assured
never to see him againe) the selfe same love, that she did, when he
was alive, howe much more then was it impossible for any other
to forget that love, which one doth hope sometimes to see againe.
I cannot answer thee *Belisa* (saide the Nymph *Cynthia*) so sufficiently as perhaps this matter doth require, because as it is a thing
impertinent to our condition, so the resolution thereof is it not
expected of a Nymphes witte and profession. But yet this is my
opinion, that though one departs from the presence of her lover,
yet the remembrance of him afterwards remaines in her eies, by
the present occasions wherof she still sees the Idea of the thing
that she desireth. The charge and office of this remembrance is to
represent that to the understanding, which it conteineth in it, and
of thinking of the person whom she loveth, commeth will (the
thirde power of the soule) to engender desire, by meanes wherof

the person absented suffereth paine, by not seeing that which she
loveth well : So that all these effects are derived from the memorie,
as from a fountaine, from whence the beginning of desire springeth.
But you must now knowe (faire Shepherdesses) that as the
memorie is a thing, that the more it encreaseth, the more it
looseth her strength and vertue, forgetting that which the eies
did deliver and put into it; so likewise do the other powers, whose
workes had their beginning in it, in the verie same sort as rivers
should want their streames, if the fountaines from whence they
spring, did cease to flowe. And as this is understoode of him that
departs, so is it likewise of her that remaines still. And whereas
thou dost thinke (faire Shepherdesse) that time will not cure thy
greefe by committing the remedie thereof into my Lady *Felicias*
handes, thou art much deceived, because there is not any, whom she
doth not helpe, and lovers more then any other kinde of people.

The sage Lady *Felicia* (though she was somewhat from them)
heard what *Cynthia* saide, and answered. It might be thought no
small point of crueltie in me, to put the remedie of her greefes
(who needes it so much) in the hands of so slowe and tedious
a phisition as time is : For though it be sometimes a helpe, yet it
fals out in the end, that the greatest malladies (if they have no
other remedies then their own) do last so long a time, that before
they have an ende, they ende their lives that have them. And therefore because I meane to bethinke me of that, which toucheth
Felismenaes ease, and the remedy of her greefes, and those of all
her companie, and that now the beames of golden *Apollo* seeme
to make an ende of their daies journey; I thinke it best to seale up
our discourses, and to go in, bicause supper (I thinke) by this time
is staying for us. And so they went into the great Ladies Pallace,
where they founde the tables ready furnished and set under an
arbour of greene vines, in a pleasant and fresh garden within the
house. And supper being ended, the sage Lady praied *Felismena*
to tell them some discourse, were it a historie, or some notable
accident, that had befallen in the Province of Vandalia? Which
Felismena did not denie : for with a sober and gentle grace she
began to tell this history following.

IN the time of the Valiant Prince *Don Fernando*, who was afterwards King of Aragon, lived a knight in Spaine called *Rodrigo*
of *Narvaez*, whose singular virtues and approved manhood were

so great, that as well in peace, as in war, he got the Sirname of the
best knight of all those that lived in his time; and where he did
especially winne it, when the same noble Prince overcame the
power of the *Moores* at the citie of *Antiquera*, shewing by his
great enterprises and martiall feates in this warre, an absolute 5
minde, an invincible hart, and a noble kinde of liberalitie, by
meanes whereof a good Captaine is not onely beloved, and highly
esteemed of his owne souldiers, but also of strangers and his
chiefest enimies: In regarde of which worthie service, hee was
guerdoned after the subduing of that countrey (although but 10
meanely in lieu of his high desertes and excellent deedes) with the
regiment of *Antiquera* and *Allora*, where hee spent most of his
time with fiftie choise gentlemen at the Kings paie, for defence
and garrison of both those frontier townes. All which by the good
government of their Captaine enterprised many valiant deedes in 15
defence of the Christian faith, atchieving them with great honour,
and registring their perpetuall fame with notable adventures done
in maintenance of the same. Whose mindes therefore being so
great enemies to idlenes, and the exercise of armes so agreeable
to the generous hart of their valiant Governour; it fell out that 20
upon a certaine sommers night, *Cynthia* inviting them to take part
of the bright and coole aire, *Rodrigo* with nine of his gentlemen
(for the rest remained in garrison of the towne) armed at all
points, went out of *Allora*, to surprise the Moores which lay on
their frontiers, carelesse (perhaps) in their charge and negligent. 25
And emboldened by the priviledge of the night, they passed by
certaine waies neere unto their townes. The valiant Captaine
therefore going on with his gentlemen as secret as he might, and
verie carefull not to be discried, came to a way that parted into
two, where consulting to divide themselves into two companies 30
of five a peece, and in such sort, that if the one company perceived themselves to be in any danger, by sounding of a cornet
they might be presently aided by the other five. The Governor
and fower of them tooke one way, and the other five an other:
who riding in severall companies together, and talking of divers 35
matters, everie one desiring some adventure to trie his manhood,
and to shew himselfe a couragious man at armes, as almost
everie day they were wont to doe, they heard not far from them a
mans voice sweetly singing, and now and then breathing out a

25 (perhaps) *Ed.*] (perheps) *Y.*

profound sigh; wherby they conjectured that some amorous passion did trouble his thoughts. The horsmen therefore that heard this, rode into a little wood hard by the way, and because the moone did shine as cleere as day, they might perceive a *Moore* comming that way they went, so gallant and comely a gentleman, that his personage did well testifie that he was of noble bloud, and singular valour. He came mounted upon a daple graie horse, and the garments he had on was a horse-mans coate of crimosin damaske, and upon that a Barberie mantell fringed about with golde, and embrodered all over, and edged with many workes of silver twist. He ware by his side a faire Moresco Cymitarre, with tassels of carnation silke and golde hanging at it; on his head a Tunez Turbant or roll of silke and white cotton, which was lifted with golde, and fringes of the same, which being wrapped many times about his head, did serve him for an ornament, and a defence of his person. He carried a great Target on his left arme, and in his right hande a Launce of two punches: and with so goodly grace and countenance came the enamoured *Moore*, that they coulde not wish to see a better sight. But giving attentive eare unto his song, they heard that the dittie (although it was in the Arabicke toong) saide thus.

First in Granada *I was borne,*
In Cartama *brought up and bred,*
To Allora *fronter, which I scorne,*
And in Coyn *enamoured.*

Though in Granada *I was borne,*
And brought up in Cartama *brave;*
My faith in Coyn *I have sworne,*
And there my libertie I gave.
There doe I live, where I doe die,
And where my care is thither led
To Allora *Fronter am I,*
And in Coyn *enamoured.*

The five horsemen, who had perhaps but small experience in amorous passions, or whether they had or no, regarding more the interest, which so brave an adventure did promise them, then the song of the enamoured *Moore*, issued out of the woode, and ranne

with great violence upon him. But the valiant *More*, who in like
assaultes was a tried champion (though love at that time was
Lorde of his thoughtes) was not a whit dismaied, but couching
his launce in rest, with woonderfull courage began to skirmish
with them all, whom he made immediately knowe, that he was no 5
lesse valiant then amorous. Some say, they set upon him by one
and one, but they that have sought out the truth of this historie,
affirme, that they ranne all upon him at once, which is most like
they did so, to take him prisoner, but when they sawe him begin
to defende himselfe, that then perhaps the other fower did stande 10
by, whilest one of them did fight with him alone. But howsoever
it was, he drove them to such a narrowe streight, that casting
three of them to the ground, the other two very fiercely set upon
him, who needed not to use their ordinarie strength against so
valiant an adversarie; for though he was wounded in one of his 15
thighes, yet his strength and courage was not of such a temper,
that mortall wounds could daunt his minde, nor make him leave
of that, which so highly touched his honour. But having by chance
let fall his launce, he put spurs to his horse making a shewe of
flight, whom the two Christians pursued at his verie heeles, 20
which when he perceived, he turned backe against them both, and
passing thorow them like a furious and swift lightning, came to
the place where one of the three laie, which he had unhorsed,
where stooping downe from his horse to take up his launce that
lay by him, he mounted nymbly into the saddle againe: which 25
one of the two horsemen seeing, and thinking they were not able
to make their partie good, he sounded his Cornet; but the *Moore*
in the meane time so fiercely assailed them, that if the valiant
Governour had not come, they had kept company with their other
three companions, that lay hurt on the ground. But when the 30
governour was come, and sawe how valiantly the *Moore* did fight,
he made great account of him in his minde, and having an eagre
desire in single combat to proove his manhoode with him, he
saide unto him. Such is thy noble valour and rare strength (brave
knight) that by overcomming thee, there cannot be but great 35
honor and glorie got; which singular favour if gentle Fortune
would but grant me, I could not (by my life) request any other at
her handes. Wherein though I put my person in no small danger,
by offring him the combat, that can so bravely defende himselfe,
yet for a worlde I will not leave it, when by so brave an enterprise, 40

and howsoever I speede, I cannot chuse but winne great honor and renowne. And saying this, he badde his men stande aside, appointing the conquered the prise of the victorie. When they were both asunder, a hot fight began betweene these valiant men at armes. The magnanimious *Narvaez* desired the victorie, because the valour of the brave *Moore* encreased the glorie, that he hoped to get by it: And the stout *Moore*, to no other ende but to attaine to the effect of his hope and desire. And so they belaied about them, passing active and nimble in lending blowes, and so hardie in assayling each others person, that had it not beene for the former wearines, and wound that the *Moore* had, (who by this time grewe somewhat faint by leesing his blood) with great difficultie had the Govenour got the happie victorie. But these impediments, and being not able to manage his horse any longer, did promise it *Narvaez* cleerely; and not bicause he knew there wanted one jot of courage or valour in the *Moore*, who (when he sawe that in this single combat his life was in hazard, which he woulde have willingly changed for the contentment, which Fortune did then deny him) he r'enforced himselfe with all his might, and standing upright in his styrrops, gave the Govenour a dangerous thrust, which he received upon his target, who was not slacke in answering him with another upon the right arme, and trusting to his strength, if the matter came to handie gripes, at last he ranne in, and closed with him, and with such force shaked him, that casting him out of his saddle, he also fell with him to the ground, saying. Yeeld thy selfe knight, if thou makest any account of thy life, which is now in my hands. It is in thy hands (said the *Moore*) to kil me as thou saist, but fortune shal never do me such despite, to make me overcommed by any, but onely by whom I have long since suffered my self to be conquered. And this onely content doth remaine to me of my prison, whereunto my misfortune hath now brought me. The Governour did not then marke the *Moore* his words so much, nor to what end he spake them, but using the mercy that the valiant conquerour is woont to use to the forlorne man of Fortune, he helped him to rise up, and to binde up his woundes, which were not so great, but that he might get upon his horse, and so all of them with their prisoner tooke the next way home to *Alora*. The Governour as he rode, did continually cast an eie upon the *Moore* whom he thought with himselfe, a goodly man of person, and gracious of visage,

remembring therewithall, howe stoutly he had defended himselfe;
but thought his sadnes too great for so brave a minde as he carried; and because he intermixed his sorrow with sighes, which
were tokens of greater greefe, then could be imagined in so brave
a man, and also desirous to knowe more of the matter, he said 5
unto him. Behold Sir knight, how the prisoner that leeseth his
hart and magnanimitie for feare of imprisonment, doth hazard
the law of his libertie, and that in Martiall affaires, adversitie must
be entertayned with as merrie a countenance, as by this greatnes
of minde it may deserve to enjoy prosperitie againe. And these 10
sighes are not (me thinkes) beseeming that valour and courage,
which thou hast shewed by tryall of thy person; neither are thy
wounds so mortall, that thy life is in hazarde, whereof besides
thou hast shewed not to make so much account, but that thou
wouldest willingly have left it for thine honours sake: If there be 15
then any other occasion of thy heavines, tell it me: for by the
faith of a gentleman, I sweare unto thee, that I will use as much
curtesie and friendship towards thee, as thou shalt not have
occasion to repent thee, that thou hast tolde me it. The *Moore*
hearing the Governours gentle speech, whereby he argued in 20
him a brave and noble minde, and his curteous and friendly offer
to helpe him, thought it no point of wisedome to conceale the
cause of his greefe from him, because by his milde wordes and
gracious countenance he had such great hope of helpe and favour,
that lifting up his face, which with the waight of sorrow he went 25
carying in his bosome, he saide unto him. How art thou called
Sir Knight, that dost thus comfort me in my sadnesse, whereof
thou seemest to have some feeling, and the which thou dost
enforce me to tell thee. My name is *Rodrigo* of *Narvaez*, and
Governour I am of *Alora*, and Antiquera, of both which townes 30
of garrison the King of Aragon my Lord and Master, hath appointed me Chiefetaine. When the *Moore* heard this, with a merrier
countenance then before, he said: I am glad that my misfortune
hath beene so fortunate, to make me fall into thy handes; of
whose force and manhoode I have beene long since informed, the 35
triall whereof though it had cost me deerer, coulde not have
greatly greeved me, since it doth so greatly content me to see my
selfe his prisoner, whose vertues, valour, and dexteritie in armes
doth importune every ones eares so much. And because the subduing of my person doth oblige me to esteeme thee the more, and 40

that thou maist not thinke it is any kinde of pusyllanimitie, or feare in me (without some other great occasion, which lies not in my power to forsake) that makes me so sad and pensive, I praie thee gentle Knight, by that thou art, to command thy gentlemen to ride on before, because thou maist know, that neither the paine ₅ of my greene woundes, nor the greefe of my present captivitie is cause of my heavie thoughts. The Governour hearing these words, made greater reckoning of the *Moore*, and because he was verie desirous to be thorowly resolved what he was, he willed his gentlemen to ride on before: and they two comming on faire ₁₀ and softly behind, the *Moore* fetching a profound sigh from his soule, began thus to saie.

IF time and triall of thy great virtues (most valiant Governour) and that golden fame wherewith they are spread in every place, had not penetrated my hart with desire of knowing them, ₁₅ and now put them manifestly before mine eies, these words, which thy will doth enforce me to relate, should be now excused, and the discourse, which I meane to tell thee of a life, continually environned with disquiets and suspects (the least whereof being (as thou wilt judge no lesse) worse then a thousand deaths) re- ₂₀ maine untold. But as I am on the one side assured of that I speake, and that (on the other) thou art a worthie knight, and noble gentleman, and hast either heard, or els thy selfe passed the like passion to mine, *Know, that my* name is *Abyndaraez* the yoonger in difference of an uncle of mine, my fathers brother who is also ₂₅ called so. Descended I am from the noble house of the *Aben- cerrajes* in *Granada*, by whose unluckie destinies I did learne to be unfortunate. And because thou maist know what theirs was, and maist by them the better conjecture, what may be expected of mine, *Thou* shalt understand, that in *Granada* was a noble linage of ₃₀ Lords, and Knights, called *Abencerrajes*, whose valiant deeds, and grave personages, as well in martiall adventures, as in peaceable and wise government of our common-wealth, were the mirrours of that kingdome. The olde men were of the Kings counsell; the yoong gentlemen exercised their minds, and bodies in feates of ₃₅ armes, in the service of Ladies and gentlewomen, and by shewing in every point their valour and gentilitie. And as they were honoured of the popular sort, and welbeloved among the princi-

22 knight *Ed.*] kinght *Y*.

pall, (for in all those good parts that a gentleman should have,
they farre excelled others) so were they very well thought of with
the King: They did never any thing in war abroad, nor in counsell
at home, that their experience was not correspondent to their
expectation: whose valour, bountie, and humanitie was so highly 5
commended, that for a common example it was ever alleaged,
That there was never *Abencerraje* coward, niggard, or ill disposed
person. In the citie they were the masters of brave inventions for
apparell: In the Court, of maskes, daunces, and triumphes, and
in the court and citie, in the service and courting of Dames passing 10
gracious: For never did *Abencerraje* love and serve any Ladie, of
whom he was not favoured, nor any Ladie (were she never so
faire and amiable) thinke her selfe worthie of the name and title
of an *Abencerraje* his mistresse. They living therfore in as great
prosperitie, honor, and reputation, that might be, came fortune 15
(an enemie to the rest and contentment of happie men) to cast
them downe from that joyfull estate, to the most unfortunate and
greevous condition of disgrace that might be. The beginning
whereof was, that the King having done a certaine injury to
the *Abencerrajes*, they made an insurrection, wherein, with ten 20
gentlemen more of their kinred, they conspired to kill the King,
and to divide the kingdome amongst themselves, and so to be
revenged of the unworthie disgrace received by him. This conspiracie (whether it was true or false) was discovered before it
could be put in practise, and they apprehended, and condemned 25
to die, before the citizens had intelligence thereof; who, without
all doubt for the great love they bare them, would have risen, not
consenting that justice should have beene done upon them: For,
carying them to exequution, it was the strangest spectacle in the
world, to see the lamentations that some made; the privie mur- 30
muring of one to another; and the bootlesse excuses, that for
compassion of these gentlemen were generally made in all the
citie. They ran all to the King, and offered to buie his mercie with
great summes of gold and silver; but such was his severitie,
that it expelled all motions of pitie and clemencie: Which when 35
the people beheld, they began to weepe, and lament againe: The
Lords, Knights and gentlemen did weepe and mourne, with
whom they were wont to keepe companie: The tender Ladies and
Damsels of the Court wept, whom they loved and served: And
all the whole citie wept, for the great honour and auctority, that 40

such noble citizens gave them. The lamentations, and outcries
were so many, and so loud, as if the earth had sunke, or the world
beene drowned anew. But the King, who to all these teares,
lamentations, and pitifull outcries did stop his eares, commaunded,
that his definitive sentence should be presently executed: So
that, of all that house, and linage there remained not one man
alive, that was not beheaded that day, except my father and
mine uncle, who were not found complices in that conspiracie.
These ils resulted to them (besides this miserable chaunce) that
their houses were ruinated; they proclaimed traitours to the
King; their goodes, lands, and possessions confiscated: And that
no *Abenceraje* should live any longer in *Granada*, except my father
and mine uncle; and they but with this condition, that if they had
any issue, they should send the men children (as soon as they
were borne) to be brought up out of the citie, never to returne
into it againe; and if they were women, and marriageable, to be
married out of the Realme. When the Governor heard the strange
discourse of *Abyndaraez*, and the termes wherewith he com-
playned of his misfortune, he could not stop his teares, but did
shew by them the sensible greefe, which of such a disastrous
accident could not be but felt. And therefore turning himselfe to
the Moore, saide unto him. Thou hast good cause *Abyndaraes*, to
be sorrie for the fall of thy noble house and kinred, whose heads
(I thinke) coulde never hatch so great treason: And were it for
no other proofe, but that so worthie a gentleman as thy selfe
came out of it, this onely were sufficient to make me beleeve, that
they never pretended such wickednes. This gentle opinion, which
thou hast of me (said the Moore) and of the goodnes of my
auncestors, I know not (worthie Governour) how to requite,
but onely with unfained and humble thankes. But now, when
I was borne into the world, with the inheritance of the selfe same
mishap of my kinred, they sent me (because they would not
infringe the Kings edict) to be nursed, and brought up in a certaine fort, belonging sometimes to the Christians, called *Cartama*,
committing the charge and care of me to the Governor thereof,
with whom my father had ancient familiaritie and acquaintance:
A man of great account in the kingdome, upright in the maner of
his life, and verie rich, but chiefly in a daughter that he hath,
which is the greatest felicitie, which I account of in this life, the
which I wish I may never enjoy, if in any thing (but onely her)

I ever tooke content and pleasure. With her was I brought up from my childhood, (for she was borne but three yeeres after me) and as we were generally thought of all to be brother and sister (for like such was our education) so did we also thinke our selves to be. The love that I did beare *Xarifa* (for thus is the Lady called that is mistresse of my libertie) were but little, if I could tell it: Let it suffice that time hath so confirmed the same, that I would give a thousand lives (if I had them) but to enjoy one momentarie sight of her faire face. Everie day encreased our age, but everie hower augmented our love, and so much, that now (me thought) I was made of another kind of mettall, then of consanguinitie. I remember that *Xarifa* being on a day in the orchard of the Jesemynes, dressing her faire head, by chaunce I espied her, amazed at her singular beautie, and how (me thought) it greeved me, that she was my sister. And by the extreme passion of my love, driven out of my musing, I went to her, who, as soone as she saw me, with open armes came to receive me: And sitting upon the fountaine by her, she said unto me. Why hast thou (good brother) left me so long alone? It is (sweete Ladie) said I againe, a good while since I having sought thee in everie place, and not found any, that could tell me what was become of thee, my hart at last conjectured where thou wert: But tel me now (I pray thee) what certaintie hast thou, that we are brother and sister? No other (saide she) then of the great love I beare thee, and to see, how everie one doth call us so, and that my father doth bring us up like his sonne and daughter. And if we were not brother and sister (saide I) wouldest thou then love me so much as thou dost? Oh seest thou not (saide she) that we shuld not be suffered to go so continually together, and al alone, if we were not. But if we were deprived of this joy, that which I feele in my selfe is a great deale more: At which words her faire face being tainted with a vermillion blush, she said unto me. What couldest thou leese by it, if we were brother and sister? My selfe and thee to, said I. I understand thee not said she, but (me thinkes) (being brother and sister) it binds us to love one another naturally. Thy onely beautie (said I) doth oblige me to this brotherhood, which rather qualifieth my love, and sometimes distempers my thoughts: At which words blushing for too much boldnes, casting downe mine eies, I saw her divine figure in the cristalline foun-

8 thousand *Ed.*] thousands *Y*.

taine so lively represented, as if it had beene she her selfe, and in
such sort, that wheresoever she turned her head, I still beheld her
image, and goodly counterfaite truely translated into verie hart.
Then said I softly to my selfe. O, if I were now drowned in this
fountaine, where with pride I behold my sweete Lady, how more 5
fortunate should I die then *Narcissus*? And if she loved me as
I do her, how happie should I be? And if fortune would let us
live ever together, what a happie life should I then lead? These
words I spake to my selfe, and it would have greeved me, that
another had heard them. But having spoken this, I rose up, and 10
reaching up my hand to certaine Jesemynes that grew round
about that fountaine, I made of them, and of some Orenge
flowers a faire and redolent garland, and putting it upon my head,
I sat downe againe crowned, and conquered. Then did she cast her
eies upon me (to my thinking) more sweetly then before, and 15
taking it from my head, did put it upon her owne, seeming then
more faire then *Venus*. And looking upon me, she said. How dost
thou like me now *Abyndaraez*? That in beautie (said I) and sweete
perfections, thou overcomest al the world, and that crowned
Queene and Ladie of it. At which words rising out of her place, 20
she tooke me by the hand, and said unto me. If it were so indeed
(brother) thou shouldest leese nothing by it; and so without
answering her againe, I followed her out of the garden. But now
from that time certaine daies after, wherein cruell Love thought
he was too long from discovering unto me the deceit that I had 25
of my selfe, and time meaning then to lay open hidden and secret
things, we came to perfect knowledge, that the kinred between
us was as much as nothing, whereupon our firme affections were
confirmed more strongly in their former and true places. All my
delight was in her, and my soule cut out so just to the proportion 30
of hers, that all, that was not in her face, seemed to mine eies
foule, frivolous, and unprofitable in the whole world. And now
were our pastimes far different from our first, and I beheld her
with a certaine kind of feare, and suspect to be perceived of any:
And now had I also a certaine envie and jealousie of the sunne, 35
that did touch her. Who, though she looked on me againe with
the verie same desire and intent, wherewith she had beheld me
before; yet I thought it was not so, bicause ones owne distrust is
the most assured and certaine thing in an enamoured hart. It fell
out afterwardes, that she being on a day at the cleere fountaine of 40

the Jesmynes, I came by chaunce thither, and beginning to talke
with her, her speech (me thought) and countenance was not like
to her former lookes and communication. She prayed me to sing,
for she was greatly delighted with songs and musick: And I was
then so trustles and misconceiving of my selfe, that I thought she 5
bad me sing, not for any pleasure that she took by hearing me,
but to passe away the time, and only to entertaine my companie
with such a request: so that I then wanted time to tell her the
whole summe of my greefe. But I who employed my minde in
nothing else, but to do whatsoever my Lady *Xarifa* commanded 10
me, in the Arabicke toong began to sing this song, whereby I gave
her to understand the crueltie that I suspected of her.

IF *thy soft* Haires *be threds of shining gold,*
Under the shade of which are two faire Eies,
(Two sunnes) whose Brow *like heaven doth them uphold,*   15
Rubie thy Mouth, *and lips where* Corall *lies?*
   Could Cristall *want, to frame thy* Necke *so white,*
   And Diamond, *to make thy* Brest *so bright?*

Thy hart is not unlike unto thy Brest,
Since that the flight of mettall of thy Haire   20
Did never make thee turne thy Necke *at lest,*
Nor with thine Eies *give hope, but cold despaire.*
   Yet from that sugred Mouth *hope for an I,*
   And from that snowe-white Brow, *that makes me die.*

Ah beautifull, and yet most bitter Brow,   25
And may there be a Brest *so hard and faire,*
So sweete a necke, and yet so stiffe to bow,
So rich, and yet so covetous a Haire?
   Who ever sawe so cleere and cruell Eies,
   So sweete a Mouth, *yet mooves not to my cries.*   30

Envious Love my Necke *doth chaine with spite,*
His passions make my Brow *looke pale and swart,*
He makes mine Eies *to leese their deerest light,*
And in my Brest *doth kill my trembling hart.*
   He makes my Haire *to stand in ghastly wise,*
   Yet in thy Mouth *all wordes of comfort dies.*   35

O sweetest face, and lips more perfect faire,
Then I may tell; O soft and daintie Necke,
O golden Raies of yonder Sunne, not Haire,
O Cristalline Brow, *and* Mouth *with Rubie deckt,*
   O equall white and red, O Diamond Brest,   5
   From these faire Eies *when shall I hope for rest?*

But if a (No) *by turning of thine* Eies,
Harke yet what saith her sweetest Mouth *to me?*
See if her hardnes in her Brest *yet lies,*
And if she turnes her whitest Necke *to thee?*   10
   Marke well the beckning of her fairest Brow,
   Then from her Haire *what may I hope for now?*

If that her Lilly Brest *and* Necke *doe once affirme their* (No)
And if her shining Eies *and* Haire *will not conclude an* (I)
What will her Ruby Mouth *then doe, and* Brow *as white as snowe,*   15
Nay what shall I my selfe expect but with denials die?

These wordes were of such force, that, being helped by the love
of her, in whose praise they were sung, I saw her shed certaine
teares, that I cannot tell you now (noble Governour) how much
they moved my hart, nor whether the content, that I had by 20
seeing so true a testimonie of my Mistresse love, or the greefe,
(my selfe being the occasion of her teares) was greater. Calling me
to her, she made me sit downe by her, and thus began to say unto
me. If the Love *Abyndaraez*, whereunto I am obliged (after I was
fully assured of thy thoughts) is but small, or such, that cannot 25
but with extinction of life be ended, my wordes (I hope) before
we leave this onely place, shall make thee sufficiently knowe. And
blame thee I will not for thy mistrust, which hath made thee conceive amisse; for I knowe it is so sure a thing to have it, as there is
nothing more proper and incident to Love. For remedie whereof, 30
and of the sorrow that I must needes have, by seeing my selfe
at any time separated from thy sweete companie, from this day
forth for ever thou maist hold and esteeme thy selfe such a Lord
and Master of my libertie, as thou shalt be indeede, if thou art
willing to combine thy selfe in sacred bondes of marriage with 35
me, the refusall whereof is (before every other thing) no small
impediment to both our contents, a prejudice to mine honour,

and the sole obstacle of enjoying the great love which I beare
thee. When I heard these wordes (Love working my thoughts to
things cleane contrarie) I conceived such great joy, that had it not
beene but by onely bowing downe my knees to the ground, and
kissing her faire handes, I was not able to doe any other thing. 5
With the hope of these wordes I lived certaine daies, in the greatest
joy in the world, whilest mutable Fortune (envying my prosperitie
and joyfull life) bereaved us both of this sweete contentment: for
not long after, the King of *Granada* minding to prefer the Governour of *Cartama* to some higher charge, by his letters commanded 10
him foorthwith to yeeld up the charge of that Fort, which lies
upon the frontires, and goe to *Coyn*, where his pleasure was he
should be captaine and Governour, and also to leave me in
Cartama under the charge of him, that came to be Governour in
his place. When I heard these unluckie newes for my Mistresse 15
and my selfe, judge you (noble Gentleman, if at any time you
have beene a lover) what a world of greefe we conceived. We
went both into a secret place to weepe, and lament our misfortunes, and the departure and losse of each others companie.
There did I call her my soveraine Mistresse, mine onely joy, my 20
hope, and other names, that Love did put into my mouth: with
weeping I saide unto her. When the viewe of thy rare beautie
shall be taken from mine eies, wilt thou then *Xarifa*, sometimes
remember me? Heere did my teares and sighes cut off my words,
and inforcing my selfe to speake more (being troubled in minde) 25
I uttered I know not what foolish wordes unto her: for the
apprehended absence of my deere Mistresse in my thoughts did
utterly carry away my wits, senses, and memorie with it. But who
can tell what sorrow my deere Lady felt for this departure, and
what bitter potions of greefe her orientall teares, (which for this 30
crosse of fortune she powred forth) made me sup up? She did
then speake such wordes unto me, the lest of which was ynough,
to have made the hardest hart thought of a sorrowfull departure
for ever: which (valiant Governour) I will omit to tell thee,
bicause thou wilt thinke them (if thy brest was never possessed 35
with love) impossible. And if it hath beene for feare, lest by hearing some of them, thou couldest not, but with hazard of life,
stay out to heare the rest. Let it suffice, that the end of them, was
by telling me, that, having any fit occasion by her fathers sicknes,
or by his absence, she would sende for me, that, that might have 40

effect, which was betrothed and agreed upon betweene us both.
With this promise my hart was somewhat lightned, and for this
infinite curtesie, (which she did promise me when time and
occasion served) I kissed her daintie hands. The next day after,
they went away, and I tarried still behinde, like one that (wandring
upon craggie and wilde mountaines, and having lost the comfortable light of the sunne) remained in hideous darknes: with
great greefe I began to feele her absence, and sought all the false
remedies (I could) against it: for sometimes I did cast mine eies
up to the windowes, where she was woont to looke out; sometimes upon the bed where her tender body was accustomed to
take rest; and went somtimes into the garden, where daily she
used to disport herselfe, and in the heate of the day to the christalline fountaine, where she bathed and refreshed herselfe under
the shade of Limon and Pomegranate trees: I walked and went all
her stations, and in every one of them I found a certaine representation of my sorrowfull thoughts. Truth it is, that the hope that
she gave me (to send for me) eased my paines a little, and with it
I dissembled some part of my woes. But for as much as the continuall thought of my desire so long deferred, did encrease my
paine the more, me thought sometimes I would have beene glad,
if I had beene left altogither without hope, for desperation doth
but trouble one, untill it be certainly knowen; but hope, untill
the desire be accomplished. But my good Fortune did so much
favour me, that this morning my Lady stoode to her worde, by
sending for me by a gentlewoman of hers (a trustie secretarie of
her thoughts) for the Governour her Father was gone to Granada,
who being sent for thither by the king, was to returne home in
a short time againe. Awaked out of my heavie slumber and
melancholike cares with these inopinate and happie newes, I prepared my selfe to go with winged speede unto her: yet staying for
night, and because I might the better escape unknowne, I did
put on this habite, as thou seest, and the bravest I could devise, to
make the better shewe to my Lady of my proud and joyfull hart.
In which journey (truely) I would not have thought, that two of
the best knights at armes had beene sufficient to abide me the
fielde, because I carried my Mistresse with me. Wherefore *Rodrigo*
if thou hast overcomed me, it was not by pure strength, which was
impossible, but it was either my harde fortune, or the determination of the heavens, that woulde prevent me of such a supreme

good. Whereupon consider nowe in the end of my true tale, and
of the good that I have lost, and the ill which I possesse: I came
from Cartama to go to Coyn, but a short journey, although the
desire of the proudest *Abencerraje* that ever lived, made it a great
deale longer. I went, sent for by my Lady, to see my Lady, to 5
enjoy my Lady, and to marrie my sweetest Ladie. But now I see
my selfe wounded, captive, and in subjection to him, who will
doe, I know not what with me. And that which greeves me most,
is, that the time and enjoying of my desire, endeth with this
present night. O suffer me then Christian to comfort my selfe at 10
the least with my secret lamentations: let me evacuate out of my
sorowfull brest my choking and smothering sighes, and water
mine eies with burning teares: All which impute not any to
imbecillitie or feare of minde, though it were a great deale better
for me that I had a hart, that coulde beare and suffer this harde 15
and sinistrous chance of Fortune, then to do that which I now do.

The discourse of the enamoured *Moore* pearced deepely into the
valiant *Narvaes* his soule, who was not a little amazed at the
strange successe of his love. And thinking with himselfe, that for
the better dispatch of his affaires, nothing might hinder them 20
more, then his long staying, he said unto him. I am minded
Abyndaraes, to make thee knowe how much my vertue surmounteth thy ill fortune, for if thou wilt but promise me to returne to my prison within three daies, I will set thee at libertie,
bicause thou maist not leave of thy amorous enterprise. For it 25
woulde greeve me to cut off so good, and honest an endevour.
The *Abenceraje* hearing this, in token of thankes would have
fallen downe at his feete, and saide unto him. If thou dost me this
unexpected favour (noble Governour of *Alora*) thou shalt restore
me againe to life, and shew the greatest gentilitie of minde, that 30
ever any Conquerour did. Take what securitie thou wilt of me,
for whatsoever thou dost demaund, I will not faile to accomplish.
Then *Rodrigo* of *Narvaes* called his gentlemen unto him, and saide.
Gentlemen, trust me for this prisoner, for whose raunsome my
selfe will be a pledge. They answered him againe, that he might 35
dispose of him at his owne pleasure, for whatsoever he did, they
would be well content withall. Then the Governour taking the
Abenceraje by his right hand, saide unto him. Dost thou promise
me as thou art a Gentleman to come to my Castell of *Alora*, there
to yeelde thy selfe my prisoner within three daies? I doe (saide he) 40

and with solemne othe binde it. Then goe (saide the Governour) and good fortune with thee, and if thou standest in neede of mine owne person to accompany thee, or of any other thing for thy way, speake, and thou shalt have it. The *Moore* thanked him very much, but tooke no more but a horse, which the Governour gave him, for his owne was hurt in the late encounter betweene them, and went very heavie, being also wearied and faint with much blood, which he lost by the way: and so turning the raines, he rode as fast as he coulde towardes *Coyn*. *Rodrigo* of *Narvaes* and his Gentlemen returned homewardes to *Alora*, talking by the way of the valour and goodly behaviour of the *Abenceraje*. The *Moore* was not long (according to the great speede he made) in comming to the Fort of *Coyn*, where, going directly as he was commanded, he first went about all the wals, untill at last he found a posterne gate, and the Centrinels on the wals fast asleepe, who though he had a great desire, and made no lesse haste to enter in, yet he staied a little, looking about him on every side, least happily he might be espied, or in danger of some thing else. But when he perceived that all was quiet, he knocked with the punch of his launce at the wicket (for that was the watchworde, that his Mistresse had given him by the gentlewoman that went to call him) the which was immediately opened unto him by the same gentlewoman, who saide unto him: Sir your long tarying hath put my Ladie in a great feare, for she hath staide this good while for you. Alight and I will bring you up where she is attending your presence in great perplexitie: he then dismounted from his horse, and set him up in a secret place, that he founde there, where also leaving his Launce against a wall with his Target and Cymitarre, the gentlewoman tooke him by the hande, and very softly led him up a paire of staires, for feare of being heard by them in the castle, and brought him into *Xarifaes* chamber. Before whom when he was come, with a sudden sursault of joye she ranne to receive him, and both of them with such extreme passions of love and gladnes embracing one another, were not able to speake one worde, for the infinite joy they had at each others sight: But comming to themselves againe, at the last she saide thus unto him. What the cause may be, that thou hast staied so long (my loving Lord) I knowe not, but what sorrowe and anxieties of minde I have passed for thy slowe comming, my impatient love is able to testifie. I hope, thou dost imagine faire

Lady (saide he againe) that it is not by my fault and negligence, but mens disseignes doe not alwaies fall out fit to their desires: So that if there be any trueth in me, thou maist well beleeve me, that it was not in my power to come sooner then I have done. But breaking him off in his excuses, she tooke him by the hand, and leading him into a rich chamber, they sat them downe upon a faire bed, where thus she said unto him. I was desirous my thrise beloved *Abyndaraes*, to have thee see, how captives in love can fulfill their promise; for, from the very day, that I gave thee my word for pledge of my hart, I have sought the meanes to discharge me of it. I sent for thee to come to this Castell, to be my prisoner, as I am thine. But now I have brought thee in hither, to make thee Lord of me, and of my fathers treasure, under the honourable name of a lawfull husband, whereunto my estate, nor thy loyaltie cannot otherwise consent. I do knowe well, that my fathers will wilbe contrarie to our workings, who being ignorant of thy valour, and not knowing thy deserts, as well as I doe, will perhaps bestowe some richer husband on me: but I esteeme thy noble personage, and thy vertuous and valiant mind more, then the greatest riches in the world. And having saide thus unto him, she hung downe her head, blushing not a little, that she had so much discovered her selfe, and in so plaine and open termes declared her affection unto him. The noble *Moore* tooke her in his armes, and many times kissing her white hands for such loving and curteous wordes, saide thus unto her. I have no new thing (sweete Lady of my soule) to give thee in requitall of such great good as thou dost offer me, bicause I am no lesse (as I was before) wholy thine. Onely this pledge I give thee in token of my unspeakable love, that I receive thee for my beloved Lady and wife: And heerewithall thou maist lay aside for a while that modest shamefastnes, and maidenly teynt, which continually thou hast had, since thou hast taken me for thine owne. Unwillingly she did the same: And upon this conclusion they went to bed, where with a new experience they rekindled the flames of their enamoured harts. In which amorous enterprise, passed on either side many loving wordes, and deedes fitter for imagination, then to be written. The *Moore* being in so great joy and pleasure, fetched on the sudden a profound and painfull sigh, and turning from her, began to lie so sad and pensive, that faire *Xarifa* perceiving it, was much amazed and troubled in minde to see so sudden an alteration: who lying still, heard him breath foorth a deepe and dolefull sigh with turning his body on every side. The Lady unable to suffer so great an injurie to her beautie and loyaltie, thinking he was displeased with the one or both, rising up a little in the bedde, with a milde and merrie voice (though somewhat troubled) saide unto him. What meanes this *Abyndaraes*? It seemes thou art offended with my mirth. I heard thee sigh, and tumble, and tosse thy body on every side: why man, if I am wholy thy joye, and thy delight, why dost thou not tell me for whom thou dost sigh; and if I am not, why hast thou thus deceived me? If thou hast found any fault in my person, that hath abridged the delight of thy imagination, cast thine eies and minde upon my will, which is sufficient to supply many wants, and upon my zealous and loving hart, that wisheth it the fairest and finest in the world for thy sake. If thou servest any other Lady, let me know her, that I may serve her to: And if thou hast any other greefe (which shall not offend me) tell it me, for I will either die, or rid thee from it. And clasping him with a kinde of violent and forcible love, she turned him to her againe, who being then confounded, and ashamed for that he had done, and thinking that it might be an occasion (if he did not tell her the cause of his sorrow) to fill her head full of jealousie and suspicion, with an appassionate sigh he said unto her. If I did not (my sweetest life) love thee more then mine owne soule, I woulde never have made such signes of inwarde greefe, for the wounding thoughts, which I brought with me (when I came with my selfe all alone) I passed away with a better hart; but now that I am constrained to go from thee, I have no force to endure them at all. And because thou shalt be no longer in suspence of knowing the cause of my sorrow, I will tell thee what lately passed: And then he told her all the matter, not leaving any thing out, in the end of his tale with many teares saying thus unto her. So that thy captive (faire Lady) is also prisoner to the Governour of *Alora*: And the paine of that imprisonment, which thou hast cast upon me, and taught my hart to suffer, I feele not, but the torment and bondage by living without thee, I account woorse then any death: Wherupon thou seest, that my sighes are rather arguments of greater loyalty, then of any want thereof. And with this, he began againe to be so pensive and sad, as he was before he had tolde her his greefe. But then with a merrie countenance she said unto him: Trouble

not thy minde *Abyndaraes* with these thoughts, for I will take the
care and remedie of this greefe upon mee, as a thing that toucheth
mee most of all; and the more, since it is not denied any prisoner
that hath given his worde to returne to prison, to satisfie it, by
sending the ransome that shall be demaunded of him: Wherefore 5
set thy selfe downe what summe thou wilt, for I have the keyes of
al my fathers treasure, which I will put into thy hands, and leave
it all at thy disposition. *Rodrigo* of *Narvaez* is a curteous gentleman,
and a good knight, and one who gave thee once thy libertie: And
as thou hast acquainted him with the trust of these affaires; so 10
is he now the more bound to use greater virtue and gentlenes
towardes thee. I am sure he will be contented with reason; for
having thee in his power and prison, he must perforce set thee at
libertie, when he hath the value of thy ransome. I see well faire
Ladie (said the *Abencerraje* againe) that the love which thou dost 15
beare me, will not suffer thee to give me the best counsell, for
I will never commit so foule a fault as this. For if I was bound to
fulfill my word, when I was alone, and without thee, now that
I am thine, the bond is greater: I will therefore returne to *Allora*,
and yeeld my selfe into the Governors hands, and when I have 20
done what I am bound to do, let Fortune do with me what she
will. Nay let me rather die, saide *Xarifa* (if thou goest to be
prisoner) then once desire to remaine here at libertie. For being
thy captive, by duetie I am bound to accompanie thee in this
journey for the extreme love that I beare thee, whereas also the 25
feare of my fathers frownes, which I have purchased by offending
him, will let me do no lesse. The *Moore* weeping for joy, to heare
these words, embraced her saying. Thou never ceasest (my deerest
soule) to heape favours upon my happie head, do therefore what
thou wilt, for this is my resolution. With this determination they 30
rose before it was day, and providing some necessarie things for
their journey, they went verie secretly towards *Allora*: and when
the day began to waxe cleere, *Xarifa* went with her face covered
with a maske, for feare of being knowen, and by reason of the
great haste they made, they came in good time to *Alora*, where 35
going directly to the castle, and knocking at the gate, it was
opened to them out of hand by the Centrinels, who had notice of
that was past, and what they should do. The valiant Governor
received them curteously: and *Abyndaraes* going to the gate and
taking his wife by the hand brought her unto him, and said. 40

Behold *Rodrigo* of *Narvaez* if I keepe not well my word and appointed time? For promising thee to returne thy prisoner, insteed
of one, I bring thee two, for one was enough to overcome many.
Behold here my Ladie, and judge if I have not justly suffered for
her sake: accept us now for thine, for in thy virtuous and noble 5
minde I repose my whole trust and confidence, and into thy
hands commit her deere and chiefest honour. The Governor was
verie glad to see them both, and said to *Xarifa*: I know not faire
Ladie which of you have conquered each other in love and
curtesie, but truely thinke my selfe greatly bound unto you both. 10
Come in therefore, and rest you in your owne house, the which
from henceforth, as also the master of it, accept for none other.
After this friendly entertainement, they went with him into his
dining chamber, where after a little while they refreshed themselves, bicause they came somewhat wearie. The Governor asked 15
the *Moore* how he did for his wounds. I thinke (said he) that what
with the way, and what with paine, they are somewhat rankled:
which faire *Xarifa* hearing, with an altered and appalled countenance said unto him. Alas how comes this to passe my Lord?
Have you any woundes about you, and I not knowe them? Who 20
escapes (saide he) from thine, needes little to care for any other.
Truth it is, that at our late skirmish in the night I got two little
woundes, which my troublesome journey and negligence in curing
them hath made somewhat worse, but all is but little or nothing.
It is best (saide the Governour) that you lay you downe, and I will 25
send for a Chirurgeon that is heere in the Castell to cure them.
Following which counsell, faire *Xarifa* caused him to put off his
apparell, and though she set a good face on the matter (bicause
she woulde not give him any occasion to feele her inwarde greefe)
yet was she altered much and troubled in her minde. The Chirur- 30
geon came, and searching his wounds saide, that they were not
dangerous, bicause the signe was not in those places when he
received them; and also, bicause they were smitten overthwart,
would not be long in healing: For with a certaine ointment that
he made out of hand, the paine of them was somewhat asswaged; 35
and in fower daies (by meanes of the great care the Chirurgeon
had in healing them) hee was as sound and whole as ever he was
before. But one day, after dinner was done, the *Abenceraje* saide
thus unto the Governour. As you are wise, *Rodrigo* of *Narvaez*,

18 and appalled *Ed.*] an appalled *Y*.

so can you not choose, but by the manner of our being at *Coyn*, and of our comming hither, imagine more then you have seene, which affaires of ours by our owne misfortunes (driven to this desperate (though happy) event, wherein they nowe are) must be (I hope) by your advise and helpe brought to some good end. This is faire *Xarifa*, of whom I tolde you: This is my Lady, and my deerely beloved wife: In *Coyn* she woulde not stay for feare of her Father. For though he knowes not what hath passed betweene us, yet she feared least this accident at some time or other might be discovered. Her Father is nowe with our King of *Granada*, whose highnesse I know, doth beare you especiall good will, and loveth you, (though you be a Christian) for your valour and vertuous disposition. Wherefore I beseech you (gentle knight) to sollicite our pardon at his gracious hands for dooing what is past without his leave and privitie, since Fortune hath brought it (though happily) to this doubtfull passe. Comfort your selves *Abyndaraes* and faire *Xarifa* (said the noble Governour) for by the faith of a gentleman I promise you to do what I can for you in this behalfe, whereupon he presently called for inke and paper to write a letter to the king of *Granada*, which in a few words and true, opening their estate unto him, said thus.

MOst mightie king of *Granada*, *Rodrigo* of *Narvaez* the Governour of *Alora*, by these letters kisseth your royall hands, and gives your Majestie to understande, that *Abyndaraez Abencerraje* borne in *Granada*, brought up in *Cartama* and being under the charge and government of the captaine of that Forte, was enamored of *Xarifa* his faire daughter: And after that it pleased your Majestie to preferre the saide captaine to the government of *Coyn*, the two lovers (to binde themselves in a mutuall and indissoluble bonde) betrothed their faith to each other before her departure, who sent to *Cartama* for the *Abencerraje* in her Fathers absence (being now in your Majesties Court) to whom as he was going to *Coyn*, in the way I met him, and in a certaine skirmish betweene us, (wherein he shewed himselfe a valiant and couragious man at armes) made him my prisoner: who telling me his pitifull case (my hart being mooved with compassion of his greefe, and with his earnest praiers) I set him free for two daies, who went his way, and got him to his wife, so that in that journey he woone his

29 mutuall *Ed.*] mutall *Y.*

wife, and lost his libertie. But seeing the *Abencerraje* (according to his worde) woulde needes returne to my prison, she came also with him, and so they are both now in my power. Let not the name of *Abencerraje*, I beseech your Majestie offende it, for this Gentleman and his Father were not privie (as I have heard) nor 5 consenting to the conspiracie pretended against your royall person, in testimonie whereof, they are yet both living. Wherefore I humblie beseech your Majestie to impart betweene your Grace and me a remedie for these haplesse lovers, whose raunsome I will frankely forgive, and freely let them go. May it onely please your 10 Majestie to procure the Ladies pardon with her Father, who is your subject, and to intreat him to receive the gentleman into his affinitie and good liking: By doing whereof (besides the singular favour that your Highnesse shall do me) your Majestie shall do no lesse, then is expected of the woonted vertues and bountie of your 15 Royall and magnificent minde.

   With this letter he dispatched away one of his gentlemen, who comming before the King, gave it him into his owne handes, the which he gratefully received, when he knew from whom it came, for he loved this Christian, especially for his valour and goodly 20 personage: and reading it, he turned his face, and by chaunce espied the Governor of *Coyn*, to whom (taking him aside) he gave the letter, saying unto him. Read this letter, who read it, and seeing what was past, by his countenance did manifest how much he was grieved in mind. Which thing the King perceiving, 25 said unto him. Be not offended, nor sorrie, although thou hast good cause; for there is not any reasonable thing, that the noble Governor of *Alora* requesteth at my hands (if it lies in my power) which I will not doe for him. And therefore I commaund thee by deferring no time, presently to goe to *Alora*, and to pardon 30 thy daughter and son in law, and carrie them with thee to thy Castle; in recompence whereof I will not forget to bestow on thee continuall favours. It greeved the old *Moore* to the verie hart, when he understood of this event; but seeing he must not disobey the Kings commaund, by counterfeiting a merie countenance, 35 and borrowing a little courage of his daunted spirits, as wel as he could, he said That he would do it. The Governor of *Coyn* departed from the Court in all haste, and came to *Alora*, where (understanding by the way of the Governors Gentleman that went with him, all that had passed in this adventure) he was 40 curteously received: The *Abencerraje* and his daughter teynted and appalled with shame and feare came before him, and kissed his hands, who receiving them joyfully, said unto them. I come not hither of mine owne accord to repeate, nor entreat of things past, but by the commaundement of the King, who willed me to 5 pardon your misdeeds, and your sudden marriage without my consent. And as for the rest daughter, thou hast chosen a better husband for thy selfe, then I could have given thee. *Rodrigo* of *Narvaez* was very glad to heare this gentle greeting of the olde *Moore*, for whose entertainment he made many feastes and ban- 10 quets. And one day when dinner was done, he said unto them. I am not so glad, as proud, that I have beene some part and meanes, whereby these occurrents are brought to so good a passe; in proofe whereof, and that nothing else could make me more content, for the ransome of your imprisonment, I will have but onely 15 the honour, that I have enjoyed by getting and keeping such brave prisoners. Wherefore *Abyndaraes*, thou art free, in testimonie whereof I give thee leave to goe whither it please thee, and whensoever thou wilt. He humbly thanked him, and so they prepared themselves to bee gone the next day, when *Rodrigo* of 20 *Narvaez* bearing them company, they went from *Alora*, and came to *Coyn*, where great triumphes, banquets, and feasts were made in publicke celebration of the marriage: The which being past, their father taking them both one day aside, spake these words unto them. Now that you are (my beloved sonne and daughter) 25 possessours of my riches, and live in rest, it is not reason that you forget the manifolde good turnes done you by the Governor of *Alora*, for which you are yet indebted unto him; and it stands not with our honors, for using you with such great virtue and humanitie, that he should leese the right of your ransome, which 30 should be rather (if you consider the matter well) more then ordinarie. I will give you fower thousand double duckats, send them unto him, and behold them here, which he well deserves (as a friend indeed) though there be different lawes betweene you and him. The *Abencerraje* thanked him verie humbly, and taking 35 them, sent them in a little rich coffer to *Rodrigo* of *Narvaez*. And because he would not of his own part shew himselfe unthankfull, he sent him therewithall six faire Barbary horses with rich saddles and furniture, and six targets and launces, the bars and punches being of fine golde. Faire *Xarifa* wrote a sweete and 40

loving letter unto him, wherein she gave him infinite thankes for
the benefits she had received by his meanes, and for the gentle
entertainment she had in his Castle. And willing to shew her selfe
as liberall and thankefull as the rest, she sent him a sweete
Cypresse chest, finely wrought and carved for a present, and 5
within it most curious and costly white garmentes for his owne
person. The valiant Governor accepting the presents, with great
thankes to them that sent them, gave the horses, targets, and
launces incontinently amongest the gentlemen that did accompanie him that night in the skirmish, taking the best of each, and 10
also the Cypresse chest, with that which faire *Xarifa* had sent
him for himselfe, and returning the fower thousand double
peeces to the messenger againe, he saide unto him. Tell thy Lady
Xarifa, that I receive the Duckets for her husbandes raunsome,
and (to doe her service) sende them backe againe, towardes the 15
charges of her marriage, and, that for her friendship and sweete
sake, I woulde change all the interests that I have in the world,
in lieue that she would make an account of this Castell, as her
owne, and her husbandes also. The messenger returned backe to
Coyn, where he was well received, and the liberalitie of the noble 20
Captaine of every one highly commended, whose linage doth
continue in flourishing estate to this day in *Antiquera*, equivalent
in Heroicall and Martiall deedes with the first originall, from
whence they are descended. The historie being ended, *Felicia* did
commend the grace, and good wordes wherewith faire *Felismena* 25
did tell it, and so did all the rest, that were present, who taking
their leave of the sage Lady, went all to take their rest.

The end of the fourth booke.

The fifth Booke of Diana of George of Montemayor.

THe next day in the morning the Lady *Felicia* rose up, and went
to *Felismenas* chamber, whom she found, not with few teares,
newly making an end of apparelling her-selfe, thinking every

hower she staied there a thousand yeeres. And the sage Lady
taking her by the hande, they went into a gallerie that looked into
a garden, where they had supped the night before, and having
asked her the cause of her teares, and giving her som comfort and
assured hope, that her greefes should have such an end, as she 5
her-selfe desired, she saide unto her. There is nothing in the
world more ready to take her life away, whom I love well, then
with incertaine hope to deprive her of the remedie of her greefe,
for there is not an hower that seemes not so long unto her (living
in this sort) as she thinkes the howers of her life short and speedie. 10
Because therefore my desire is to fulfill thine, and after some fewe
troubles to have thee obtaine the sweet content and rest, that
Fortune hath promised thee, thou shalt depart from thine owne
house heere, in the same habite that thou camest, when thou didst
defend my Nymphes from the force and violence of the brutish 15
and cruell Savages; assuring thee besides, that when my helpe and
favour may stande thee in steede, unsent for, thou shalt alwaies
have it. So that thy departure faire *Felismena* must be presently;
and trust in God, that thy desire shall have a happie end: For if
I knew it to be otherwise, thou maist well thinke, I woulde not be 20
without other remedies to make thee forget these thoughts, as
I have done to many other Lovers more. *Felismena* was glad to
heare the grave Ladies wordes, to whom she replied thus. I know
not howe with words (discreete Lady) I may give you condigne
thankes, nor with what deeds and humble service make any part 25
of satisfaction of this infinite favour, which I receive at your
Ladiships hands. God grant I may live so long, that by proofe
your Ladishippe may know the great desire I have to do you all
the service I may. That which your Ladiship commands me to do,
I will presently go about, which cannot but have good successe, 30
being directed by her counsell, that can in every thing give the
best. The sage Lady embraced her, saying. I hope to see thee,
faire *Felismena*, in this house more joyfull and contented, then
now thou art. And bicause the two Shepherdes and Shepherdesses
are staying for us, it is reason that I go, to give them also some 35
remedy for their sorrowes, that need it so much. Wherfore both
of them going out of the hall, and finding *Syrenus* and *Sylvanus*,
Selvagia and *Belisa* attending their comming, the Lady *Felicia* saide
to *Felismena*. Entertaine this company faire Lady, while I come
hither againe: and going into a chamber, it was not long before 40

she came out againe with two cruets of fine cristall in either
hande, the feete of them being of beaten golde, and curiously
wrought and enameled: And comming to *Syrenus*, she saide unto
him. If there were any other remedy for thy greefe (forgotten
Shepherd) but this, I woulde with all possible diligence have 5
sought it out, but because thou canst not now enjoy her, who
loved thee once so well, without anothers death, which is onely
in the handes of God, of necessitie then thou must embrace
another remedie, to avoide the desire of an impossible thing.
And take thou, faire *Selvagia*, and despised *Sylvanus*, this glasse, 10
wherein you shall finde a soveraine remedie for all your sorrowes
past and present; and a beginning of a joyfull and contented life,
whereof you do now so little imagine. And taking the cristall
cruet, which she helde in her left hande, she gave it to *Syrenus*, and
badde him drinke; and *Syrens* did so; and *Sylvanus*, and *Selvagia* 15
drunke off the other betweene them, and in that instant they fell
all downe to the ground in a deepe sleepe, which made *Felismena*,
and *Belisa* not a little to woonder, to whom the sage Ladie said.
Discomfort not thy selfe *Belisa*, for I hope in time to see thee as
glad, as ever any was after their many sorrowes and paines. And 20
untill thy angrie fortune be not pleased to give thee a needfull
remedy for thy great greefes, my pleasure is, that thou still remaine heere in my companie. The Shepherdesse woulde have
kissed her hands at these words, but *Felicia* did not let her, but
did rather imbrace her, shewing how greatly she loved her. But 25
Felismena standing halfe amazed at the deepe sleepe of the Shepherdes, saide to *Felicia*: If the ease of these Shepherds (good
Ladie) consisteth in sleeping (me thinkes) they have it in so ample
sort, that they may live the most quiet life in the worlde. Woonder
not at this (saide *Felicia*) for the water they drunke hath such 30
force, that, as long as I will, they shall sleepe so strongly, that
none may be able to awake them. And because thou maist see,
whether it be so or no, call one of them as loude as thou canst.
Felismena then came to *Sylvanus*, and pulling him by the arme,
began to call him aloud, which did profite her as little, as if she 35
had spoken to a dead body; and so it was with *Syrenus* and *Selvagia*, whereat *Felismena* marvelled very much. And then *Felicia*
saide unto her. Nay, thou shalt marvell yet more, after they
awake, bicause thou shalt see so strange a thing, as thou didst
never imagine the like. And because the water hath by this time 40

wrought those operations, that it shoulde do, I will awake them,
and marke it well, for thou shalt heare and see woonders. Whereupon taking a booke out of her bosome, she came to *Syrenus*, and
smiting him upon the head with it, the Shepherd rose up on his
feete in his perfect wits and judgement: To whom *Felicia* saide. 5
Tell me *Syrenus*, if thou mightest now see faire *Diana*, and her
unworthy husband both togither in all the contentment and joy
of the worlde, laughing at thy love, and making a sport of thy
teares and sighes, what wouldest thou do? Not greeve me a whit
(good Lady) but rather helpe them to laugh at my follies past. 10
But if she were now a maide againe, (saide *Felicia*) or perhaps
a widow, and would be married to *Sylvanus* and not to thee, what
wouldst thou then do? My selfe woulde be the man (saide
Syrenus) that woulde gladly helpe to make such a match for my
friende. What thinkest thou of this *Felismena* (saide *Felicia*) that 15
water is able to unloose the knottes that perverse Love doth
make? I woulde never have thought (saide *Felismena*) that anie
humane skill coulde ever attaine to such divine knowledge as this.
And looking on *Syrenus*, she saide unto him. Howe nowe *Syrenus*,
what meanes this? Are the teares and sighes whereby thou didst 20
manifest thy love and greefe, so soone ended? Since my love is
nowe ended (said *Syrenus*) no marvell then, if the effects proceeding from it be also determined. And is it possible now (said
Felismena) that thou wilt love *Diana* no more? I wish her as much
good (answered *Syrenus*) as I doe to your owne selfe (faire Lady) 25
or to any other woman that never offended me. But *Felicia*, seeing
how *Felismena* was amazed at the sudden alteration of *Syrenus*,
said. With this medicine I would also cure thy greefe (faire
Felismena) and thine *Belisa*, if fortune did not deferre them to some
greater content, then onely to enjoy your libertie. And bicause 30
thou maist see how diversly the medicines have wrought in
Sylvanus and *Selvagia*, it shall not be amisse to awake them, for
now they have slept ynough: wherefore laying her booke upon
Sylvanus his head, he rose up, saying. O faire *Selvagia*, what a great
offence and folly have I committed, by imploying my thoughtes 35
upon another, after that mine eies did once behold thy rare
beautie? What meanes this *Sylvanus* (said *Felicia*.) No woman in
the world even now in thy mouth, but thy Shepherdesse *Diana*,
and now so suddenly changed to *Selvagia*? *Sylvanus* answering her,
said. As the ship (discreete Lady) sailes floting up and downe, and 40

well-ny cast away in the unknowen seas, without hope of a secure haven: so did my thoughtes (putting my life in no small hazard) wander in *Dianas* love, all the while, that I pursued it. But now since I am safely arrived into a haven, of all joy and happinesse, I onely wish I may have harbour and entertainment there, where my irremooveable and infinite love is so firmely placed. *Felismena* was as much astonished at the second kinde of alteration of *Sylvanus*, as at that first of *Syrenus*, and therefore saide unto him laughing. What dost thou *Sylvanus*? Why dost thou not awake *Selvagia*? for ill may a Shepherdesse heare thee, that is so fast asleepe. *Sylvanus* then pulling her by the arme, began to speake out aloud unto her, saying. Awake faire *Selvagia*, since thou hast awaked my thoughtes out of the drowsie slumber of passed ignorance. Thrise happy man, whom fortune hath put in the happiest estate that I could desire. What dost thou meane faire Shepherdesse, dost thou not heare me, or wilt thou not answere me? Behold the impatient passion of the love I beare thee, will not suffer me to be unheard. O my *Selvagia*, sleepe not so much, and let not thy slumber be an occasion to make the sleepe of death put out my vitall lightes. And seeing how little it availed him, by calling her, he began to powre foorth such abundance of teares, that they, that were present, could not but weepe also for tender compassion: whereupon *Felicia* saide unto him. Trouble not thy selfe *Sylvanus*, for as I will make *Selvagia* answere thee, so shall not her answere be contrarie to thy desire, and taking him by the hand, she led him into a chamber, and said unto him. Depart not from hence, untill I call thee; and then she went to the place againe where *Selvagia* lay, and touching her with her booke, awaked her, as she had done the rest, and saide unto her. Me thinks thou hast slept securely Shepherdesse. O good Lady (said she) where is my *Sylvanus*, was he not with me heere? O God, who hath carried him away from hence? or wil he come hither againe? Harke to me *Selvagia*, said *Felicia*, for me thinkes thou art not wel in thy wits. Thy beloved *Alanius* is without, and saith that he hath gone wandring up and downe in many places seeking after thee, and hath got his fathers good will to marrie thee: which shall as little availe him (said *Selvagia*) as the sighes and teares which once in vaine I powred out, and spent for him, for his memorie is now exiled out of my thoughts. *Sylvanus* mine onely life and joy, O *Sylvanus* is he, whom I love. O what is become of my *Sylvanus*? Where is my *Sylvanus*? Who hearing the Shepherdesse *Selvagia* no sooner name him, could stay no longer in the chamber, but came running into the hall unto her, where the one beheld the other with such apparaunt signes of cordiall affection, and so strongly confirmed by the mutual bonds of their knowen deserts, 5 that nothing but death was able to dissolve it; whereat *Syrenus*, *Felismena*, and the Shepherdesse were passing joyfull. And *Felicia* seeing them all in this contentment, said unto them. Now is it time for you Shepherds, and faire Shepherdesse to goe home to your flocks, which would be glad to heare the wonted voice of 10 their knowen masters: And make this account, that you shall never want any helpe and favour at her handes, who is so ready to pleasure you in what shee may. And the holy end (*Sylvanus*) and consummation of thy love shall be, when with her, whom thou dost so deerly love, thou shalt combine thy selfe in the sacred 15 bonds of chaste and lawfull mariage, whereof I will be carefull to put you both in minde, when time and opportunitie shal serve. And (faire *Felismena*) prepare thy selfe also for thy departure, for to morrow is the day, wherein it behooves thee to go from hence. After this, all the Nymphes came in at the hall doore, who now 20 knew of the remedies, that their gracious Ladie had given the Shepherds for their griefes, which thing made them not a little glad, *Doria* especially, *Cynthia* and *Polydora*, bicause they were the principall occasions of their content. The two new lovers did busie themselves in nothing else, but in looking upon one another 25 with such affection and tendernes, as if a thousand yeeres had bin past since their loves had first begon between them. And that day they all taried there, with as great joy and pleasure, as by such a new commenced love might be imagined, until the next day in the morning, when the two Shepherds and the Shep- 30 herdesse, taking their leave of the sage Ladie *Felicia*, and of *Felismena*, and *Belisa*, and likewise of all the Nymphes, with great joy returned to their villages, whither they came the verie same day. And faire *Felismena* (who had that day put on againe her Shepherdesses weeds) taking her leave of the sage Ladie, and 35 being particularly and well advised what to doe, with many teares embraced her, and, accompanied of all those Nymphes, went forth into the great Court before the Palace gate, where embracing everie one by her selfe, shee went that way that they did direct her. *Felismena* went not alone, neither did her imaginations 40

give her leave so to do: for on the one side she went thinking of that, which the wise Ladie had told her; and considering on the other, what little hap and lesse successe, she had
yet in her love, which made her doubt of her future happines.
With these contrarieties of thoughts did she go warring in her 5
minde, which though on the one side they made her wearie; yet
on the other they did entertaine her with their company, so that in
the meane time she forgot her solitarie and painefull way. She
had not travelled far in the mids of a faire valley, when towardes
the west part therof, she espied a far off a shepherds coat, which, 10
at the entrance of a green wood stood, amongst many high Okes,
and invited thither by her importunate hunger and wearines, and
also bicause the heate of the day began to come on so fast, that
shee was forced to passe it away under the shadow of those
braunchie trees, she bended her steps directly towards it. Com- 15
ming to the coate, she heard how a Shepherd said unto a Shepherdesse, that sat neere unto him, these wordes. Entreate me not,
good *Amarillis*, to sing, since thou knowest what great causes
I have to sigh, and weepe all the dayes, whilest my languishing
soule shall not forsake this wearied and fainte bodie. For though 20
musicke is no small meanes to encrease his melancholie, that is
ever sadde and pensive, as his joye and mirthe, whoe lives a merry
life; yet my greefe is not of such a qualitie, that by any humane
arte or industrie may be increased or diminished. Heere hast thou
thy baggepipe, play and sing, faire Shepherdesse, for well maist 25
thou do it, having thy hart as free, as thy wil exempt from the
bondage of love. Then the Shepherdesse answered him againe.
Be not such a niggard of thy skill, *Arsileus*, which the heavens
and nature have so bountifully bestowed on thee: for, she that
doth aske it at thy hands, will not denie to pleasure thee in any 30
thing she may. Sing if it be possible that song, which (at the
request of *Argastus*) thou didst make in the name of thy father
Arsenius, when, for hir love, you both served and sued to the
faire Shepherdesse *Belisa*. Thy condition is strange *Amarillis*
(saide the Shepherd againe) still demanding that of me, which 35
doth least of all content me. What shall I do, for perforce I must
please thee, and yet not perforce, since he were very discourteous
(to say the truth) that would not of his own accord do thee any
service he could. But now thou seest, how my ill fortune doth

37 discourteous *CTr² CUL BM¹⁻² Sus*: discourous *CTr¹ Bodl.*

ever narrowly pursue me, when I woulde faine take some small respite, and ease from my greevous thoughts. And seeing the great reason I have (*Amarillis*) to burst out in continuall lamentations and teares, why dost thou then command me to sing? What pleasure dost thou take to offende the occasions of my 5 sorrowe? I pray God thou maist never have the like, to feele the greefe that I do, bicause Fortune might not (so greatly to thy cost) informe thee of my paine. Thou knowest well enough I have lost my *Belisa*, and that I live without hope of her recoverie. Why dost thou then commaund me to sing? But since I will not have 10 thee conceive an opinion of me to be discourteous (for it was never my manner and condition to be accounted so amongst faire Shepherdesses, to whom we Shepherdes, and my selfe especially for my *Belisas* sake, owe all respect of love and dutie, and are so much beholding) I will endevour (though most 15 against my minde) to content thee: Whereupon taking up his Rebecke that lay hard by him, he began to tune it, and doe that, which the Shepherdesse requested him. *Felismena*, that was listening to their talke, might heare very well what speeches passed betweene them; And when she sawe they talked of *Arsenius*, and 20 *Arsileus*, servants to faire *Belisa*, (both which she tooke to be long since dead, as *Belisa* had told, not only her, but the Nymphes also, and the Shepherds, when they found her in the Shepherds coat in the Iland) she verily thought, that all, that she heard, and sawe there, was but a meere dreame, or some fantastick illusion. But 25 giving attentive eare, she perceived how the Shepherd began to touch his Rebecke so divinely, that she thought it to be some celestiall musicke, who having plaide on it a little with a more heavenly then humane voice, began to sing this song following.

O *Vainest hopes, Alas, how many* Daies 30
   Have I beene bondslave to a brave Deceite?
And how, in vaine, have these two wearied Eies
With show'rs of teares watred this pleasant Vale?
Appai'd I am of cruell Love, *and* Fortune,
And knowe not yet whereof I doe Complaine. 35

   No small harmes I must passe, since I Complaine,
For, to endure, framed are all my Daies,
The traunces, and deceites of Love *and* Fortune:

But whence *Complaine I, of a brave* Deceite,
Of such a Shepherdesse within this Vale,
On whom (to my great harme) I cast mine Eies?

Yet am I much beholding to my Eies,
(*Although with greefe of them I doe* Complaine)
Since by their meanes I sawe within this Vale
The fairest thing, which never in my Daies
I thought to see, And this is no Deceite;
In proofe whereof, aske it of Love and Fortune.

Though on the other side, instable Fortune,
And time, occasion, and my dolefull Eies,
And not suspecting this most brave Deceite,
Caus'd all the ill, whereof I doe Complaine:
And so I thinke to end my wofull Daies,
Counting my greefes, and passions to this Vale.

If that the river, hill, the meade, and Vale,
Earth, heaven, and fate, and cruell Love, and Fortune,
The howers, and the moments, yeeres, and Daies,
My soule, my hart, and these two wearied Eies,
Doe aggravate my greefe when I Complaine,
Who then can say, I live by fond Deceite?

Deceiv'd I was, but this was no Deceite,
For, that I have beheld within this Vale
So rare perfection, I doe not Complaine,
But to behold, how Love and cruell Fortune
Would signifie unto these wearied Eies,
That there should come a helpe after some Daies.

And now the yeeres are past, the months, and Daies
Upon this confidence, and cleere Deceite:
Wearie with weeping are my watrie Eies:
Wearie to heare me is the hill, and Vale.
And in the end thus answered of false Fortune,
Jesting at that, whereof I doe Complaine.

But wofull man, whereof doe I Complaine,
But of the length of my prolonged Daies?
Perhaps, a slave to me is cruell Fortune,

That for my fault she must pay this Deceite?
Went he not free, exempted in this Vale,
Who did command me to lift up mine Eies?

But who againe can tame his greedie Eies,
Or can I live, if I doe not Complaine   5
Of th'ill, which Love hath done me in this Vale.
Curst be that ill, that lastes so many Daies:
But death cannot (if this be no Deceite)
Stay long to give an end unto my Fortune.

Calmes wonted are to come after hard Fortune,   10
But never shall be viewed of mine Eies.
(Nor yet I thinke to fall in this Deceite)
O well, let the first suffice, which I Complaine,
And will (faire Shepherdesse) as many Daies,
As the remembrance lasteth of this Vale.   15

If (Shepherdesse) that day, when in this Vale
I did behold thee (to my hardest Fortune)
The finall end had come of all my Daies,
Or I had lesse beheld those coyest Eies,
The cause should cease, whereof I doe Complaine,   20
And I would fall no more into Deceite.

But purposing to worke me this Deceite,
When by and by thou sawest me in this Vale,
Milde thou didst seeme: See then if I Complaine
Unjustly of false Love, and cruell Fortune?   25
And now I knowe not, why thou turn'st thine Eies
Away, unlesse thou greevest at my Daies.

My song of Love and Fortune I Complaine,
And since a brave Deceite *so many* Daies
Did last, water mine Eies *this hill and* Vale.   30

This did the Shepherd sing, keeping time with his teares, and
resting with his sighes, and the Shepherdesse sat harkening unto
him with great content, to see with what a grace he did both play
and sing. But after the Shepherd had made an end of his song,

laying his rebecke out of his hand, he said to the Shepherdesse. Art thou now pleased *Amarillis*, for (to content thy minde) thou maist make me do that, which doth utterly displease me. And accursed *Alfeus*, I wish that Fortune would bring thee to that passe, wherunto by thy detested sorceries I am come, bicause thou mightest then know what good cause I have to hate thee, for the cruell despite that thou hast done me. O sweet *Belisa*, is there any in the world more bound to thee then I am? God graunt I may deduct this sorrowfull life so long, that mine eies may once again enjoy thy peerlesse beautie, and that thine may see, if I do not acknowledge, how much I do owe unto them. These words the Shepherd spake with such plentie of teares, that there was no hart (had it beene never so hard) that by hearing them, would not have melted. But now that thou hast told me *Arsileus* (said the Shepherdesse unto him) the beginning of thy affection, and how thy father *Arsenius* was the principall occasion of thy service and great love to *Belisa*; bicause when he sued unto her, she did participate, and thou profit thy selfe by thine owne letters and songs, and some times by thine owne musicke, (of all which he might have well excused himselfe) I pray thee now tell me, how thou didst leese her. This is a thing (said the Shepherd) which I would seldome repeat, but bicause it is ever thy qualitie, to commaund me to tell thee that, which is most grievous unto my soule, hearke then, and in a few words I will tell it thee.

There was a man in our towne called *Alfeus*, who had the name amongst us to be a great Magician, and he loved *Belisa* extremely, before my Father ever began to serve her, but she could not abide, not onely to see him, but not to heare of his name, which if any had but sounded in her eares, they could not have angred her worse. Now when this Conjurer understood (I know not how) of the appointed meeting betweene me and *Belisa*, to talke together in the night from the toppe of a Mulberie tree in her fathers Orchard; *Alfeus*, full of divels, commanded two spirits to take the shape of my father *Arsenius*, and mine upon them, and that he, that took upon him my shape, shuld go to the appointed place; and the other, that took my fathers, should come thither, and shoot at him in the tree with a crosbow arrowe, thinking he was not his Son, but another, and then to come presently unto him, and knowing him to be his Son, should kill himselfe, for greefe that he had slaine his owne Son, to the end that the Shepherdesse

Belisa should kill her-selfe, seeing my selfe and my Father dead, or at least do that, which afterwards she did. This villany did the traitor *Alfeus* work, for despight of that great love, which he knew *Belisa* did beare me; and for the contempt, which she had of his unwoorthy affection. When this was in maner aforesaide done, 5 and *Belisa* thought that my Father and I were both slaine, like a careles and desperate woman, she forsooke her Fathers house, and is gone where none can yet tel where she is, or any tydings of her. This did the Shepherdesse *Armida* tel me, and I do verily beleeve it, according to that which succeeded after. When *Felis-* 10 *mena* had heard what the Shepherd had tolde *Amarillis*, she wondred not a little, imagining with her-selfe, that all that he tolde, did seeme to be true, and by the signes that she sawe in him, knewe that he was the same *Arsileus*, *Belisas* servant, whom she thought to be dead, and therefore saide to her-selfe. It is not 15 reason, that Fortune should give her any content, that would denie it a Shepherd, that doth so well deserve it, and that stands so much in neede thereof. I will not at the least, depart from this place, without giving him such joy, as he will receive at the newes of his beloved Shepherdesse. Whereupon comming to the dore of 20 the coate, she saide to *Amarillis*. Will it please thee (faire Shepherdesse) to give the forlorne woman of Fortune, that hath lost her way, and the hope to finde it out againe, leave to passe away the heate of the day in this place with thee? The Shepherdesse seeing on a sudden such exceeding beautie, and so comely a 25 feature, was so amazed, that she was unable to answer one worde againe: but *Arsileus* saide unto her. There wants no other thing (faire Shepherdesse) for the performing of thy request, but the place, which is not so good as thou deservest: but if thou art wont to bee served with such homely lodging, Come in, and 30 wherein wee may doe thee any service, our good wils shall excuse the wants of our abilitie. These wordes *Arsileus* (saide *Felismena* againe) seeme well to come out of thy mouth, but the joye, that I will leave with thee in requitall of them, I wish may befall to me of that, which I have so long desired. And saying 35 thus, she went into the Coate, and the Shepherd and Shepherdesse rose uppe, offering her their places, and all three sitting downe againe, *Arsileus* saide to *Felismena*. Have you ever seene mee before (faire Shepherdesse,) or hath any body tolde you of my name? I knowe more of thee *Arsileus* (saide *Felismena*) and of 40 thy estate, then thou thinkest, although thou art in a Shepherdes weede, far different from that I sawe thee in, when thou wert a student in the famous Academie of *Salamanca*: If there be any thing heere to eate, I pray thee give it me, for I will tell thee afterwardes a strange and true thing, which thou hast desired 5 long since to knowe. This will I doe with a good will (saide *Arsileus*) though I can doe no kinde of service, due ynough to the great apparance of thy vertues and deserts. Whereupon *Arsileus* and *Amarillis*, taking of their severall scrips, gave *Felismena* such victuals, as they had. And after she had refreshed her selfe, 10 desirous to make him a joyfull man, who lived so long a time in greefe and sorrow, she began to speake to him in this sort. There is nothing in the world (*Arsileus*) that ought more religiously to be kept then firmnesse, and most of all in a womans hart where it is seldomer wont to be found. But the reason thereof I plainly 15 perceive, that men for the most part are occasions of their small constancie towardes them. I speake this for the great bond wherein thou art obliged to a Shepherdesse, that I knowe, who would not (if she knew thou wert alive) exchange her joy and content for all that the whole world could affoord. And then she 20 began to tell him in order all that was past, from the time that she killed the three Savages, untill she came to the Lady *Felicias* house: In which discourse *Arsileus* heard the golden newes of the thing, which he so deerely loved, and all that had passed betweene her and the Nymphes, when they found her sleeping in 25 the *Iland of the Lake*, as you have heard before: And that joie, which he then felt, when he understood, that the love and faith which his Shepherdesse did beare him, remained yet sincere, and inviolate in her hart, and the place certaine, where he might finde her out, was so extreme, that he fell downe in a traunce 30 betweene them both, by putting his life in hazard, with surfet of that sudden passion: But comming to himselfe againe, he said to *Felismena*. With what wordes shall I sufficiently (faire Shepherdesse) thanke thee for the great curtesie thou hast done me, and with what deedes acquite that singular content, wherewith 35 thou hast now blessed me, the like whereof I pray God so amply in every thing may give thee, as thy hart can either wish or desire. O my sweete *Belisa*, is it possible that I shall see those eies so soone againe, that had so great power over mine, to kisse those delicate hands, that made so intricate a knot in my hart, to heare 40

those angelicall words, and see that singular beauty, that ravished
so much my admiring senses. And that after so many troubles of
minde, and turmoiles of Fortune, such soveraine felicitie to succeede in their places? And speaking this with many teares, he
tooke *Felismenas* hands, and with great reverence kissed them. 5
And so did the Shepherdesse *Amarillis*, saying. Thou hast revived (faire Shepherdesse) the most sorrowfull man that ever I did
see, and filled him full of joye, who did lest deserve to have it.
Sixe monethes hath *Arsileus* lived in this Cotage so sorrowfull and
desolate a life, as none coulde imagine the like, without all 10
manner of consolation, but that certaine Shepherdesses, feeding
their flockes in these plaines (of the which I am one) sometimes
come in to visite him, and to affoord him that comfort, which his
greefe (were it at the lest capable of any at all,) woulde give him
leave to embrace. This is not such a greefe (saide *Felismena* 15
againe) that he, that hath it, may thinke to take any comfort in
any thing, but in the first causer thereof, or by whom he heareth
such newes, as I have now tolde him: which are so good for me
(faire Shepherdesse) saide *Arsileus*, that they have revived a living
hart in me, which was mortified and worne almost out with the 20
clogge of continual care. So much did the Shepherds words and
teares, uttered and powred foorth for joy, mollifie her tender hart,
as by her owne, she gave manifest proofe thereof. And in this
sort they tarried there, untill the heate of the day was past; and
then *Arsileus*, taking his leave with great thankes to both the 25
Shepherdesses, with infinite joy went towards the Temple of
Diana, the same way that *Felismena* did direct him.

   Sylvanus, and *Selvagia* with that content, as they are wont to
have, which after a long absence, enjoy the sight of their desired
Love, did goe towardes the pleasant meadowes, where their 30
flockes went feeding in companie of the Shepherde *Syrenus*, who
went also free and delivered from that kinde of content, that hee
behelde in them, and from the paine, which the want thereof is
wont to procure; bicause hee neither thought of loving well, nor
cared, whether he was beloved or no? Whereupon *Sylvanus* said 35
unto him. Everie time that I see thee (my deere friend *Syrenus*)
thou shouldest not be the man (me thinkes) that thou wert wont
to be, but that jointly with thy former thoughts and affection,
thou art thy selfe also chaunged: On the one side, I have in

14 all,) *Ed.*] all, *Y.*

a manner pitie of thee; on the other, it greeves me not to see thee carelesse of loves misfortunes. In what respect (said *Syrenus*) hast thou pitie on me? Bicause I thinke it (saide *Sylvanus*) the most malecontent and worst estate of life, not to love well, nor to be beloved againe. It is not long since that thou didst understand 5 this cleane contrarie (said *Syrenus.*) And for mine owne part, I pray God that Fortune may still preserve me in this ill estate, and thee in that joy and pleasure which thou takest in seeing thy *Selvagia.* For though there might arise some emulation of thy love, and being beloved of so faire a Shepherdesse; yet can I assure 1 thee, that Fortune doth not neglect to tune you the content, that you receive of your mutuall love. The hurt, said *Selvagia*, that she may doe us with her disordinate effects, can never be so great, as my joy is to see my selfe so well bestowed. Ah *Selvagia* (said *Syrenus* to her) I have also seene my selfe as well beloved, as none 1 might be more, and thought as little to see an end of my love, as you do now: but let none account without Fortune, nor lay his foundation without the consideration of the mutabilitie of time. But I doe owe no small respect of love and duetie to the sage Ladie *Felicia*, whom the heavens requite: For I never imagined to 2 speake so freely of mine ill in such a time, when I thought to feele it so little. But I am more indebted to her (saide *Selvagia*) bicause shee was the cause, that I loved him well, whose sight I ever enjoyed before mine eies: But *Sylvanus* turning his eies to her, saide. This debt I shoulde with great reason (my life) requite, 2 if it were such a thing, that might with life bee paied, which God grant thee (saide *Selvagia*) since without the same mine shoulde be woorse then a continuall death. *Syrenus* seeing the amorous words on both sides, with a smiling countenance saide unto them. It is well that every one can so well acquite himselfe for his good turne 3 done him, that the one will neither be in debt, nor the other have any indebted to him; and yet in mine owne opinion it is better, that you rejoyce so much, and so lovingly entreate of your amorous affections, my selfe not being a thirde in them. With these and other speeches the newe Lovers and carelesse *Syrenus* 3 passed away the time and length of the way, which they made an end of about sunne set: And before they came to the fountaine of the Sicamours, they heard a voice of a Shepherdesse sweetely singing, whom they knew by and by, for *Sylvanus* hearing her, saide unto them. This is *Diana* doubtlesse, that singes at the 4

fountaine of the Sicamours. It is she indeede (said *Selvagia.*) Let
us go behinde these Myrtle trees neere unto her, bicause we may
heare her the better. Agreed saide *Syrenus*, although the time
hath beene, when her musicke and sight delighted me more then
now. But all three going into the thicket of Myrtle trees, and 5
bicause it was about the going down of the Sunne, they sawe
faire *Diana* neere to the fountaine, shining with such surpassing
beautie, that they stoode (as men that had never seene her before)
amazed and in a woonder. Her haire hung downe loose from her
head behinde, and gathered up with a carnation stringe, which 10
parted them in the middes : her eies were fixed on the ground,
and somtimes looking into the cleere fountaine, and wiping
away some teares, that nowe and then trickled downe her beautifull cheekes, she sung this Dittie.

> *Hen that I poore soule was borne,*   15
> *I was borne unfortunate:*
> *Presently the Fates had sworne*
> *To foretell my haplesse state.*

> Titan *his faire beames did hide,*
> Phoebe *'clips'd her silver light,*   20
> *In my birth my mother dide,*
> *Yong, and faire in heavie plight.*

> *And the nurse, that gave me sucke,*   25
> *Haplesse was in all her life:*
> *And I never had good lucke*
> *Being maide or married wife.*

> *I lov'd well, and was belov'd,*
> *And forgetting, was forgot:*
> *This a haplesse marriage mov'd,*
> *Greeving that it kils me not.*   30

> *With the earth would I were wed,*
> *Then in such a grave of woes*
> *Daily to be buried,*
> *Which no end nor number knowes.*

Yong my father married me,
Forc't by my obedience:
Syrenus, *thy faith, and thee*
I forgot, without offence.

Which contempt I pay so far,   5
Never like was paide so much:
Jealousies doe make me war,
But without a cause of such.

I doe goe with jealous eies
To my foldes, and to my sheepe,   1
And with jealousie I rise,
When the day begins to peepe.

At his table I doe eate,
In his bed with him I lie,
But I take no rest, nor meate,   1
Without cruell jealousie.

If I aske him what he ailes,
And whereof he jealous is?
In his answere then he failes:
Nothing can he say to this.   2

In his face there is no cheere,
But he ever hangs the head:
In each corner he doth peere,
And his speech is sad and dead.

Ill the poore soule lives ywisse,   2
That so hardly married is.

The time was once, when *Dianas* teares and dolefull song and
the sorrow, that by her sadde lookes she expressed, might have
so much mooved *Syrenus* hart, as put the Shepherdes life in such
danger, that all other remedies (but onely proceeding from the 3
same) had beene impossible to have helpt it; whose eies and hart,
since now they were delivered out of that dangerous prison, tooke
no delight to beholde *Diana*, nor greeved at her sorrowfull

lamentations. And the Shepherd *Sylvanus* had lesse cause in his minde to be condolent for any greefe that *Diana* had, considering she never had the smallest regard of the greatest woes which he passed for her sake. Onely *Selvagia* helped her with her teares, fearefull (by the fall of her joy) of her own fortune, whereupon she said to *Syrenus*. There is no perfection, beautie, nor favour, in natures gift, which she hath not liberally bestowed on *Diana*, bicause her beautie is peerelesse, her wit and discretion admired, her good graces excellent, and all other her commendable parts, which a Shepherdesse should have, not to be seconded: since in the lest of them, that made her such a woonder in our age, there was never any yet that excelled her. Onlie one thing she wanted, which I ever suspected and feared, and this was her good Fortune, which woulde never accompanie her, to have made her live a contented and joyfull life, which (to speake the truth) she ever well deserved. She that so unjustly hath taken it from so many (saide *Syrenus*) by great reason should not enjoy such a happie estate; which I speake not, that I am not sorrie to see this Shepherdesse so sorrowful, but for the great reason I have, not to wish her any content at all. Saie not so (said *Selvagia*) for I cannot thinke, that *Diana* hath offended thee in any thing. What offence did she by marrying, compelled thereunto by the constraint of her parents, and kinsfolkes, and not by her owne will? And after she was married, what could she do (having due regarde to her honor and honestie) but forget thee? Truly *Syrenus*, thou shouldest have greater cause to complaine of *Diana*, then I have heard thee hitherto alledge. In truth *Syrenus* (saide *Sylvanus*) *Selvagia* hath so great reason for that she saith, that none can well disproove it. And if there be any that of ingratitude can justly accuse her, it is I, who loved her more then my selfe, she requiting it so ill againe, and with such cruell contempt as thou knowest well enough. *Selvagia* casting an amorous eie upon him, saide. But thou didst not deserve (my beloved Shepherd) to be so ill entreated, since there is no Shepherdesse in the worlde, that may not thinke herselfe blest to enjoy thy happy love. About this time *Diana* perceived, that their talke was of her, for the Shepherds were so loude, that she might heare them very well: Wherfore rising up, and looking among the Myrtle trees, she knew the Shepherdes, and the Shepherdesse that was sitting betweene them. Who, perceiving that she had espied them, came to her, and curteously

saluted her, and she them againe with a good grace and countenance, asking them, where they had beene so long a time. Whom
they answered with another kinde of wordes and countenance,
then they were wont to do, which seemed so strange to *Diana*,
that though she tooke no care for any of their loves, yet in the end
it greeved her, to see them so much altered from that they were
wont to be, and especially when she perceived what great joy
Sylvanus tooke in beholding faire *Selvagia*. And bicause it was now
time to go home, and that the flockes tooke their accustomed way
towards the village, they went after them, and by the way faire
Diana saide to *Syrenus*. There are many daies past, Shepherd,
since I sawe thee in these valleyes. But more (saide he) since
I woulde have lost my life, in lieu she had not seene me, that made
me passe it away in such great greefe, whereas in the end it contents me not a little to talke of my passed fortunes, that finde my
selfe now in a safe haven. Dost thou then thinke this to be a sure
estate, (saide *Diana*) wherein thou now livest? It cannot be
dangerous (said he) when I dare speake thus before thee. I never
remember (saide *Diana*) that I sawe thee so much lost for my love,
but that thy toong might have had as much libertie, as now it
hath. Thou art as discreet in imagining this (said he) as in all
other things else. Why so (saide *Diana*?) bicause there are no
other meanes (saide he) to make thee not know that, which thou
hast lost in me, but onely by thinking that I did not love thee so
much, that my toong might not have that libertie, as thou sayest.
But yet for all this I pray God give thee so much content as
sometimes (faire *Diana*) thou hast wished me: For though my
love be now past, yet the relickes therof that remaine in my soule,
are sufficient to wish thee al the happines in the world. Every
word that *Syrenus* spake was a dagger to *Dianas* hart. For God
knowes, if she would not have rather given a more willing eare
to his wonted complaints, then occupied her minde in beleeving
such apparant signes of his newe libertie. And though she answered
to every thing the Shepherd spake unto her, with a certaine kinde
of carelessenes, and did helpe her-selfe by her owne discretion
(bicause she would not shew any signe of sorrow for their
libertie) yet in her minde she ruminated the discontent, that by
their speeches and semblances she had so deeply conceived.
And with talking of these and other matters, they were come
to their village by that time the Sunne had hidden all his

beames, and taking leave one of another, they went to their owne
houses.

But comming to *Arsileus* againe, who went with great joye and
desire towards the wood where *Dianas* Temple was, to see his
Shepherdesse, he came to a little brooke, that ranne hard by the 5
Temple amongst a row of greene Sicamours, under whose coole
shadowes he sat him downe, hoping that Fortune would send
some body that way, by whom he might make his *Belisa* understand of his being there, bicause he thought it somwhat dangerous
to come upon her on the sudden, especially when she thought 10
him long since to be dead : And on the other side, the unpatient
desire that he had to see her, would not suffer him to take any
rest at all. But the Shepherd consulting with himselfe what was
best to be done, espied by chaunce a Nymph of wonderfull
beautie comming towardes him with her bowe in her hand, and 15
her quiver at her necke, looking on everie side, if she could espie
any Deare or wilde beast, to trie how she could bestow an arrow,
that she carried in her bow ready bent. But seeing the Shepherd,
she went straight unto him, who rising up, did her such reverence
as was due to so faire a Nymph, whom she curteously saluted 20
againe : For this was faire *Polydora*, one of the three that *Felismena*
and the Shepherds delivered from the violent hands of the Savages,
and a deere friend to *Belisa*. But both sitting downe againe upon
the greene grasse, *Polydora* asked him what countrey man he was,
and the cause of his comming thither. Whom *Arsileus* answered 25
thus. The countrey where I was borne (faire Nymph) hath so ill
intreated me, that (me thinkes) it greeves me to call it mine,
although on the other side, I am bound to love it much, and
more then I am able to expresse. And to tell thee the cause, that
Fortune had to bring me to this place, it were first needefull for 30
thee (faire Nymph) to tell me, if thou dost belong to the sage Lady
Felicia, in whose Palace (I heard say) my deerest *Belisa* doth remaine, the onely cause of my exile out of my native town, and of
that infinit sorrow, which her long absence hath made me feel.
I am of Lady *Felicias* house (said *Polydora*) and the gretest friend 35
in the world to the Shepherdesse that thou hast named : and
bicause thou maist also make such an account of me, if I thought
I might profit thee any thing by giving thee some counsel, I would
advise thee to forget hir, if it were possible, or (if it lay in thy

32 *Belisa* Ed.] *Belisia* Y.

power) not once to have an amorous thought of hir, bicause the
remedie of thy griefe is no lesse impossible, then the helpe of
that, which she suffers, since the cruell ground doth now feede
on him, who was once the hope of al her sorrow. And may this
be true (said he) that the earth doth consume hir servant *Arsileus*? 5
most true (said *Polydora*) for this was he, whom she loved more
then her selfe, and he, whom I may justly call the most unfortunate man besides thee, bicause thou hast setled thy thoughts in
such a place, where it is impossible for them to have any remedie.
For though I was never in love my selfe, yet do I hold it for 10
a firme opinion, that the passion of death is not so ill, as that,
which one suffers by loving, her that hath her affection setled in
another place. I beleeve it well faire Nymph (said *Arsileus*) and
that such are *Belisas* golden virtues and rare constancie, that as
imperious death cannot make her settle her affection in any other 15
place, so there is none in the world, that can make her chaunge
her minde, wherein (faire Nymph) the whole summe of my
felicitie consisteth. How doth thy felicitie consist Shepherd (said
she) by loving so as thou saist, when as her love is so strongly
fixed in another place? This is a strange kinde of affection, and 20
never heard of before. Bicause thou maist no longer (faire Nymph)
marvell at my words, nor at the maner of the love which I beare
to *Belisa* the soveraigne mistresse of my thoughts, give eare
a while (said *Arsileus*) and I wil tel thee that, thou never thought'st
to heare, although the beginning of it, thy friend, and the load- 25
starre of my life hath perhaps told thee. And then he told her
from the beginning of their loves to *Alfeus* his inchauntments
and brave deceit, and everie thing else, that till then in his loves
aforesaid befell unto him: which the Shepherd told sometimes
with teares, being loth to recall to memorie his passed mishaps; 30
sometimes with sighes, that he fetcht from the centre of his hart,
imagining what his mistresse *Belisa* might feele in these occurrents
and greevous accidents. And by his dolefull words and alterations
in his countenance, he gave so great a spirit to that he said, and
shewed such signes of inwarde griefe, that as it strooke the 35
Nymph in a great admiration, so likewise in no lesse compassion
of his paines: but when she understood, that undoubtedly he was
Arsileus, the joy that she conceived thereof was so great, that
with words she could not tell it, and thought her selfe unable at

20 another *Ed.*] anothet *Y.*

that present to do any more, but with inward sence to surfet on
the sweet joy of such happie newes. Behold then what might be
expected of comfortlesse *Belisa*, when she should understand of
these gladsome tydings. The Nymph therfore casting hir eies on
Arsileus, not without teares of inward gladnes said unto him, 5
I would I had thy ripe wit and fluent toong (*Arsileus*) to make thee
know what infinite pleasure I conceive by the good successe,
that Fortune hath solicited for my *Belisa*, because I might otherwise be deceived, by thinking that so simple a conceit and barren
wordes as mine are, could declare it. I ever thought that the con- 10
tinuall griefe of my *Belisa* should be at length converted into
great gladnes, induced thereunto by the great deserts of her
singular beautie, wisdome, and faith that she hath ever kept
firme and inviolate, but did ever feare on the other side, that
Fortune never made account to give it her so amply, and in such 15
sorte, as I did desire it, bicause it is her condition (for the most
parte) to bring her effectes to passe cleane contrarie to their
desires that love well. Happie maiest thou call thy selfe *Arsileus*,
since thou didst deserve to bee so well beloved in life, that
couldest not bee forgotten after death. And bicause the deferring 20
of such great joy, for a hart that needes it so much, may not be
too long, give me leave to goe and carrie so good newes to thy
Shepherdesse, as those of thy life, and of her deceived minde. And
depart not from this place untill I come againe with her whom thou
dost so much desire, and most deserve to see. As I can expect 25
nothing else (saide *Arsileus*) from such excellent wisdome, and exceeding beautie as thine, but all joy and contentment whatsoever:
even so faire Nymph (bicause thou dost so greatly desire to give it
me) thy will be done, whereby I hope to governe my selfe as well in
this, as in all things else, that shall ensue thereof. Whereupon they 30
taking leave of one another, *Polydora* went to tel *Belisa* these inopinate newes, and *Arsileus* remained still, tarying for them under the
pleasant shadow of those green Sicamours, who (to entertaine the
time with something) as they are wont to doe, that are attending
some joyfull thing, tooke out his Rebecke, and to the tune of it, 35
began with sweetest voice to sing these verses following.

10 continuall *Ed.*] coutinuall *Y.*

NOw Love, and fortune turne to me againe,
  And now each one enforceth and assures
A hope, that was dismaied, dead, and vaine:
And from the harbour of mishaps recures
  A hart, that is consum'd in burning fire,   5
  With unexpected gladnes, that adjures
My soule to lay aside her mourning tire,
  And senses to prepare a place for joy.
  Care in oblivion endlesse shall expire:
For every greefe of that extreme annoy,   10
  Which when my torment raign'd, my soule (alas)
  Did feele, the which long absence did destroy,
Fortune so well appaies, that never was
  So great the torment of my passed ill,
  As is the joy of this same good I passe.   15
Returne my hart, sursaulted with the fill
  Of thousand great unrests, and thousand feares:
  Enjoy thy good estate, if that thou will:
And wearied eies, leave of your burning teares,
  For soone you shall behold her with delight,   20
  For whom my spoiles with glorie Cupid beares.
Senses which seeke my star so cleere and bright,
  By making heere and there your thoughts estray,
  Tell me, what will you feele before her sight?
Hence solitarinesse, torments away   25
  Felt for her sake, and wearied members cast
  Of all your paine, redeem'd this happy day.
O stay not time, but passe with speedie hast,
  And Fortune hinder not her comming now.
  O God, betides me yet this greefe at last?   30
Come my sweete Shepherdesse, the life which thou
  (Perhaps) didst thinke was ended long ago,
  At thy commaund is ready still to bow.
Comes not my Shepherdesse desired so?
  O God what if she's lost, or if she stray   35
  Within this wood, where trees so thicke doe growe?
Or if this Nymph, that lately went away,
  Perhaps forgot to go and seeke her out.
  No, no, in her oblivion never lay.
Thou onely art my Shepherdesse, about   40

Whose thoughts my soule shall finde her joy and rest:
Why comm'st not then to assure it from doubt?
O see'st thou not the sunne passe to the west,
And if it passe, and I behold thee not,
Then I my wonted torments will request   5
And thou shalt waile my hard and heavie lot.

When *Polydora* went from *Arsileus*, not far from thence she met
with the Shepherdesse *Belisa*, who was going to recreate her selfe
in the greene wood, in the companie of the two Nymphes *Cynthia*
and *Doria*, who seeing her comming in such haste, began to be 10
afraid, thinking that she ran away from some thing, from the
which it behoved them also to flie away. But now when she came
neerer unto them, the joy that they perceived by her milde eies
and countenance did warrant them from danger, and being come
to them, she went presently to the Shepherdesse *Belisa*, and 15
imbracing her with great joy and gladnes, saide thus unto her. If
thou knewest from whom this imbracement came, thou wouldst
with greater content (faire Shepherdesse) receive it then now thou
dost. It can come from no part faire Nymph (said she) where
I may more joyfully accept it, then from thine owne selfe, since 20
he, from whom with the supremest joy in the world I should
entertaine it, is not now in the world: And I would desire to live
no longer, if I were now altogither deprived of the content, that
this miserable life may at some times affoorde me, which onely
I account, faire Nymph, thy friendly and gracious companie. This 25
life (saide *Polydora*) from henceforth I hope thou shalt enjoy with
more content then thou canst imagine: And bicause thou maist
knowe how, let us sit under the shade of this greene Sicamour,
and I will acquaint thee with such matters, as shall revive thy
spirits, and decaied soule. *Belisa*, and the Nymphes sat them downe 30
taking *Polydora* in the mids, who said to *Belisa*. Tell me (faire
Shepherdesse) how certaine art thou of the death of *Arsenius* and
of *Arsileus*? *Belisa* unable to stop the sudden eruption of her
violent teares, answered. So certaine, as one that beheld that
tragicall spectacle with her owne eies, the one shot thorow with 35
an arrowe, the other killing himselfe with his owne Faulchion.
But what wilt thou say to one, that will tell thee, that these two,
whom thou didst see dead, are alive, and in perfect health? Her
would I answere (saide *Belisa*) that told me this, that she had

a desire to renew my teares, and to bring those to my thoughts
againe, whose remembrance is my death, or that she tooke
a delight to sport her selfe with my greefes. I am certaine (saide
Polydora) thou thinkest not so of me, for thou knowest how thy
cares have touched me neerer then any other, to whom thou 5
didst ever impart them. But tell me what is that Shepherd of thy
towne, that is called *Alfeus*. The greatest Conjurer (said *Belisa*)
and the most cunning Magician that is (I thinke) in *Europe*, who
did once fondly spend his time in loving and serving me. He is
a man (faire Nymph) whose dealing and conversation is altogether 10
with Divels, which he makes to take such shapes upon them as
he list himselfe, so that many times thou wouldst thinke, thou
wert talking with thy familiar acquaintance (into whose shape he
transformeth some spirit or other) when indeede thou art talking
with a very Divell. Thou must therefore knowe faire Shep- 15
herdesse (saide *Polydora*) that the same *Alfeus* with his enchantments and divellish devises hath beene the cause of the deceite,
wherein hitherto thou hast lived, and of the infinite teares, that
for the same thou hast powred forth, bicause knowing that
Arsileus was to speake with thee that night (as it was concluded 20
betweene you) he caused two spirits to take the shapes of *Arsileus*
and his father upon them. And *Arsileus* desiring to talke with
thee, effected that, that should fall out, which with thine eies thou
didst that night beholde. Bicause thinking they were dead, thou
mightest despaire and kill thy selfe, or do that (at the least) 25
which thou hast already done. When *Belisa* heard what faire
Polydora did tell her, she was so farre beside her-selfe, that for
a while she could not speake one word, but comming to her-selfe
again, she said unto her. Thou hast told me (faire Nymph)
strange things, if my sorrow woulde give me leave to beleeve 30
them. By that love which (thou saiest) thou dost beare me, tell
me (I beseech thee) how thou knowest it, or of whom thou hast
understoode that those two, which I sawe dead before mine eies,
were not *Arsenius* and *Arsileus*? Of no other saide *Polydora*, but of
Arsileus himselfe. What, of *Arsileus*, saide *Belisa*? Is it possible 35
that my *Arsileus* doth live, and so nigh to blesse me with these
happy newes? I will tell thee how possible it is (saide *Polydora*) if
thou wilt go with me, for before we come yonder to those three
hedges, which thou seest before thee, I will shew thee the man,

14 talking *Ed.*] talkiug *Y.*

that shal restore thy decayed hope, and restore thee thy life
againe. O soveraigne Deities (said *Belisa*) what words do I heare?
That the renuing of my joyes and felicitie is so apparant, and that
my *Arsileus* is there? Why dost thou not leade me (faire Nymph)
to the place, where I may see him, and die at his feete with joy of
his happy sight? Ah thou dost not love me (*Polydora*) so much as
thou saiest. This did the faire Shepherdesse speake with an uncertaine kinde of joy, and doubtfull hope of that, which she so
much desired. But *Polydora* rising up, and taking her by the
hand, and the Nymphes *Cynthia* and *Doria*, who for joy also to
see *Belisas* good happe, would not stay behinde, went to the
brooke, where *Arsileus* was. And before they came, a temperate
aire, that came from the place where he sat, ravished their sences
with the sweete voice of the enamoured Shepherd, who had not
yet left off his musicke, but still began afresh to sing upon this
old proverbe.

> *Good fortune come and tarie.*

With the glosse that he himselfe did descant upon it to his owne
purpose.

The Glosse.

WHat motions, times and changes,
  What waies, what uncouth ranges,
What slights, what disillusions,
What gladnes (in conclusions)
Have risen of such sorrowes?
One faith yet all these borrowes,
And one good love assureth,
And my misfortunes cureth.
And since from greefe they varie,
  Good fortune come and tarie.

Good hap thou still dost moove thee,
So light as not behooves thee,
And if, thus to content me,
Thou thinkest to repent thee?
Then better is my smarting:
For if thou goest, At parting

My sense and wits forsake me:
But if (more sure to make me)
Thou com'st, my soule to marrie,
     Good fortune come and tarrie.

But if I come in vaine heere,   5
Or live deceiv'd, to plaine heere:
For, wretched men what feare not?
To loose my life, then weare not
The same more safe each hower?
O feare, strange is thy power,   10
For th'ill thou figurest ever.
But since such beautie never
Did any falshood carrie,
     Good fortune come and tarrie.

When *Belisa* heard *Arsileus* his musicke, she felt such inward
joy, as the like did never any, whereupon resolving with her selfe
to shake off all former sorrowe that had appalled that surpassing
beautie, which nature had bountifully bestowed on her, and
decaied those pleasant lookes, and comely favour (the onely
source of *Arsileus* his teares and sighes) in her sweete and alluring
face, now on a sudden with a renewed grace and excellent beautie
(whereat the Nymphes were not a little amazed) she spake in this
sort, saying. This is, without doubt, the voice of my *Arsileus*, if
I do not deceive my selfe by calling him mine. When the Shepherd
did see the cause of all his passed cares, and present contents
before his eies, the ineffable joy that he conceived thereat was so
great, that his hart unable to comprehend it, was troubled in such
sort, that at that instant he could not utter a word: To whom the
Nymphes, perceiving in what a traunce the sight of his Shepherdesse had put *Arsileus*, most lovingly came, when the Shepherd, suspending that for a litle while, which the present joy
wrought in him, with many teares saide. With what wordes am
I able to expresse the satisfaction that fortune hath made me for
so many greefes and troubles, as for thy sake (sweete Shepherdesse
Belisa) I have endured. O who may give me now a new hart, and
not so distempered with sorrowfull thoughts, to receive into it

10 *power, Ed.*] *power.* Y.

such unspeakable joy as thy happy sight presents me! O fortune,
I have no more to request of thee, and thou no more to give me:
yet onely one thing I aske thee, That, since it is thy fashion to
give no supreme happinesse without extreme heavinesse, the
great force of this unexpected joy, which thou hast given me this 5
sevenfold happy day, may with little sorrowe (in liew of such
a soveraigne sweete) and with such an opposite, as may but
a while countermaund this sweete content, be mildly and with
favour tempered. And faire Nymphes, in whose sacred guard
and ampare, such great treasure hath bin divinely preserved, and 10
where it could never have beene better imployed, let your harts
rejoice with mine, at this infinite joy that revives it, which thing
(if you your selves have sometimes loved well) shall seeme no
lesse then due to my restored good. O faire Shepherdesse, why
dost thou not speake unto me, doth it greeve thee to see me, or 15
dost thou take no delight in seeing thy *Arsileus*? hath his greevous
sight troubled thy toong, or the extreme joy thereof hindered the
passage of thy golden wordes? Whom *Belisa* answered thus. The
joy which I have to see thee (my deere *Arsileus*) were but little, if
with words it might be told. Let it suffice thee to know in what 20
continual panges and dangers of my life, thy supposed death
hath put me, and by that thou shalt see what a world of joy thy
renewed life hath brought to this my mournfull soule. At the ende
of which words, by reason of an issue of swelling teares ascending
up from the center of her sorrowfull hart into her eye brinkes, she 25
was not able to utter out the rest of her minde, which the tender
harted Nymphes, being mollified with the milde and pitifull
words of both these lovers to one another, did helpe and accompany with theirs. And bicause night was comming on, they went
all to *Felicias* house, telling to each other the discourse and 30
accidents of their lives, which till then they had both passed.
Belisa asked her *Arsileus* for his father *Arsenius*, who told her,
that, as soone as he knew she was gon, he went to one of his
Farmes not far from thence, where he lives as quiet and contented
a life, as he could wish, having put all mundane affaires in 35
oblivion: whereat *Belisa* was verie glad, and so they came to the
Palace of sage *Felicia*, where they were welcommed with great
joye and feast, whose hands *Belisa* kissed many times, saying
evermore that shee was the cause of her good Fortune. And so

38 saying *Ed.*] saying, Y.

did *Arsileus*, to whom *Felicia* shewed an earnest will to do ever for him, what lay in her power.

The end of the fifth booke.

The sixth Booke of Diana of George of Montemayor.

AFter that *Arsileus* was gone, *Felismena* staied still with the Shepherdesse *Amarillis*, that was with him, demaunding of one an other the course of their lives, a common thing to them, that finde themselves in like places. And as *Felismena* was telling the Shepherdesse the cause of her comming thither, a jolly Shepherd came to the Coate, though very sad by his countenance and gate. When *Amarillis* sawe him, she rose up in great haste to be gone, but *Felismena* taking hold by her garment, and suspecting what the cause of her sudden departure might be, said unto her. It were not reason Shepherdesse, that I should receive this discourtesie at thy hands, who desires so much to serve thee. But as she strived to be gone from thence, the Shepherd with many teares said unto her. My desire is (*Amarillis*) having respect to that, which thou makest me suffer, not to see thee sorie for this unfortunate Shepherd, but to consider what belongs to thy wisedome and beautie, and that there is nothing in the worlde worse beseeming a Shepherdesse of thy brave qualities, then to intreate one so cruelly, that loves thee so entirely. Beholde these wearied eies (*Amarillis*) that have shed so many teares, and then thou shalt see what reason thine have to shew themselves so angrie against this miserable man. Alas, that thou fliest away from me, not seeing the reason thou hast to abide my presence. Stay *Amarillis*, and harken to my complaints, and to my just excuses, and if thou wilt not answere me at all, yet I will be content, so that thou staiest still. What can it hinder thee to heare him, whom it hath so deerely cost to see thee? And looking upon *Felismena*, with many teares he besought her, not to let her goe, who with sweete and gentle wordes intreated the Shepherdesse not to use him with so small pitie, whom he shewed to love more then himselfe, or that she would (at the lest) harken unto him, since she could

not hurt hir selfe much by doing so litle. But *Amarillis* said:
Intreat me not (faire Shepherdesse) to give eare to him, who
beleeves his thoughts, more then my words. For behold, this
Shepherd that stands in this fained sort before thee, is one of the
most disloyall men, that ever lived, and one of them that most of 5
al troubles our simple loving Shepherdesses with his false deceits
and dissimulations. Then said *Filemon* to *Felismena*. My onely
request and desire is, faire Shepherdesse, that thou wouldst be
judge in the cause betweene *Amarillis* and me, wherein if I am
found culpable, or the just provoker of that anger, and ill opinion 10
that she hath wrongfully conceived against me, that then I may
loose my life; and if she be, that I may have no other thing for
satisfaction, but her confession, how much she hath injured, and
owes me. To leese thy life (said *Amarillis*) I am sure thou wilt
not, bicause thou wilt not wish thy selfe so much harme, nor me 15
so much good, as for my sake to put thy life in adventure. But
I am content, that this faire Shepherdesse be judge (if it please
her) betweene us, to consider of our reasons, and to declare which
of us both is more worthie of blame. Agreed (said *Felismena*) and
let us sit downe at the foote of this greene hedge neere to the 20
flourishing meadow before our eies, for I will see what reason you
have to complaine of one another. After they were all three set
downe upon the greene grasse, *Filemon* began thus to say. I trust
faire Shepherdesse, if thou hast at any time beene touched with the
force of Love, that thou shalt plainly perceive what small reason 25
Amarillis hath to be angrie with me, and to conceive so ill an
opinion of the unstained faith I beare her, which makes her surmise that, which never any other Shepherdesse hath ever yet
imagined of her loving Shepherd. Knowe therefore (faire Shepherdesse) that the fates (not onely when I was borne, but long 30
before) determined, that I should love this faire Shepherdesse,
which sits before thy faire and my sorrowfull eies, whose intents
I have answered with such effect, as there is no love (I thinke)
like mine, nor any ingratitude like to hers. It fell out afterwardes,
that from my childehood, serving her in the best manner I coulde, 35
there are five or six moneths past, since my mishap brought
a Shepherd hither called *Arsileus*, who went up and downe seeking a Shepherdesse called *Belisa*, which by some ill successe of
Fortune, wandred like an exile heere and there amongst these
woodes and groves. And as his sorrow was very great, it fell out, 40

that this cruell Shepherdesse, either for great pittie she tooke of
him, or for the little she had of me, or for what cause else (she
knowes best herselfe) woulde never be out of his companie: To
whom if by chance I did but speake thereof, she was ready to kill
me with anger; for those eies which thou seest there, procure
death no lesse, when they are angry, then life when they are milde
and gentle. But now when all my sences were thus occupied,
mine eies with teares, my eares with hearing denials, my thoughts
with a bitter taste of sorrow, my soule with a rare and unspeake-
able kind of affection, and my understanding with the greatest
jealousie, as the like never any had, I made my complaint to
Arsileus with sighes, and to the earth, and these groves with
pitifull and bitter lamentations, shewing them what injuries
Amarillis did me. Her deceived imagination of the suspect, that
I had of her honestie, hath bredde in her so great despite and
hatred against me, that to be revenged of me, she hath hitherto
persevered therein, which greevous torment she is not onely content to lay upon me, but when she sees me before her eies, flies
from my presence, as the fearefull Hinde from the hungry and
pursuing Hounde. So that by the love which thou owest thy selfe,
I pray thee (good Shepherdesse) judge whether this be a sufficient
cause to make her thus abhorre me, and if my fault on the other
side, be so great, that it deserves such endles and extreme hate.
Filemon having made an end of the cause of his greefe and injurie,
wherewith his Shepherdesse tormented him; *Amarillis* began to
shape her answer thus. This *Filemon* (faire Shepherdesse) that sits
before thee, hath loved me well (I must needes confesse) or at the
least, made a fine shewe thereof, and such have his services beene
towards me, that to say otherwise of him, then he deserves, it
would ill beseeme me. But if for his sake, in lieu and recompence
of that affection, I have not rejected the suites and service of many
jolly Shepherds that feede their flockes upon these downes, and
in these pleasant vales; and also (for his love) have not contemned
many countrey youthes, whom nature hath enriched with no
lesse perfections then himselfe, let himselfe be judge. For the
infinite times, that with their amorous sutes I have beene importuned, and those wherein I have kept that firmnes due to his faith,
have not (I thinke) beene at any time out of his presence, which
neverthelesse should be no sufficient cause for him to make so
small account of me, as to imagine or suspect any thing of that,

wherein I am most of all bounde to my selfe. For if it be so, (as he knowes well enough) that for the love of him I have cast off many, that died by mine occasion, how coulde I then forget or reject him for the love of another? A thousand times hath *Filemon* watched me, not leesing a steppe that the Shepherd *Arsileus* and I have troden amiddes these greene woods, and pleasant vales, but let him say, if he ever heard *Arsileus* talke to me of love, or if I answered him any thing touching such matter. What day did *Filemon* ever see me talke to *Arsileus*, whereby he might conceive any thing else by my words, but that I went about to comfort him in such great sorrow, as he suffered: And if this be a sufficient cause to make him thinke ill of his Shepherdesse, who can better judge it, then him selfe? Behold then (faire Shepherdesse) how much he was given to false suspects and wrongfull jealousie, that my wordes could never satisfie him, nor worke with him, to make him leave off his obdurate minde by absenting himselfe from this valley, thinking therby to have made an end of my daies, wherein he was deceived, when as he rather ended his owne joy and contentment, if for me at the least he had ever any at all. And this was the mischiefe besides, that *Filemon* being not onely content to beare mee such a kinde of unjust jealousie, whereof he had so small occasion, as now (faire Shepherdesse) thou hast seene, hee did likewise publish it at everie feast, in all bridales, wrestlings, and meetings, that were made amongst the Shepherds of these hilles. And this thou knowest (good Shepherdesse) howe it did prejudice mine honour more then his contentment: In the ende hee absented himselfe from mee, which course since hee hath taken for a medicine of his malladie (which it seemes hath the more increased it) let him not finde fault with me, if I have knowne how to profit my selfe more thereby then he hath. And now that thou hast seene (faire Shepherdesse) what great content that I felt, when thou toldst the Shepherd *Arsileus* so good newes of his Shepherdesse, and that I my selfe was most earnest with him to have him go and seeke her out, it is cleere, that there could not be any thing between us, that might ingender such cause of suspition, as this Shepherd hath wrongfully conceived of us. So that this is the cause, that hath made me not only so cold in the love that I did beare him, but not to love any more, wherby to put mine honor and good name in hazard of false suspects, since my

20 mischiefe *Ed.*] michiefe *Y.*

good hap hath brought me to such a time, that (without forcing my selfe) I may do it at mine own choise and libertie. After *Amarillis* had shewed the small reason the Shepherd had to give so great credit to his jealous imaginations, and the libertie wherein time, and her good fortune had put her (a naturall thing to free harts) the woefull Shepherd replied in this sort. I doe not denie (*Amarillis*) but that thy wisedome and discretion is sufficient to cleere thee of all suspition. But wilt thou now make novelties in love, and invent other new effects, then those which we have heretofore seene? When a lover would love well, the least occasion of jealousie torments his soule, how much more when those were greater, which by thy privie conversation and familiaritie with *Arsileus* thou hast given me. Dost thou thinke (*Amarillis*) that for a jealousie certainties are needfull? Alas thou deceivest thy selfe, for suspicions be the principall causes of their entrance: which was also no great matter, since I beleeved that thou didst beare *Arsileus* good will, the publishing whereof was as little prejudiciall and lesse offensive to thine honour, since the force of my love was so great, that it made mee manifest the ill that I did feare. And though thy goodnes assured mee, when, at stealth and deceite of my suspectes, I thought thereof, yet I alwaies feared, least some adverse successe might befall unto me, if this familiaritie had beene still continued. But to that thou saiest (faire Shepherdesse) that I absented my selfe, I answere, that upon a stomacke, or to give thee any offence or greefe thereby, I did it not; but to see if I could have any remedie in mine owne, not seeing the cause of my great mishap and greefe before mine eies, and bicause my pursutes might not also offende thee. But if by seeking remedy for so great an ill, I went against that, which I owed thee, what greater punishment can I have, then that which thy absence hath made me feele? If thou saiest thou didst never love *Arsileus*, it gives me greater occasion to complaine of thee, since for a thing of so small importance, thou didst forsake him, who so greatly desired to serve thee. So that I have the more cause to accuse thee, the lesse thy love was to *Arsileus*. And these are the reasons *Amarillis* and manie more, which I do alleage, not in mine owne excuse and favour, whereby I thinke not to helpe my selfe at all, since in matters of love they are woont to profite so little; only requesting thee (gentle *Amarillis*) that thy clemencie and the faith which I have ever borne thee, may be of my side, and moove thee unto pittie, the want whereof can prescribe no ende to my greefe, nor meanes of reconciliation in thy hard condition and crueltie. And with this the Shepherd made an ende of his words, and began to poure forth so many teares, that they were sufficient (with the requests and sentence that *Felismena* gave 5 in his behalfe) to mollifie *Amarillis* hard hart, and to make the enamoured Shepherd come againe into her good grace and liking, for which he was so glad a man, as never more; and *Amarillis* not a little joyfull, by shewing how much *Filemon* was deceived in his false suspicions of her. And after this, they passed away that day 10 with great content of the two reconciled lovers, and with greater sorrow of faire *Felismena*, who next day early in the morning departed from them after many embracings, and promises, to sende to each other newes of their affaires.

But *Syrenus* being now free from love, and *Sylvanus* and *Selvagia* 15 more enamored then ever before, and faire *Diana*, not a little discontent for the sorrowfull success of her affaires, passed away her melancholike life, feeding her flocke along the bankes of the great river *Ezla*, where, many times meeting with one another, they talked of that, which pleased their fancies best. And discreete 20 *Selvagia* being on a day at the fountaine of the Sicamours, the Shepherdesse *Diana* came thither by chance, to seeke a lambe that had runne out of the foulde, which *Sylvanus* had tyed to a myrtle tree, for when they came thither, they founde it drinking at the cleere spring and by the marke knewe it to be faire *Dianas*. But 25 being come (as I say) and curteously welcommed of the newe lovers, they sat them downe upon the greene grasse, leaning to one of the Sicamours, that stoode about the fountaine, and after they had talked of many matters, *Sylvanus* saide unto her. Why dost thou not aske us (faire *Diana*) for *Syrenus*? Bicause I woulde not 30 talke of matters past (said *Diana*) for the great greefe which present things do give me: The time was, when I tooke more delight to aske for him, and hee for mee, and to speake and converse with one another then now, which gives neither of us the like contentment; but time doth cure infinite cares, that seeme 35 remedilesse to many men, which if I understood not so, there could not be now a *Diana* in these faire meades and plaines, in regard of the sorrowes and care that are daily offred me. God never graunt so much harme to our pleasant fieldes (saide *Selvagia*) by depriving them of such great beautie as hers is. That 40

shall not be wanting as long as thou livest (saide *Diana*) and wheresoever thy grace and perfections are, little may be lost by my
want, in truth whereof, behold thy *Sylvanus*, who (I thought)
would never have forgotten me for any other Shepherdesse, and
yet in the end hath shaken hands with me for thy love, which 5
deserved a great deale more. This did *Diana* speake with a gracious
smile, although she laughed not so much in minde at these things,
nor with so good a hart as they thought. For though she once
loved *Syrenus* more then her owne life, and despised *Sylvanus*, as
nothing so much, yet it greeved her more, that *Sylvanus* had for- 10
gotten her for the love of another, whose sight he now enjoyed
every day with great contentment of his newe love, then that
Syrenus had freed himselfe out of her love, whom nowe no new
affection mooved. When *Sylvanus* heard what *Diana* said, he
answered her thus. Time, and the revolutions of the heavens shall 15
first cease (faire *Diana*) before I will forget thee, for thy beautie
and wisedome is not such, that may be ever put in oblivion.
Truth it is that I am now bound to my *Selvagia*, bicause (besides
many other good parts in her obliging me to her love) she never
esteemed her Fortune to bee woorse by this, that she is nowe 20
beloved of him, whom thou did'st alway so reject and make so
small account of. No more of this (saide *Diana*) for thou art well
bestowed, and I was not well advised by not loving thee, as thy
love deserved it at my hands. But if at any time thou didst desire
to give me some content, I beseech thee (al I may) and thy faire 25
Selvagia, to sing some song, to entertaine the time, and to passe
the heate of the day away; which now beginnes so fast, that we
must be faine to passe it under these Sicamours, and there enjoy
the bubling of this cleere spring, which shall not a little helpe the
sweetenes of your song. The new lovers were not daintie to be 30
praied, though faire *Selvagia* was not very well content with this
kinde of talke that *Diana* had with *Sylvanus*. But bicause in her
song, she thought to be revenged on her, to the tune that *Diana*
plaied on her Bagpipe, both of them began to sing as followeth.   35

> *I See thee jolly Shepherd merry,*
> *And firme thy faith and sound as a berry.*
> *Love gave me joy, and fortune gave it,*
> *As my desire could wish to have it.*

What didst thou wish, tell me (sweete lover)
Whereby thou might'st such joy recover?
　　To love where love should be inspired,
　　Since there's no more to be desired.
In this great glory, and great gladnes,   5
Think'st thou to have no touch of sadnes?
　　Good fortune gave me not such glory,
　　To mocke my love, or make me sorie.
If my firme love I were denying,
Tell me, with sighes would'st thou be dying?   10
　　Those wordes in jest to heare thee speaking,
　　For very greefe my hart is breaking.
Yet would'st thou change, I pray thee tell me,
In seeing one, that did excell me?
　　O noe, for how can I aspire,   15
　　To more then to mine owne desire.
Such great affection dost thou beare me
As by thy wordes thou seem'st to sweare me?
　　Of thy deserts, to which a detter
　　I am, thou maist demaund this better.   20
Sometimes me thinkes, that I should sweare it,
Sometimes me thinkes, thou should'st not beare it.
　　Onely in this, my hap doth greeve me,
　　And my desire, not to beleeve me.
Imagine that thou dost not love mine,   25
But some brave beautie that's above mine.
　　To such a thing (sweete) doe not will me,
　　Where faining of the same doth kill me.
I see thy firmnes gentle lover,
More then my beautie can discover.   30
　　And my good fortune to be higher
　　Then my desert, but not desier.

About this time came *Syrenus* downe from the village towards
the fountaine of the Sicamours, with great desire to meete *Selvagia*
or *Sylvanus*, for hee nowe tooke no greater delight in any thing, 35
then in the company of these two lovers. And if he had (perhaps)
a touch of *Dianas* love in his memorie, the time that he had spent
in loving her, did not leave him altogither without some pensive
thoughts, not, for that her love now gave him any paine; but

because the remembrance of a good estate, doth breed some small
kind of griefe and discontent in him that hath lost it. Before he
came to the fountaine, in the mids of the greene meadow which
was beset round about with Myrtles and Laurels, he found *Dianas*
sheepe, that went by themselves all alone feeding amongst the 5
trees under the keeping of two fierce masties. And as the Shepherd
staied to looke upon them, thinking of the time, wherein he had
greater care of them, then of his owne, the masties with great
furie came running upon him. But when they came somewhat
nigh and knew him, by wagging their tailes, and holding downe 10
their necks (that were armed with collers of sharpe nailes) the
one fell downe at his feete; and the other by skipping upon him
fawned on him with the greatest joy in the world. And the sheepe
did no lesse, for the Bell-wether with his rurall bleating came to
the Shepherd, whom all the rest followed, and knowing *Syrenus*, 15
came round about him, which sight he could not behold without
teares, calling to mind that sometimes in the company of faire
Diana he had fed that gentle flocke. And seeing that in the silly
beasts that love and knowledge did abound, which wanted in their
mistresse, it was so forcible a motion in his minde, that if the 20
vertue of the water, which sage *Felicia* had given him, had not
made him forget his olde love: it might well have beene, that
there was nothing else in the worlde that coulde have let him
from renewing it againe. But seeing himselfe thus in the mids of
Dianas sheepe, and with the thoughts, that the memorie of such 25
a thing did put before his eies, to the tune of his merie Rebecke he
began to sing this song.

> *P*Assed contents,
>   *O what meane ye?*
> *Forsake me now, and doe not wearie me.* 30
>
> *Wilt thou heare me, O memorie,*
> *My pleasant daies, and nights againe,*
> *I have appaid with sevenfold paine:*
> *Thou hast no mor to aske me why,*
> *For when I went, they all did die:* 35
> *As thou dost see,*
> *O leave me then, and doe not wearie me.*

26 Rebecke *Ed.*] Recbecke *Y.*

Greene field, and shadowed valley, wheare
Sometime my chiefest pleasure was,
Behold what I did after passe:
Then let me rest, and if I beare
Not with good cause continuall feare,   5
Now doe you see.
O leave me then, and doe not trouble me.

I sawe a hart changed of late,
And wearied to assure mine:
Then I was forced to recure mine   10
By good occasion, time and fate,
My thoughts, that now such passions hate,
O what meane ye?
Forsake me now and doe not wearie me.

You lambes and sheepe that in these layes,   15
Did sometimes follow me so glad:
The merry howres, and the sad
Are passed now with all those daies:
Make not such mirth, and wonted plaies,
As once did ye: 20
For now no more you have deceived me.

If that to trouble me you come,
Or come to comfort me indeede:
I have no ill for comforts neede.
But if to kill me, Then (in summe)   25
Full well may ye
Kill me, and you shall make an end of me.

After *Syrenus* had made an ende of his song, faire *Diana* knewe him by his voice, and so did the two enamoured Shepherdes *Sylvanus* and *Selvagia*. They called to him, telling him, that if he 30 was minded to passe away the heate of the day in the field, there was the fresh fountaine of the Sicamours, and faire *Diana*, both which should be no small allurements to invite him thither. *Syrenus* answered him, that he must needs stay all day in the field, untill it was time to go home againe with his sheepe to the towne, 35 and comming where the Shepherd and Shepherdesses were, they sat round about the cleere fountaine, as they were commonly woont to do. But *Diana*, (whose life was so sorrowfull, as one may imagine, that ever sawe a Shepherdesse, the fairest and wisest that was then knowne, married so greatly to her greefe) went day by day seeking out new occasions to entertaine the time, and to passe her life away, and studying often to prevent her con- 5 tinuall and sorrowfull thoughts. But the Shepherds sitting and talking of other matters touching the feeding of sheepe, and their profite, *Diana* brake off the substance of their talke, saying to *Sylvanus*. It is a proper thing, Shepherd, that, sitting before thy faire *Selvagia*, thou talkest of other impertinent things, and not of 10 praising her beautie, nor of the great love, that she beares thee: Let the field and lambes alone, the good or ill successe of time and fortune, and enjoy the good hap that (Shepherd) thou hast nowe, by being beloved of so faire a Shepherdesse, for where there is so great reason to have continually such contentment of minde, thou 15 need'st not care for that, which Fortune doth but sometimes give. How much I am beholding to thee *Diana* (answered *Sylvanus*) none can expresse but he, that knowes what great reason I have to acknowledge this debt, bicause thou didst not onely then teach me to love well, but now also shewest me the way to use the con- 20 tentment, that my love affoordes me: The reason thou hast to warne me, not to talke of any other matter (my Mistresse being in presence) but onely of the content that by her sight I receive, is great and infinite, the which I promise thee (faire *Diana*) to do, while my happy soule shall be conteined in this joyfull body. 25 But I marvell at one thing, to see how thy *Syrenus* doth cast his eies another way, when thou speakest unto him, it seemes thy wordes please him not, or that he is not satisfied with thy answers. Blame him not (said *Diana*) for carelesse men and enimies to their own good will do more then this. Enimy to mine own good 30 (said *Syrenus*?) If I was ever such an one, let death punish me for my error. This is a pretty shift to excuse thy fault. To excuse my fault (said *Diana*?) If I have not yet the first offence to do thee, I pray God I may never have any other content, then that, which I now enjoy: It is wel that thou dost finde fault with me for being 35 married having parents. But it is wel (said *Syrenus*) that thou didst marry having another Love: And what power had that Love (saide *Diana*) where obedience was due to parents? And what power had those parents (saide *Syrenus*) that obedience, those times, those favourable or sinistrous successes of Fortune, to 40

overrule so true a Love, as before my departure thou didst shew
me? Ah *Diana*, I never thought there was any thing in the worlde,
that could dissolve so great a faith as that, and how much more
Dianas, considering that well thou mightest have married, and
not forgotten him, who loved thee so entyrely. But thinking of 5
the matter unappassionately, it was now better for me, since thou
wert resolved to marrie, and being married, to forget me quite.
For what reason saide *Diana*? For what, saide *Syrenus*? Bicause
there is no woorse thing in the worlde, then for a Shepherd to
love a Shepherdesse that is married, nor that makes him, (that 10
beares her true love and affection) sooner to loose his wits and
sences: the reason whereof (as wee all know) is, that the principall
passion which doth torment a lover (after the desire of his Mistres)
is cruell jealousie: For what dost thou then thinke, that a poore
unfortunate Lover that loves wel is able to do, what griefe 15
(thinkest thou) he passeth, when he knowes, that his Shepherdesse
is in the armes of her new married husband, and he bewailing and
weeping his disgrace and ill Fortune in the streete. And this is not
all the torment, when such a mischeefe and death remaines yet
thereof, that he must not complaine of it at all, but must suffer 20
(silly man) and holde his peace, bicause by complaining he shall
be thought no lesse then a foole or a madde man (a thing as
contrarie to his rest as may be:) For if the jealousies were of some
other Shepherd, that served her, by complayning of the favours
she doth him, and by hearing her excuses, the Lover might better 25
passe away his greefe; but this is such a kinde of torment, that in
an instant one shall loose it, if he have no stay in his desire. Leave
of this talke (said *Diana*) for thou hast no neede to love, nor to be
beloved. In respect of not having it to love (saide *Syrenus*) I am
glad in not having it also to be beloved. Strange is thy libertie 30
(said *Diana*) but stranger was thy forgetfulnes (said *Syrenus*) if
thou dost remember well the words thou spakest to mee at my
departure. But let us (as thou saiest) leave of to speake of things
which are past, and let us thanke time and Lady *Felicia* for those
that are present. And thou *Sylvanus*, take thy Pipe, and I will tune 35
my Rebecke to it, and let us sing some verses togither, although
so free a hart as mine cannot sing of anie thing, that may give
content to thine, that is of another qualitie. I will give thee a good
remedie for this (saide *Sylvanus*:) For let us imagine that we are
both in the same case, as this Shepherdesse made us live, when we 40

filled these hils and dales with our amorous complaints. *Sylvanus*
devise liked them all well, but *Selvagia* was a little displeased
thereat, who for that time, (bicause she would not seeme to be
jealous, where she was ascertained of so great love) helde her
peace: And the Shepherds began to sing in manner following.   5

Syrenus.

*I*F *teares cannot with tendernesse relent thee,*
  How can my song thy cruelty assured,
  Since nought of mine could ever yet content thee:
What hart was ever that so much endured?   1
  That to deride thou never canst suffice thee,
  A greefe that hath the worlds wonder procured.
Ah blinde conceite, let love nor time disguise thee,
  And such a thought of change that never told me
  But to thy good and my content advise thee.   1
Ah wilt thou in such cares and greefes enfold me,
  Fierce Shepherdesse, and in such lamentations
  To spend my dolefull yeeres, wilt thou behold me?
A hart that's thine, dispos'st thou in such fashions?
  Intreat'st thou thus a soule to thee affied,   2
  That the lest greefe it is to suffer passions?

Sylvanus.

Love such a knot, that's endles thou hast tied,
  That's blinde, and thou, and I more blinde intended:
  And she is blinde, for whom my life's denied: 2
For I sawe not my life, and pleasure ended,
  Nor she how I for her to death imploy me,
  Nor thou, that I in flames am thus incended.
Fell Love, shall faire Diana *now destroy me*
  With absence? then conclude (since hate surrounds it)   3
  To end my life, and fortunes that annoy me.
Joy's slowe, time flies, and with his shortnes wounds it,
  Hope dies, an amorous thought lives still augmented:
  Love shortens it, prolongs it, and confounds it.
To speake I am ashamed thus tormented,   3
  And though it greeves me, yet with ceaslesse payning
  Without the same I cannot live contented.

18 *me? Ed.] mo? Y.*

Syrenus.

O soule, forsake not now thy dolefull plaining,
 And you my wearied eies
 Cease not in swelling teares my cheekes to steepe,
 Since you have learn'd to weepe, 5
And waile the chiefest cause of all my cries.

Sylvanus.

And waile the chiefest cause of all my cries:
 Yet (cruell Shepherdesse)
 Sometimes they were of my most sweete content. 10
 O thoughts in sorrow spent,
How small time lasts a joy and happines?

Syrenus.

How small time lasts a joy and happines,
 And that sweete gracious smile, 15
 (Fortune) wherewith I sawe thee not accoyd?
 Now all is well imployd
In him, whom time doth counsell and beguile.

Sylvanus.

In him, whom time doth counsell and beguile, 20
 Love works his behest:
 But in his things who can him well advise?
 Or his deceites who spies?
O cruell Shepherdesse, O cruell brest.

Syrenus. 25

O cruell Shepherdesse, O cruell brest
 Whose crueltie is no
 Whit lesse then her brave beautie and her grace,
 And my mishap and case:
How to my cost my sorrowes doe I knowe? 30

Q

Sylvanus.

My Shepherdesse, in white and red more cleere,
Then both those roses pluckt, in May we see:
And brighter then the sunne beames sent
From their coruscant Orient
By morning, that upon thy foldes appeere: 5
How can I live, if thou forgettest me?
My Shepherdesse, thy rigour then impaire,
For crueltie becomes not one so faire.

Syrenus.   10

My faire Diana *more resplendant, then*
The Emerauld, or Diamond in the night:
Whose beautious eies doe cease
My sorrowes, that increase,
If gently that (perhaps) to me they bend.   15
So maist thou thy flocke so faire and white,
Come to my shadowed sheepefold in the heate,
That such a wretch thou would'st not ill intreate.

Sylvanus.

My Shepherdesse, when that thy yellow haire   20
Thou combest in the beames of shining sunne,
Dost thou not see the same obscured?
My pride and joy by them procured?
That am from hence beholding it so faire,
Woon now with hope, now with despaire undone,   25
But so maist thou thy beautie brave enjoy,
As thou wouldst give, a meane in such annoy.

Syrenus.

Diana, whose sweete name in all these hils
The wilde beastes tames, and crueltie rebates: 30
And whose surpassing beautie to it
Doth subject fortune, and undoe it.
And feares not love, but wars against his wils:
Respecting not occasion, time, nor fates.
*   To thee thy flockes and folds such joy may give,*   35
*   As carelesse of my greefe thou wouldst not live.*

Sylvanus.

The heate is past (Syrenus) *and doth cease,*
  The Shepherds to their folds begin to goe,
  And wearie grashoppers doe hold their peace:
The night will not stay long, which, hid belowe,   5
  Is comming in, while Phœbus in our skie
  Doth heere and there his vading light bestowe:
Therefore before the darkest shade shall lie
  Upon the ground, and while the wren doth sing
  In top of this greene Sicamour on hie,   10
Our wandring flockes together let us bring,
  And drive them where Diana *now doth stay*
  For us, while in the woods our voices ring.

Syrenus.

My friend, Sylvanus, *goe not yet away,*   15
  Since all his beames not yet the sunne doth hide,
  And that we have sufficient of the day.
There's time for us and for our flocke beside,
  And time to drive them to the river cleere.
For in this meade to day they shall abide: 20
  And, Shepherd, let my song be ended heere.

All the while that the Shepherds were singing, the Shepherdesse
Diana was leaning her faire face upon her hand, whose sleeve falling downe a little from her wrest, discovered an arme whiter then
the driven snow, she held her eies downe to the ground, powring 25
out such plentie of teares, as were sufficient arguments of more inward griefe and paine, then she would (though faine) have then
uttered. And as the Shepherds ended their song, with a deepe sigh,
in company whereof it seemed that her soule would have flowen
out, she rose up, and without taking her leave, went downe along 30
the valley, dressing her golden haire, whose vaile hung intangled
behinde in a bow, when she rose up. And if the Shepherds had not
tempered the great pitie which they had of her, with the little that
she had of them, neither the one nor the others hart had beene able
to indure it. And so all of them went to gather up their sheepe, that 35
(scattered abroad) went skipping up and downe the greene meadow.

The end of the sixth booke.

The seventh Booke of Diana of George of Montemayor.

AFter that *Felismena* had reconciled *Amarillis* and *Filemon*, and
left them with full purpose and resolution, the one never to
do any thing to the discontentment and complaint of the other: being now gon from them, she went downe along the valley,
wherein she wandred many daies without hearing any newes, that
might affoorde her the least content, that she desired: and yet
carrying with her an assured hope of sage *Felicias* wordes, she
did not let it passe out of her minde, but thought, that after so
many travels, Fortune would be wearie at the last of troubling
her any more: And these imaginations supported her somewhat in
the greatest torments of her desire. But travelling one morning
on her way, thorow the mids of a woode, and at the going out of
certaine thick bushes which appeared from the top of a high hill,
she beheld before her a most pleasant and greene Champaine
that lay all along beneath the hill, and of such length, that she
could scarce see to the end of it; for twelve miles right out it
butted upon the bottoms of certaine hils, that might hardly be
discerned. Thorow the mids of this pleasant plaine a goodly river
ranne, which in many places made fresh and faire bankes on both
sides, whereon grew thicke Birches, greene Sicamours, and divers
other trees; and in other places leaving the cristalline waters discovered to the wandring view, and in some (brinked with sandie
plats) did from a far off more bravely beautifie the faire river
bankes. The graine which was sowne in all those fields, was at
hand to yeeld up the desired fruit, and by reason of the fertill
soyle was verie well growen: which being mooved by a little gale
of winde, waved up and downe some in greene, and some in
yellow colours, which made most pleasant shades and delightfull
objects to the greedie eie. The greene and delectable vale was in
some places three miles broad, and in others a little more, and in
none lesse then this. The faire Shepherdesse therefore comming
downe her way from the hil above, entered into a great wood full
of Sicamours and wilde Olive trees; in the middes whereof were
many stately houses so sumptuously built, that they made her not
a little to marvell: And lifting up her eies on a sudden, there
appeared to her sight a great and faire Citie, which being full of

faire houses and stately buildings, from the top of a rockie hill that was right before her, reached in breadth with the wals to the great river that ranne thorow the mids of the plaine. The buildings of that famous citie were high, and wrought with as great arte, as humaine industrie could devise. Amongst the which were 5 many towres, Pyramydes, and shining pinnacles, reared up to the skies. The Temples were many, and sumptuous, the houses strong, the wals loftie and strongly embattelled; the bulwarkes thicke and full of munition: so that excelling in stately structure and even proportion, it made a faire show, and gave a goodly 10 glorie to the great and auncient Citie: all which from that place she severally beheld. The Shepherdesse was amazed to see that brave sight, and on the sudden to be so neere so faire a Citie; from whence, as from all other popular concurse with great care she endevored to flie. And yet she could not choose, but sat her 15 downe a little under the shadow of an Olive tree, to behold from thence all in particular which you have heard; and seeing that populous Citie, great *Soldina* her native Citie and Countrey came to her musing thoughts; from whence, the love that she bare *Don Felix* had exiled her, which was an occasion not to make her passe 20 it out of her memorie without teares, bicause the remembrance of a good thing lost, doth for the most part offer occasions of no lesse. But the faire Shepherdesse leaving that place and citie on the right hand, went softly on by a path hard by the river towards that part, where the Cristalline waters with a gentle and pleasant 25 noise runne smoothly into the Ocean. And having gone sixe miles by the pleasant bankes of that river, she espied two Shepherdesses at the foote of a great Oke neere to the river side, passing away the heat of the day, both which (though they were but meanely faire) yet in sweete favour and gentle behaviour, 30 were passing gracious. The hew of their faces was a nutbrowne sanguine, but amiable, the colour of their haire, a darke browne-abram; their eies and eiebrowes blacke, and yet of a sweete and mild aspect in their countenances. Upon their heades they had severall garlandes of greene Ivie, tied up togither with many roses 35 and sweete flowers. The fashion of their attire seemed to her to be different from any other kind of apparell, that she had seene till that time. But one of them rising up in great haste, to drive a flocke of sheepe out of a flaxe field, where they had broken in, and the other going to drive her goates to the river to drinke, 40

they went and sat them downe againe under the shadow of that
leafie Oke. *Felismena*, that had hid her selfe in a plat of high
bulrushes, and so neere to the Shepherdesses, that she might well
heare what passed betweene them, understood that the language
they spake, was the Portugal toong, and that the kingdome where- 5
in she was, was Portugall; for one of the Shepherdesses taking the
other by the hand with a sweete grace in her owne toong said
thus to the other. Ah my *Duarda*, what small reason hast thou to
despise him, who loves thee more then himselfe? How better
beseeming thee were it, not so ill to entreate a thought that is so 10
much employed in thy perfections? It greeves mee that so faire
a Shepherdesse shoulde bee so farre from pitying him that hath
so great neede thereof. The other, that seemed to bee more at
libertie, with a certaine disdaine, and a fillippe of her hande
(a common note of carelesse and free mindes) answered her thus. 15
Wilt thou have me tell thee, *Armia*? If I should trust him another
time, who hath so ill apaied the love I bare him, he shall not beare
the blame of the ill, that I shall procure by mine owne desire,
but my selfe. Lay not before mine eies the services, that this
Shepheard hath sometimes done me, nor tell me the reasons that 20
he gives thee to moove me, for the time is now past, when they
once helpt him. He promised to marrie me, and behold he hath
married another. What would he nowe have? Or what pretendes
this enemie of my quiet rest? What, now that his wife is dead,
would he have me marrie him? O God forbid that I should doe 25
my selfe so great injurie. Let him go, *Armia*, let him go: for if
he loves me so much as he saith, this love shall serve me for a
revenge of his deepe deceite. The other joyning her smiling face to
Duardas frowning countenance, and lovingly imbracing her, with
milde and gentle wordes replied thus. How wel hath all becomen 30
thee, gracious Shepherdesse, which thou hast said? I would
never desire to be a man, but even now, to love thee more then
mine owne selfe. But tell me, *Duarda*, why art thou so desirous to
have *Danteus* leade so sorrowfull a life? He saith, the reason that
thou hast to complaine of him, serves him for his excuse. For, 35
before he married, being with thee one day neere to the hedge of
Fremoselle, he saide unto thee. *Duarda*, my father wil marrie me,
what is thy advise in this matter? And that thou didst answere
him roughly. How now *Danteus*? Am I so olde, or have I so great

28 revenge *Ed.*] renenge *Y*.

power over thee, that thou dost aske my opinion and leave for
thy marriage? Thou maiest doe what thou list, and what thine
owne will and thy fathers shall oblige thee to: for in the like case
I my selfe would do no lesse: And this was spoken with an
estranged countenance, and not with that woonted kinde of 5
milde and gentle speech, but as if it had beene quite past thy
memorie, that thou didst once love him well. Callest thou this an
excuse (said *Duarda*) If I knew thee not *Armia*, so well as I doe,
thy wisedome and discretion should hazard their credit with me.
What should I answere a Shepherd, who published every where, 10
that there was nothing in the world whereon he would cast an
affectionate eie, but on me, how much more then, that *Danteus*
was not so ignorant, but that he understood by my countenance
and manner of my wordes, that with my will I would not have
answered him, as I did. What a mockerie was this (I pray thee 15
Armia) for him to meete me one day before this came to passe,
neere to the fountaine, and with many teares to say thus unto me.
Why art thou so ungratefull (*Duarda*) to the good will which
I beare thee, that thou wilt not be married to me without thy
fathers consent? when time (thou knowest) will weare out the 20
anger, that they may conceive thereof. Whom I then answered
thus. Content thy selfe *Danteus*, that I am thine, and that I can
never be any others, whatsoever shall befall unto me. And thy
word and promise, which thou hast given me to be my husband,
contents me well ynough: desire not then, in respect of staying 25
a little time longer, a thing, whereof such mischiefe may ensue.
At which wordes he tooke his leave, telling me the next day that
his father would marrie him, and requesting me to give him
leave, and not content with this, but to be married in deede three
daies after. Dost thou not therefore thinke this (*Armia*) a sufficient 30
reason for me, to use the benefite of that libertie, which with such
trouble of my thoughts I have at last obtained? These are things
(saide the other) soone spoken and passed betweene the truest
lovers, but must not be taken so much at the hart, nor so narrowly
interpreted, as thou dost understand them. For those, which are 35
spoken, thou hast reason, *Armia*; but for those that are done,
thou seest it well ynough, if they touch not our soules too neere,
that love well. In the ende *Danteus* married, and it greeves me not
a little, that so faire a Shepherdesse lived so small a time, and more,
to see that one whole moneth after her buriall being scarce past, 40

new thoughts began to occupie his minde againe. God tooke her away (said *Armia*) to the end that *Danteus* might be thine, for indeede he could be no others but thine. If this be so (said *Duarda*) that he that is ones, cannot be anothers, I finde my selfe now to be mine owne; and therefore cannot be *Danteus* his. But let us leave ₅ of a thing not worth the losse of time that is spent about it, which shal be better imployed in singing a song: And then both of them in their owne toong with a sweete grace began to sing that which followeth.

> *Times change and shall (as we doe see)*   10
> *And life shall have an ende:*
> *But yet my faith shall ever bee*
> *Whereon my eies depende.*
>
> *The daies, and moments, and their scope,*
> *The howres with their changes wrought,*   15
> *Are cruell enemies to hope,*
> *And friendes unto a loving thought.*
> *Thoughts still remaine, as we doe see,*
> *And hope shall have an end;*
> *But yet my faith shall not leave me,*   20
> *Her honour to defend.*
>
> *Inconstancie in trust contrived,*
> *Causeth great danger in conclusion,*
> *And life that is of hope deprived,*
> *Standes not in feare of disillusion.*   25
> *Times goe and come, as we doe see,*
> *And life shall have an end,*
> *But yet my faith shall never bee*
> *Distan'd for foe or friend.*

This song being ended, *Felismena* came out of the place, where ₃₀ she had hid herselfe, directly to that place where the Shepherdesses were, who amazed at her sudden sight, but more at her rare grace and beautie, went to her, and with loving embracings welcommed her, asking her of what countrey she was, and from whence she came. To which demaundes faire *Felismena* could not answer, but ₃₅ with manie teares asked them what countrey that was, wherein they nowe were. For by her owne toong she cleerely made them knowe, that she was of *Vandalia*, and that for a certaine mishap she was banished from her countrey. The Portugall Shepherdesses with their pitifull teares did the best they could to comfort her, being very sorrie for her exile, a common thing to that nation, 5 and more proper to the inhabitants of that province. And *Felismena* asking them what citie that was, which she had left, where the river with his christalline streames, and speedy course came running on with great force: and bicause she also desired to know, what castle that *Montemayor* was, which was scituate on the 10 hill, higher then the rest, and many other demands, one of them called *Duarda*, tolde her, that the citie was *Coymbra*, one of the most famous and principall cities, not onely of that kingdome, but of all Europe, for the brave territories and fieldes about it, which that great river (called *Mondego*) watred with his cleerest 15 waters. And that all those fieldes, where with great swiftnes it ranne, were called the fieldes of *Mondego*: And that the castle which she sawe before her, was the ancient light and glory of Spaine; which name (she saide) did better fit it, then the right name of it, bicause in the mids of the infidelitie of *Marsilius* the 20 Mahometicall king, who had so many yeeres encompassed it with a cruell and continuall siege, it did ever so strongly defend it selfe, that it was alwaies the conquerour, and never subdued, and that it was called in the Portugall toong *Montemor*, or *Velho*, where the vertue, valour, wisedome, and magnanimitie remained 25 for trophees of the noble deedes, that the Lords and Knights of it did in those daies, and that the Lords and Ladies that now dwelt in it, flourished in all kinde of vertues, and commendable parts. And so did the Shepherdesse tell her manie other things of the fertilitie of the soile, of the antiquitie of the buildings, of the riches of the 30 inhabitants, of the beautie, discretion, and vertues of the Nymphes and Shepherdesses, and of the aptnes and activitie of the jolly Shepherdes, that dwelt about that impregnable castle: All which things did put *Felismena* in great admiration. But the Shepherdesses requesting her to eate somthing (bicause they thought 35 she needed it) she thankfully accepted their curteous offer. And whiles she was eating that which the Shepherdesses had set before her, they sawe her shed so manie teares, that caused no small sorrow in them both. And desirous to aske her the cause of them, they were hindred by the voice of a Shepherd, that came 40

sweetely singing to the tune of his Rebecke, whom the Shepherdesses knewe to be the Shepherd *Danteus*, for whom *Armia*
pleaded so much to the gracious *Duarda* for pitie and pardon.
Who saide to *Felismena*. Although these are but homely cates
(faire Shepherdesse) and countrey Shepherdesses fare, yet fals it 5
out to be a dinner for a Princesse, for thou didst but little thinke
when thou cam'st hither, to dine with musicke. There is
not any musicke in the world (saide *Felismena*) that pleaseth me
better then thy sight and conversation, gracious Shepherdesse,
which by greater reason makes me thinke, that I am a princesse, 1
then the musicke thou talkest of. These words should be adressed
(said *Duarda*) to one of more woorth, and higher deserts then
I am, and that had a riper wit, and deeper conceite to understande
them. But howsoever I am, to my poore abilitie, thou shalt finde
an earnest will and an unfained affection in me readie to do thee 1
all the service it may. Ah *Duarda* (saide *Armia* to her) how discreete art thou, and how mightest thou not win the onely praise
of wisedome, if thou wert not cruell? Is there any woman in the
worlde like thee heerein, who of purpose art offring occasions of
impertinent speech, and to busie thy head with other matters, 2
bicause thou hast no list to harken to the wofull Shepherd that
by dolefull song is breathing out his sorrowes and mishaps.
Felismena understanding what that Shepherd was by *Armias*
wordes, praied them to be still and to give eare unto him, who
to the tune of his Rebecke did in his owne toong sing this song 2
following.

> SIghes, since you lighten not my hart,
>   Why go you not, why stay you still?
> For in the end hope doth impart
> A remedie unto mine ill.   3
>
> Yet hope to helpe me never stood,
> Where reason worketh all in vaine:
> Nor ever promis'd so much good,
> As crueltie doth give me paine.
> But love and trust give me an art,   3
> And qualitie of such a skill,
> That neither hope revives my hart,
> Nor crueltie the same doth kill.

Mine eies you neede not then complaine,
With which her faire ones I have seene,
And what neede you to feare againe,
Since viewed by her you have beene?
And therefore change shall have no part,   5
Nor entrance in my constant will,
Though crueltie doth kill my hart,
Or whether hope remaineth still.

The Shepherds musicke pleased *Felismena* better then the Shepherdesses meat, for she thought the song was made to complaine 10 more of his owne griefe, then to lament an others. And as he made an ende, she said. Shepherd, it seemes thou hast truely learned by my ils to complaine of thine owne. Unfortunate woman, that can neither heare, nor see any thing, which sets not before me the small reason I have, to desire life. But yet God 15 grant I may so long enjoy it, until mine eies may see the cause of their burning teares. Thinkest thou faire Shepherdesse (said *Armia* to her) that these words deserve not to be heard, and that the hart, from whence they came forth, to be more esteemed then this Shepherdesse regards them? Talke not saide *Duarda* of his 20 words, talke of his works; speake not of his dittie, but of his deeds, for by them his intent and meaning is to be judged. If thou dost enamour thy selfe of songs, and delightest in Sonets compacted of industrie of fine and flattering words; Thinke not, that I do so: for as they are things wherein I take least pleasure; so by 25 them I lesse perswade me of the love he beares me. *Felismena* then favouring *Duardas* reason, said. Behold *Armia*, how many ils might be avoided, and great mischiefes not effected, if we would not hearken to smooth and filed speeches, and lightly credit words framed by free harts: for, by nothing else they shew their 30 properties more, then by a cunning and false tale, uttered by an eloquent and fine toong; that when we thinke it most true, there is nothing more false. Unhappie me, that could not in time helpe my selfe with this counsell. But by this time was the Portugall Shepherd come where the Shepherdesses were, who in his owne 35 language saide to *Duarda*. If the teares of these eies, and the sighes of this my hart are not sufficient (Shepherdesse) to mollifie that hardnes, wherewith thou dost so ill intreate me, I require nothing else, but that my company may not be troublesome unto thee in these fields, and that the sorrowfull verses (which my griefe makes me sing, like to the dying swanne neere to this river) may be no occasion of thy miscontent and trouble. Passe away (faire Shepherdesse) the parching heate of the day under the shade of these greene Osiars, for thy swaine will drive thy goates to the river to drinke, and tarrie with them, while they are washing themselves in the cristalline waters. Kembe and adresse (lovely Shepherdesse) thy silke soft haire upon the brinke of this cleere fountaine, from whence issueth out the running brook, that round about watereth this sweete meadow: And in the meane time I will carrie thy faire flocks to feed, and keepe thy sheep from going into the corne, that growes along the river side. I pray thee (sweet Shepherdesse) take no care for any thing, for I have no rest all the while that I am not travelling about thy busines. If this seemes to thee but a small token of love, tell me then, wherein I may shew the good will and entire affection that I beare thee? For no especiall love doth wrong (to speake the truth) in any thing whereof it offers any experience at all. *Danteus* having made an end, the Shepherdesse *Duarda* answered him thus. If it be true (*Danteus*) that there is any love in the world, I have borne it thee, and as great, as thou thy selfe knowest. Never any of these Shepherds, that bring their flockes to feede in the fieldes of *Mondego*, and to drinke in these cleere waters, obtained so much as one onely word of me, whereby thou mightest have occasion to complaine of *Duarda*, nor of the love that she hath ever showen thee. Thy teares, and burning sighes have never touched any neerer at the hart then me. The day, mine eies beheld thee not, could not see any thing that pleased them. The bullocks that thou didst keepe, were of more account to me, and I had a greater care of them, then of mine owne. And (for the most part) fearing, least the keepers of this delightfull Champaine might hinder their feed, I went to the top of this little hill, to see if I could espie them, whereas I brought mine in place, when they could not feed the grasse of these faire river bankes, without feare of being impounded. And I was not afraid to put my selfe in this subjection and danger, to put thee in assurance and safetie. I know well, that of this my subject and apparant kind of love thy affiance did arise; and of thy affiance, that which thou dost. Thou did'st marie *Andresa* (whose soule is now in glorie) a thing that in times past, made me to die for griefe: but I prayed to God, that I might see my selfe at last revenged of her and thee, and after thy marriage I have suffered that, which thou and others sufficiently knowe: And in the end my Fortune hath concluded, that thine shall give me no more paine and care. Let me then injoy my libertie, and hope not to regaine that with me, which by thine owne folly and default thou hast so fondly lost.

The Shepherdesse having made an ende of her sharpe answer, and *Felismena* beginning to arbitrate the matter between them; they heard a great noise in the other side of the meadow, like to the sounde of blowes, and smiting of swordes upon harneies, as if some armed men had fought togither, so that all of them with great haste ranne to the place, where they heard the noise, to see what the matter was. And being come somewhat neere, they saw in a little Iland, (which the river with a round turning had made) three knights fighting against one. And although he defended himselfe valiantly, by shewing his approoved strength and courage, yet the three knights gave him so much to do, that he was faine to helpe himselfe by all the force and pollicie he could. They fought on foote, for their horses were tied to little trees, that grew thereabouts. And now by this time, the knight that fought all alone and defended himselfe, had laide one of them at his feete with a blowe of his good sword, which ended his life: But the other two that were very strong and valiant, redoubled their force and blowes so thicke on him, that he looked for no other thing then death. The Shepherdesse *Felismena* seeing the knight in so great danger, and if she did not speedily helpe him, that he could not escape with life, was not afraide to put hers in jeopardy, by doing that, which in such a case she thought, she was bound to performe: wherefore putting a sharpe headed arrowe into her bowe, shee saide unto them: Keepe out knights, for it is not beseeming men that make account of this name and honour, to take advantage of their enimies with so great oddes. And ayming at the sight of one of their helmets, she burst it with such force, that the arrow running into his eies, came out of the other side of his head, so that he fell downe dead to the ground. When the distressed knight sawe two of his enimies dead, he ran upon the third with such force, as if he had but then begun the combat; but *Felismena* helped him out of that trouble, by putting another

26 *Felismena Ed.*] *Filismena Y.*

arrow into her bow, the which transpiercing his armour, she left
under his left pap, and so justly smot his hart, that this knight also
followed his two companions. When the Shepherds and the knight
beheld what *Felismena* had done, and how at two shootes she had
killed two such valiant knights, they were all in great woonder. 5
The knight therefore taking off his helmet, and comming unto
her saide. How am I able (faire Shepherdesse) to requite so great
a benefite, and good turne, as I have received at thy hands this
day, but by acknowledging this debt for ever in my gratefull
minde. When *Felismena* beheld the knights face, and knew him, 1
her sences were so troubled, that being in such a traunce she could
scarce speake, but comming to her-selfe againe, she answered
him. Ah my *Don Felix*, this is not the first debt, wherein thou art
bound unto me. And I cannot beleeve, that thou wilt acknowledge
this (as thou saiest) no more then thou hast done greater then this 1
before. Beholde to what a time and ende my fortune and thy
forgetnesse hath brought me, that she that was woont to be
served of thee in the citie with Tilt and Tourneyes, and honoured
with many other things, whereby thou didst deceive me, (or
I suffered my selfe to be deceived) doth nowe wander uppe and 2
downe, exiled from her native countrey and libertie, for using
thus thine owne. If this brings thee not into the knowledge of
that which thou owest me, remember how one whole yeere
I served thee as thy page in the Princesse *Cesarinas* Court: and
how I was a solicitor against my selfe, without discovering my 2
selfe, or my thoughts unto thee, but onely to procure thy remedie,
and to helpe the greefe, which thine made thee feele. How many
times did I get thee favours from thy mistresse *Celia* to the great
cost of my teares and greefes: all which account but small *Don
Felix* in respect of those dangers (had they beene unsufficient) 3
wherein I would have spent my life for redresse of thy paines,
which thy injurious love affoorded thee. And unlesse thou art
weary of the great love, that I have borne thee, consider and weigh
with thy selfe the strange effects, which the force of love hath
caused me to passe. I went out of my native countrey, and came 3
to serve thee, to lament the ill that thou did'st suffer, to take upon
me the injuries and disgraces that I received therein; and to give
thee any content, I cared not to lead the most bitter and painefull
life, that ever woman lived. In the habite of a tender and daintie

26 onely *Ed.*] onley *Y.*

Ladie I loved thee more then thou canst imagine, and in the
habite of a base page I served thee (a thing more contrarie to my
rest and reputation then I meane now to reherse) and yet now in
the habite of a poore and simple Shepherdesse I came to do thee
this small service. What remaines then more for me to doe, but 5
to sacrifice my life to thy lovelesse soule, if with the same yet,
I could give thee more content: and if in lieu therof thou wouldest
but remember, how much I have loved, and do yet love thee: here
hast thou thy sword in thy hand; let none therefore, but thy selfe
revenge the offence that I have done thee. When the Knight 10
heard *Felismenas* words, and knew them all to be as true as he was
disloyall, his hart by this strange and sudden accident recovered
some force againe to see what great injurie he had done her, so
that the thought thereof, and the plenteous effusion of blood that
issued out of his woundes, made him like a dead man fall downe 15
in a swoune at faire *Felismenas* feete. Who with great care, and no
lesse feare, laying his head in her lap, with showers of teares that
rained from her eies, upon the Knights pale visage, began thus to
lament. What meanes this cruell Fortune? Is the periode of my
life come just with the last ende of my *Don Felix* his daies? Ah 20
my *Don Felix* (the cause of all my paine) if the plenteous teares,
which for thy sake I have shed, are not sufficient: and these which
I now distill upon thy lovely cheekes, too fewe to make thee come
to thy selfe againe, what remedie shall this miserable soule have
to prevent, that this bitter joy by seeing thee, turne not into 25
occasion of utter despaire. Ah my *Don Felix*, Awake my love, if
thou dost but sleepe, or beest in a traunce, although I would not
woonder if thou dost not, since never any thing that I could do,
prevailed with thee to frame my least content. And in these and
other lamentations was faire *Felismena* plunged, whom the Portu- 30
gall Shepherdesses with their teares and poore supplies, endevored
to incourage, when on the sudden they saw a faire Nymph
comming over the stony causey that lead the way into the Ilande,
with a golden bottel in one hand, and a silver one in the other,
whom *Felismena* knowing by and by, saide unto her. Ah *Doria*, 35
could any come at this time to succour me, but thou faire Nymph?
Come hither then, and thou shalt see the cause of al my troubles,
the substance of my sighs, and the object of my thoughts, lying
in the greatest danger of death that may be. In like occurrents
(saide *Doria*) vertue and a good hart must take place. Recall it 40

then (faire *Felismena*) and revive thy daunted spirits, trouble not
thy selfe any more, for nowe is the ende of thy sorrowes, and the
beginning of thy contentment come. And speaking these wordes,
she besprinkled his face with a certaine odoriferous water which
she brought in the silver bottle, whereby he came to his memorie
againe, and then saide unto him. If thou wilt recover thy life,
Sir Knight, and give it her that hath passed such an ill one for
thy sake, drinke of the water in this bottle: The which *Don Felix*
taking in his hande, drunke a good draught, and resting upon it
a little, founde himselfe so whole of his wounds, which the three
knights had given him, and of that, which the love of *Celia* had
made in his brest, that now he felt the paine no more, which
either of them had caused in him, then if he had never had them.
And in this sort he began to rekindle the old love, that he bare to
Felismena, the which (he thought) was never more zealous then
now. Whereupon sitting downe upon the greene grasse, hee tooke
his Lady and Shepherdesse by the hands, and kissing them manie
times saide thus unto her. How small account would I make of
my life (my deerest *Felismena*) for cancelling that great bond,
wherein (with more then life) I am for ever bound unto thee: for
since I enjoy it by thy means, I thinke it no more then right, to
restore thee that, which is thine owne. With what eies can I behold
thy peerelesse beauty, which (though unadvisedly) I knew not to
be such, yet how dare I (for that which I owe thee) cast them in
any other part? What wordes are sufficient to excuse the faults,
that I have committed against thy faith, and firmest love, and
loyaltie? Wretched and accursed for ever shall I be, if thy condition and clemencie be not enclined to my favour, and pardon:
for no satisfaction can suffice for so great an offence, nor reason to
excuse me for that, which thou hast to forget me. Truth it is,
that I loved *Celia* well, and forgot thee, but not in such sort that
thy wisedome and beautie did ever slide out of my minde. And
the best is, that I knowe not wherein to put this fault, that may be
so justly attributed to me; for if I will impute it to the yoong age
that I was then in, since I had it to love thee, I shoulde not have
wanted it to have beene firme in the faith that I owed thee. If to
Celias beautie, it is cleere, that thine did farre excell hers and all
the worlds besides. If to the change of time, this shoulde have
beene the touchstone which should have shewed the force and
vertue of my firmenes. If to injurious and trayterous absence, it

serves as little for my excuse, since the desire of seeing thee
should not have been absent from supporting thy image in my
memorie. Behold then *Felismena*, what assured trust I put in thy
goodnes, that (without any other meanes) I dare put before thee,
the small reason thou hast to pardone me. But what shall I doe to 5
purchase pardon at thy gracious hands, or after thou hast par-
doned me, to beleeve, that thou art satisfied: for one thing
greeves me more then any thing else in the world, and this it is.
That, though the love which thou hast borne me, and wherewith
thou dost yet blesse me, is an occasion (perhaps) to make thee 10
forgive me, and forget so many faults: yet I shall never lift up
mine eies to behold thee, but that everie injurie, which I have
done thee, will be worse then a mortal incision in my guiltie
hart. The Shepherdesse *Felismena*, who saw *Don Felix* so penitent
for his passed misdeedes, and so affectionately returned to his 15
first thoughts, with many teares told him, that she did pardon
him, bicause the love, that she had ever borne him, would suffer
her to do no lesse: which if she had not thought to do, she would
never have taken so great paines and so many wearie journeyes to
seeke him out, and many other things, wherewith *Don Felix* was 20
confirmed in his former love. Whereupon the faire Nymph *Doria*
came then to the Knight, and after many loving words and
courteous offers in the Ladie *Felicias* behalfe passed betweene
them, she requested him and faire *Felismena* to goe with her to
Dianas Temple, where the sage Ladie (with great desire to see 25
them) was attending their comming. *Don Felix* agreed thereunto,
and taking their leave of the Portugall Shepherdesses (who
wondered not a little to see what had happened) and of the woefull
Shepherd *Danteus*, mounting upon the horses of the dead Knights
that were slaine in the late combate, they went on their waie. 30
And as they were going, *Felismena* told *Don Felix* with great
joy, what she had past since she had last seene him, which made
him to marvell verie much, and especially at the death of the
three Savages, and at the Palace of the sage Ladie *Felicia*, and
successe of the Shepherds and Shepherdesses, and at everie thing 35
else contained in this booke. And *Don Felix* wondred not a little
to understand how his Ladie *Felismena* had served him so many
daies as his page, and that he was so far gon out of his wits and
memorie, that he knew her not all that while. And his joy on the
other side, to see that his Ladie loved him so well, was so great, 40

that by no meanes he could hide it. Thus therefore riding on
their way, they came to *Dianas* Temple, where the sage *Felicia*
was looking for their comming: and likewise the Shepherds
Arsileus, and *Belisa*, *Sylvanus*, and *Selvagia*, who were now come
thither not many daies before. They were welcommed on everie 5
side, and with great joy intertained; but faire *Felismena* especially,
who for hir rare vertues and singular beautie was greatly honored
of them all. There they were all married with great joy, feasts,
and triumphes, which were made by all the goodly Nymphes, and
by the sage and noble Ladie *Felicia*; the which *Syrenus* with his 10
comming augmented not a little, of whom, and of the Portugall
Shepherds *Danteus*, and *Duarda*, more shall be spoken in the
second part of this booke.

The end of the seaven Bookes of Diana of

George of Montemayor.   1

THE FIRST PART OF ENAMOURED DIANA,

made by *Gaspar Gil Polo*.

To the most noble and vertuous Lady
Doña Maria de Austria
y fuentes.

IF you were (my singular good Lady) that heavenly muse and divine fire from whence this little creature hath borrowed life and light, being most happie that it was borne under such a constellation, whose beames and influence have guided and indued it with those perfections, which now it presumeth by vertues thereof to possesse: Reason and dutie then it were to offer up unto your woorthines all the service it may, and humbly to crave of the same, That since now it commeth abroad to every ones view, it may in the forhead carie the imprinted golden character and warrant of your noble and renowned name: wherewith being protected, it feareth not any malignant spirit that may bite it. And little though this be which my zealous and dutifull affection, which I have ever borne to you and your honorable house (from whence many gallant personages, and rare and learned wits have sprung out) can present to such great bountie and vertue, the which nature having placed in a most beautifull and christalline figure, in every part spread foorth their beames with love and admiration: Yet respecting the minde of him that offers it, and the good will wherewith like bookes have beene received by Kings and great Lordes, I hope faire Lady, you will not condemne me of too much presumption by dedicating this unto your high patrocinie, when as the affiance which I have in your gentle Graces, noble minde and sweete perfections inforceth me heereunto, the which duly to be recommended and recounted, require a finer wit and fitter place. Which if at any time heereafter my happy fortune shall grant me, in nothing else so justly it shal be imploied, then in the deserved praise and

service of your Ladiship, whose illustrous person and house our
Lord defend and prosper many yeeres with increase of all happinesse. From VALENCIA the ninth of Februarie 1564.

The first Booke of *Enamoured*
DIANA.   5

AFter that appassionate *Syrenus* by the vertue of the mightie
liquor which sage *Felicia* had given him, was now delivered
out of *Cupids* handes, Love (working after his accustomed maner)
wounded anewe the hart of carelesse *Diana*, reviving in her brest
forgotten loves, bicause she should be captive to one that was 10
free, and live tormented for the love of one, who from the same
was most exempted: her greefe being thereby the more augmented, when it occurred to her thoughts that the small regard
that in times past she had of *Syrenus*, was now an occasion of his
forgetfulnes, and of that great contempt that he did beare her. 1
She was not only with these griefs, but with many more so
fiercely assaulted, that neither the holy bonde of matrimonie,
nor the reynes of seemely shame and modestie were able to staie
or mitigate the furie of her immoderate love, nor remedie the
sharpnes of her cruell torments, untill with lamentable com- 20
plaints, and pitifull teares she mollified the hardest rockes, and
savage beasts. Wherefore being by chance on a sommers day at
the fountaine of the Sicamours, about that time when the Sunne
was elevated to the Meridian point, and there calling to minde the
great content, that in that very place she had many times received 2
of her beloved *Syrenus*, and counting her passed delights with her
present greefes, and knowing that the beginning of her sorrowes,
and the fault was onely in herselfe, she conceived thereof such
greefe and anguish of minde, and was with such dangerous
affrightes sursaulted, that even then she thought desired death 30
would have made an end of all her troubles. But after she had
recovered some small vigour, yet the force of her passion, and the
violence wherewith love reigned in her brest, was neverthelesse
so great, that it compelled her to publish her torments to the
simple birdes, which from the greene boughes were listening to 3
her, and to the branchie trees that seemed to take compassion of

her greefe, and to the cleere fountaine, that with the solemne
murmur of the Christalline waters accorded with the notes of
her dolefull song: And so to the sound of a sweete Baggepipe,
which commonly she caried about her, she began to sing these
verses following.   5

LOng have I felt a silent paine of sorrow,
   Cruell, by that my senses it importunes
To such extremes, that I am forc't to borrow
   This last releefe against my heavie fortunes,
     To publish them unto the windes, that stay them   10
     Thorow out the world with pitie to convay them.

Then gentle Aire, performe this due of pitie,
   Let every region know my greevous anguish,
Breath out my paines, and tell in every citie
   The life of her, that in Loves want doth languish: 15
     Forgotten of a Shepherd that disdaines her,
     Who once did die even for like love that paines her.

O that this ill (death to my vitall powers)
   Hardly maintain'd amids these cruell fashions,
Springs of my late oblivion and those howers,   20
   Which I bestow'd, and thought not of his passions:
     And that the fault, that heertofore did blame me
     Causeth my paine, and with my paine doth shame me.

Hart breake in two for greefe when thought assailes thee
   Of those fell torments which thou once didst lend him,   25
Thou lov'st him now, but little it prevailes thee
   To pardon that, wherewith thou didst offend him.
     Who cried once for that which now I crie for,
     And died once for that which now I die for.

These present greefes of passions that confound me   30
   With ceaselesse paine, torment not in such measure,
As thoughts of my late crueltie doe wound me,
   Or when I thinke, I lost so deere a treasure:
     For they are heaven, to thinke that now I prize him,
     And these are hell, to thinke I did despise him.   35

22 blame me Bodl. Sus; blame me. CTr¹⁻² CUL BM¹⁻²

For if my little love (more fitly named
  Injurious hate) (whereof I now repent me)
Were not in fault (alas too lately blamed)
    Of all these present greefes, that thus torment me;
      Then with complaints I would not cease t'importune   5
      Ungentle love, and raile on cruell Fortune.

But I so proude for my admired beautie
  That flattred me, of sense was so bereaved,
That carelesse of my fault, and forced dutie
    I owde to Love, I never once perceaved,   10
      That Love did take revengement at his pleasure,
      And Fortune change without all meane or measure.

But Loves revenge wrought never such a woonder,
  Nor to so great despaire did ever drive one,
As thus on every side to breake asunder,   15
    And ruinate a hope that might revive one:
      And Fortune in her change made never any
      So great, as from one life to deathes so many.

Syrenus then, how art thou now assured
  Of thy revenge, which thou hast deepely taken   20
In my disgrace, which I my selfe procured:
    That since of late my love thou hast forsaken,
      No remedie for any greefe is left me,
      That of my woonted comfort hath bereft me.

For heeretofore as thou hast even, and morrow,   25
  Seene me disdaine thy sight with so small reason,
So maist thou now take pleasure in my sorrow,
    And with thy scornes my feeble comforts season:
      For now to love me, lies not in thy power,
      Though I must love thee till my dying hower.   30

So far from Cupids *force thy haps have blest thee,*
  And in thy libertie thou tak'st such glorie,
That (gentle Shepherd) I doe not request thee
    To cure mine ill (which cannot make thee sorie)
      But to beguile these paines by Love ordained,   35
      With one poore favour, though it were but fained:

And though mine ils, which thou art not contented
To remedie, nor dost pretend to cease them,
When to thy carelesse thoughts they are presented,
Whose hot revenge have vowed to increase them:
    Yet turne thine eies, and see how mine are flowing   5
    With rivolets of teares, that still are growing.

Behold my ruine, and my life decaied,
  My little hope, which in despaire I borrow,
My teares, my sighes, my senses all dismaied,
  Though not to take compassion of my sorrow,   10
    Yet see how with them all I am affreighted,
    In thy revenge to be the more delighted.

For though with greefe, wherewith I still am calling
  To mollifie thy hart, and have no power,
Nor that my teares, which evermore are falling,   15
  Cannot excuse my death one little hower,
    Then will I die for love of thee, and never
    Enjoy this breath without I love thee ever.

Enamoured *Diana* had not so soone made an end of her delightfull musicke, if on the sudden she had not beene interrupted by 20
a certaine Shepherdesse, which behinde a tuft of Hasels was
hearkening unto her: Who therefore espying her, gave a pause to
her sweete voice by cutting off the substance of her song, and
was not a little greeved (which by a naturall blush that tainted
her faire face, might easily be conjectured) that her song was 25
heard, and her griefe unknowen; especially perceiving the same
Shepherdesse to be a stranger and never seene in those parts
before. But she, who from a far off had heard so sweete a sound,
with silent steps drew neere to enjoy such daintie melodie; and
understanding the cause of her dolorous song, made on the sudden 30
so goodly a shewe of her excellent beautie before her, as the
Nocturnall Moone is woont to doe, when with her shining
beames it pearseth and overcomes the foggie thicknes of the
darke clouds. But seeing *Diana* to be somewhat troubled in
minde at her sight, with a merrie countenance, she thus began to 35
say unto her.

I have not a little (faire Shepherdesse) with my interrupting presence (which to small purpose hath thus disturbed thee) offended the great content, which I had to heare thee; but the desire I have to know thee, and to give thee some lightning for thy griefe, that causeth thee so pitifully to moane, may serve (if it please thee) for my excuse, and make me blamelesse heerein. For the which griefe, though it is bootelesse, as some say, to seeke any comfort; yet by a free will and reasons devoide of passion there may be sufficient remedies applyed. Dissemble not therefore with me thy sorrowes, and thinke it not much to tell me thy name, and the cause of thy sad complaints, since for this I will make no lesse account of thy perfections, nor judge thy deserts to be of lesse value.

Diana hearing these words, stoode a while without answering her againe, having her eies fastened on the rare beautie of that Shepherdesse, and her minde occupied in a doubtfull construction of that, which she should answere to her gentle offers and loving words, and in the end answered her thus againe.

If the great pleasure, which I take in beholding thee (unknowen Shepherdesse, and curteous without compare) and the comfort, which thy sweete words do promise me, might finde any small kinde of confidence or hope in my afflicted hart, I would then beleeve that thou wert able to remedie my sorrowes, and would not doubt to manifest my paines unto thee. But my griefe is of such tenour, that when it begins to molest me, it seiseth in such sort on my heart, that it stops up all the passages against remedie: Yet know (Gentle Shepherdesse) that I am called *Diana*, knowen too well in all the fields and villages hereabouts; and so let it content thee to knowe my name, and not to enquire further of sorrowes, since thou shalt profit thee no more, then to make thy selfe compassionate and condolent for my tender yeeres, seeing them oppressed with so many cares and troubles.

Thus are they deluded (answered the Shepherdesse) that make themselves slaves to fonde Love, who but beginning to serve him, are become so much his vassals, that they desire not to be free, and thinke it impossible to be manumitted from his servitude. If love be thy greefe (as by thy song I am sure it is) then know (faire Shepherdesse) that in this infirmitie I have no small experience: For I my selfe have beene manie yeeres a captive in like bondage, but now am free; blinde I was, but now have found out the way of truth: I have passed in the amorous Ocean manie

dangerous stormes and tempests, and now am safely arrived in
the secure haven of content and rest: And though thy paine be
never so great; yet hath not mine, I dare boldly say, beene lesse:
And since for the same I found out a happie remedie, banish not
hope from thy minde, shut not up thine eies from the truth, nor 5
thine eares from the substance of my words.

Are they words (said *Diana*) that shall be spent to remedie my
love, whose workes exceed the compasse and helpe of wordes.
But yet for all this faine would I know thy name, and the cause
that hath brought thee into our fields; the which if thou wilt 10
vouchsafe to tell me, shall so greatly comfort me, that I will for
a while suspend the complaints that I have begun, a thing perhaps which may not a little availe for the lightning of my griefe.

My name (said the Shepherdesse) is *Alcida*: but the rest which
thou demandest of me, the compassion which I have of thy 15
voluntarie greefe, will not suffer me to declare, before thou hast
embraced my wholsome remedies, though (perhaps) unsaverie
to thy distempered taste.

Every comfort, said *Diana*, shall be most gratefull to me that
commeth from thy hands, which neverthelesse is not able to 20
roote out the strong love in my brest, nor to remoove it from
thence, without carying my hart with it burst in a thousand
peeces: And though it might, yet I woulde not live without,
bicause I woulde not leave to love him, who being once forgotten
of me tooke so sudden and extreme a revenge of my unjust 25
crueltie.

Nay then (said *Alcida*) thou givest me no little hope and confidence of thy recoverie, since now thou lovest him, whom thou
hast heeretofore hated, having learned thereby the pathway to
oblivion, and acquainted thy will with contempt, and the more, 30
since betweene these two extremes love and hate there is a meane,
which thou must embrace and follow.

To this *Diana* replied and said. Thy counsell (faire Shepherdesse)
contents me very well, but I thinke it not sure enough for my
safetie, nor the best in common reason for my availe. For if my 35
will were put betweene love and hate, I shoulde sooner yeelde to
love then to hate; bicause being neerer to it, mightie *Cupid* with
greater force woulde assaile, and overcome me.

To this *Alcida* answered. Do not honor him so much, who
deserves it so little, calling him mightie, who may be so easily 40

overcommed, especially by those that choose out the meane abovesaid: for therein doth vertue consist, and where that is, all harts are armed with force and constancie against love.

Thou mightest better terme those harts cruell, harde, untamed, and rebellious, said *Diana*, which pretend to repugne their proper nature, and to resist the invincible force of love. And yet when they have oppugned it as much as they list, in the end they have little cause to bragge of their stoutnes, and lesse helpe to defende them with their foolish hardines. For the power of love overcomes the strongest holdes, and makes most way thorow, where it is most resisted: of whose marvels and memorable deedes my beloved *Syrenus* did on a day sing in this verie place, at that time when his remembrance was so sweete, as now most bitter to my soule. The which Sonnet, and all his other Ditties, which he then made and sung, I well remember, having ever a great care not to forget them for certaine causes, which perswaded me to register the words and deeds of my deerest *Syrenus* in perpetuall memory: But this which intreats of the mightie force of Love, saith thus.

> *T*Hat *mighty Love, though blinde of both his eies,*
>   *Doth hit the Center of the wounded hart:*
> *And though a boy yet* Mars *he foiles with dart,*
> *Awaking him, where in his net he lies:*
> *And that his flames doe freeze me in such wise,*
>   *That from my soule a feare doth never start*
>   *Most base and vile: yet to the highest part*
> *(Strengthned by land and sea) of heaven it flies.*
>   *That he, whom Love doth wound or prisoner take,*
>   *Lives in his greefes, and with his gives content:*
>   *This is his might that many woonder at.*
>   *And that the soule which greatest paine doth shake,*
>   *If that it doth but thinke of Loves torment,*
>   *The feare of such a thought forgetteth that.*

No doubt, said *Alcida*, but the forces of love are well extolled: But I would rather have beleeved *Syrenus*, if after having published the furie of *Cupids* arrowes to be so great, and after having commended the hardnes of his chaines, he had not also found out the meanes to set himselfe at libertie: And so I marvell that thou wilt so lightly give credit to him, who makes not his word and deed all one. For it is very cleere, that the Songs and Sonnets are a kinde of a vaine and superfluous praises, whereby lovers sell their ils for dangerous things, when that so easily of captives they become free, and fall from a burning desire to a secure oblivion. And if lovers feele passions, it proceedeth of their owne will, and 5 not of love, which is not but a thing imagined of men; a thing neither in heaven, nor earth, but in his hart, that entertaines it: whose power (if any he have) onely by the default of those he usurpes, who of their owne accord suffer themselves to be over-commed, offering him their harts for tribute, and putting their 10 libertie into his hands. But bicause *Syrenus* Sonnet may not so easily passe without an answere, give eare to this, which as it seemes was made in countermaund of that; and long agoe it is, since I heard a Shepherd called *Aurelius*, sing it in the fields of *Sebetho*, and as I remember, thus it said.   15

LOve is not blinde, but I, which fondly guide
    My will to tread the path of amorous paine:
  Love is no childe, but I, which all in vaine,
Hope, feare, and laugh, and weepe on every side:
Madnes to say, that flames are Cupids *pride,*   20
    For my desire his fier doth containe,
    His wings my thoughts most high and soveraine,
And that vaine hope, wherein my joies abide:
  Love hath no chaines, nor shaftes of such intent,
    To take and wound the whole and freest minde,   25
      Whose power (then we give him) is no more,
  For love's a tale, that Poets did invent,
    A dreame of fooles, an idoll vaine and blinde:
    See then how blacke a God doe we adore?

Dost thou therefore thinke *Diana*, that any one endued but 30 with reasonable understanding, will trust to things in the ayre as thou dost? What reason hast thou so truely to worship a thing so unruly and false, as the supposed God of love is, who is fained by fond and vaine heads, followed by dishonest mindes, and nourished in the braines of idle wantons? These are they, 35 who gave to Love that name which makes him so famous thorow out all the world. For seeing how fonde men for loving well did suffer so many sursaults, feares, cares, jealousies, changes,

and other infinite passions, they agreed to seeke out some principall and universall cause, from whence, as from a fountaine all
these effects should arise. And so they invented the name of
Love, calling him a God, bicause he was of many nations and
people feared, and reverenced, and painted him in such sort, that 5
whosoever sawe his figure, had great reason to abhorre his
fashions. They painted him like a Boy, bicause men might not
put their trust in him; Blinde, bicause they might not followe
him; Armed, bicause they might feare him; with flames of fire,
bicause they might not come neere him; and with wings, because 10
they might knowe him vaine and inconstant. Thou must not
understande (faire Shepherdesse) that the power which men
attribute to Love is, or may be any waies his: But thou must
rather beleeve, that the more they magnifie his might and valour,
the more they manifest their weakness and simplicitie. For in 15
saying, that Love is strong, is to affirme, that their will is weake,
by suffering it so easily to be overcommed by him: To saie, that
Love with mightie violence doth shoote mortall and venemous
arrowes, is to include that their harts are too secure and carelesse,
when that so willingly they offer themselves to receive them. To 20
say, that Love doth streightly captivate their soules, is to inferre,
that there is want of judgement and courage in them, when at the
first bruntes they yeelde; nay when sometimes without any combate they surrender their libertie into their enimies hands: and
finally all the enterprises which they tell of Love, are nothing 25
else but matter of their miseries, and arguments of their weakenes.
All which force and prowesse admit to be his, yet are they not of
such qualitie, that they deserve any praise or honour at all. For
what courage is it to take them prisoners, that are not able to
defend themselves? What hardines to assaile weake and impotent 30
creatures? What valour to wounde those that take no heede and
thinke least on him? What fortitude to kill those that have
alreadie yeelded themselves? What honour with cares to disturb
those, that are mery and joyfull? What woorthie deede to persecute unfortunate men? Truely faire Shepherdesse, they that would 35
so much extoll and glorifie this *Cupid*, and that so greatly to their
cost serve him, should (for his honour) give him better praises.
For the best name that amongst them all he gets, is to be but
a cowarde in his quarrels, vaine in his pretences, liberal of troubles,
and covetous in rewards. Al which names, though of base infamie 40

they savour, yet are those woorse which his affectionate servants give him, calling him fire, furie, and death, terming (Loving) no better then to burne, to destroy, to consume, and to make themselves fooles, and naming themselves blinde, miserable, captives, madde, inflamed, and consumed. From hence it comes, that 5 generally all complaine of Love, calling him a Tyrant, a Traytour, unflexible, fierce and unpitifull. All Lovers verses are full of dolour, compounded with sighes, blotted with teares, and sung with agonies. There shalt thou see suspicions, there feares, there mistrustes, there jealousies, there cares, and there all kindes of 10 paines. There is no other speech amongst them but of deathes, chaines, darts, poysons, flames, and other things which serve not but to give torments to those, that emploie their fancies in it, and feare when they call upon it. *Herbanius* the Shepherde famous in *Andolozia*, was troubled too much with these termes when in the 15 barke of a Poplar, with a sharp bodkin, instead of his pen, in presence of me wrote these verses following.

*H*E *that in freedome jets it proude and brave,*
   Let him not live too carelesse of himselfe:
For in an instant he may be a slave   20
   To mighty Love, and serve that wanton elfe:
     And let that hart, that yet was never tamed,
     Feare at the last by him to be inflamed.

For on that soule that proudly doth disdaine
   His heavie lawes, and lives with loftie will,   25
Fierce Love is woont t'inflict a cruell paine,
   And with most sharpe and dire revenge to kill:
     That who presumes to live without his power,
     In death he lives tormented every hower.

O Love, that dost condemne me to thy jaile,   30
   Love, that dost set such mortall coles on fire,
O Love, that thus my life thou dost assaile,
   Intreated ill, tormented by thine ire:
     Hencefoorth I curse thy chaines, thy flames, thy dart,
     Wherewith thou bind'st, consum'st, and kill'st my hart. 35

11 other *Ed.*] orher *Y.*

And now let us come to *Syrenus* Sonnet, whereby he seemes to make men beleeve, that the imagination of Loves enterprises sufficeth to overcome the furie of the torment. For if his operations be to kill, to wound, to make blind, to burne, to consume, to captivate, and to torment, he shall never make me beleeve, that 5 to imagine things of paine doth lighten the griefe, which must rather (as I thinke) give greater force and feeling to the passion: For when it is more in imagination, it remaineth longer in his heart, and with greater paine torments it. And if that be true which *Syrenus* did sing, I much marvell that he receiving so deepe 10 a taste in this thought, hath now so easily changed it, by meanes of so cruell oblivion, not onely of loves operations, but also of thy beautie, which ought not for any thing in the world to be forgotten.

Alcida had scarce finished these last words, when *Diana* lifting 15 up her eies (for she suspected somewhat) perceived her husband *Delius* comming downe from the side of a little hill bending his steps towards the fountaine of the Sicamours, where they were togither: whereupon cutting off *Alcidas* discourse, she said unto her.   20

No more, gentle Shepherdesse, no more; for we will finde fitter time hereafter to heare out the rest, and to answer thy weake and common arguments: For behold my husband is comming downe yonder hill towards us, and therefore I thinke it best to turne our talke to some other matter, and with the tune of 25 our instruments to dissemble it: and so let us begin to sing, bicause when he is come neere unto us, he may not be displeased at the manner of our conversation: whereupon *Alcida* taking her Cytern, and *Diana* her Bagpipe, began to sing as followeth.   30

Provencall Rythmes.

Alcida.

*W*Hile Titan *in his Coach with burning beames*
    Over the world with such great force doth ride,
That Nymphes, and their chaste companies abide   35
In woods, and springs, and shallowe shadowed streames:
And while the prating grashopper replies
Her song in mourning wise,

Shepherdesse sing
So sweete a thing,
That th'heavens may bee
By hearing thee
Made gentle, on their owne accord to power   5
Upon this meade a fresh and silver shower.

Diana.

Whiles that the greatest of the Planets staies
Just in the mids betweene the East and west,
And in the field upon the mowers brest   10
With greater heate doth spread his scorching raies:
The silent noise this pleasant fountaine yeeldes,
That runs amids these fieldes,
Such musicke mooves,
As woonder prooves,   15
And makes so kinde
The furious winde,
That by delight thereof, their force they stay,
And come to blowe as gently as they may.

Alcida.   20

You running rivers pure and christalline,
That all the yeere doe make a lively spring,
And beautifie your banks and every thing,
With Cowslips, Lillies, and sweete Colombine,
The cruell heate of Phœbus *come not neere*   25
To heate this fountaine cleere,
Nor that such sweete
Liquour, with feete
Troubled be not
Of sheepe or goat: 30
Nor that the teares, which faithlesse lovers wast
In these fine waters never may be cast.

Diana.

Greene flowrie meade, where natures curious die
Hath showen her colours divers in their kinde,   35
With trees, and flowers, whereto they are combinde,
Which paintes thee foorth so faire unto the eie:

In thee thy boughes of verdure may not knowe
The blustring windes that blowe,
Prosper, and give
Flowers, and live:
Not to be lost
By heate or frost:
Nor angrie heaven in furie doe not spoile,
Nor hurt so faire a meade, and fertill soile.

Alcida.

Heere from the hurly burly, and the noise
Of stately courtes sequestred, every one
Reposedly lives by himselfe alone,
In quiet peace, in harmlesse sportes and joies:
In shades sometimes, laide downe on Floras *pride*
Neere to some rivers side,
Where birdes doe yeeld
Sweete notes in field,
And flowers fine
Odours divine:
And alwaies with an order soveraine
The meadow laughes, the wood, the hill, and plaine.

Diana.

The noise made heere by silent gentle windes
In flowrie boughes, the leaves that softly shake,
Delighteth more, then that the people make
In great assemblies, where their sundrie kindes
Of proud demeanours, and high majesties,
Are foolish vanities:
Their solemne feastes
Breede but unrestes,
Their honours name
Blinde errours frame:
And all their holy wordes cleane different
From that, that in their harts was ever ment.

Alcida.

Ambition heere no snares nor nets regardes,
Nor avarice for crownes doth lay her bates:
The people heere aspire not to estates,
Nor hungers after favours, nor rewardes: 5
From guile and fraude, and passion, as we see,
Their harts are ever free.
Their faith's not vaine,
But good and plaine:
Their malice small, 10
They just to all,
Which makes them live in joy and quiet peace,
And in a meane sufficient for their ease.

Diana.

To new found worlds, nor seas, that rage and swell, 15
The simple Shepherd never sailes in vaine:
Nor to the furdest Indias, *for his gaine,*
Thousandes of leagues, and duckates there to tell:
Unto the field he comes as well content,
With that that God *hath sent;* 20
As he that spendes
Rents without endes:
And lives (perdie)
As merily
As he, that hath great flockes upon his hils, 25
And of good ground a thousand acres tils.

Delius from a far off heard the voice of his faire wife *Diana,* and
perceiving that another answered her, made great haste to goe see
who was in her companie: wherefore hiding himselfe behind
a great Mirtle, neere to the fountaine, he listened to their singing, 30
as one that still sought occasions of his woonted jealousie. But
when he understoode that their songs were far from that which
he suspected, he was well pleased in minde: But yet the great
desire he had to know the other, that was in companie of his wife,
made him draw neere unto the Shepherdesses; who courteouslie 35
saluted him, but especially *Diana,* whom with a smiling and

angelicall countenance she most sweetely entertained. And being
set neere unto them, *Alcida* saide.

I thinke my selfe (*Delius*) greatly bound to Fortune, who hath
not onely favoured me, by presenting to mine eies the excellent
beautie of thy *Diana*, but also by making me knowe the man, 5
whom she hath onely chosen, and thought most worthy to
possesse so rare a gem, by yeelding her libertie so frankly into his
hands; which choise no doubt (as she is wise) cannot be but
deemed most high and soveraigne: So I marvell much againe,
that in lieu thereof, and of that intire love which she beares thee, 10
thou makest so small reckoning of her, as to let her goe one step
without thy company, or be a minute out of thy sight. If she be so
firmely rooted in thy hart, which I may well presume, how can
that love thou owest her be so small as only to content thy selfe
with her lively figure engraven therein, and not feede thine eies 1
with the continuall sight of her singular beautie.

Then *Diana* (least *Delius* by his answere might have hazarded
his blunt wit and rude education) tooke him by the hand and said
unto her.

Delius hath but little reason to thinke himselfe so happie (as 20
thou saist) to have me for his wife, or so much in his presence,
as by meanes thereof to forget his flocks, and granges, matters
of more consequence, then the poore delight which he may take
by viewing that beautie, which thou dost unworthily attribute
unto me. 2

Do not to so small purpose (said *Alcida*) prejudicate thy comely
graces, *Diana*, nor offer such injurie to the generall voice the world
hath of thy perfections, since it is no lesse beseeming a faire
woman to have some small conceit and opinion of herselfe, then
a point of rash judgement to terme her proud and arrogant, that 3
doth moderately acknowledge the same. Therefore hold thy selfe
(*Delius*) for the happiest man in the world, and with pride injoy
this favour that Fortune hath bestowed on thee, who never gave,
nor can give any thing, that in felicitie may be comparable with
the husband of *Diana*. 3

These words so sweetely delivered by *Alcida*, and that faire
face, and eies of hers, which (all the while she was talking) *Delius*
both marked and gazed on, made so deepe an impression in his
hart, that at the ende of her gentle and discreet words, he was so
greatly enamoured of her, that, like a sencelesse and astonished 4

man, he had not one word to answere her againe, onely giving, with a new burning sigh, a manifest token of the greene wound, that *Cupid* had made in his conquered hart.

But now about this time they heard a voice, the sweetnes whereof delighted them marvellously. They gave therefore atten- 5 tive eare unto it, and casting their eies from whence it resounded, they saw a Shepherd comming with a wearie pace towards the fountaine, and going like one that was surcharged with griefe and anguish of minde, singing as followeth.

> *I Cannot be by Loves wrath more tormented,* 10
> *Nor Fortune can to me be more unstable:*
> *There is no soule in hope so little able,*
> *Nor hart that is with paine so much contented:*
> *Love doth inforce my fainting breath, that striveth*
> *The better to endure my hard rejection,* 15
> *And yet with hope my suffrance, and affection,*
> *And life will not consume, that yet reviveth:*
> *O vainest hart, sad eies, whose teares have spent me,*
> *Why in so long a time, and with such anguish,*
> *End not my plaints, and spirits deadly languish?* 20
> *O woes, sufficeth it not what you have sent me?*
> *O Love, why dost thou thus my torments nourish,*
> *And let* Alcida *in her freedome flourish?*

The Shepherd had scarce ended his song, when *Alcida* know-ing who he was, trembled like an Aspen leafe in everie part of 25 her bodie; wherefore she rose up in great haste to be gone before he came to them, requesting *Delius* and *Diana* not to tell him that she had beene there, since it was as much as her life was worth, if that Shepherd whom she hated more then death, did either finde or had any knowledge of her. They promised her so to do, though 30 verie sorie for her sudden and hastie departure. *Alcida* as fast as she could hye her, recovered a thicke wood not far from the fountaine, and fled with such celeritie and feare, as if she had beene pursued by some hungrie and cruell Tygre.

Immediately after the Shepherd wearied with extreme travell 35 and trouble, came to that place, which Fortune (it seemed) condolent for his griefe, had offered him, and that cleere foun-taine, and *Dianas* companie for some lightning of his paine: who

being faint after his painfull journey, and seeing the Sunne in the
pride of his heat; the place verie pleasant; the trees casting forth
coole shades; the grasse fresh and greene; the fountaine cleere
and cristalline, and *Diana* passing faire; thought good to rest
himselfe a while, though the earnest care and haste of that he 5
went seeking, and the ceaselesse desire he had to finde it, gave his
wearied bodie no place of rest, nor ease to his afflicted minde:
The which *Diana* perceiving, shewed her selfe as courteous towards him, as *Delius* jealous eie (who was present) would give
her leave; and yet entertained the strange Shepherd with sweete 10
words, as well for his owne deserts, which she deemed not small;
as also for that she perceived him tormented with the like grief
that she was. The Shepherd cheered up by *Dianas* friendly welcome and seemely favours, of a miserable man, thought himselfe
happie by finding out so good a chaunce. But they being thus 15
togither, *Diana* by chaunce casting her eie aside, could not see
her husband *Delius*, who newly surprised in *Alcidas* love, when
Diana tooke least heed of him, and while she was entertaining the
newe Shepherd, pursued amaine the Shepherdesse that fled away,
and tooke the verie same way with a strong resolution to follow 20
her even to the other part of the world. *Diana* not a little per-
plexed to see her husband wanting so on the sudden, called and
cried a good while togither on the name of *Delius*, but all in vaine
to get an answere from him in the wood, or to make him leave of
his fonde pursuite, who rather running after her as fast as he 25
could, thought at the last to sease upon his beloved *Alcida*.
Whereupon when *Diana* perceived that *Delius* appeared in no
place, she shewed her selfe a most sorrowfull woman for him,
and lamented in such pitifull sort that the Shepherd to comfort
her, said thus unto her.   30

Afflict not thy selfe thus without reason (faire Shepherdesse)
and beleeve not thine owne imaginations so greatly prejudiciall
to thy rest and quiet: for the Shepherd whom thou missest, is
not so long since wanting, that thou maiest have anie cause to
thinke that he hath forsaken thee. Pacifie then thy selfe a little, 35
for it may be that when thy backe was turned, he having some
desire to change place, secretly got away, unwilling (perhaps)
that we shoulde see him go for feare of staying him, being invited
by the coole shades of those greene Sicamours, and by the fresh
and pleasant winde that is gently blowing them; or else perhaps 40

discontented for my comming hither, thinking my companie troublesome, whereas now without it he may merrily passe the heate of the day away.

To this answered *Diana*. By these words (gracious Shepherd) which thy toong hath uttered, and forced cheere which thou dissemblest, who cannot conceive the greefe that consumes thy life? Thou shewest well that love is thy torment, and art accustomed to deceive amorous suspicions by vaine imaginations. For it is a common tricke of lovers, to work their thoughts to beleeve false and impossible things, bicause they would not credite things that are certaine and true. Such comforts (gentle Shepherd) availe more to quote out the sorrow of my greefe by thee, then to remedie my paine. For I know well enough, that my husband *Delius* is fledde after a most faire Shepherdesse, who went but even now from hence, and in regarde of the great and fervent love wherewith he beheld her, and sighes, which for her sake came smoking from his hart, I do verily beleeve (knowing moreover how stedfastly he performes that he imagines or takes in hand) that he will not leave following that Shepherdesse, though he thinke to come never in my sight againe. And that which greeves me most is, that I know her disposition to be so rigorous, and her hart so great an enimie to Love, that she will not onely shew him no pitie, but with great despite contemneth the most soveraigne beautie, and greatest deserts that may be.

At these very wordes the sorrowfull Shepherd thought that a mortall dart pierced his chill hart, and therefore saide. Unhappie me most wretched Lover, what greater reason have not these harts (not made of stonie flint) to be sorrowfull for me, when thorow out the worlde I seeke the most cruell and pitilesse Damsell that lives on earth? Ah faire Shepherdesse, thou hast good cause to be sorrie for thy husband, for if she whom he followes, be so cruelly conditioned as this, then must his life be in great danger.

By these words *Diana* cleerely perceived, what his greefe was, and that the Shepherdesse that ranne away at his comming, was the very same, whom in so many parts of the worlde he had sought. And so she was indeede; for when she began to flie from him, she tooke the habite of a Shepherdesse, by that meanes not to be knowne nor discovered. But for that present time *Diana*

1 discontented *Ed.*] discontended *Y*.

dissembled with the Shepherd, and woulde tell him nothing of
the matter, to keepe her worde and promise which she had given
Alcida at her departure: And also bicause it was now a good
while since she was gone, and ranne with such haste thorow the
thicke wood, that it was impossible for him to overtake her. All 5
which if she should tell the Shepherd, she thought would serve
for nothing else but to adde a fresh wounde to an old sore, and to
trouble his minde more, by giving him some little hope to attaine
to his purpose, when by no meanes he was able to obtaine it.
But bicause she desired to know what he was, the summe of his 10
love, and the cause of her hate, she said unto him.

Comfort thy selfe (Shepherd) in these thy complaints, and of
curtesie tell me their cause: for to lighten them, I would be glad to
know who thou art, and to heare the successe of thy mishap, the
report whereof will be no doubt delightfull to thee, if thou beest 15
so true a lover as I do take thee.

He then without much entreatie, both of them sitting downe by
the cleere fountaine began thus to say. My greife is not of such
quality, that it may be told to al kind of people, though the good
opinion I have of thy deserts and wisedome, and the confidence 20
which thy vertues and peerelesse beautie do suggest to mee,
urge me to lay open before thee the totall summe of my life (if so it
may be called) which willingly long since I would have changed
for death.

Know therefore faire Shepherdesse, that my name is *Marcelius*, 25
and my estate far different from that, which my habite doth
testifie: for I was borne in *Soldina*, the chiefest citie in *Vandalia*, of
parents for birth and bloud renowned, and in all wealth and
power abounding. In my tender yeeres I was caried to the king of
Portugalles court, and trained up there, where, not onely of all the 30
chiefest Lords and Knights I was beloved, but especially of the
king himselfe, insomuch that I had never his good will and leave
to depart from thence, untill at the last he committed to my
government a charge of certaine men of warre, which he had in
the coast of *Africa*. There was I a long time captaine of the 35
townes, and fortresses that the king had on the sea side, remaining
with my chiefest garrison in *Ceuta*, where the originall of all my
hard haps was first commenced. For in that towne (to my great
harme) dwelled a noble and renowned Knight called *Eugerius*,
who had also a charge by the King, and government of the same 40

towne, whom God (besides that he had adorned and inriched him with the gifts of nature, and Fortune) had blessed with a Sonne called *Polydorus*, valiant without compare, and with two daughters, called *Alcida* and *Clenarda*, women of most rare and excellent beautie. *Clenarda* was verie skilfull in drawing of her 5 bow and in shooting; but *Alcida* which was the eldest, endowed with incomparable beautie: whose vertues so inflamed my hart with burning love, that they have caused me to leade this desperate kinde of life, which I now passe away, wishing for death, which everie day I call upon and attend. Her father was so tender and 10 charie over her, that few times he suffered her to be out of his sight, which thing was no small impediment to the opening of my griefe and great love I bare her, except sometimes when it was my fortune to see her by an appassionate eie, and many sighes (maugre my will) came forciblie out of my brest, I signified my paines unto 15 her. At one time among the rest, I wanted not opportunitie to write a letter unto her, which fit occasion by favourable fortune granted me, I omitted not but wrote to her this letter following.

Marcelius *his letter to* Alcida. 20

*T*Hat majestie so princely, grave, and sweete,
  That modest blush, that gentle seemely grace,
   Those lookes so chaste, and haviour so discreete,
Those golden vertues, that thou dost imbrace
  (Besides thy beautie, which the world resoundes   25
   With famous name) from heaven that brought their race,
In such a narrow streight, with bleeding woundes
  Have set my hart (Alcida *heavenly faire*)
   That every thing my woonted rest confoundes;
For that which breedes my love, is my despaire,   30
  And so restraines my soule, that faine it would
   Say nought, although it cost my vitall aire.
What man of flint, that ever did behold
  The burning beames that thy faire eies doe cast,
   But waxed dumbe, and died with mortall cold?   35
Who ever sawe those beauties rare and chaste,
  More perfect then the starrie skie above,
   Or any living now or gone or past,

That presently felt not a fervent love?
   The cause whereof his senses so would use,
   As not to let him speake for his behove:
So much I passe by silence, that I muse
   That sad complaintes my hart doe never kill,   5
   Nor breake my brest with anguish so confuse:
My joies are none, my woes continue still,
   My paine is firme, and all my hope is vaine,
   I live alas, and die in greevous ill:
And take revenge upon my selfe againe,   10
   That which I most eschew, doth take me straight:
   And what I most desire, I lest obtaine:
For that, that lest behooves me, I awaite,
   Not comfort for my greefe, that never endes,
   Joying in paine, wherewith my soule I fraight: 15
Yet my delight and life so far extendes,
   As thought of that great distance doth abide,
   That twixt thy beautie, grace, and me dependes:
For in my soule I doe conceive a pride,
   That I have put it in so high a place: 20
   Where constancie and hope my hart doe guide.
But yet thy gentle, and sweete Angels face
   Against my soule such mortall war doe threate,
   That thousand lives dare not abide the chace.
To feare me yet the passage's not so great,   25
   Nor way so steepe, nor craggie, that shall stay
   My forward steps with danger, or deceate:
I follow then my ruine and decay,
   The path of paine, and seeke not to decline
   From greevous plaints, that force me every day.   30
Yet endlesse joy my heavie hart doth shrine,
   And glads my life, by wished paine opprest:
   That glories strangely in these greefes of mine.
Paine's my delight, my plaints my sport and jest,
   My sighes sweete soundes, my death my glory makes,   35
   My woundes my health, my flames my happy rest,
Nothing I see, which stirs not, and awakes
   My furious torment and her endlesse wheele;
   But happy fortune by the same it takes:
These ils (sweete Mistresse) for thy sake I feele,   40

And in these passions live, and die tormented
With equall paine, and suffrance, well contented.
Let then a man despairing of releefe,
Who to thy love his doubtfull life assignes,
Moove thee to some compassion of his greefe, 5
By reading of these hart-breake written lines,
   Since that he craves no helpe for all his mone,
   But onely that his torment may be knowne.

This was the letter I wrote unto her; the penning whereof, had
it beene as fine, as the purpose fortunate, I would not have 10
changed my skil in posie for famous *Homers.* It came to *Alcidas*
hands, in whose hart (when finally she knew the summe of my
griefe, though at the first the contents of my letter with my too
great presumption did somewhat offend her) it made deeper
impressions then I imagined, or hoped for. Then I began to 15
manifest my selfe for her open Lover, by making manie brave
Justes, and encounters at Tilt and Tourney, running of wilde
Buls, and *juego de Cannas,* by celebrating for her sweete sake and
service Moresco sportes on horsebacke in the day time, and
maskes and stately dances in the night, causing consorts of sundrie 20
musicke to delight her, and making verses, impresas, and Ana-
grammes of her love and name, and many other gallant shewes
and inventions more for the space of two whole yeeres togither.
At the ende whereof, *Eugerius* thought me woorthie to be his
sonne in law, and by the request of some great Lords in those 25
parts, offered me his faire daughter *Alcida* for wife. We concluded
that the espousall rites should bee solemnized in the citie of
Lysbone, bicause the king of *Portugall* might with his presence
honour them: and therefore dispatching a Poste with all haste,
by him we certified the king of this marriage, and requested his 30
majestie to give us leave (having commended our charges and
affaires to persons of trust) to celebrate it there. Whereupon the
report of this solemne day was published thorow all the citie,
and places farre and neere, which caused so generall a joy, as was
due to so faire a dame as *Alcida,* and to so faithfull a lover as my 35
selfe. Unto this passage my good fortune conducted me, thus
high she reared me up to throw me downe afterwardes headlong
into the depth of miseries, wherein (wretched man) I still remaine. O transitorie good, mutable content, vading delight, and

inconstant firmenes of mundaine things! What greater joy could
I have wished for, then that I had alreadie received, and what
greater crosse am I able to suffer then this, which I now carie
about me? Oh faire Shepherdesse, entreat me no more to molest
thy eares with so large and lamentable a historie, nor to pierce 5
thy compassionate hart with recitall of my ensuing calamities.
Let it content thee, that thou hast knowen my passed felicities,
and desire not to search out farther my present greefes, bicause
I assuredly know, that as my long and pitifull historie will be
tedious to thy eares, so will my continued disgraces alter thy 10
reposed minde.

    To which *Diana* answering said. Leave off (*Marcelius*) these
excuses, for I would not desire to know the successe of thy life,
onely thereby to rejoice my minde with thy contents, without
sorrowing for thy calamities, but woulde rather heare everie 15
part of them, to bewaile them also in my pitifull hart.

    How greatly woulde it please me, faire Shepherdesse (saide
Marcelius) if the good will I beare thee did not force me to content thee in a matter of so great grief. And that which greeves me
most, is that my disgraces are such, that they must needs fill thy 20
hart full of sorrow, when thou knowest them; for the paine that
I must passe by telling them, I reckon not so great, but that I
would willingly suffer it in lieu of thy contentment. But bicause
I see thee so desirous to heare them out, although they shall
force me to make thee sorrowfull; yet I will not seeme to leave 25
thy will herein unsatisfied.

T Hen Shepherdesse, thou must knowe, that after my un-
    fortunate marriage was agreed upon, the Kings licence being
now come, her old father *Eugerius*, who was a widower, his sonne
Polydorus, and his two daughters *Alcida* and *Clenarda*, and the 30
haplesse *Marcelius*, who is telling thee his greevous accidents,
having committed the charges left us by the King to sufficient
and trustie Gentlemen, embarked our selves in the port of *Ceuta*
to goe by sea to the noble citie of *Lisbone*, there to celebrate (as
I saide) the marriage rites in presence of the King. The great 35
content, joy, and pleasure which we all had, made us so blinde,
that in the most dangerous time of the yeere, we feared not the
tempestuous waves which did then naturally swel and rage, nor
the furious and boysterous winds, which in those moneths with

greater force and violence are commonly woont to blow: but committing our fraile barke to fickle Fortune, we launched into the deepe and dangerous seas, heedlesse of their continuall chaunges, and of innumerable misfortunes incident unto them. For we had not sailed far, when angrie Fortune chastised us for our bold attempt, bicause before night came on, the warie Pilot discovered apparant signes of an imminent and sudden tempest. For the thicke and darke cloudes began to cover the heavens all over, the waves to roare and murmur, and contrarie windes to blow on everie side. O what sorrowfull and menacing signes, said the troubled and timorous Pilot? O lucklesse ship, what perils assaile thee, if God of his great goodnes and pitie do not succour thee? He had no sooner spoken these words, when there came a furious and violent blast of winde, that puffed and shooke the whole bodie of the ship, and put it in so great danger, that the routher was not able to governe it, but that tossed up and down by this mightie furie, it went where the force of the angrie waves and windes did drive it. The tempest by little and little with greater noise began to increase, and the raving billowes covered over with a fomy froth mightily to swell: The skies powred downe abundance of raine with throwing out of everie part of it fearful lightnings, and threatned the world with horrible thunders. Then might there be heard a hideous noise of Sea monsters, lamentable outcries of passengers, and flapping of the sailes with great terrour. The winds on everie side did beat against the ship, and the surges with terrible blowes shaking her unsteadie sides, rived and burst asunder the strong and soundest plaunchers: Sometimes the proud billowe lifted up us to the skies, and by and by threw us downe againe into deepe gulphes, the which also with great horrour opening themselves, discovered to our fearfull eies the deepe and naked sandes. The men and women ran on everie side to prolong their ensuing and haples death; and did cast out, some of them dolefull sighs; other some pitifull vowes; and others plentie of sorrowfull teares. The Pilot being appalled with so cruell Fortune, and his skill confounded by the countenance and terrour of the tempest, could now no more governe the tottered routher. He was also ignorant of the nature and beginning of the windes, and in a moment devised a thousand different things. The marriners likewise agast with the agonie of approching death, were not able to execute the Masters

commaund, nor (for such lamentations, noise and outcries)
could heare the charge and direction of their hoarse and painfull
Pilot. Some strike saile, others turne the maine yarde; some make
fast againe the broken shrouds; others mende and calke the riven
planks; some ply the pompe apace, and some the routher; and in 5
the end, all put their helping hands to preserve the miserable ship
from inevitable losse. But their painfull diligence did not helpe
them, nor their vowes and teares profit them to pacifie proud
Aeolus and *Neptunes* wrath: but rather, the more the night came
on, the more the winds blew, and the storme waxed greater and 10
more violent. And now darke night being fully come, and angrie
Fortune continuing still her severe punishment, the olde Father
Eugerius being past all hope of helpe and remedie, looking on his
children and son in lawe, with an appalled and altered countenance, felt such great sorrowe for the death that we had to 15
passe, that his greefe and compassion for us, was more bitter to
our soules, then the thought of our proper and present misfortunes. For the lamenting olde man, environed on every side with
care and sorrowe, with a pitifull voice and sorrowfull teares, said
thus. Ah mutable fortune, common enimie to humane content, 20
howe hast thou reserved so great mishap and miserie for my
sorrowfull olde age? O thrise blessed are they, who fighting in the
middes of bloudie battails, with honour die in their yoong and
lustie yeeres, bicause not drawing foorth their line to wearied old
age, have never cause with greefe to bewaile the untimely death 25
of their beloved children. O extreme sorrow! O balefull successe!
who ever ended his daies in so heavie a plight as I poore distressed man, that hoping to have comforted my naturall death, by
leaving them to the worlde, that might have survived, not onely
to performe the due of my last obsequies, but to continue my line 30
and memorie, must now (miserable man) perish in their deerest
companie. O my deere children, who would have thought that
my life and yours should ende at one time and by one misfortune!
Faine woulde I (poore soules) comfort you; but what can a
sorrowfull father tell you, in whose hart there is such aboundance 35
of greefe and want of consolation. But comfort your selves my
children, by arming your invincible soules with patience, and lay
all the burden of your sorrow upon my backe, for besides that
I shall once die for my selfe, I must suffer so manie deaths more,
as you have lives to leese.   40

This did the olde and sorrowfull man abruptly deliver with so many teares and sobbes, that he could scarce speake, embracing first one and another, and then altogither for his last farewell, before the very point of danger and death was fullie come. But now to tell thee of *Alcidas* teares, and to recount the greefe that I endured for her sake, were too difficult and long a narration. Onely one thing I will not omit to tell thee, that that which did most torment me, was to thinke, that the same life which I had offered up for her service, should now be jointly lost with hers.

In the meane while, the forlorne and tossed ship, by the force and violence of the fierce westerne windes, which by the streights of *Gibraltar*, came blowing as they were madde, sailed with greater speede then was expedient for our safetie, and being battered on every side with the cruell blowes of envious fortune by the space of a daie and a night (unable also to be guided by the skill and ceaselesse labour of the marriners) ran many leagues in the long *Mediterranean* sea, wheresoever the force of the waves and windes did carrie her. The next day following Fortune seemed a little while to waxe more calme and gentle, but on a sudden turning againe to her accustomed crueltie, she drove us into such danger, that nowe we looked not for one halfe hower of life. For in the ende a fierce and mightie tempest came so suddenly upon us, that the ship driven on by the force of a boisterous blast, that smit her on the starboord, was in so great danger of turning bottome up, that she had now her forepart hidden under the water: whereupon I undid my Rapier from my side (espying the manifest and imminent danger) bicause it might not hinder me, and imbracing my *Alcida*, leaped with her into the Sciffe that was fastened to the ship. *Clenarda*, that was a light and nimble damsell, followed us, not forgetting to leave her bowe and quiver in the ship, which she esteemed more then any treasure. *Polydorus* imbracing his old father *Eugerius*, had also leapt in with him amongst us, if the Pilot of the ship with another mariner had not beene before him: But at that very instant when *Polydorus* with olde *Eugerius* were next to them, preparing themselves to leape out of the ship, a mighty great blast of winde smiting on the larboord, brake the cockboate from the ship, and drove them so far asunder, that those miserable men that were in her, were constrained to tarrie there still, from which time (unlesse a little while after) we

20 accustomed *Ed.*] acccustomed *Y*.

lost sight of them, and knew not what became of the ship, but
doe verily thinke, that it was either swallowed up by those cruell
waves, or else smiting upon some rocke or sandes neere to the
coast of Spaine, is miserably cast away. But *Alcida, Clenarda,* and
I remaining in the little Sciffe that was guided by the industrie of 5
the Pilot, and of the other mariner, went floting up and downe
a day and a night attending every minute of an hower apparant
death, without hope of remedie, and ignorant in what coast we
were. But the next morning finding our selves neere to land, we
made towardes it amaine. The two mariners that were very skilfull 10
in swimming, went not alone to the wished shore, but taking us
out of the boate caried us safely thither. After that we were
delivered from the perils of the sea, the mariners drew their
Sciffe to lande, and viewing that coast where we arrived, knew
that it was the Iland *Formentera,* woondering not a little that in so 15
small time we had run so many miles. But they that had so long
and certaine experience of the casuall effects, which outragious
tempests are woont to cause, marvelled in the end not much at
the preposterous course of our navigation. Now were we safely
com to land, secure from the dangers of passed fortune, but yet 20
surcharged with such sorrow for the losse of *Eugerius* and *Polydorus,* so ill intreated by greef and care, and so weakened by hunger
and cold, that we had no lesse sure hope of our safety, nor recovery of our lives, then joy of our passed perils. I passe over
with silence, faire Shepherdesse, the great complaintes that *Alcida* 25
and *Clenarda* made for the losse of their father and brother,
bicause I wold quickly com to the period of this lacrymable
historie, and to the haples successe that befell to me since I came
to that solitary Iland: For after that in the same I was delivered
from Fortunes crueltie, Love envying that poore content of 30
mine, became my mortall foe so extremely, that sorrowing to
see me escaped from the tempest, with a new and greater greefe
(when I thought my selfe most safe) he tormented my scarce
revived soule. For alas, wicked love wounded the Pilots hart
(whose name was *Sartofano*) and so enamoured him on *Clenardas* 35
beautie, that (to come to the end of his desire, by imagining and
hatching in his wicked hart a strange and inopinate treason) he
forgat the lawe of faith and friendship. And thus it was: That
after that the two sisters had with bitter teares and lamentations
offered up the sorrowfull effectes of their loving harts as obsequies 40

to the ghostes of their deceased parents, it fell out that *Alcida*, wearied with the long greefe and troubles that she had passed, laide her selfe downe upon the sand, and being overcome with deepe melancholie, fell fast asleepe. The which when I perceived, I said to the Pilot.   5

My friend *Sartofano*, unlesse we seeke out somthing to eat, or if in seeking, our hard fortune will not conduct us where we may finde some foode, wee may make full account that we have not saved our lives, but rather changed the manner of our death. Wherefore I pray thee, my good friend, to goe with thy fellow 10 marriner to the first village thou canst finde in this Iland to seeke out some victuals for the sustenance of our hungrie bodies.

Whereunto *Sartofano* answered. Though Fortune hath sufficiently favoured us by bringing us safe to lande, yet thinke not (*Marcelius*) to finde any thing heere to eate; this being an Iland, 15 of townes desert, and of people inhabited: But to comfort you againe, I will tell you a remedie, how to save our selves from dying for hunger. For, see you yonder little Iland right over against us, and so neere to this? There is so great store of venison, conies, and hares, and many other wilde beasts, that in great 20 heardes they go togither without feare or danger at all. There also dwelleth a certaine Hermite, whose celle is never without bread, oyle, and meale. I therfore thinke it best that *Clenarda* (who is cunning in shooting, and having her bowe and arrowes heere so fit for the purpose) passe over in the boate to the Ilande to kill 25 some of those wilde beasts, whom my fellowe and I will transport whilest you staie heere to beare *Alcida* companie: for it may fall out that we will returne before she awake, and come hither againe with good store of fresh and savorie provision.

Although *Clenarda* and I liked *Sartofanos* counsell well, least of 30 all suspecting his suttle and secret treacherie, yet she would never consent to go into the Iland without my company, for feare of committing herselfe alone to the rude marriners; whereupon she requesting my companie, I made many excuses to staie behinde, telling her that it was not meete to leave *Alcida* alone and sleeping 35 in so solitarie a place: Who answered me againe, that since the distance of the place was but small, the game much, and the sea somwhat calme (for by that time that we were a litle while on lande, the tempest began to cease) we might go hunt and come

22–23 without bread, oyle, *Ed.*] without, bread, oyle *Y.*

againe before *Alcida* (who had not slept so long before) awaked.
In the end she shewed me so many perswasions, that forgetting
what I had to do in such a case, without more adoo I agreed to go
with her; which thing greeved *Sartofano* to the hart, who had
rather had *Clenardas* company alone for the better effecting of his 5
wicked purpose. But yet the Traytour for all this wanted not
suttletie to prosecute his divelish pretence. For *Alcida* being left
asleepe, and both of us got into the Sciffe, and lanched into the
deepe, before we came to the Iland all unawares and unprovided
of weapons (for I had left mine in the ship, when I skipt out of it 10
to save my life) I was assayled by both the marriners, and unable
to helpe my selfe, bound both hand and foote. *Clenarda* seeing
their treason, for sudden griefe would have lept into the sea; but
she being staied by the Pilot, and carried from the place where
I was to the other ende of the boate, he said thus in secret to her. 15
Trouble not thy selfe (faire gentlewoman) to see us so rudely
entreate this Traitour, but quiet thy minde, for what is done, is
all for thy service. For know (faire Mistresse) that this *Marcelius*,
when we arrived at the desert Iland, had some private talke with
me, and prayed me to perswade thee to goe a hunting into this 20
Iland; and when we should be at sea, to steere the boate directly
from that place, telling me, that he was greatly in love with thee,
and that he would leave thy sister in the Ilande, onely and without
impediment to enjoy his pleasure of thee: And the deniall of his
companie with thee to this place, which faintly he used, was but 25
dissembled to colour his wicked intent the more. But I considering with my selfe what a vile and barbarous a part it was to offer
violence to so singular beautie, and to so good a Ladie, to prevent
this inhumanitie from thy great goodnes, even at the verie point
when he would have committed his treason, resolved to be loyall 30
unto thee, and so have bound *Marcelius* as thou seest, with
determination to leave him in this case at the shoare of a little
Iland which is neere at hand, and afterwards to returne with thee
to the place where we left *Alcida*: This is the reason that makes me
do thus, and therefore consider well what thou meanest to doe. 35
When *Clenarda* heard this smooth tale, which the wicked Traitour
so cunningly had told her, she beleeved it so truely, that presently
she bare me mortall hatred, and was well pleased, it seemed, that
I was carried to the place, where *Sartofano* did meane to lande me.

12 hand and foote *Ed.*] hand foote *Y*.

For with a frowning countenance she beheld me, and for very
anger could not speake a word, untill she had a pretie while
rejoyced in her secret hart to thinke of the revenge and punishment, that should light upon me, not telling me one word of that
brave deceit, wherewith she was so much abused. All which when 5
by her joyfull countenance I perceived, and that my bonds did
not grieve her, it made me say thus unto her. What meanes this
sister, doest thou esteeme so lightly of both our paines, that so
soone thou hast ended thy complaints? Perhaps thou art in good
hope to see me by and by at libertie to be revenged of these vil- 10
lanous Traitours? Then like a fierce Lyonesse she told me, that
my imprisonment and bonds were for no other cause, but for the
cruell intent I had to leave *Alcida*, and to carrie her away, and the
rest, whereof the false Pilot had wickedly informed her. When
I heard these words, I never felt like griefe in my life, and instead 15
of laying violent hands upon these Traitours, with vile and outragious words I railed upon them; and with good proofes so well
perswaded her of the truth, that she perceived by and by that it
was a manifest peece of treason, sprung up of *Sartofanos* vile and
filthie love: Whereupon she made so great lamentation, that she 20
fell foorthwith into the pitifull discourse of their deceite, which
was forcible enough to have mollified the craggie rockes we
passed by with ruthe and compassion, though it wrought nothing
in the hard harts of those two wicked monsters. Imagine then
now how the little sciffe that floted up and downe the wide seas, 25
was in a small time carried a great way from the Ilande, when
unfortunate *Alcida* awaking, and seeing her selfe all alone, and
forsaken, turned her sorrowfull eies to the maine sea, and not
finding the sciffe, how in everie part of the shoare thereabout, she
went seeking up and downe and found no creature at all. Ah thou 30
maist conceive (faire Shepherdesse) what anguish of minde she
felt in these crosses of unjust Fortune! Imagine besides, what
plenty of teares she powred forth, in what extremities and wants
she was, how sometimes (perhaps) she would have cast her selfe
into the sea, and how often in vaine she called upon my name. 35
But alas we were gone so far, that we could not heare her pitifull
outcries, and might onely perceive (how by shaking a white
scarffe up and downe in the Aire) she incited us to turne backe
againe, which the wicked Traitour *Sartofano* would never agree to.

12 were *Ed.*] where *Y.*

But making the greatest haste away that he could, he brought us
to the Iland of *Yviça*, where disimbarking us, they left me fast
bound to an anchor that was pitched in the ground. That way by
chance came certaine Marriners of *Sartofanos* acquaintance, companions like him selfe, whom though *Clenarda* never so much   5
informed of her estate, innocencie, and misfortune, yet it availed
her nothing to make them take pitie on her, but they rather gave to
the Traitour sufficient provision, who went to imbarke himselfe
againe with *Clenarda*, whom poore soule (at her perill) she must
needes follow; from which time hitherto I never saw nor heard   10
any newes of them. There was I left all alone bound hand and
foote, and pinched with intolerable hunger. But that which most
of all greeved me, was *Alcidas* want and sorrow, who was likewise left alone in the Iland *Formentera*, and in lieu thereof regarded not mine owne, which was presently remedied. For at the   15
noise of my loude and lamentable outcries, certaine Marriners
came to me, who being more pitifull then those before, gave me
some meate to stanche my extreme hunger. And at my incessant
request, they armed for my sake a Fregantine, and carrying with
them some store of meate and wine, with weapons, and other   20
necessaries embarked themselves in my companie, and within
a short time, with swift and speedie oares it came to the Iland of
Formentera, where *Alcida* was left a sleepe. But for all that I could
doe by seeking up and downe in it, and hallowing in everie
place, and calling aloud on *Alcidas* name, I could neither finde her, 25
nor by any signe perceive that she was there. I then thought that
she had desperately throwen her self into the sea, or else that
she had beene devoured of wilde beasts. But yet seeking up and
downe the plaines and shoares, and all those rockes and caves,
and most secret corners of the Ilande, in a peece of a rocke,   30
made in forme of a quarrie, I found these verses with a sharpe
point of steeled knife, engraven, which said thus.

> O Sandie desart, and drie barren meade,
>   Thou that hast heard the sound of my lament,
> O swelling seas, fierce winde to changing bent,   35
> Chang'd with my sighes, that are in sorrow bread,
> Hard rocke, wherein for ever may be read

36 *bread, Ed.*] *bread Y.*

My torment heerein graven, and permanent:
Truly report my paines which you present.
For that Marcelius *heere hath left me dead,*
(My sister stolne, he hath forgotten mee)
His faith, his sailes, and then my hope forlorne 5
Commend I to the windes, and witnes yee
That love I will not any man that's borne,
To scape those seas where calmes are never any,
Nor combat foes, that are so fierce and many.

I cannot tell thee (faire Shepherdesse) how deepe a wound my 10
soule felt, when I read these letters, knowing that for anothers
fault and vile deceit, and by the hard event of cruell fortune I was
so suddenly abhorred of *Alcida*: wherefore resolving with my
selfe not to leade a life replenished with such woes and miseries,
I woulde forthwith with one of their swordes have pierced my 15
heavie hart, had not one of those marriners who suspected such
a thing, by maine force hindred mee from it. With comfortable
words therefore they brought me backe againe halfe dead into their
Fregatte, and being mooved at my importunate and pitifull praiers,
for a peece of money caried me towards the coast of *Italy*, and 20
landed me in *Gayeta* in the kingdome of Naples. Where enquiring of
every one that I knew and met, after *Alcida*, and publishing certaine tokens of her, at the last by certaine Shepherds which came
thither in a ship of *Spaine*, I heard some newes of her, which
ship passing by *Formentera*, found hir there al alone, and tooke 25
her in; and that she had taken upon her the habite of a Shepherdesse; with as strong a resolution to hide her-selfe from me,
as strange to live unknowne in those disguised weedes. Which
when I understood, I also apparelled my selfe like a Shepherd,
the better to finde her out, and wandring up and downe, and 30
seeking her thoroughout all that kingdome, coulde never finde
her, nor heare which way she was gone, untill a long time after
I understoode that she knew how I had notice of her, which made
her flie the farther from me, and to passe into *Spayne* in a shippe of
Genua. Then I embarqued my selfe presently to follow her, and 35
hither I am come into *Spayne*, where having troden the greatest
part of it in seeking her up and downe, have not yet found any
one, that coulde tell mee any newes of this cruell one, whom with

4 *Brackets supplied. Ed.*

so great greefe and trouble of minde and bodie I am continually
seeking, and can never finde.

   This is (faire Shepherdesse) the tragedie of my life, this is the
cause of my death, and this the processe of al mine ils: In which
so sad discourse if I have been too tedious, the fault is thine, since 5
my unwilling toong, by thy importunate requestes was constrained to tell it. And that which now I crave of thee (gentle
Shepherdesse) is, that thou wouldest not trouble thy selfe to
applie any remedies to my sorrowe, nor comfort my cares, nor to
stop the teares, which with so just cause are due to my cordiall 10
greefe. *Marcelius* having ended his sorrowfull historie, began to
make a most dolefull complaint, and to sigh so forciblie, that it
was great pittie to beholde him. Faine would *Diana* have told him
tidings of his *Alcida*, which was not long since in her companie;
but to performe her worde, which she had promised not to dis- 15
cover her unto him, and also for that she sawe it would but have
tormented him more, by giving him notice of her, who extremely
hated him, helde her peace: And rather wished him, to comfort
himselfe by entertaining an assured hope and confidence of his
future gladnes, since she herselfe doubted not before it was long 20
to see him very joyfull in the presence of his beloved Mistresse.
For if it was true (as he beleeved) that *Alcida* went wandring up
and downe in the companie of Shepherdesses and Nymphes of
Spaine, she could not then (saide *Diana*) bee long unhidden from
him, and so she promised him to cause an enquirie and search to 25
bee made in the strangest, remote, and solitarie places, and in the
fieldes most frequented by them, but especially charging him to
have a regarde to his owne life, and promising him to performe
that which she had offered. For which unexpected curtesies,
Marcelius yeelding her infinite thankes, would have taken his 30
leave, saying, that after a fewe daies he thought to returne thither
againe, and to give her a full account of al those accidents that in
seeking out *Alcida* might happen unto him. But *Diana* staying
him, saide. I will not be so great an enimie to mine owne content,
to let thee goe out of my companie, but would rather (bicause 35
I see my selfe forsaken of my husband *Delius*, as thou art of thy
Alcida) have thee staie and eate (if it please thee) a little of my
simple cheere to refresh thy selfe, who hast (it seemes) no
small need thereof. And after when the shadowes of the trees
and hils waxe greater, we will both go home to our village, 40

where with that rest (which continuall greefe will suffer us to take)
we will passe the night away, and in the morning betimes hasten
us towardes the Temple of chaste *Diana*, where the sage Lady
Felicia makes her abode, whose secret wisedome will minister
remedies to our painfull passions. And bicause thou maiest the 5
better enjoy the rurall conversation and countrey plaines of the
Shepherds and Shepherdesses of our fieldes, it shall be best for
thee, not to change thy pastorall habite, nor to discover thy selfe,
but to name thy selfe, and in apparell and fashions live wholly
like a Shepherd. *Marcelius* being willing to do that, which *Diana* 10
told him, did eate a little of that which she had taken out of her
neat scrip, and quenched his thirst with the savorie water of the
cleere fountaine, both which were so needfull for him, as for one
that travelling all the day before, had neither eaten nor drunke:
and then they went on their waies towards the village. But they 15
had not gone foorth many paces, when in a little thicket not farre
from the path way, they heard the resounding voices of certaine
Shepherds, who sweetely sung to the tune of their mery Bagpipes,
and bicause *Diana* was delighted much in musick, she praied
Marcelius to go to the place where they were, who being come 20
neere unto the wood, *Diana* knew the Shepherds *Taurisus* and
Berardus, two great corrivals in her love, and commonly wont to
go togither in company, and sing in emulation the one against
the other. Whereupon *Diana* and *Marcelius* not entring into the
place where the Shepherds were, but yet hiding themselves 25
behinde certaine Okes so nigh, that they might heare the sweetenes
of the musicke, listened to the Shepherds songs, being not perceived of them at all, who though they knew not the cause and
effect of their songs, was so neere at hand, yet divining (as it
were) that their enimie was harkening unto them, by cleering up 30
their pastorall voices, and making most delicate and different
stops with them, they began to sing this Eglogue following.

Taurisus.

N<small>OW</small> *that the sunne doth hide his golden beames*
  Behinde the hils, whose shadowes doe increase: 35
And labouring men unyoke their wearie teames
  And leave of worke, their wearied lims to ease:

---

1 where with *Ed.*] wherewith *Y.*

My sheepe forsake your pastures, and attend
  Unto my fainting voice and hollow cries,
Which without stint or pause of time, I send
  Disorderly unto the carelesse skies:
Harke how my poore and miserable hart   5
  Is in the deepest of a burning flame,
And how my bowels and every inward part
  Are melted with the scorching of the same:
    That flame I meane and heate, wherewith my sencelesse soule doth
      trace   10
    Th' Angelicall and peerelesse beautie of Dianas *face.*

Berardus.

Before the sunne in radiant Coche doth glide
  Downe to the West, to leave our Hemisphere,
And suffers not the deaw of evening tide   15
  To fall upon the meadowes any where,
Thou simple Sheepe that oft hast heard my voice,
  And gentle lambes which all the sommer long
With merrie glee doe in these meades rejoice,
  Now lend a gentle eare unto my song: 20
My ruthfull song and verse shall not intreate
  (Though all the same within my brest I beare)
Of any flames, or coles, or burning heate:
  But of that mortall cold and frozen feare,
    Wherewith doth bridle and correct the sencelesse soule apace   25
    Th' Angelicall and peerelesse beautie of Dianas *face.*

Taurisus.

When that my painefull thoughts and pensive minde
  Doe but imagine of her comely graces,
Then burnes my soule so strangely, that I finde   30
  My vitall spirits to leave their proper places:
Love doth inforce this suffrance, weake by kinde,
  And hope, that's flowne away with feathered paces,
    To make my flames still burning in my brest,
    Which gives me not one hower of wished rest.   35

Berardus.

When I consider of my base estate,
And high perfections of my Shepherdesse,
Then doth my hart retire with fearefull gate,
And pinching frost my timorous soule possesse: 5
Love wills I live in hope of happinesse,
And so I doe sometimes, but fortunes hate
To quaking feare subjecteth every power,
Which makes me not enjoy one happy hower.

Taurisus. 10

In such ill time, I sawe the burning light
Of those cleere stars, whose like was never seene,
That face, that grace, those vertues infinite,
With which Diana *raignes as fairest Queene:*
That my desires are kindled by those bright 15
And shining beames, that I doe never weene
To hope for ease of these excessive flames
That burnes my soule, and breedes a thousand blames.

Berardus.

In such ill time I sawe those daintie handes 20
Of whitest Ivorie, fram'd for thousand smartes,
And those two eies, where little Cupid *standes*
Wounding the freest mindes with mortall dartes:
That my small forces with his mighty bandes
Confounded, foiled, and fearfully departes, 25
And then remaines so weakned with his ire,
That shivering feare doth conquer my desire.

Taurisus.

Didst ever see a lightning from the skies
With mightie force to rend an aged Oke? 30
So strong is that and terrible, which lies
Within my brest, all smoothered in the smoke:

6 *wills Ed.*] *will Y.*

Didst ever see the violent force of brookes,
   That from the highest rocks fall headlong downe?
So proud, so fierce, and angrie in her lookes
   Diana seemes, when she begins to frowne:
      But her pretences are too far   5
To make me sad by base and servile feare,
      For greater that the dangers are,
   The greater is the firmenes which I beare.

Berardus.

Didst ever see the snowe in any hill   10
   To lie, and melt before the sunnie beames?
So doe I waste with sighes, and teares distill
   Before those lights that from her beautie streames:
Didst ever see in any bloodie broile
   Some simple Shepherd put to fearefull flight?   15
With no lesse feare (poore man) I doe recoile,
   Leaving my sheepe (whilome my best delight)
      And in this cold and frozen feare
I merit more, and in my trembling brest
      More comfort and content doe beare,   20
   Then in that heate so bold and manifest.

Taurisus.

My greefe (Berardus) *which I feele, is of such suttell* Art,
   That it doth trouble still my soule and every part consume
Thereof, which never to resist, durst once presume *for* feare,   25
But even as gently as it may, and must with meare consent
Yeeld up her life into the hands of him that's bent *to* tame
The proudest harts: And joyfull in his burning flame *I* live:
   And as they doe of comfort give *me* store
   For more content, so would I wish for more.   30

Berardus.

The Gods (Taurisus) *and the heavens have made so passing* faire
   This star Diana, *whose golden gleames of glittring* haire *and* face
Doe with their lights illuminate my life, and chace away
   The darkest cloudes, restoring to mine eies a day *so* bright,   35

That if I am beholding her the shining light *and* blaze
Of those two stars, mine eies and senses doe amaze *and* blinde,
That casting them unto the ground, my hopes I finde *so* bare,
  That, though I would, not once I dare complaine
  Or see, or sue, or tell her of my paine.   5

Taurisus.

This lovely Nymph would never list
    Unto my wofull cries,
But in her rigour doth persist
    And from my succour flies: 10
And pitilesse to see my death would never turne her eies.
O cruell eies, O cruell paine,
    O beautie, cruell foe:
Yet doth my faith so firme remaine,
    That all my cares and woe   15
It doth encourage in such sort, and feares doth overthrowe,
That like a sturdie rocke it standes
    Against the cruell raves
(Though sencelesse in the naked sandes)
    Of beating windes and waves.   20
And how much more with conquering hand my hart she doth controule,
By so much doe I adde more heate unto my burning soule.

Berardus.

The woods and mountaines doe not beare
    Woolves of such crueltie,   25
Whose howling threats I feare not theare,
    And yet a jealousie
Doth make my hart to quake for feare,
    And yeeld most cowardly.
I am not able to defend   30
    My weake and feeble brest
From thousand feares, where they pretend
    To build their strongest nest:
And with their entrance drive away my hopes, my joy and rest.

There they commaund and governe all,
　　And proudly tyrannize
And there my soule to endlesse thrall
　　And bodie sacrifice.
O cruell Love, whom cruell death must needes at last succeede,　　5
O why with such consuming tortures die I not in deede?

Taurisus.

Neere to this Christall fountaine on a day
　　I sawe Diana *sitting with her spouse,*
And as by chaunce I crost the woods that way,　　10
　　Espied them behinde these hasell bowes:
　　　　Dying with greefe, impatience, and despite
　　　　To see (which I would not have seene) that sight.
Nothing he spake, but with his clownish hand
　　Did rudely touch, and claspe her round about:　　15
(Her tender corpes, the smallest in this land,
　　Too daintie and fine for such a homely lout.)
　　　　And so he sat, and did not stir
　　　　In this unseemely sort with her.
But when my jealous eies so base a thing espied　　20
With mortall rage I burn'd and cruell envie died.

Berardus.

To walke the woods in sweetest moneth of May
　　When winter hides his hoarie head for shame,
Diana *with her husband on a day*　　25
　　The glorie of the fairest women came.
　　　　A vaile of Lawne upon her golden haire
　　　　With silver pins enfolded every where,
A thousand sportes and pastimes did I see
　　How she found out, his minde to recreate:　　30
And as I lurk'd behinde a Poplar tree,
　　How lovingly she dallied with her mate:
　　　　Whom I did see reach foorth his hand
　　　　Unto her necke as white as swan,
Wherewith he did undoe her vaile, and loose her shining haire,　　35
Which sight did kill my hart with feare enwrapped in despaire.

The Shepherds after they made an end of singing, began to gather their flockes togither, that went feeding up and downe the woode. And comming towardes the place where *Marcelius* and *Diana* were, they could not otherwise chuse but see them, for they had no handsome shift to hide themselves, although they 5 woulde faine have stept aside. At which joyfull and unexpected sight, they received no meane content and gladnes. And though *Berardus* was somwhat altered and appalled thereat, yet inflamed *Taurisus* to see the cause of his griefe before his eies, kindled more and more his hot desire. They curteously saluted the Shep- 10 herds, and requested them not to denie them their companie to the village, since good fortune had made them all so happely meete togither. *Diana*, whose custome was never to be coy nor discurteous, was well content to do it. So that *Taurisus* and *Berardus* praied the other Shepherds that were with them, to 15 come after by little and little with their flockes, that they had now gathered up togither, towards the village, whilest they in companie of *Diana* and the other Shepherds went on before; which they willingly performed. *Taurisus* by the way as he went, praied *Diana* to answere verse for verse to the song that he would 20 sing, which she denied him not to doe, and so they sung as followeth.

Taurisus.	*THe cause why that thou dost denie*
	To looke on me, sweete foe impart?
Diana.	*Bicause that doth not please the eie,* 25
	Which doth offend and greeve the hart.
Taurisus.	*What woman is, or ever was,*
	That when she looketh, could be mov'd?
Diana.	*She that resolves her life to passe,*
	Neither to love nor to be lov'd. 30
Taurisus.	*There is no hart so fierce nor hard,*
	That can so much torment a soule.
Diana.	*Nor Shepherd of so small regard,*
	That reason will so much controule.
Taurisus.	*How fals it out Love doth not kill* 35
	Thy crueltie with some remorce?
Diana.	*Bicause that Love is but a will,*
	And free will doth admit no force.

Taurisus.	*Behold what reason now thou hast,*
	To remedie my loving smart?
Diana.	*The very same bindes me as fast,*
	To keepe such danger from my hart.
Taurisus.	*Why dost thou thus torment my minde,*
	And to what end thy beautie keepe?
Diana.	*Bicause thou call'st me still unkinde,*
	And pitilesse when thou dost weepe.
Taurisus.	*It is bicause thy crueltie*
	In killing me doth never end:
Diana.	*Nay for bicause I meane thereby*
	My hart from sorrowes to defend.
Taurisus.	*Behold so foule I am no way*
	As thou dost thinke, faire Shepherdesse:
Diana.	*With this content thee, that I say,*
	That I beleeve the same no lesse.
Taurisus.	*What after giving me such store*
	Of passions, dost thou mocke me too?
Diana.	*If answers thou wilt any more*
	Goe seeke them without more adoo.

5

10

15

20

It greatly contented *Taurisus* that *Diana* sung with him, whereby though hee heard the rigorous answers of his Shepherdesse, yet he was so glad in his minde, that she deigned to answer him, that it made him forget the greefe, which by the crueltie of her wordes he might have otherwise conceived. But nowe timorous *Berardus* forcing his heavie hart, and casting a pittifull eie on *Diana* (not unlike the sorrowfull Swanne, that a little before her death singes sweetely in the cleere and christall brookes) lifted up his faint and fearefull voice, which came foorth with great paine out of his panting brest, and to the sound of his Baggepipe sung these verses following.

25

30

*E*Nd now my life, with daily paines affrighted,
   Since that for all that I have wept and greeved,
     My teares are not requited,
  And trustie faith not any whit beleeved.

35

1, 13 *Behold* Ed.] *Bebold* Y.

I am in such a haplesse state of sorrowe,
  That I would be content (and so releeve me)
Unjust rewardes and scornes of her to borrow,
  Onely that she would credit and beleeve me.
But though my life is thus with woes despited,   5
  And though to be most constant, never greeved,
    My paines are not requited,
And trustie faith not any whit beleeved.

After that *Berardus* had ended his song, both the Shepherds cast
their eies upon *Marcelius,* and bicause he was unknowne to them, 10
they durst not entreat him to sing. But in the end bold *Taurisus*
praied him to tell them his name, (and if it pleased him) to sing
them a song, wherein they would thinke themselves beholding to
him for either curtesie. At which words *Marcelius* looking upon
Diana, and making her a signe to touch her instrument, without 15
giving them any other answere, with one song pleased them both,
and satisfied their desire. Whereupon fetching out a great sigh,
he began thus.

*A*H *such an one I ever was, since that*
  My Shepherdesse so cruell I did see,   20
That now I knowe not who I am, nor what
  My hap shall be, or shall become of mee.

I knowe right well that if I were a man,
  Greefe had my life consumed long agoe:
And if a stone, I am most certaine then,   25
  That dropping teares had melted me like snowe.

Marcelius *is my name, who knowes not that?*
  And I am hers, since first I did her see,
That now I knowe not who I am, nor what
  My hap shall be, or shall become of mee.   30

Now did the light begin to give place to darknes, and the
countrey villages with their domesticall fires began to smoke
apace, when the Shepherds being neere to their towne made an
ende of their singing. Everie one went to his owne house, as
men not meanely glad for their passed conversation: but *Diana* 35

founde no rest at all, especially when she remembred that her
beloved *Syrenus* was not in the towne. She lodged *Marcelius* well in
Melibeus house, cousen to *Delius*, where with great kindnes, and
their best countrey cheere he was welcommed: and after comming home to her owne house, she called her husbands and her 5
owne kindred togither, and tolde them how *Delius* had forsaken
her at the fountaine of the Sicamours by following a strange
Shepherdesse, that by chance came thither. At which wordes she
seemed to make so greevous complaints, and indeed to be so
sorrie, that in the end she told them all, that earely in the morning 10
she was purposed to go to *Dianas* Temple, to enquire of sage
Felicia some newes of her husband *Delius*. They were all well
content, that she should go, and offered her all the favour and
helpe they could in her journey, but the intent therof was for no
other end but to see *Syrenus*, whom she knew assuredly to be 15
there. Wherefore with many thankes she remained verie glad,
that her determination had so good successe; and so with hope of
her future joy, she gave some rest that night to her wearied bodie,
and felt in her heavie hart a touch of unwoonted pleasure and
content.   20

The end of the first booke.

The second Booke of Enamoured
DIANA.

UNjust and lawlesse love is of such force, that, to augment his
crueltie, it hath the helpe of all things in the world, his enter- 25
prises being favoured and maintained by those things, which are
of most might and valour, but especially aided so much by Fortune, and by her mutabilities, as for bestowing his paines and
torments abroad, he needs no better friend nor furtherer. All
which is verified by *Marcelius* disgraces, since Fortune wrought 30
so hard a conceite in his betrothed *Alcidas* brest, that she was
forced to give credite to such a suspicion, that (though most
false) she held for an assured, or at least an apparant ground of
his inconstancie, whereof ensued the hating of her husband, who
loved her deerer then his owne life, and who in any thing had 35

never offended her. Heereupon it may be gathered, how strong and certaine a presumption ought to be, to make a wise and discreete person give faith and credite to it, since this, that had but a colour of certaintie was so farre indeede from the truth of the matter. But now though Love and Fortune so ill entreated *Marcelius*, yet in one thing they highly pleasured him, which was, that Love wounded *Dianas* hart, and Fortune conducted him to the fountaine, where he found her, whereby they might go both togither to sage *Felicias* house, and passe away his sorrowes with lesse annoy in her comfortable and delightfull companie. But the time being come, when the redde morning with her golden habite did overcome the starres of the passed night, and the birdes with their chirping noise gave warning that day was come, Enamoured *Diana*, wearied with the long and tedious night, rose up, to walke the path of her desired journey : and committing the charge of her flockes to the Shepherdesse *Polyntia* her friend, she came out of her towne accompanied onely with her rurall Baggepipe, (the deceiver of her sorrowes) and with her scrippe stored with some fewe victuals. She came downe from the side of a hill, which ledde from the towne to a thicke woode, where in the bottome of it she sat her downe underneath a rowe of greene Sicamours, attending for *Marcelius* companie, as she had promised the night before. But in the meane time, whilest he came not, she began to tune her Baggepipe and to sing this song following.

A Wake a little, light of cleerest day, 25
With calme aspect, with milde and gentle grace,
A poore soule to beguile in sorrowes plight:
Stretch out that light Apollo *from thy face,*
That joies the desert Champians in decay,
And driest plants with life and secret might: 30
In this most pleasant wood, that doth invite
To sweetest rest,
Tormented thou shalt see my brest
With carefull greefe (my heavie lot)
To see it selfe by him forgot, 35
Who for my scorne a thousand plaintes did waste,
The fault is Cupids *taste,*
Who gives and takes on purpose discontent,
Where he perceives he may the more torment.

What beastes with mildnesse doe not complaints acquaint,
    What stone by sighes is not to softnes wrought,
    The which a wearied brest doth yeeld with paine?
What Tigres, or what lions are not brought
    To ruth and pitie, hearing a complaint   5
    Which hath almost undone my soule in twaine.
But to Syrenus *I recount in vaine*
    My sorrowfull mishap,
    Who doth as little care for that,
    As furious windes in raging seas   10
    The teares, that all to little ease,
    The mariners with carefull hart doe spill:
For more they crie, the more it rageth still.

Thy love Syrenus *was not fine and good,*
    Which in these fieldes to me thou didst once beare,   15
    When as my errour might offend it so:
*Remember (*Traitour*) what thou then didst sweare,*
    Neere to the river sitting in this wood:
    What then doth now thy hardnes seeme to show?
Shall not a small oblivion long agoe   20
    Be helpt by extreme love?
    And such, that shall be far above
    My passed hate, and fault before?
    Then since I cannot love thee more
    Nor satisfie the same with greater heate;   25
    For remedie, my death I will intreate.

Live yet in paine, the which I feele at last
    For thee who mak'st my sorrowes lesse appeere,
    Though more it hurtes my wretched soule, I see,
Bicause to have thy present figure heere,   30
    Gives to her thought a sweete delightsome tast,
    Who paining for thy sake doth thinke on thee.
But bend thy hart a little unto me,
    Ardent in my request.
    Thou seest I live in paine opprest,   35

---

² *by* Ed.] *hy* Y.

Sustain'd by this desire alone,
In all my life to heare but one
(No) if thou wilt, in that I most doe love:
But from a man so fierce what shall I prove?

Tell me, the favours how canst thou requite   5
In that time past, Syrenus, *when thy hart*
Thou hadst more tender, now in hardnes dead:
When (Traitour) *for my cause, with envies smart*
A thousand Shepherdes thou didst kill outright:
O joyfull time, and life that I did leade: 10
The vale shall witnes, and the pleasant meade,
Where I of Roses white
And sweetest flowers, with delight
Brave garlands for thy head I had
Compacted, and sometimes did adde   15
(Only for thy content) some of my haire,
Which greevous thought my life doth now impaire.

Now free, thou dost abhorre me, in the end,
Who, for thy sake her selfe in paine consumes:
But yet take heede of Cupids *fine deceates:*   20
For that proud hart, that overmuch presumes,
From cruell love his senses to defend,
The more he yeeldes, the more to strive he sweates:
O that thou wert so wounded in his heates,
As now my selfe I see: 25
But ever it is unto mee
The best advise, no good to crave:
For whatsoever it would have,
Though heaven, and earth the more it doth importune,
It ever was denied by Love, *and* Fortune.
      30

My song, in pine I will no wise ingrave thee,
Nor hardned Oke, but rather will commend thee
Unto the windes, where they will tosse and wave thee,
And to the deafe and desart Champian send thee:
Bicause my torments, of their hope deprived,   35
And memorie of them, which makes me sorie,
May be forgot, and never be revived,
Now that my life is lost and chiefest glorie.

The delicate voice and excellent graces of *Diana*, surmounted farre the praises of the fairest and most skilfull Shepherdesses of her time. And the quavers and fine conceits wherewith so sweetely she brake her voice, and adorned her songs, made her to be the more admired: For they were so rare and singular, that they rather seemed to be fetcht from some majesticall court, then knowen in the homely countrey. The which ought not to be so much wondred at, nor thought so strange, since Love is able to make the simplest Shepherds discourse of high and learned matters, especially if it finde a lively wit and spirit, which in those pastorall cottages is seldome wanting. But as the enamoured Shepherdesse was now ending her song, about that time that the cleere Sunne began to lessen the shadowes of the high hils, despised *Marcelius* taking his leave of his pastorall lodging, to come to the place where he had appointed to meete *Diana*, came downe from the hill above, at the foote whereof she was sitting to attende him: whom when she had espied a far off, she held her peace, bicause he might not understand the cause of her griefe. When *Marcelius* was come to the place where *Diana* stayed for him, he saide unto her. The cleere light of this day (faire Shepherdesse) which with the more resplendant beames of thy shining beautie did arise, be as joyfull and happie to thee, as to me most sorrowfull, if in thy good company I passe it not away. Truely I am ashamed to see, that my slownes hath made thee stay heere all alone so carefull for my comming; but this is not the first fault that (faire *Diana*) thou must pardon me during the time that I shall converse with thee. As that pardon should be vaine (answered *Diana*) where there is no fault; so thou art not to be blamed for any such small care, but rather the earnest desire that I had to rise so early, and to come hither, where I have passed away the time in sundrie fancies, and in thinking of the effects which belong to a troubled minde. But here is no time nor place for us to stay, since the desire I have to be at *Dianas* Temple is great, though the way is very short: as also for that the morning being somewhat fresh, we may before the Sunne begins to powre downe his beames with greater heat, begin to take our journey, the better to refresh our selves, and in

25–26 comming; but this is not the first fault that (faire *Diana*) thou must pardon me *CTr² CUL BM¹⁻² Sus*: comming, thou (faire *Diana*) must pardon me; but this is not the first fault that *CTr¹ Bodl.*   34 morning *CTr² CUL BM¹⁻² Sus*: morning, *CTr¹ Bodl.*

the heate of the day to rest our wearied bodies. When she had
saide thus, they both went on their way, crossing over a thicke
wood that was before them, and for lightning of their journey,
began to sing that which followeth.

Marcelius.

5

*I*Nconstant love and cruell, which hast lately
   Setled my happy thoughts, my love and fire,
In such a place so famous, high and stately,
   Where mortall mens desarts cannot aspire:
      Well hast thou shew'd thy power
      By quailing of my sorrow,
      To double it each hower
And make my torments greater even and morrow:
Thou mightst have left my hart in former sadnes,
   Bicause lesser harme it were to die with anguish,
      Then to receive a gladnes
So full of paine: And so by fits to languish.

10

15

Diana.

Thou must not thinke it strange, and must not woonder
   That thus the mighty Boy of paine and pleasure
After one small delight, doth send a hunder
   Nay thousand paines and torments without measure:
      For firme repose to any
      He yet did promise never,
      But cruell deathes, and many
Sobs, sighes, and teares, complaintes, and chaines for ever:
The Lybian sandes, and Aprils fairest flowers
   Passe not the greefes, with which fierce love doth murder
      Each harte, and into showers
Distraines the eies: And yet proceedeth furder.

20

25

30

Marcelius.

Before that ever Love my soule inflamed,
   His slightes, wherein he most of all abounded,
I knew right well, wherewith mens harts he tamed
   And captives made, and after deepely wounded:

35

17 *languish*. Ed.] *languish*, Y.

> *Our lives with great offences*
> *Not onely he annoieth,*
> *But yet our wits and senses*
> *And soundest judgements wholy he destroieth.*
> *And so torments a soule, and so encumbers,*   5
>   *That one poore joy it hardly doth recover:*
>   *So by ten thousand numbers*
> *Most greevous thoughts surcharge a wretched lover.*

Diana.

> *If Loves deceites and his dissembling proffers,*   10
>   *Wherewith he takes us, are so knowne and tried,*
> *Why then presents the soule it selfe and offers*
>   *So easily to be taken, and applied?*
>   *If that the hart so tender*
>   *The troubles intertaineth*   15
>   *That* Cupid *doth engender,*
> *Why after then laments it, and complaineth?*
> *Reason it were in love he should be pained,*
>   *That to his dartes doth yeeld, and is consenting*
>   *With fetters to be chained:*   20
> *For ill affoords us nought but paines tormenting.*

They sung this song and many more, the which having ended,
they were nowe out of the wood, and then they began to walke
over a pleasant and flowrie meade, which caused *Diana* to use
these words. They are no doubt marvellous and strange things, 25
which the industrie of man hath invented in populous and great
cities, but yet those, which nature hath produced in the wide and
solitarie fieldes, are more to bee admired. For who woulde not
woonder at the lively greene of this wood? and not be amazed at
the beautie of this goodly meadow? For, to beholde the diversitie 30
of coloured flowers, and the pleasant melodie of chirping birdes,
is a thing so full of content and delight, that the glorious pompe
and wealth of the bravest and most famous Court is not comparable to it. There is indeed (said *Marcelius*) in this pleasant soli-
tude great store of content and joy, and namely for those that are 35
free from passions of love, since they may lawfully, and when
they list, enjoy such rare sweetenes, and abundant pleasures. And

I am certaine, that if Love, (which is now so much my mortal enimy, remaining in these sequestred places) had in the village where I was of late, given me halfe the grief, which now I feele, my life durst never abide it, since with such like delights I coulde not have mitigated the crueltie of my torment. To this *Diana* 5 answered not a word, but putting her snowe white hande before her eies, and therewith supporting her golden head, she staied a great while very sadde and pensive: and after sending foorth now and then a sorrowfull and painefull sigh, said thus. Then woe is me (unfortunate Shepherdesse) that can finde no remedie 10 sufficient to comfort my sorrowes, when those, which take away from others a great part of their paine, doe bring to me a continuall and burning greefe. I can now (*Marcelius*) no longer hide the paine which I suffer, the force whereof, though it compels me to publish it, yet for one thing I am bound to thanke it, that 15 it constraines me to tell it in such a time and place, where thou art onely present, since thy noble minde and experience in like passions will not (I hope) condemne it for a meere and trifling follie, especially when thou knowest the cause thereof. I am (to be plaine with thee *Marcelius*) tormented with the like greefe that 20 thou art, and am also forgotten (as thou art) of a Shepherd called *Syrenus*, of whom in times past I was greatly beloved. For cruell Fortune, which overturneth humane intents, married me to *Delius* (enforced more by the hard commandement of my parents, then by mine owne will) and to my great greefe, made me a bond- 25 slave to such a husband, the intollerable thought of whose continuall jealousie (besides the sufferance of many other greefes more) is onely sufficient to kill this miserable soule. Whose injurious suspects I could be content yet to suffer, if I might but enjoy the presence of *Syrenus*; who, taking a just occasion by my 30 forced marriage to forget me, forsooke our towne, (bicause he would not see me) and (as I understande) is in the Temple of *Diana*, whither we are now going. Whereupon thou maiest imagine what kinde of life I leade, being alwaies troubled with the jealousie of my husband, and tormented with the absence of 35 my lover. Then *Marcelius* said. I cannot chuse but pittie thy greefe, nowe I know it (gracious Shepherdesse) and am sorrie that I have not heard it till now. God grant I may never enjoy any happie content, if I wish it not as well to thy hart as to mine owne. But bicause thou knowest how generall Loves arrowes are, and with 40

what small partialitie they hurt the stoutest harts, and most free
and vertuous mindes, then blush not to manifest his wrongs,
since it shall never the more be an empeachment to thy good
name, but an occasion to make me esteeme the better of thee. And
that which comforts me heerein is, that I knowe, that the torment 5
of thy husbandes jealousie (a greater corsive to the hart then the
absence of the thing beloved) will suffer thee to take a little rest,
since *Delius*, who is following the flying Shepherdesse, shall now
be separated from thy companie. Enjoy therefore the time, and
occasion that Fortune presents thee, and comfort thy selfe, for it 10
shall be no small ease unto thee, to passe away the absence of
Syrenus, being now free from the importunous trouble of thy
jealous husband. I wold not esteem these jealousies so hurtful to
me (said *Diana*) if *Syrenus* had them aswel as *Delius*, bicause
I would then thinke that they had their foundation and beginning 15
of love. For it is manifest, that they that love, would be glad to be
loved againe, and must esteem the jealousie of the thing beloved,
to be good and lawfull, since it is a manifest token of love,
springing from love, incident to love, and ever accompanied with
it. And for my selfe I am able to assure thee, that I never thought 20
my selfe more in love, then when I was a litle jealous, and never
judged my self to be jealous, but when I was ascertained that
I was most in love. To the which *Marcelius* replied thus, I never
thought that a pastoral plainnes was able to alledge such wise
reasons, in so difficult a question; whereupon I must needes con- 25
demne that for an olde approoved errour, that maintaines, that
onely in cities and in the court the finest wits, and exquisite
conceits do dwell, when I finde them as well to be amongst the
thicke woodes, and in countrey and plaine cottages. Yet for all
this I will gainsay thy opinion, whereby thou wouldst seeme to 30
proove that jealousie is the messenger and companion of love, as
if love could not be where jealousie is not joyned with it. For
though there are fewe lovers but are a little jealous; yet we must
not therefore say, that the Lover that is not jealous, is not a more
perfect and truer lover. For he rather sheweth (being exempt 35
from jealousie) what valour and force he hath in love, and the
qualitie of his desire, which is pure and cleere, and not troubled
with the miste of jealous imaginations. Such an one was I (with
modestie be it spoken) in my most happie and passed times, and
so highly then prised my good Fortune, that with my publike 40

verses I did manifest the same. And amongst many other times that *Alcida* marvelled to see me so much in love, and free from jealousie, I tooke in hand on a time to write this Sonnet to her to that effect.

*T*Hey say Love *sware, he never would be frend,*
   If mortall Jealousie *were not in place:*
   And Beautie *never be in any face,*
Unlesse that Pride *did on her thought attend:*
These are two hags, which hideous hell doth send, 10
   Our sweete content to trouble, and disgrace:
   The one the joy of love to paine doth chace,
The other pitie from the hart defend.
Beautie *and* Love *were both forsworne, by mee*
   And thee, by making my unsure estate 15
   In joy and happinesse so fortunate:
Bicause since first thy figure I did see
   Being so Faire, *yet* Prouder *wast thou never*
   Nor I in Love, *that could be* Jealous *ever.*

The pleasure that my *Alcida* tooke when I rehearsed this Sonnet 20 to her, was so great (perceiving thereby the integritie of my love) that a thousand times shee would sing it, knowing that I had well pleased her fansie with it. And truely (faire Shepherdesse) I hold it for a great errour, that such a horrible monster as jealousie is, should be accounted a good thing, as to say, that it is the token of 25 Love, and that it is not but in an enamoured hart. For by this assertion we may say, that a feaver is good, bicause it is a token of life, for it is never but in a body most likely to live. But both are manifest errours, since jealousie affoords no lesse paine then a feaver: For it is a plague of the soule; a frensie disturbing the 30 thoughts; a madnes that weakens the bodie; an anger consuming the spirits; a feare abasing the minde, and a furie that fils the will with folly. But bicause thou maist the better judge of jealousie to be most abhominable, imagine the cause of it, and thou shalt finde that it is nothing else, but a little feare of that which is not, 35 nor shall be, a vile contempt of ones owne deserts, and a mortall surmise, which cals the faith and sinceritie of that which is beloved, in doubt and suspition. The pangs of jealousie with words (gentle Shepherdesse) cannot be decyphered: for they are such that do infinitely exceed in quantitie and qualitie the paines, that are incident to love. For all the rest (saving they) may be converted in the end to a great sweetnes, and content. And as the burning thirst in the hottest day makes the cold and fresh fountaine water to taste more sweete and savorie, and as the danger and garboiles in warre and sedition, make us esteeme the more of quietnes and peace; so the torments of Love serve us for greater pleasure, whensoever any small favour is graunted unto us, and when we enjoy but the least content and happines. But this frantike jealousie powres such bitter poyson into mens harts, that it spoiles and drives away all delights that harbour in it. To this effect I remember that an excellent Musition in *Lisbone* did sing this Sonnet on a day before the King of *Portugall*, which said thus.

A Sonnet.

VVHen cruell absence woundes a soule with paine,
Then thought is fed with fancies in their kinde:
For further of the good remaines, the minde
Receives more joy, when that it comes againe:
He that on hope his ground doth yet sustaine,
For all his greefe a remedie shall finde,
And for his paines rewardes shall be assign'd:
Or dies at lest in love content and faine:
A thousand paines away one joy doth chace,
And to a thousand scornes revenge presents
The onely viewing of an Angels face:
But when a soule vile jealousie torments,
Though thousand joyes doe afterwards succeede,
Yet bitter greefe and rage the same doth breede.

O how true was his opinion, how sure was this conclusion? For in very truth this pestilent jealousie leaves not one part of the soule whole, nor the least corner of the hart unsearched, where any small delight may hide it selfe. There is no content in Love, where there is no hope; and hope will never be there, where jealousie is a meane betweene them both. There is no stedfast pleasure where jealousie is, no delight which is not consumed with it, and no griefe but jealousie torments us with it. The enraged furie of poysoned jealousie is so extreme, that it grieveth the hart infected with it, to heare the praises of the thing beloved, 5 and would never have the perfections of that which one loveth neither seene nor knowen of any but of himselfe, offering great injurie by meanes hereof to the woorthines of that gentilitie, that holds him in captivitie. And the jealous man doth not onely live in this slavery and paine, but to her also whom he loveth, he 10 giveth such incessant griefe, that more he could not give her, if he were her mortall enimie. Wherefore it is verie cleere, that a jealous husband (like thine) would rather have his wife seeme foule and lothsome to the world, and that she might be never seene, nor praised; no, not by the most virtuous and modest 15 mindes. What griefe is it for the wife to have her honesty condemned by a false suspect? What greater punishment, then without all reason to be locked up in a secret corner of her house? What hart breake sorrowe with austere words, and somtimes with unseemely deeds to be continually checked? If she be merie, 20 her husband thinks her dishonest; if she be sad, he imagines himselfe lothsom in her eie; if she be musing, he judgeth her ful of fansies; if she looke on him, he thinks she deceives him; if she lookes not on him, he thinkes she hates him; if she use any daliance with him, he thinkes it to be but fained; if shee be grave 25 and modest, he thinkes her a counterfaite; if she laughes, he thinkes her to be loose; if she sigh, he counts her naught: And in the end jealousie converteth everie thing that is poisoned with it, to an endlesse griefe and miserie. Whereupon it is verie cleere, that there is no paine in the world like to this, and never out of 30 hell came fouler *Harpyes* to contaminate and putrifie the sweete and savourie foode of an enamoured soule: wherefore care not greatly *Diana* for the absence of jealous *Delius*, for it availes thee not a little to make thee suffer the paine of Love more gently. To this *Diana* answered. Now am I thorowly ascertained, that this 35 passion which thou hast so lively depainted, is a most ugly and horrible thing, which deserves not a place in amorous harts; and also beleeve, that this was the verie same griefe that tormented *Delius*. But I must tel thee by the way (*Marcelius*) that I never

37 horrible *Ed.*] horrble *Y*.

meant to defend the like grief, and that it never found harbour in my brest: for as I never thought amisse of *Syrenus* worthines and deserts; so was I never tormented with such like passion and follie, as thou hast told of, but I had onely a certaine kinde of feare to be rejected in respect of another. And in this suspition 5 I have not beene much deceived, for to my great griefe I have tried *Syrenus* forgetfulnes. This feare, said *Marcelius*, cannot be properly termed jealousie, which is rather an ordinarie passion in the best and wisest lovers. For it is verified, that that which I love, I esteeme and hold it for good, and thinke it deserves to be 10 beloved: which being so, I am afraide least another might know the goodnes, and worthines of it, and so love it like my selfe. And so it fals out, that a lover is put betweene hope and feare. That which the one denies him, the other doth promise him; and when the one doth cast him downe, the other lifts him up againe. 15 And in the ende, the wounds that feare makes in this contentious quarrell, hope heales againe, untill one of the two remaines conqueror. And if it happen that feare overcomes hope, the lover then becomes jealous; but if hope conquers feare, then the lover lives in a joyfull and happie estate. But in the time of my 20 good fortune I had ever so strong and sure a hope, that feare was unable, not onely to overcome it, but durst never attempt to assaile it; whereby, I ever enjoyed so great delight, that in exchange of that, I never cared to be troubled with continual griefes. And I was so greatly in her favor, that I sustained my 25 hope in such firmnes, that there was no grief that came from her part, that I accepted not for a singular joy, and pleasure. I accounted her cruelties, courtesies; her disdaines, daliances; her angrie answers, amiable promises. *Diana* and *Marcelius* going on their waies, had these and divers other speeches togither. And 30 having passed over the greene meade in sweete communication, and going by the side of a little hill, they entred into a pleasant wood, where the thicke Sicamours did spread abroad fresh and coole shadowes. There they heard a passing cleere voice, which joyned with the tune of a sweete harpe, sounded forth strange 35 melodie; and comming neer to hearken to it, they might perceive, that it was the voice of a Shepherdesse, that sung in maner following.

24 troubled *Ed.*] ttoubled *Y.*

A Sonnet.

AS many stars as Heaven *containeth, strive*
  To frame my harme, and lucklesse hap to show:
  And in th'Earth *no grasse nor greene doth growe,*
That to my greefe may any comfort give: 5
Love *unto feare subjected, ever drive*
  A soule to coldest ice: O bitter woe,
  That he, whom Fortune *did contrarie so,*
Continually with jealousie must live.
The fault I must (Montanus) *lay on thee,*   10
  And all my greefe: on thee I doe complaine
  (O cruell soule) that pitie dost disdaine;
For if thou hadst but taken part with mee,
  I would not care though gainst me did conspire
  Heaven, Earth, *and* Love, *and* Fortune *in their ire.*   15

After that the Shepherdesse had sweetely sung, enlarging the
raines of her bitter and dolefull complaint, she powred out such
abundance of teares, and gave so many sighes, that by them, and
by the wordes she spake, they knew that a cruell deceit of her
jealous husband was the cause of all her greefe. But bicause they 20
would know better what she was, and the cause of her passion,
they went to the place where she was, and found her sitting al
alone in the shadowe, which the thicke boughes made on everie
side upon the fine and greene grasse, neere to a little spring, which
rising out of the foote of an oke, ranne by divers waies thorow 25
that little woode. They curteously saluted her, and she (although
it greeved her that they had interrupted her lamentation, yet
judging by their countenances that they were Shepherds of good
regard) was not greatly discontented at their comming, hoping to
have had the fruition of their good company, and therefore said 30
unto them. To my remembrance (faire Shepherd and Shepherdesse) I never received so great contentment that might be
compared with this in seeing you now, since the time that I was
unjustlie forsaken of my cruell husband; which is so great, that
though continuall greefe compels me to ceaselesse plaints, yet 35
will I make a pause of them a little while to enjoy your peaceable
and discreete companie. To this *Marcelius* answered. I praie God
I may never see my torments cease, if that it greeves me not to

see thine, and the same maiest thou also beleeve of faire *Diana*, whom thou seest in my companie. The Shepherdesse hearing *Dianas* name, running unto her, did with the greatest gladnes that might be, embrace her, shewing a thousand loving signes, and making the most on her in the world, bicause she was desirous 5 long since to knowe her, for the great report that she heard of her wisedome and beautie. *Diana* marvelling to see herselfe so entreated by a Shepherdesse, whom she knewe not, requited her yet with like curtesies againe, and desiring to know who she was, saide unto her. The great favours that thou hast done me, and the 10 pittie which I take of thy complaints, make me desirous to know what thou art, wherefore tell us (faire Shepherdesse) thy name, and discourse unto us the cause of thy greefe, bicause that after thou hast tolde it, thou shalt see how our harts will helpe thee to passe it away, and our eies readie to bewaile it. The Shepherdesse 15 then with a gracious speech began to excuse herselfe, from telling the substance of her owne fall, yet urged in the ende by their importunate requestes, she sat downe againe upon the grasse, and began thus to saie. By the report of *Selvagia* that was borne in my towne, and in thine too faire *Diana*, which is now married to the 20 Shepherd *Sylvanus*, thou hast beene told (I thinke) of the unfortunate name of *Ismenia*, that is now beginning to tell her sorrowfull tale. And I thinke that she tolde thee at large when she was in thy towne, howe against my will I deceived her in the Temple of *Minerva* in the kingdome of *Portugall*, and how by my 25 owne deceite I was overtaken; then perhaps she hath also tolde thee how I fained to love *Montanus* her mortall enimie, to be revenged of *Alanius*, who for the love that he did beare her, forgot me quite, and how this fained love with the riper knowledge of his vertues, and accomplishments fel out at last so true, 30 that by means of it, I suffer this intolerable sorrow and greefe, which even now I complained of. Therefore passing on farther in the history of my life, thou shalt understand, that when *Filenus* father to *Montanus* came sometimes to my fathers house about certaine of his affaires, and bargaines that he had with him for 35 flockes of sheepe, and had espied me on a time, although somewhat aged, yet he was so extreemely enamoured of me, that he became almost out of his wits. A thousand times a daie he wooed me, and every hower reckoned up to me his greefes, but all in vaine, for I would neither harken unto him, nor regard his 40

wordes. Yet bicause he was a man of more sufficiencie, and of
fewer yeeres then many other in his case, I did not altogither
forget him, and the rather for his sonne *Montanus* sake, whose
love had made me now his captive before. The old man knew not
of the love, that *Montanus* did beare me, for he was alwaies so 5
carefull and dutifull a son, and so discreetly handled the matter,
that the father had not any notice thereof, fearing mightilie (if
it had beene knowne) his fathers displeasure, and that with bitter
and angrie wordes he might have justly corrected him for it.
And as wisely did the father conceale from his sonne *Montanus* 10
his owne follie; for, the better to chastise and amend what he
thought amisse in his sonne, he was very vigilant not to discover
his owne and greater faults. Although for all this he never ceased
with continuall suites to sollicite my love, and importuned me to
take him for my husband. He discoursed to me a thousand odde 15
matters, and made me as many great offers: he promised me many
costly garments, rich jewels, and sent mee many letters, thinking
by those meanes, if not to overcome me, at least to mollifie my
hard refusals. He was a Shepherd in his flourishing age no lesse
commended for al youthful sports, then cunning in all pastorall 20
exercises, one that could tell a smooth tale, and with great wisedome and discretion bring his purpose to good effect. And
bicause you may the better beleeve me, I will rehearse unto you
a letter that once he wrote unto me, the which although it altered
my minde nothing, yet it greatly contented me, and thus it said. 25

Filenus *letter to* Ismenia.

*F*Aire Shepherdesse, The cause was Love,
   Who (to acquaint thee with his paine)
This fault and blame in me did move
To write to thee: But to be plaine,
   Who would not be both shent and blamed,   30
   In thy sweete loves to be inflamed?

But if my letter doe offend
Thy modest eares, as to too bold:
Then understand, that in the end
The feare I have to be controld,   35
   My soule with paine and greefe hath fild,
   And hath the same already kild.

I have to thee ten thousand times
My torments told, wherein I live,
Sometimes by speech, sometimes by rimes,
Which first to me thy selfe didst give,
   The which no more thou dost requite,   5
   Then mocke, unto thy great delighte.

With open mouth thou laugh'st at mee,
And makest it thine onely game
To see me die for love of thee:
And I doe joy to see the same: 10
   Although thou laughest at my paine,
   Which laughter is to me no gaine.

And so when that in me I finde
The greevous ill, which makes me die,
I thinke (when that comes to my minde)   15
No remedie thou wilt apply.
   Bicause to see thou joi'st thy fill,
   How much my comforts thou dost kill.

A remedie thou dost disdaine:
And then my soule with hope to feede   20
I see it is as much in vaine,
When as it is by love decreede
   To have my life lie in thy hand,
   And death in thy desire to stand.

I sawe thy shining beauties beames,   25
Faire Shepherdesse, upon a day
Neere to great Duerus *Christall streames,*
Making the fields so fresh and gay,
   And goodly banks to joy and flourish,
   The which thy beauties feedes and nourish.   30

And there I sawe thee leane and stand,
Among those banks not long agoe,
Upon thy sheepehooke with thy hand,
With naked necke as white as snowe,
   And to thine elbowe (seeming greeved)   35
   With naked arme, that was unsleeved.

Where, if there had beene any one,
That well had viewed every part,
Admit he were as hard as stone,
And had not lov'd thee from his hart:
    Reason would move me then to say,   5
    That he his folly did bewray.

And therefore thus when I had knowne
Thy goodly giftes, and beautie rare,
From thinking of them one by one
No time, nor rest I did not spare: 10
    Thus I began loves force to trie,
    And in his torments thus to die.

But if against me thou dost move
Saying, It is to me a shame
Being an old man thus to love   15
So yoong a maide, and so to blame:
    O give me no advice at all,
    But remedies for which I call.

For I will never thinke this part
Of mine hath made so great a crime,   20
By loving thee with all my hart,
As having lost so long a time,
    Before I ever came to knowe
    Thy beauties which adorne thee so.

Alas I knowe that I am olde,   25
And that my prime long since did fall,
Which now I wish I had not tolde:
But that which greeves me most of all,
    Is that my loving paine appeeres
    Not equall with so many yeeres.

                                    30

Bicause since first I came into
This life, I would in all that space
Have loved thee as now I doe,
Since first I sawe thy sweetest face,
    And as I must with Cupids *powre*   35
    Unto my last and dying howre.

And let it not thy minde dismay
To see my haire so gray and white,
For it is ill to take away
The place from any, that of right
  Belongs to him in any reason,   5
  Though it comes out of time and season.

And though my valour not my hart,
And force, not will thou dost exceede,
It is not yet so just a part
That any man should leese his meede   10
  For being old, or be unpaide
  Bicause a souldier now decaide.

The buildings newer that they are,
And lately built in any sort,
By no proportion may compare,   15
For statelines and princely port,
  (The which antiquitie doth showe)
  With those of Rome built long agoe.

And so in things of woorthines,
Of prime or goodnes any way,   20
Of profit, joy or happines,
Commonly unto this day
  They say, (and yet do say most true)
  That th'old is better then the new.

Love wise in that he went about,   25
Till now gave me no sense of paine,
Bicause he sawe it did fall out,
That for the most part did remaine,
  In aged men, and like to mee,
  More firmnesse as we daily see.   30

To love thee more then I can tell,
I am resolved till I die,
And in my firmnesse doe excell
Of all loves torments which I trie:
  But olde againe and not to proove   35
  In all my life, the sweete of love.

Yoong youthes that most of all doe faine
Themselves to burne in Cupids *heate*
Are false and double, but to traine
Beleeving women to deceate:
    For when they say, That they doe die   5
    Then doe they live most merily.

And so their false and changing love,
And paines alledged in the same,
And all the torments which they proove
Is but their pastime, sport and game,   10
    It is their jest and common fashion,
    It is no will, nor any passion.

Besides, Ismenia *doe not feare*
That I am like to one of those
Yoong lovers, that doe every wheare   15
Their favours openly disclose:
    For sooner they receive not one,
    But straight to many it is knowne.

For though I doe receive at lest
Three hundred favours one by one,   20
Yet in my love I doe protest
To be as much a very stone
    In hiding favours which I gaine,
    As that I am in suffring paine.

But yet as far as I can see,   25
Resolved as thou art in minde
To kill me with thy crueltie,
Suer I am that I shall finde
    Much to endure to be reveal'd,
    Little ynough to be conceal'd.   30

For now ingratefull Shepherdesse,
The greatest favour which I misse
And faine the same would heere possesse,
Of all the rest is onely this
    To die, bicause I would no more   35
    Complaine against thee, as before.

Time onely will I thee accuse,
O time that art so great a friend
To greefes, and makest her refuse
My love, who loves her without end.
    For he that hath most part in thee   5
    Is little woorth in love we see.

Alas that ever I did love
Too late a thing so passing faire,
And reason therefore that I proove
To die for her in deepe despaire: 10
    Since when her birth day did appeere
    I was not borne that very yeere.

If I had beene, faire Shepherdesse,
With thee, when I was in my prime
As now thou art, then more or lesse,   15
I had not wanted any time,
    Delights and pastimes to present thee,
    Nor thy sweete favours to content mee.

For as for playing on a Pipe,
Or Rebecke with most sweetest sound   20
To touch with many a daintie stripe,
And dauncing best in all the towne,
    Amongst the youthes to win the prise
    All in my favour did arise.

And therefore marvell not a whit,   25
If that in song I doe excell
Famous Amphion, *as unfit*
(Compar'd with me) to beare the bell,
    Since that my singing hath surmounted,
    Better then he was ever counted.

                                                       30
Of fields that goodly graine doe beare
I plowe more acres then the rest:
And all my mountaines every where,
And plaines that are for pastures best,
    With flocks of sheepe and goates I cumber,   35
    Mark't with my mark that have no number.

But now what bootes my present store
(O cruell hap) for my delight?
Or that that hath beene heeretofore?
Since now it is forgotten quite.
 Nay which is more, scorn'd and despis'd,   5
 And unto cruell death devis'd.

Then (sweetest foe) let this availe
To make thy hardest hart relent,
Strike downe of pride thy puffed saile,
When to thine eies age shall present,   10
 That in the same thy brave perfection
 Shall vade, and be in times subjection.

O Shepherdesse, thou art more hard
Then sturdy rocke consum'd in time:
But yet perhaps for thy reward   15
When thou hast lost thy golden prime,
 Then freedomes want shall be thy paine,
 Wherewith thou dost me now disdaine.

Wherefore let Love take such despite,
Revenging one so much unkinde,   20
That when all hopes forsake thee quite,
And comforts for thy troubled minde,
 Then he may give thee store of greefe,
 And make despaire thy best releefe.

These and many other letters and songs he sent me; the which, 25
if they had wrought their effect so much as my delight, he might
then perhaps in his owne conceit have thought himselfe a happie
man, and I have beene by this time an ill married wife. But there
was not any thing able to blot *Montanus* image out of my hart,
who apparantly also satisfied my will with like words and deeds. 30
We passed our lives away certaine yeeres in this joy, untill we
thought with holy marriage to accomplish our happie daies, and
rest. And though *Montanus* would have tolde his Father of it
before, to have shewed the dutie of a good sonne, yet he would
not do it, when I told him, how hardly his Father would thinke of 35
it, by reason of the doting desire that he had to marrie me himselfe: Having therefore greater respect to the contentment of his

owne life, then to the dutie he owed his Father, without making him privie, we performed our unluckie marriage. Which was done by the consent of my Father, in whose house there were great feastes made in solemnitie of it, besides other pastimes, as dancing, plaies, and such great sports, that the noise of them was bruted in all the countrey towns about. Whereupon the loving old man understanding his own son had deceived him of his love, he became so incensed against us both that he hated us like death, and therfore would never after that see us, if he could otherwise choose. On the other side there was a certaine Shepherdesse of that towne called *Felisarda*, that died almost for the love of *Montanus*, whom (in regard of his great love to me, and of her bad conditions and declining age) he could never abide: When she perceived that *Montanus* had married me, she had almost hanged her selfe for griefe, so that by our unfortunate marriage we got us two mortall enimies. The wretched old dotard, because he would disinherit his sonne, purposed to marrie a yoong and faire wench, to have had children by her. But though he was rich, yet did not any Shepherdesse of our towne love him, *Felisarda* onely excepted, who, bicause she thought by these meanes to enjoy the dishonest love of *Montanus* (the which she bare yet fresh in memorie) married with old *Filenus*. And being now his wife, she practised divers waies to winne *Montanus* to her love, and especially by meanes of a maide she had, called *Sylveria*, sending him word, that if he would condiscend to her will, she would make an attonement betweene his Father and him, offering him besides many great rewards, and gifts. But she could never corrupt his minde, nor pervert his chaste intent: Seeing her selfe therefore so much contemned, she began to beare such mortal hatred to *Montanus*, that by and by she instigated his Father against him; and not content with this, wrought moreover this vile piece of treacherie against him. For she in such sort overcame *Sylverias* minde with flatterie, gifts, good cheere, and other favours, that she was content to do whatsoever she commaunded, although it had beene to the prejudice of *Montanus*, whom sometimes she respected greatly, for that she had beene a long time servant in his Fathers house. Both of them agreede secretly togither upon that they had to doe, and upon the hower of putting it in practise: Whereupon *Sylveria* went out of her towne, and comming to a forrest neere to the river *Duerus*, where *Montanus* was feeding his

sheepe, she came to talke with him secretly, as though she had
beene troubled much in minde about the weightiest matter in the
world, saying. Ah *Montanus*, how wise wert thou in despising
thy wicked Stepdames love, though I my selfe by her importunate
request did what I could to bring thee to it. But since I know 5
what hath passed, she shall never make me any more the messenger of her dishonest lusts. I have seene, and know certaine
things by her, which touch thy Fathers credit and thine too neere,
and such, that, if thou knewest them (though thy Father is so
cruell to thee) in such a case thou would'st not care to leese thy 10
life for safegard of his honour. I tell thee no more but this,
bicause I know thee to be so wise and discreete, that I neede
make no longer discourse unto thee. *Montanus* was amazed at
these wordes, suspecting by and by some dishonest tricke of his
Stepmother: But bicause he would be thorowly informed of the 15
matter, he prayed *Sylveria* to tell him all that she knew concerning
that matter. The more she was entreated, the more she denied,
making it verie daintie, and no lesse dangerous to discover so
secret a thing; but in the end satisfying his request, and her owne
desire, she told him a notable and cunning lye, saying. Bicause it 20
is a thing that so greatly toucheth thy credit, and *Filenus* my
Masters good name, I will therefore tell thee truely what I know,
hoping that thou wilt tell none in the worlde, that this secret
treacherie was discovered by me. Thou must therefore knowe,
that *Felisarda* thy stepmother is working a great disgrace against 25
thy father, with a certaine Shepherd, whose name I will not tell
thee, bicause thou maiest heereafter knowe him, if thou wilt:
for if thou wilt come this night, and follow me where I will
leade thee, thou shalt finde the adulterer and the trayteresse
togither in *Filenus* house: for so they have appointed, bicause 30
Filenus lieth this night at a Farme he hath, by reason of some
busines there, and cannot come home again before to morrow at
noone. Wherfore look wel about thee, and at eleven of the clocke
at night come to mee, for I will bring thee in, where thou maiest
doe that, which may turne to thine own credit, thy fathers honor, 35
and perhaps greatly to thine owne profit by obtayning pardon at
thy fathers hands. This tale *Sylveria* told so smoothly, and with
such cunning dissimulation, that *Montanus* was resolved to put
himselfe in the greatest danger to be revenged of him, who

19 secret *Ed.*] secrct *Y.*   36 obtayning *Ed.*] obtaying *Y.*

shoulde offer any dishonour to his father. And so the vile and
wicked *Sylveria* very glad that this deceit which *Felisarda* hatched,
had so good successe, went home againe, where she tolde *Felisarda*
her Mistresse what was agreed on betweene *Montanus* and her.
Nowe had the darke night overspred the earth with her blacke 5
mantell, when *Montanus* being come to the village, tooke a dagger
with him which his uncle *Palemon* the Shepherd had given him,
and just at eleven of the clocke went to *Filenus* his fathers house,
where *Sylveria* was staying for him, as she had appointed. O wicked
treason, the like never seene, nor heard of before! Oh trayterous 10
wickednes, such as was never thought of before! She tooke him
by the hand, and going very softly up a paire of staires, ledde him
to the chamber doore where *Filenus* his father, and *Felisarda* his
stepdame were a bedde togither, and when she had set him there,
she saide unto him. Now thou art come to the place *Montanus*, 15
where thou must shew that thou hast courage and no abject
minde, that is requisite in so good a cause: goe into this chamber,
and there thou shalt finde thy mother a bed with the adulterer.
When she had saide so, she ranne away, as fast as ever she could.
Montanus being thus deluded with *Sylverias* falshood, gave credite 20
to her words, and in a furie plucking his dagger out of the sheath,
brake open the chamber doore with a thrust of his foote, like
a mad man with these loud exclamations rushed into it, saying:
Here must thou die (traytour) by mine owne hands: now shall
the strumpet *Felisardas* foule loves helpe thee nothing at all: And 25
speaking these words, he was so wroth, that he knew not who he
was that lay in the bedde, and thinking to have slaine the adulterer,
he lifted up his arme to stabbe his Father as he lay a bedde. But
yet good Fortune awoke the old man, who knowing his sonne by
the light that was there, thought verily that for the austere words 30
and unkind disgraces, which he had done him, he came to kill
him; wherefore lifting himselfe quickly out of the bedde, with
holding up his hands he saide. O my sonne! what crueltie is this
that makes thee the butcher of thine owne Father? For Gods
sake remember thy selfe, and spill not nowe my innocent bloud, 35
nor ende my life before the appointed hower from above doth
come. For if I have heeretofore used any rigour against thee,
heere upon my knees I crave pardon for it, with protestation,
that from hencefoorth I will entreate thee as lovingly and gently

17 requisite *Ed.*] reqnisite *Y.*

as any father in the world may use his sonne. When *Montanus* perceived the treacherie that was wrought, and the danger that he had almost incurred, by killing his owne Father, he stoode there so astonished, that his hart and arme so failed him, whereby the dagger fell out of his hands and never felt it. Being thus striken in a maze, he could not utter a worde; but ashamed and confounded in his owne enterprise, he went out of the chamber, and out of the house wonderful sorrie for the treacherie that *Sylveria* had buzzed into his eares, and for that which he had almost done, but that his fortune was the better. *Felisarda*, who knew all the matter before, and how it would fall out, when she saw *Montanus* come into the chamber, she lept out of the bed, and ranne into another inward chamber, and locking the doore after her, saved her selfe from her sonne in lawes furie. But when she saw her selfe free from danger (for now *Montanus* was gone out of the house) shee came into the chamber againe where *Filenus* was yet shaking for feare, and then she incensing the Father against the Sonne, with loude vociferations began thus to say unto him. Now *Filenus*, thou knowest well what kinde of Sonne thou hast, and now canst tell if it be not true which I have so often told thee of his wicked conditions and nature. O cruell wretch! O vile Traytour *Montanus*! why doe not the heavens confound thee? Why doth not the earth swallow thee up? Why do not the wilde beasts devour thee? Why do not men persecute thee to death? Accursed by thy marriage, thy disobedience, thy loves, and thy *Ismenia*, that hath brought thee to this barbarous crueltie, and to commit so horrible a sinne. Traytour as thou art, thou dost not punish *Alanius*, who to thy shame and disgrace, hath too familiar companie with thy *Ismenia* using her dishonestly, and whom she loves more then thy selfe; and carest not to kill thy owne Father, who with tendernes of thy life, and credit hath ever made account of thee. Bicause he gave thee good counsell, would'st thou therefore kill him? O woefull Father! O unfortunate gray haires! O grievous old age! What fault didst thou ever commit, that thine owne sonne should kill thee for it, even he, whom thou hast begotten, brought up, and for whom thou hast passed a thousand cares? Plucke up thy hart now; leave of thy fatherly love; give place to justice; let him be duely punished: for, if he, which perpetrated such wicked crueltie, hath not his deserved punishment, disobedient sonnes will not be afraide to do the like, nor thine owne hereafter to murder thee once againe with his owne hands. Old *Filenus* full of feare, griefe, and despite, hearing the speech that his wife told him, and considering his sonnes treason, tooke so great displeasure at it, that taking up the dagger that *Montanus* had let fall, early in the morning he went to the market place, and there assembling the chiefest men of the towne, and the Justices togither, after many teares and sobs, said thus unto them. I invoke God for witnes (most worthie Shepherdes) that the discourse, which I must tell you, torments my soule so much, that I am afraide it will flye out of my bodie before I have told it out. Let not any therefore thinke me cruell or unnatural, by comming to publish my sonnes wickednes openly in this place, since it is so strange and detestable, that the greatest punishment that I am able to give him, is not sufficient for the enormitie thereof. The which for that I am unable my selfe to remedie it, I will lay open before your eies, that you may see, how just and needfull a thing it is to give him condigne punishment, and to forwarne all other sonnes by his grievous example. Needlesse it is to tell you, with what tender love and affection I have brought him up, how carefully I have kept him; with what diligence I have instructed him in commendable qualities; what thoughts I have suffered for him; what good counsell I have given him, and how mildly I have chastised him. To my great griefe he married *Ismenia*; and bicause I found fault with him for it, in lieu of being revenged of *Alanius* the Shepherd, who (as all the countrey knowes) lives dishonestly with his wife *Ismenia*, turned his anger towards me, and this night would have done me to death. For this last night he found the meanes to get into the chamber where I was a bed with my wife *Felisarda*, and with this naked dagger would have killed me: And had done it, but that God did cut off his strength, and abated it in such sort, that being halfe astonished and afraide, he went out from thence, not able to put his damnable intent in practise, leaving the dagger (that fell out of his hands) in the chamber. This is the true report of that which this last night passed, whereof you may be better informed by my loving wife. But bicause I certainly know that my sonne *Montanus* would never have committed so foule a deed against his Father, if his wife *Ismenia* had not perswaded him to it, I therefore beseech you all to consider well of this matter: First, that my sonne may be sufficiently punished for his wicked attempt; and then, that false *Ismenia*, especially for the treacherous counsell she gave her husband, as also for her dishonest love, and life that she leades with *Alanius*, may likewise receive due correction. *Filenus* had scarce ended his tale, when there arose such a noise amongst the people, that all the towne seemed to have suncke: And the harts of all the Shepherds and Shepherdesses were so much altered at these words, that they conceived a mortall hatred against *Montanus*. Some saide, that he deserved to be stoned to death; others, to be throwen into the deepest place of the river *Duerus*; others, that he should be cast forth to be devoured of hungrie woolfes, so that there was not one almost amongst them all, who allotted not his doome and manner of his death. It mooved them also not a little to despite to heare that which *Filenus* falsely reported concerning my life: but they were so incensed with anger and hate against *Montanus*, and his pretenses, that they had no leysure to thinke of mine. When *Montanus* understoode how his Father had openly before all the towne accused him of this deed, and of the hurly burly and awaite, that was laide to catch him, he fell into a woonderfull desperation. And besides this knowing what his Father had told of me before them all, he tooke such a deepe conceit and griefe thereat, that the like was never heard of. From hence did all my sorrowes rise, this was the cause of my perdition, and here did my painfull life begin. For my beloved *Montanus* knew that in times past I had loved *Alanius*, and was beloved of him againe; and imagining that old and mortified loves might oftentimes be revived, and seeing *Alanius* (whom now for his sake I had quite forgotten) to be in love with me as much as ever he was, by making daily suites to me for my love, with those kinde of pastorall feasts and sports, that lovers are woont to please their Shepherdesses withall, he vehemently suspected, that the false report which his Father *Filenus* had told of me was true; and the more he thought of it, the more he beleeved it to be so indeed: In so much that waxing almost mad and desperate for the treacherie that *Sylveria* had wrought him, and for that which he suspected I had done him, he fled from the towne and countrey thereabouts, and since was never more heard of. And I then, who knew of his departure and the cause thereof, by the report of certaine Shepherds his friends, whom he fully acquainted with his unfortunate estate, left also our town to seeke him out, and while I live will never leave seeking, until I have found my deere husband, to acquite my selfe of this crime which he suspectes, although I shoulde die by his owne handes for my labour. It is a good while since I have gone up and downe wandring and enquiring after him, and for all that I have sought in the cheefest townes, and amongst all the Shepherdes and cottages, Fortune 5 never yet gave me any notice of my *Montanus*. The greatest accident, that in these my travels chanced unto mee, since I forsooke my towne, was, that I found the trayteresse *Sylveria*, who knowing the voluntarie exile of *Montanus*, went up and downe following, to tell him the plot and drift of the secret trecherie 10 that she had done him, and to aske him forgivenes for it, being verie penitent that she had committed such abhominable wickednes. But as yet till then she had not spoken with him, and when she sawe me, she told me openly howe the matter stoode, which was no small ease unto my minde, to know the maner how we were 15 betraied. I thought with mine owne handes to have killed her, though I was but a weak woman, yet I did it not, bicause it lay in her only to helpe my greefe by confessing her owne wickednes. I praied her, to seeke out my beloved *Montanus* in all the haste she could, to certifie him of the matter, and how it stoode, and so 20 I left her to seeke him out some other way. I came hither to day to this woode, where being invited by the pleasantnes of the place, I rested mee to passe the heate of the day away. And since that Fortune (for my great comfort) hath brought you hither, and that it is now the hottest part of the day, I beseech you let me enjoy 25 your gracious companie, while the heate of the sunne shall last. *Diana* and *Marcelius* were glad to heare the historie that *Ismenia* tolde them, and to knowe the cause of her greefe. It pleased them also well to heare the discourse of her life, who then gave her some comfort to ease her greefe, promising her all the favour and 30 helpe, that they might possiblie bestow on her for remedie of her paine and travels. They praied her also to go with them to *Felicias* pallace, bicause it was most like that there she should finde out some kind of comfort to make her glad againe. And they both thought good to passe the time away there, while the heate of the 35 Sunne did last, as *Ismenia* requested them. But bicause *Diana* was very skilfull in that ground, and knew very well the woods, fountaines, forrests, and the pleasant and shadowed places of it, she told them, that there was not farre from thence a more delightfull and pleasant place then that was, for it was not yet full 40

midday: So that all three of them rising, went a little way, and
came by and by to a forrest, where *Diana* led them, which was as
pleasant, coole, and delightful a place, as any of those hils, or
fieldes that ever was with fame renowned in the pastorall *Arcadia*:
There were in it faire and greene Sicamours, Sallowes, Ashes, 5
Byrch, and Beech trees, which round about the brinks of the
chrystalline fountaines, and in every part thereabout, being softly
blowen with a coole and sweete winde, made a pleasant and
gentle noise. There the aire did so sweetely resound with the
tuned melodie of the little birdes, which went skipping up and 10
downe the greene boughes, that it cheered up the minde with
a gracious kinde of welcome. It was covered all over with greene
and small grasse, amongst the which were many faire and coloured
flowers, which painting the place with knots in many places, did
with their sweete smell recreate the most sorrowfull and melan- 15
cholike spirits. There were the Hunters woont to finde Heardes
of fearefull Harts, wilde Goates, and of other little beasts, in which
games and sports they tooke no small pastime and delight. They
came into this forrest following *Diana* their guide that went in
first, for she went before to seeke out a little thicke grove of 20
trees, that she had marked out in that place (where she was woont
to resort) to rest and refresh herselfe many times. And they had
not gone farre, when *Diana* comming neere to the place, that she
thought the most pleasant of all the wood, and where shee minded
to have passed away the heate of the daie, putting her finger to 25
her mouth, she made signes to *Marcelius* and *Ismenia* to come on
softly without making any noise. The reason was, bicause she
heard amongst those thicke trees certaine Shepherds singing. By
their voices they seemed to be *Taurisus* and *Berardus*, both extremely tormented in pursute of her love, as it is saide before. 30
But bicause she would be more sure of it, stealing on neerer unto
them betweene certaine bushes, she was harkening to them, to
see if she knew them, and she perceived that they were the very
same, and that they had in their companie a faire yoong gentlewoman, and a gallant and woorthie gentleman, both which 35
(although they seemed to be somewhat troubled in minde, and
wearied by much travell) shewed neverthelesse in their gesture
and disposition notable tokens of valour and vertue. After she
had viewed who they were, she went backe againe bicause she
woulde not be seene. And now was *Marcelius* and *Ismenia* come, 40

and all three togither began to sit them downe behinde certaine
Hasels, where they might not bee seene, but where they might
distinctly heare the Shepherds songs, whose voices resounding
over all the forrest, made a singular sweete melodie, as you shall
heare in the Booke that followeth.

The end of the second Booke.

The third Booke of Enamoured
DIANA.

THe treacherie and malice of an injurious and envying stepdame is commonly woont to enterprise so detestable acts,
that it would discourage the stoutest hart, not onely to doe them,
but make it tremble to thinke of them. And that which is worst, is,
that Fortune is so great a friend in changing good and prosperous
estates, that she sheweth them all the favour she may in their
unjust attempts: for she knoweth that most of them endevour to
stirre up strange novelties, and mutinies, and to be the occasion
and meanes of much sorrow and trouble. The crueltie of *Felisarda*
was great, when by her vile and suttle slightes she made the father
so mortally abhorre his owne sonne, and a husband to forsake his
loving wife; the one deceived by an apparant shewe of love and
dutie misconstrued; the other by a false report, and with a vaine
and simple suspect stinged: but yet her happe was the better,
that brought her malicious and wicked purpose to that effect,
that she herselfe desired. And I speake not this, to make men
thinke the woorse of all such kinde of women, but bicause
everie one may live advisedly by taking good heed of such as
Felisarda was, which are but fewe (I hope) since so many of that
noble sexe are the glorie of the worlde, and the lanterns of life,
whose sinceritie, faith, discretion, and vertues with golden verses
deserve to be eternized. For proofe whereof, *Diana* and *Ismenia*
may give sufficient testimonie, Shepherdesses adorned with singular beautie, chastitie, and wisedome, whose histories do blazon
foorth their infinite and woorthie praises. In following the discourse whereof, you must understand, that when *Marcelius* and

they were sitting behinde the Hasels, they heard that *Taurisus* and *Berardus* did sing as followeth.

Berardus.

*T*He *coole fresh winde,* Taurisus, *that inviting us*
  Amongst the trees, the leaves is gently shaking,   5
  Our sences joying, and with ease delighting us:
The Cotes, and Sicamours sweete shadowes making:
  The Cristall fountaines, that in copious swelling
  Doe flowe, our thirst with savourie liquours slaking:
The coloured flower, whose sweete and fragrant smelling   10
  To banish melancholie greefes sufficeth,
  Which makes the hart from sweete content rebelling,
    His might, that all despiseth,
Cannot subdue, nor malice, nor the braverie,
Of that most cruell king, whose sway doth wearie us,   15
    Whose punishment, and slaverie
Is absolute, unjust, and meere imperious.
For amorous greefes, to hels of paines that ferrie us,
  No remedies have yet beene salutiferous,
    But still the poison fuming   20
Infects my soule with torments most pestiferous.

Taurisus.

He that in love is evermore consuming,
  Is never glad, for such an evill tires him,
  Living in greefe, in greefe his death resuming: 25
Love gives him paines, and most with torments fires him,
  When most he seekes his pastime and his pleasure;
  For then with furious thoughts he most inspires him:
Those few times when a soule enjoies her treasure,
  Greefe doth succeede in place, whose balefull sovenaunce   30
  Makes it returne to playning without measure:
    Love will enjoy his covenants:
And whom he conquers, kils, or prisoner taketh,
He thinkes by him to get most famous glorie:
    His prisoner now, that quaketh,   35
He gives to Fortune, with his Fortune sorie,

Or sels to greefe, whom evermore it shaketh,
And paints in him her dire and tragicke storie,
And him thats burning in his hottest fires
He quite consumes, the cruell he retires.

Berardus.   5

The whole man waxeth sicke as he intreates him,
He turnes each hart from former joy to sadnes,
Still killing him, that living is, and threates him,
That is most free, with bonds, the scourge of gladnes:
Since then (my soule) thou knowest too well how cruell   1
This Tyrant is, be patient, and content thee,
That such a place contains thy amorous fuell:
(So high a place) Take greefes, and now present thee
To all those harmes, and paines he shall enure thee:
Enjoy thine ill, and in thy greefes maintaine thee,   1
Bicause by how much more thou shalt procure thee
A meanes, to rid thy selfe from that that paines thee,
The more thou shalt enwrap thee in his briers,
And shalt be furdest from thy cheefe desires:

Taurisus.   2

Love findes in me so well disposed matter,
And such a minde to amplifie his glorie,
That mongst all those, whose mournfull flockes doe scatter
On both Hisperias plaines, in love so sorie,
My daily greefes are ever more augmented: 2
Salt showers of teares mine eies have ever rained:
And more, then wretched Biblis malcontented,
When turned to a fountaine she remained.
Strange is my good, my paine is proper to me,
Faine would I see Dianas face, but twenty,   3
And twenty deaths in seeing her undoe me,
I die for want neere to the fount of plenty:
Her presence doth with paines and torments fill me,
Her absence doth with desperation kill me.

Berardus.

The woods doe murmur, and the meadow smileth,
And jugging nightingales are sweetely singing:
But death to thousand woes my hope exileth:

Taurisus.   5

The blooming trees smell sweete, that now are springing,
The grasse growes greene, with many a painted flower:
But I remaine (O woe) in sorrowes stinging:

Berardus.

My woes my wits have slaine in such an hower,   10
That now I have no power
To say by hart ten verses all along:

Taurisus.

My toong doth cleave even in my very song,
Wherefore (my friend) prolong   15
The time no more, but sing that sweetest dittie,
Which interrupted with thy sighes of pitie,
And teares, in every citie
And countrie towne, so highly did commend thee.

Berardus.   20

Singing with thee, it shall no whit offend me,
But ease and pleasure lend me:
Then answer me. But now what shall I sing?

Taurisus.

Sing that that saieth. The radiant star doth bring?   25
  Or that: Loves teares doe spring. *Etc.*
Or that: I knowe not well how it doth say,
  Which thou sung'st on a day,
Dauncing with faire Diana *on a greene.*

Berardus.

No Tigresse nor no lionesse have beene,
  But with compassion mooved
Of all my torments, able to despaire one:
  But not that cruell faire one,   5
The fierce devouresse of my life approoved.

Taurisus.

The fierce devouresse of my life approoved,
  My peerelesse Shepherdesse,
As fell in hart, as she is faire in face: 10
  How then in such a case
Can I escape (O greefe) but die without redresse?

Berardus.

Can I escape (O greefe) but die without redresse
  With deathes of racking passions?   15
But when I see Diana faire, her sight my griefes asswageth,
  Yet then my soule enrageth:
The more I have to doe with love, the lesse I knowe his fashions.

Taurisus.

The more I have to doe with love, the lesse I knowe his fashions, 20
  His servants he neglecteth
And he, that flying seeketh to escape his mortall chaine,
  With thrise redoubled paine
He wounds, and with his furious plagues his wretched soule infecteth.

Berardus.   25

Faire Shepherdesse, whose face the heavenly powers
Have graced with more beautie, then the Roses:
And sweeter then the purple golden flowers,
That deckes our meades and virgins brestes with poses:
  So may the heavens powre downe in copious plentie   30
  Upon thy flockes their favours most abounding:
  And thy faire ewes, with double twins not emptie,
  In numbers swarme, in profit still redounding:
    That to my soule, which my demerit pesters,
    Thou wouldst not shew sterne lookes, nor angrie gestures.   35

Taurisus.

Faire Shepherdesse, that with thy neighbour dwelling,
Dost cleere thy fieldes bedight with Daffodillies,
The driven snowe in whitenesse far excelling,
In beautie Gilloflowres, and stately lillies: 5
  So prosper may thy fieldes in every season
  In corne, and fruit, which thou maist taste at pleasure:
  Thy peares, and plums, and apricocks so geason
  By handfuls maist thou pull in plentious measure:
    That thou wouldst looke upon thy swaine so sorie: 10
    For of thy sight depends his cheefest glorie.

About this time the yoong Gentleman, and Gentlewoman that
were harkening to the Shepherds songs, did cut them off, and
gave them many thankes for the delight and recreation, which
with so sweete musicke they had given them. And after this the 15
Gentleman turning to the Gentlewoman said. Didst thou ever
(sister) in the magnificent and stately Cities heare musicke that
pleased the eare, and delighted the minde like this? Truely (saide
she againe) these pastorall and country songs, being full of
simplicitie and plainnes, please me more, then the delicate voices 20
set togither with curious skill, and full of newe inventions and
conceits in the brave pallaces of Kings and Princes. And when
I thinke this melodie to be better then that, you must the rather
beleeve it, bicause I have been present at the best musicke that in
any Citie of the world or Kings Court, was ever heard. For in that 25
happie time, when *Marcelius* was a sutor to our sister *Alcida*, he
did some nights sing to the tune of his Lute so sweetely, that if
Orpheus made so solemne musicke, I did not marvell then if the
Birdes, and Beastes did follow him, and that he brought backe
his deere wife *Euridice* from darke hell. Ah *Marcelius*, where art 30
thou nowe? Ah where art thou *Alcida*? Ah most haplesse woman
that I am, how often doth Fortune surcharge my memorie with
objects of greefe, when she sees me enjoy the least content and
pleasure in the worlde? *Marcelius* heard the talke of the Gentleman and the Damosell, which were with the Shepherds behinde 35
the shrubs and bushes, and when he perceived that they named
him and *Alcida*, he began to bee somewhat altered. He scarcely
beleeved his owne eares, and was doubting with himselfe whether

it was another *Marcelius* and *Alcida* whom they named. He rose
up by and by out of his place, and to cleere himselfe of all doubt,
comming neerer, he knewe that they were *Polydorus* and *Clenarda*,
brother and sister to *Alcida*: Wherupon he ran suddenly to
them, and with open armes, and abundance of teares, somtimes 5
embracing *Polydorus*, sometimes *Clenarda*, he stoode a great while
before hee could speake for inward greefe. *Polydorus* and *Clenarda*
wondring at this noveltie, could not conjecture what accident it
was, bicause *Marcelius* going in a Shepherds habite, was unknowne
unto them, untill his sobs and teares giving him leave, he saide. 10
O deere brother and sister, care not nowe for my ill fortune paste,
and to come, since I am the happiest man in the world in seeing
you. Ah, why is not *Alcida* in your companie? Is she perhaps
hidden in any part of this thicke woode! O let me know some
newes of her, if you can tell me any, to ease my cruell greefe, and 15
to satisfie my desire! In speaking these wordes, they knewe
Marcelius, and embracing him very affectionately, and weeping for
pleasure and greefe, they saide unto him. O happie day! O unexpected joy! O deere brother of our soules, what cruell Fortune
hath bin the cause, that thou dost not enjoy the company of 20
Alcida, nor we her sight? Why dost thou dissemble thy selfe with
this new habite? O cruell fortune, in the end there is not full
content of any good. *Diana* and *Ismenia* on the other side, seeing
that *Marcelius* had so on the sudden gone to the place where the
Shepherds did sing, went after him, and founde him talking with 25
Polydorus and *Clenarda*, as you have heard. When *Taurisus* and
Berardus saw *Diana*, the joye, that at so sweete and sudden a sight
they tooke, cannot be tolde. And so *Taurisus* shewing a marvellous
kinde of gladnes in his hart, and words, said unto her. This is no
small favour of fortune (faire *Diana*) to make her, that con- 30
tinually flies our companie, by unexpected and happie chances to
come so often where wee are. That is not the cause of Fortune
(woorthie Shepherds) saide *Diana*, but rather bicause you are so
excellent in singing and playing on your instruments: for there is
no place of pleasure where you are not, and where your sweete 35
musicke and songs are not heard. But now, since I am come
hither, though ignorant of your being heere, and that the parching
Sunne is now in the highest way, I shall be very glad to passe
away the heate of the daie in this pleasant place, and in your good
companie: and though it standes me upon to go quickly to 40

Felicias pallace, yet will I not thinke the time long to staie heere with you to take part of the coole and greene grasse, and to harken to your delightfull musicke. Prepare your selves therefore to sing and plaie, and to all kinde of honest myrth, for it will not become this place, and brave assemblie to be without such kinde of 5 pleasure. And you Gentleman, and faire Gentlewoman, surcease your teares a while, bicause you shall have time enough heere-after to tell to each other your Fortunes and adventures, and to bewaile, or rejoice at the ill or good successe of them. All of them liked well of *Dianas* speech, and so they sat them downe 10 upon the fine greene grasse rounde about the Fountaine. That was the pleasantest place in all the wood, and more then any of those, that were celebrated by the cleere Bagpipe of *Neapolitan Syncerus* in famous *Parthenia.* There was in this place a broad quadrant fortie paces of everie side, and compassed about with a great 15 number of thick trees. So that in a maner of a walled castle, they, that went to recreat themselves in it, could not go but by one way into it. It was covered all over with greene grasse and sweete flowers, never troden downe with the feete of sheepe or goates, nor mangled with their slicing teeth. In the mids thereof was 20 a goodly cleere fountaine, which, issuing foorth at the foote of an olde Oake, rose up fower square and deepe; not made by skil-full hand, but placed there by provident nature to such purposes, as with the abundance of the waters it made there a delightfull meeting, which the Shepherds named the *faire Fountaine.* The 25 brinkes of this fountaine were of white stone so even, that none would have thought, but that it was made with artificiall hand, if the naturall stones growing there, did not deceive his sight, which were fastened in the ground as hard, as the craggie rocke, and flint in the wilde mountaines. The water that came out of that 30 sweete fountaine, issuing out of two narrow pipes, did water the grasse and trees about it, making them continually to spring, and fertill, and keeping them in a pleasant and fine verdure. This *faire Fountaine* for everie goodly pleasure about it was so much visited of the Shepherds and Shepherdesses, that there was never wanting 35 about it pastorall mirth and joy. Who likewise had it in such veneration and account, that when they came to it, they left their flockes without, bicause the cleere and sweete waters might not be troubled, nor the fine little meadow fed, nor troden downe by the hungrie and carelesse sheepe. About this fountaine (as I saide) 40 they all sat downe, and taking necessarie foode out of their scrips, did eate it more savourly, and with greater content, then the greatest Lords their varietie and number of daintie dishes. At the end of which repast, as *Marcelius* on the one side, and *Polydorus* and *Clenarda* on the other, were greatly desirous to heare, and make relation of their passed fortunes, *Marcelius* first began to say to the other two in this sort. It is great reason (brother and sister) that I know somthing of your adventures and accidents, since last I saw you, bicause seeing not your Father *Eugerius*, nor your sister *Alcida* in your company, it makes a great alteration in my hart, not knowing the cause thereof. To whom *Polydorus* answered.

Bicause this goodly place might not be injured (me thinkes) with reports of dole and sorrow, and that these Shepherds with hearing of our hard haps might not be also greeved, with the fewest words (that possible may be) I will report the many miseries and disgraces that we have received of Fortune.

After that I was hindered by the mariners from leaping into the sciffe, having attended fit time and occasion to have delivered my father *Eugerius* (being faint and halfe dead) out of the dangerous ship, and that of force I was constrained to remaine (to my great griefe) with my fearefull father in it, the sorrowfull olde man was overcome with such bitter anguish and paine, as may be imagined of a loving father, who in the end of his aged yeeres, seeth the violent perdition of his owne life and of his loving children. He tooke no heed now to the maine blowes, which the cruell waves did beate against the ships sides, nor to the rage of the angrie windes that did bluster on everie side, but casting his eies to the little boate wherein thou wert *Marcelius* with *Alcida* and *Clenarda* (which at everie flote of the hoisting billowes seemed to turne over) the more he saw it going from the ship, the more his hart burst in peeces. And when he lost sight of you, he was in danger of yeelding up his decaied spirits. The ship driven on by the crueltie of Fortune, went floating up and downe the maine seas five daies togither, after that we parted; at the ende of which time, the Sunne going downe towards the West, we were in ken of lande: At sight whereof the Marriners were verie glad, as well for recoverie of their lost hope, as also for knowing the coast whither the ship was driven. For it was the most fertill countrey and most abounding in all sortes of pleasures, as far as the Sun

doth heate with his beames: In so much that one of the Marriners
taking a Rebecke out of a chest, with the which he was wont to
cheere up himselfe in long and dangerous voiages, began to
play and sing to it in manner following.

Welcome thy friendes from swelling seas that rore   5
   With hideous noise, and tost by Neptunes *toile,*
O fortunate and faire Valencia *shore,*
   Where nipping frost doth never hurt thy soile,
     Nor Phebus *with his woonted parching beames*
     Doth burne thy meades, nor heates thy christall streames.   10

Thrise happy he, who living without feare
   In swallowing seas and billowes to be drownd,
Enjoies thy golden beauties every wheare,
   Of thy sweete meades, greene banks, and fruitfull ground,
     Thy ground bedeckt with flowres so fine and faire,   15
     Maintainde with heavenly deaw and pleasant aire.

With greater toile the ship doth cut the seas,
   Then wearie plowmen doth thy gentle fieldes,
Then happy Earth, the joy and wished ease
   Of traveled soules, that to thy succour yeeldes,   20
     Receive into thy pleasant woods and caves,
     Before the sea doth rage in roring waves,

Receive (I say) *poore and disastrous men*
   Beaten with stormes and almost cast away,
Since now we are arriv'd within the ken   25
   Of thy brave coastes, this sevenfold happy day:
     That I may wash in Turia, *as of late,*
     These waters and accursed waves to hate.

By the Marriners song we knew, that the shoare which we
went to, was in the kingdome of *Valentia*, a countrey famous 30
throughout all the world. But whilest he was singing this song,
the ship blowen on by a mightie strong gust of winde, came so
neere unto the shoare, that if the sciffe had not beene wanting,
we might have gone into it a land. But we were hailed a far off by
certaine fisher men; who seeing our sayles lost, our maste broken, 35

our tackling torne, and the forecastle shivered in pieces, knew in what neede of helpe we were. Whereupon some of them getting in their boate, in which they went commonly a fishing, being readie at the shoare, came to us, and with great kindnes, and trouble tooke us all out of the ship. The joy at which landing we 5 made was so great, as the like may not be imagined. *Eugerius* and I gave a thousand thankes, and due rewards for so singular a courtesie to the fishermen, that of their owne accord, and without entreatie so lovingly tooke us into their boate: But they being men pitifull by nature, and of a simple and bountifull disposition, 10 cared not for our gifts, but refusing them rather, one of them saide unto us. Thanke us not so much (Gentlemen) for this kinde of duetie, considering that we are bound to succour men in their necessities, accept our good will onely that inforceth us to this small piece of service. And be assured that at all times when like 15 occasion shall happen as this, we would be as readie as now we are to hazard our lives in it. Bicause no longer agoe then this morning happened a stranger chaunce then this, wherein if we had not employed our labours to helpe it, as now we have done, it would have grieved us to death. And thus it was, that at breake 20 of day, going out of our sheds with our nets, and ordinarie tew to go a fishing, before we came to the sea side, we saw the cloudes to waxe darke, the sea to make a great noise, and the winds to rise with great force, and twise we would have turned backe againe, being halfe afeard to trust the dangerous waves in so 25 tempestuous a time. But yet some of us thought it not amisse to go to the shoare side, to see what would become of the threatning tempest, and to trie, if after lowring weather and Fortune, any faire calme (as it is woont to doe) or Sunshine would follow. But when we were come thither, we saw a boate striving and tossing 30 up and downe the swelling waves, without sayle, maste, or oares in it, and in the same danger as you were. Being mooved to compassion, we launched one of our boates into the sea, and leaping quickly into it without any feare of danger or Fortune, we made towards the boate that was in great perill to be cast away, 35 and after a little while came to it. When we were so neere unto it, that we might well discerne those that were in it, we saw a gentle-woman, ignorant of her Fortune and name, who with her eies swollen with teares, and her armes cast abroade called upon us, and with pitifull and dolefull words said thus unto us. Ah deere 40

brothers, deliver me I beseech you from this danger of cruell
Fortune, but helpe me, most earnestly I pray you, out of these
Traitours hands that come with me, who against all reason keepe
me heere captive, and by maine force would violate my deere
honour. When wee heard this, with all the haste we could make, 5
and not without great perill, we tooke them both out of the
boate, and carried them to lande. She told us of the treason and
deceit that they had done to her, and to a sister of hers and
a brother in law, which would be too long to declare. And she is
now at home in the company of our wives, free from the crueltie 10
and villanie of the two Marriners that came with her, whom we
have committed to prison in a towne not far from hence, where
after a few daies, they shall be duely punished for their wicked
treacherie. When any such chaunce therefore doth befall, as this
did not long since, who of us all would not adventure himselfe in 15
like dangers, to recover those that are in hazard of Fortune, and
to do good to miserable men? When *Eugerius* and I heard the
Marriner tell this tale, our harts leapt in our breast for joy,
imagining, that it was one of his daughters and my sister: wherefore we both tooke great comfort, knowing that we should see 20
anone whether our surmise was true or not? While the Marriner
was recounting to us this accident, the boate driven by force of
oares, went on so fast, that at last we came to shoare. The fisher
men bare feete and bare legged lept into the water, and upon
their shoulders carried us to wished land. And when we were 25
there, knowing what great neede of rest and cherishing we had,
one of the auncientest of them, taking my Father by the hand, and
making signes to me and to the rest to follow him, went towards
his house, which was not far off, to refresh and rest us, which was
verie needfull for us. Being come thither, we heard women 30
singing within, and we had not gone in before we had heard and
understoode the manner and matter of their songs, if the poore
case that we were in, would have given us leave to staie without
to hearken to them. But *Eugerius* and I thought everie minute of
an hower too long before we went in, to see what that Damosell 35
should be, whom they had set free from the tempest and Tray-
tours hands. We went on the sudden into the house, and the
women (which were the fisher mans wife and his two faire
daughters) being somewhat abashed at our sight, left of their

13 punished *Ed.*] puuished *Y.*

song: for they were sweetly singing, while they were knitting
of nets to take the silly fish, in the middest of whom was the
Damosell, which was knowen by and by; for it was my sister
Clenarda, which is heere present. The accidents that we passed
after this, and that which she escaped before, let her selfe recount, 5
bicause I dare not take in hand so hard a taske. But there were
complaints, teares, sighes, and pleasures intermingled with paines,
sweetnes, sowrenes, and such words and deeds as a wise man may
easily conjecture. At the ende of which, my Father turning to the
fisher mans daughters, said unto them. Since I came hither (faire 10
maides) to refresh my selfe, and to take some ease of my passed
troubles, it is not therefore reason that my comming should
interrupt and molest your mirth and singing, bicause they alone
shall be sufficient to cheere up my sorrowfull hart. You shall not
want this service (said the fisher man) whilest you are in my 15
house: or else I will endevour at the least to procure it for you by
all meanes possible. Let not this therefore be any part of your
care, but rather to make your selfe strong againe, with some good
foode, for such homely musicke shall not be wanting at any time.
Then his wife brought us out some victuals, and while we were at 20
them, one of the maids, called *Nerea*, did sing us this song.

Nereas *Song*.

*I*N *those most happy fieldes and plaines,*
Where Guadaljar *in goodly vaines*
  With christall streames doth glide,   25
Leaving the sweete and pleasant fieldes,
Unto the sea his tribute yeeldes
  And runs with hastie tide,

Faire Galatee *full of disdaine,*
And joyfull of the woes and paine   30
  To Lycius *that she gave,*
Played upon the sands and shore,
The which the sea sometimes before
  Doth wash with wallowing wave.

28 *tide, Ed.*] *tide. Y.*

Gathering amongst the sandes alone
Fine shels, and many a painted stone,
  As she went up and downe:
And singing many songs so sweete,
The which the roring billowes yet   5
  Did alter much and drowne.

Neere to the water side she hies,
And there the waves that fall and rise
  She view'd with great delight;
And fled, when that they came amaine,   10
And sometimes could not, but was faine
  To wet her feete so white.

Lycius, who had in suffring paines
No equall in those fieldes and plaines,
  His torments there suspended,   15
Whiles that he view'd with great content
His Shepherdesse so excellent,
  For beautie most commended.

But now comparing his unrest
With all the joy that she possest,   20
  The Shepherd halfe decaied
With dolefull voice his sad complaints
To shores and champaines he acquaints,
  And in this manner said.

O fairest Nymph, if that thou please,   25
Play not about the roring seas,
  Although thy chiefe delight
Consist therein, yet Galatee
As thou dost Licius, so the sea
  Eschew with hastie flight.   30

And now (sweete Nymph) leave of to play,
For it doth greeve me day by day
  To see thee on the sandes:
O doe not now torment me more,
For seeing thee upon the shore   35
  I feare false Neptunes hands.

And this doth fill me full of doubtes,
That I must credit these my thoughtes,
   Bicause it is most cleere,
That if he die not now for thee,
He will no doubt thy lover bee   5
   When that he sees thee heere.

And this is sure: For love doth knowe,
Since first my soule he wounded so,
   That I should never want
A stronger rivall, and more stoute,   10
Then I, who daily would seeke out
   My true love to supplant.

Leave then the barren sands and shore,
Forsake the cliffes, come there no more,
   Flie from that dangerous coast: 15
Take heede no monster of the sea
Surprise thee not (faire Galatee)
   Where many have beene lost.

Flie now, and see how I endure
Ten thousand greefes to see thee sure,   20
   Bicause with double paine
Jealous I am of thy content,
And for thy dangers imminent
   Great cares I doe sustaine.

In seeing thee so mery and glad,   25
My jealous thoughts doe make me sad,
   And thinke of Europe *faire,*
Deceived by a milke white bull,
As on the sea bankes she did cull
   Fine flowers to dresse her haire.   30

And more, my ordinarie cares
Make me to thinke, how unawares
   Disdainfull Alnade *was*
Dishivered and devour'd by
A huge sea monster, that did lie   35
   Hard by where he did passe.

But well away, that I doe see
Signes of no feare nor greefe in thee,
 For this my sorrow knowes,
That he, thats not of love afraide,
Can with no dangers be dismaide,   5
 And feares not where he goes.

O then (my peerelesse Nymph) take heede,
Lest Cupid *doe revenge with speede,*
 To see himselfe contemned,
For being such a God of might,   10
He will not suffer, but will smite,
 When he is once offended.

Come goe with me unto the woods,
Where every plant sprout foorth her buds,
 And to the goodly fieldes,   15
Where we will spend the pleasant howers,
Amongst the faire and redolent flowers,
 That nought but pleasure yeeldes.

If waters please thee, I will bring
Thee to so faire and fine a spring,   20
 That to be first in praise
Amongst the rest, thy body white
To wash within her waters bright,
 For thee it onely staies.

Disporting in this naked place,   25
Thou hast no vaile to hide thy face,
 Nor shade from parching sunne,
Pitie it were thy beauties blaze,
Which envious Titan *feares to gaze,*
 By him should be undone.   30

Heere hear'st thou no melodious voice,
But still a huge and fearefull noise
 Of monsters hideous raves,
And seas, that rore like tumbling thunder,
Tost with the windes, that beate asunder   35
 The proude and raging waves.

What joy and pleasure canst thou take,
To see the tossing billowes shake
  A ship upon the sand?
And then to see the broken plankes,
And carcases in pitious rankes   5
  Come swimming to the land.

Come to the frithes, and forrests tall,
Where nature hath beene liberall
  With many a pleasant seate.
Come to the coole and sweetest shades,   10
Where in greene pathes and open glades
  We passe away the heate.

Flie, flie, those proude and swelling seas,
Come, come and thou shalt see what ease
  We take, and how we sing   15
Ditties so sweete, that in suspence
We hold the rockes, and every sence
  Of every living thing.

And though that some be full of pitie,
Love forceth them to such a dittie,   20
  For love is full of paine:
Yet all the Shepherdes will I moove,
To sing no mournefull songs of love,
  Onely to please thy vaine.

There maist thou reade in every tree,   25
And every meade that thou shalt see
  The loves in knots disguis'd
Of jolly Shepherdes, and the names
Of chiefest Nymphes, and countrie dames
  In curious sort devis'd.   30

But it will make thee sad, I feare,
To see thy name ingraven there,
  By knowing it was carved
By him, whom thou didst ever blot
Out of thy minde, and hast forgot,   35
  And with disfavours starved.

25 *every* Ed.] *evety* Y.

And though thine anger will be such,
Yet wilt thou marvell not so much
  To see thy carved name,
As thou wilt woonder then to see,
That he doth love and honour thee,   5
  That there did write the same.

Not to be loved, and to love,
It is a greevous greefe to proove:
  But what a greefe or paine
Could it in thee (faire Nymph) procure,   10
To be beloved with love so pure,
  And not to love againe?

But now despis'd I reckon small
Faire Galatee my torment all
  So that thou wilt forsake   15
These swallowing sandes, and seas so high,
Where monsters bellow out and crie,
  And daily praies doe take.

What better pastime canst thou finde
Neere to the seas of blustring winde,   20
  Then in our woods and mountaines
To listen to the nightingales,
And gather flowers in our vales,
  And bathe in christall fountaines.

I would to God thou livedst heere,   25
In our faire fieldes and rivers cleere,
  And for to love them more,
I would to God thou wouldst but see
Before I should report to thee
  How they excell the shore.   30

Bicause I know, the more I praise
These woods, meades, springs and lovely laies,
  The lesse thou wilt beleeve me;
And wilt not come where thou dost knowe,
That part of my content doth growe   35
  Which most of all doth greeve me.

Poore Lycius *would have spoken more,*
To win her from that haplesse shore,
  But that she bad him cease:
For with an angrie face and scoule
She turn'd unto the wretched soule,   5
  And bad him hold his peace.

Then went she to her sportes againe,
He to his plaintes and woonted paine:
  And in the selfe same sort
He still remaines in woonted sorrow,   10
She in the sea bankes even, and morrow,
  Contented with her sport.

The faire maides song, and our supper ended al at one time,
which being done, we demanded of *Clenarda* what had hapned
unto her since our last departure from her, who tolde us what 15
villanie *Sartofano* offered unto her, in what case *Alcida* was left,
of thy imprisonment, her captivitie, and in the ende all that thou
knowest at large. We bewailed bitterly our hard Fortunes, which
when the Fisherman hearde, hee comforted us up as well as he
could, and tolde us especiallie how that in these parts there was 20
the sage *Felicia*, whose wisedome was enough to remedie our
greefes; giving us also notice of *Alcida*, and of thee, to the which
our desires principally tended. And so passing away that night
the best we coulde, assoone as morning came, leaving the
marriners there that came with us in the shippe, we three alone 25
went our waies, and not long after came to the Temple of *Diana*,
where the wise Lady *Felicia* keepes her court. We sawe there the
admirable temple, the most pleasant gardens, the sumptuous
pallace, there we knew the great wisedome of the most grave
Ladie, and other things that filled us so full of woonder, that wee 30
have scarce anie breath to tell them againe. There we sawe the
fairest Nymphes, examples of chastitie, many Lordes and Ladies,
Shepherds, and faire Shepherdesses, and especiallie one Shepherd
named *Syrenus*, whom every one there made great account of:
To him and many more besides, did sage *Felicia* give divers 35
remedies for their loves and greefes. But the pleasure, which but
hitherto yet she hath done us, is, to keepe our Father *Eugerius* in

27 *Felicia* Ed.] *Fe- cia* Y.

her companie, commanding us to goe towardes these parts, and
that we should not returne untill we had found out some content
or good Fortune. And for the great joy that wee have received by
thy sight, I thinke wee have good occasion to go backe againe,
especially for that we have left there our Father all alone and 5
comfortlesse: I know well that in seeking out *Alcida* is no small
ease to his carefull thoughts; but bicause Fortune hath not these
manie daies given us any newes of her, we shall take the better
course to returne backe againe, then to suffer our old Father to be
deprived so long of our companie. After *Polydorus* had made an 10
end of his discourse, every one was astonished to heare such
strange accidents; and after *Marcelius* had wept for *Alcida*, he
made a breefe relation to *Polydorus*, and *Clenarda* of that which
had hapned to him since he sawe them last. When *Diana* and
Ismenia heard *Polydorus* make an end of that sorrowfull historie, 15
they desired to go the sooner to *Felicias* court, the one bicause
she knew assuredly that *Syrenus* was there; the other, bicause she
conceived a certaine hope (hearing of the woonderfull wisedome
of *Felicia*) to have also some redresse for her greefes. Being therefore possessed with this desire, *Diana* (although she was minded 20
to recreate herselfe certaine howers in that pleasant place) altered
her determination, esteeming more of *Syrenus* sight, then of the
greene hew of that goodly and fine wood. Whereupon rising up,
she said to *Taurisus* and *Berardus*. Sit yee (merrie Shepherds) still,
and enjoy the delight and sweetenes of this pleasant place, for 25
the desire that I have to go to *Dianas* temple, will not let me stay
any longer here. We are right sorie to forsake so delightfull
a shade and so good company, but we are forced to follow our
Fortune in this behalf. Wilt thou be so discurteous (faire Shepherdesse) (said *Taurisus*) to depart so soone from our dolefull eies, 30
and to let us so small a while enjoy thy sweet sight and speeches?
These Shepherds have great reason (said *Marcelius* to *Diana*) to
demand such a gentle request, and it is therfore as great again that
their demand be not denied them in reward of their constant
faith and true love, which deserves to enjoy thy companie a little 35
while in this pleasant place, especially when thou hast time enough
to be at *Dianas* temple before the Sunne wil hide his light. All of
them were of his opinion, and therefore *Diana* woulde not seeme
discourteous to anie of them, but sitting down again in her place,
she would not rather please herselfe, then displease so brave 40

a companie as that was. Now then loving Shepherds (said *Ismenia* to *Berardus* and *Taurisus*) since faire *Diana* doth not denie us her presence, it is not reason that you denie her your songs. Sing jolly Shepherds, that in your songs and roundelaies shewe so great cunning, and so perfect love, being for the one commended 5 in al the townes and countries heereabout, and mooving the hardest harts with the other to love and pitie. True (saide *Berardus*) all harts, saving *Dianas*, and began to weepe, and *Diana* to smile. Which when the Shepherd sawe, to the sweete sound of his pipe with the swelled teares standing in his eies, he sung a glosse upon 10 this Dittie.

M Y greevous sighes and sorrowfull teares
In stones doe make their lively print,
But not in thee harder then any flint.

The glosse. 15

Let not thy Graces rare,
   Be with my service any whit offended,
Since that my greevous fare,
   And torments past, to thy devotions tended,
      Were never yet with greefe of thee lamented, 20
      Nor with my sighes thy crueltie relented.
Thy hart was never changed with my cries,
   With which I was importunate alwaies
      To wearied earth and skies:
Though thou dost see not onely nights and daies 25
      Spilt and consum'd with many feares,
      My greevous sighes and sorrowfull teares.

In thy conditions strange thou art,
   That dost not cease with stranger deathes to kill me:
But strangest is my sorrowfull hart, 30
   That suffring paines wherewith thou dost so fill me,
      And living in so strange and cruell passion,
      It dies not in most strange and cruell fashion.

For if an ill a little time relents,
  (Although it be the hardest to sustaine)
    It openeth yet some vents
To ease, and doth not give such mortall paine:
    But greefe that hath no end nor stint,   5
    In stones doe make their lively print.

Love is a daintie milde, and sweet,
  A gentle power, a feeling fine and tender,
So that those harmes, and paines unmeete,
    Which I doe passe, thou onely dost engender: 10
    Onely to him his torments love deviseth,
    That scornes his lawes, his rites, and love despiseth.
And this is now my mortall paine and death,
    That, love (since first thy beauties I did see)
      Like to my proper breath,   15
Wherewith I live, hath ever beene in mee:
    In me it lives, in me it makes his print,
    But not in thee, harder then any flint.

Berardus song pleased *Diana* well, but perceiving by it, that he made her hart harder then the stones, she would for her credite 20 have answered him againe, and therfore said. It is a merrie jest (by my life) to call her hard that is modest, and cruell, that is carefull to keepe her honestie, I woulde to God, Shepherd, my soule were no more sorrowfull, then my hart is hard. But O greefe! Fortune hath made me captive to so jealous a husband, 25 that I was many times constrained to shew discurtesie to gentle Shepherds in these hils, dales, and fieldes, bicause I woulde not have added more sorrow to my troublesome life with him. And yet for all this, the knot of marriage and reason oblige me to seeke out my rude and ill conditioned husband, although I looke 30 not for any thing else at his hands, then sorrow, care, greefe, and manie more annoies in his frowarde companie. *Taurisus* taking nowe occasion at *Dianas* complaints, which she made of her unfortunate marriage, began to play on his Baggepipe, and to sing, speaking as it were to love, and descanting upon this 35 common song that saieth.

The Song.

A Faire maide wed to prying jealousie
   One of the fairest as ever I did see,
If that thou wilt a secret lover take,
Sweete life, doe not my secret love forsake.   5

The glosse.

Beware good Love, beware, it is not well
   To let blinde Fortune have a greater part
In women, that in Beautie doe excell,
   More then thy selfe, since such an one thou art: 10
For Beautie being commended to thy power
      To grace the same,
Thou dost thy selfe dishonour every hower,
      And art to blame,
   By suffring, that this thing should ever be,   15
   A faire maide wed to prying jealousie.

Thou dost but ill, since thou didst ever make
   Beautie thy friend, who therefore had prepared
Sorrowes for him, (that viewed her) for thy sake,
   Which otherwise she would have kept and spared: 20
And so my firmnesse, and my faith so pure,
      And all my paine,
A simple sight did not the same procure,
      Nor did maintaine,
   But sight of her, and it was onely shee   25
   One of the fairest as ever I did see.

O Love! thou kilst so many without end,
   (For murdring is thy pastime and delight)
That once I hope thy selfe thou shalt offend,
   For want they shall on whom to worke thy spight.   30
Oh then how seemely shalt thou seeme to grone,
      And wounded see
Thyselfe with thine owne griefes, and then thine owne
      Captive to be.
   For thou at last thy selfe shalt not forsake,   35
   If that thou wilt a secret Lover take.

Then maist thou give to Lovers double smart,
  And then I will forgive thee all the care
And amorous paines, thou didst to me impart,
  When that thy selfe (fond Love) thou dost not spare:
And if I blame thy deedes or do reproove thee,   5
    Then shalt thou say,
(But to thy selfe) that reason yet did moove thee
    To make away
Thy selfe, and for thy selfe thy death to take,
Sweete life do not my secret love forsake.   10

All of them liked well of *Taurisus* song, but *Ismenia* especially.
For though it touched *Diana* most of all, bicause it spake of those
women that were ill married; yet the comment upon it (which
were complaints against love) was common to all those that were
tormented with it. And therefore *Ismenia*, who blamed *Cupid* for   15
her paines, did not onely like of those reprehensions that *Taurisus*
gave Love, but she herselfe to the sound of her Harpe, sung
a song to the same effect, which *Montanus* was woont to sing,
when he was a suter unto her.

A Sonnet.   20

*H*Aving no cause, why in the deepest sound
  Of amorous seas my fraile barke dost thou swallow?
O Love! I'le make thy crueltie to sound
  Swifter from East to West then flying swallow.
Though gales of windes doe bluster in my sterne,   25
  Yet from the gulfe my ship shall never part
Of thy brave might, so furious and so sterne,
  Untill my sighes doe helpe to blowe a part.
If being in a storme, my face I turne,
  Then my desire is weakned by thy might: 30
    Thy force controules my force, that strives in vaine:
I never shall arrive with happy turne
  Into the port, and therefore, if I might,
  I would let out my life in every vaine.

Marcelius deferred not his answere long after them, with another   35
song made to the same purpose, and of the same forme, saving

that the complaintes that he made, were not onely against Love, but against Fortune, and himselfe.

A Sonnet.

STep after step I followe death in sight
Through every field, and hill and troden vale,   5
For everie day my spirits he doth cite,
And warnes my selfe, to shrowde me in his vale.
O death, that once thou wouldst consume this light,
That still deducts my life in blisselesse bale:
Now that my hope hath past away so light,   10
And joies condemn'd to torments without bale.

That Goddesse, whose continuall frownes I beare,
And love, that all my joies asunder teares,
And I my selfe, are foes unto my hart:
She praying on me like a hungrie beare,   15
He chasing me like to the wounded Hart,
And I, that doe increase my bootelesse teares.

The desire that *Diana* had to go to *Felicias* pallace, would not suffer her to staie any longer there, nor harken to any more songs, but when *Marcelius* had ended his, she rose up. And so did 20 *Marcelius*, *Ismenia*, and *Clenarda*, understanding *Dianas* mind, although they knew that *Felicias* house was nigh at hand, and that they had time enough to be there before night. After they had taken their leave of *Taurisus* and *Berardus*, they went from the faire fountain that way that they came in, and walking thorow the 25 wood at their leysure, enjoying the pleasures and delights of it, at last they came out of it, and then they began to go thorow a great and wide plaine, passing goodly to behold, where they went thinking howe they might recreate their mindes with some myrth, while they were going on their waies, and every one told 30 his opinion concerning that matter. But *Marcelius*, who had ever the figure of *Alcida* engraven in his hart and thoughts, tooke no greater delight nor other joy, then to marke the sweete behaviour of *Polydorus* and *Clenarda*, and to harken to their talke. And therefore to delight himselfe fully with this desire he said. I beleeve 35

10 *light Ed.*] *lgiht Y.*

not (faire Shepherdesses) that all your pastimes are comparable
to the delight that you may have, if *Clenarda* would discourse
unto you any of those things that she hath seene in the fieldes and
bankes of *Guadalajar*. I passed that way in my peregrinations, but
tooke no pleasure in those delights, bicause my minde went 5
musing on other matters. But bicause wee have two large howers
(our journey being but halfe an howers worke) to go to *Dianas*
temple, we may therefore walke on softly, and she (if it please
her) may tell us somthing of that goodly and pleasant countrey.
Diana and *Ismenia* seemed to be very glad, shewing by their 10
amiable countenances, that they longed to have her beginne,
although *Diana* was very desirous to come betimes to the temple;
but bicause she would not make it knowne to them, she concealed
the great passions of her desire, by accommodating her will to
their pleasures. *Clenarda* then entreated by *Marcelius*, following on 15
her way, beganne to saie in this manner. Although I shall offend
your daintie eares, and offer great injurie to the worthines of the
kingdome of *Valentia*, with a rude and disordered relation, to
recount the ornaments, rarities, and pleasures of it; yet bicause
I will in some part fulfil your gentle requestes, I will say some- 20
thing that I have heard and seene therein: I will not make any
particular narration of the fertilitie of the yeelding soyle, the
pleasantnes of the flourishing fieldes, the beauties of the shrubby
hils, the shadowes of the greene woods, the sweetenes of the
cleere fountaines, the melodie of the singing birdes, the coolenes 25
of the fresh and calme windes, the riches of the profitable flockes
of sheepe and goates, the fairenes of the populous townes, the
good nature of the loving people, the strangenes of the sumptuous
temples, nor of many other things more, for which that countrey
is famous thorow out the worlde, bicause it requireth larger time, 30
and a better toong: But bicause you may knowe the cheefest
glorie of that countrey, I will tell you that, which I heard renowned *Turia* the principall river of that land sing. *Polydorus* and
I came on a day to his bankes, to aske the waie to *Dianas* temple
of the Shepherds thereabouts, bicause they coulde best tell it in 35
those parts, and comming to a cottage where certaine herdsmen
were, wee founde them sweetely singing. We asked them that we
desired to know, and they verie lovingly informed us at large of
all we demanded, and afterwards tolde us, that since we came in
so good an hower, that we should not depart from thence, untill 40

we had heard a most sweete song, that the famous *Turia* would make not farre from thence after halfe an hower. We were well content to heare it, and so we staied to go with them. After we had staied a little while in their companie, we went up along the river bankes, untill we came to a wide fielde, where we sawe 5 a great companie of Nymphes, Shepherds, and Shepherdesses, every one attending when famous *Turia* would begin to sing. Not long after we sawe old *Turia* come out of a deepe cave, with a great pot (very curiously wrought) under his arme, his head crowned with a garland of Oke and Laurell, his armes all hairie, 10 his white beard long and slimie: And sitting downe on the grounde, leaning upon his pot, and powring out of it abundance of christalline waters, he cleered up his hoarse and hollow voice, and sung as followeth.

The Song of Turia.   15

*W*Ater (*faire Springs, and purest running streames*)
   This fortunate and most abundant soile,
Comfort the meades and trees, and pleasant aire,
Defend the flowers from Titans burning spoile,
So with the favour of the highest beames   20
I will maintaine my bankes so fresh and faire,
   That these shall have great envie of my crowne,
   The Father of flouds, Rosne, Myncius, *and* Garoune.

Whiles that you goe thus hastening of your course,
Winding your streames by many a crooked way,   25
And joy Valencia *fieldes that sweetely smell*
With savourie liquours in the hottest day:
My weake and feeble breath I will enforce
With my divining spirit to foretell,
   And sing of those good haps, that shall befall   30
   By favour of the heavens unto you all.

Shepherds, and Nymphes, within these lovely dales
Whose names resound unto th' Arcadian fieldes,
Give eare to me: But of the painted flowers,
Nor pleasure, that the springs and medowes yeeldes,   35

Nor woods, nor shades, nor warbling nightingales,
I will not sing, nor of the countrie powers:
   But of those famous men and worthy peeres,
   That shall be heere not after many yeeres.

And now I see two Shepherds first in place, 5
Calixtus, *and* Alexander, *whose fames*
Surmounting the great Cesars *chiefe renowne,*
From Atlas *unto* Maurus *sounds their names:*
Whose lives the heavens adorning with their grace,
Shall make them both to weare a reverend crowne: 10
   And save from losse with their industrious heede,
   As many flockes as in the world doe feede.

Of whose illustrous stocke I see arise
That man, whose hart base feare cannot rebuke,
Well knowne for armes, and many martiall feates, 15
The Roman Cesar, *and* Valencian Duke :
A minde that mounts above the hautie skies,
Whom yet a cruell fate with murder threates,
   That that rare strength, brave hart, and noble breath
   Must have an end by rawe and bloodie death. 20

The same likewise must in a moment end
The glory of Don Hugo de Moncades,
With valour, good successe and happy praise,
Leaving the Moores subdued by Spanish blades:
For Charles *his blood most willing he shall spend,* 25
After the winning of a thousand daies,
   And fight he shall with strong and conquering hand
   Against the French and barbarous Affrican.

But ill it doth befit to talke of those,
Whom furious Mars *doth kindle with his heate,* 30
When learned lampes doe gravely come in place:
For heere they shall arise, and shine in great
And glorious blaze, as far as Europe goes:
The darkest corners shall their lights imbrace.
   Vives *shall live as long as* Daphnes *lover* 35
   Above the world with golden wings doth hover.

Whose highest skill and learning shall inherit
John Honorate, *and clime to honours hill,*
Teaching the mightie Emp'rour of our land:
The Muses with great woonder he shall fill,
Whom now (me thinkes) I see with greatest merit   5
Bearing a Bishops Crosier in his hand:
    O that such famous Shepherds, all my sheepe
    And lambes might feede, and plaines and pastures keepe.

About that time Nunnez *with praise shall flourish,*
Who for deepe learning in his tender yeeres,   10
Shall be compar'd unto the Stagarite:
Demosthenes *gives place where he appeeres*
And doth declame, whose eloquence doth nourish
His owne and strangers: But O vile despite,
    And most ingratefull place, whom thou shalt make   15
    For Ebrus *banks, thy countrie to forsake.*

But who shall tell you of that musicall,
Which many a Poet straining foorth his voice
Along my bankes so sweetely shall resound?
Heere doe I see how all of them rejoice,   20
With favours that Apollo *gives them all,*
For, singing with a spirit most profound,
    They shall enlarge this happy countries name,
    From Pole to Pole with endlesse golden fame.

And now I see that man, whose name shall bee   25
Bruted with living praise in every part:
Whom I may well for golden verse compare
To Phebe, *to* Mars *in armes and martiall art,*
Ausias March, *who (flowring meade) of thee,*
Love, vertue, and death, shall sing with verse most rare   30
    Taking for honorable and his just emprese
    To celebrate the vertues of Terese.

Well shall he shew himselfe to be the sonne
Of Peter March, *who both in peace, and war,*
Learned in verse, in armes most mighty heere,   35
Shall make his countrie famous very far:

29 Ausias *Ed.*] Ansias *Y.*

Whose noble linage (when that they are done)
Wherein renowned valour doth appeere,
   Shall give a Jayme, *and* Arnau *in those daies*
   Poets, whom heaven shall favour many waies.

Giorgio del Rey *with verse most high and stately*   5
My banks shall honour, and with garlands crown'd
By all my fairest Nymphes, that shall imbrace him,
His name with double ecchoes shall resound:
The gentle Planets favouring but lately
His fellow Poets, in such sort shall grace him,   10
   That Italie shall woonder at his verse,
   And die for spite his sweete songs to reherse.

Now Fraunces Oliver, *that with thy voice*
Lifting thee up unto the Azur'd heaven,
Dost wound the same: And thee renown'd Figueres   15
Whose verse shall be most pleasant, fine and even,
And thee Martin Garcy, *that maist rejoice,*
That (mauger death) thy fame time never weares:
   And Innocent of Cubels *I doe see,*
   Who well deserves a crowne of Laurell tree.   20

Shepherdes, you shall have heere a man of woorth,
That with the vertue of his secret skill,
And herbes, shall helpe your languors and your smartes,
And mend your lives with verses at his will:
Then Nymphes strow flowers and sweetest herbes powre foorth   25
Unto great Jayme Royg *with thankfull hartes,*
   Crowne him with Bay, with Parsley, and with Tyme,
   For famous skill in phisicke, and in ryme.

And great Narcis Vinnols, *that to the skie*
With loftie verse did blaze his woorthy praise,   30
Make him a crowne of Laurell faire and greene,
Whose fame shall not (though all the world decaies)
Another for a personage most high,
Whose verse shall reach as high as may be seene:
   He shall be matcht with him that loved Laura,   53
   His name, the famous Crespi Valladaura.

Me thinkes I see an Earle most excellent,
The noble Lord surnamed of his Olive,
Which, while the world shall last: amongst his owne
And strangers, it shall flourish and survive:
His comely verse shall shine most orient 5
With perfect light, which he derives alone
   From heate that from his Centelles *doe arise*
   Shining as bright as stars in cleerest skies.

And Nymphes, *when that the heavens shall joy you all*
With John Fernandz, *as now but with supposes,* 10
There shall no place be voide in all this land,
Where sowe ye may not Lillies, *and fine* Roses:
And thou (light fame) stretch out thy flight, and call
Thy mighty powers, and use them heere at hand:
   And give him that surname most soverayn 15
   Thou gavest unto the famous Mantuan.

And now I doe behold that Poet rare,
Jayme Gaçull, *who in* Valencian *ryme*
Did shew his pregnant and his lively wit,
Which mounted to the highest cloudes in time: 20
And Fenollar, *whom I well to compare*
To Tityrus *my thoughts cannot omit:*
   For sounding heere his sweetest verse along
   These banks, the world shall heare his solemne song.

Pinedas *songs so copious and so fine,* 25
Shall also make my sweete banks to resound,
By whose brave verse Pan *conquer'd needes must be,*
Tygres made gentle: and they shall rebound
His famous name, which never shall decline,
Unto the highest spheares in dignitie. 30
   I hope by him more honour to obtaine,
   Then proudest Smyrna *did by* Homer *gaine.*

Behold the staied, milde, and sweetest grace,
Wherewith Vincent Ferrand, *a man most grave,*
Shall shew his highest judgement, and his skill: 35
Being in his time a Poet rare and brave.

His verse shall hold king Aeolus in his place,
And stay my streames from running at their will,
   Hearing the sweetest sound and harmonie,
   Of all his verses gracious, grave, and hie.

The heavens will not, nor reason will consent, 5
That I should speake with humble stile and plaine
Of that choise squadron, and without compare,
Above mans reach an office to obtaine:
Ferran, Sans, Valdellos, and excellent
Cordero, and Blasqo a wit most rare, 10
   Gaçet, more shining lights then faire Aurore,
   Of whom my spirits now shall sing no more.

When of so great a Master I doe thinke,
As excellent Borja of Montese,
Who shewes his valour, as his wits divine, 15
As well in verse, as any high emprese:
Me thinkes, my fieldes, my rivers, and their brinks
Shall with more hap and greater glorie shine,
   Then Tybur hath, though he within her wombe
   Was borne, that built the stately towne of Rome. 20

And thee who of same father, place, and name,
And of the selfe same highest linage bred,
Most excellent Don Joan, whose surname shall
In Pindus, and Parnase be honoured.
For everie one to reare his verse shall frame 25
With pen above the globe celestiall.
   The Muses that doe dwell in Helicone,
   Make for thee there a crowne and stately throne.

The Romane people with their heroes
Was not so proud, when they did all despise, 30
As my most fertill soile, and I shall be
When that great Aguilon shall once arise,
Whom both in war, in counsell, and in peace,
In verse, and valour, his dexteritie
   Shall to the highest top of honour reare, 35
   Where Marius yet, and Fabius never were.

Now Seraphin Centellas *I doe see,*
Who lifting up his high and loftie song,
And militarie art unto the skie,
Builds for his verse a fort most sure and strong,
And shewes himselfe so brave a man to be   5
In courage, skill, and true nobilitie,
   That now begins my sweete content of hart,
   To see his valour, and his great desart.

But now I feare me that I cannot praise
Don Luys Milan, *even as I doe desire,*   10
Who shall in musicke to such skill attaine,
That to Orpheus *wreathe he shall aspire:*
His vaine shall be so stately in his daies
In heroicke verse, that I beleeve in vaine
   That they will name before this Adamant   15
   Cyno Pystoya, *and* Guido Cavalcante.

Thou that shalt get so great a part, and taste
Of Pegasus *fount, that mighty deaw and sweete,*
And whom the dwellers of Parnassus *hill*
Shall with a standard of brave poesie greete   20
(*Noble* Falcon) *heere words I will not wast*
In praising thee, for fame shall that fulfill:
   And shall be carefull that thy learned name
   In all the world with praise she will proclame.

Praising alwaies the famous Emperour   25
Charles *the great King, Fame makes the world to knowe him;*
And though above the stars she doth commend him,
Little it is to that that she doth owe him,
You shall behold him to excell so fur,
With favour that the Muses all will lend him,   30
   His surname shall the worlde so much delight,
   That Hesiodes *name shall be forgotten quite.*

He that declares the stately Romane lawes,
He that a fine and daintie verse compoundes,
He that the wise Lycurgus *doth excell,*   35
And all the Poets of Verona *groundes,*

Comes next in place, whose golden chariot drawes
Fame with her trumpe, his praises to foretell:
And this is Oliver, *whose memorie*
Controules the old and newest historie.

Knowing faire Nymphes, your good daies to begin   5
Make thousand outward signes of inward joy,
For now (me thinkes) I doe behold even then
Two famous men who shall their mindes imploy,
The one to war, the other still to win
Salvation for the soules of sinfull men.   10
    Ciurana *and* Ardevol, *who shall raise*
    Their highest verse to heaven with endlesse praise.

What? Will you see a judgement sharpe and sure,
A generall skill, a grave and setled minde,
A lively spirit, and a quicke conceate,   15
A sweete consort, poeticall and fine,
That savage beastes to mildnesse doth enure?
Of Philip Catalan *behold the great*
    Wisedome and wit, who therefore hath no meane
    A portion in the fountaine Hyppocrene.   20

Heere shall you see a high and loftie wit,
Who shall bring honour to our pleasant fieldes,
Endowed with a brave and noble spright,
Cunning in all things that good letters yeeldes,
The learned Pellicer, *whose braine shall fit*   25
For poemes, making them his chiefe delight:
    In which his skill and methode shall be great,
    His judgement deepe, a sweete and quicke conceate.

Behold the man whose noble brest containes
Knowledge most rare, and learning generall,   30
Orpheus *seemes with him to be combinde,*
Apollos *favours on his head doe fall:*
Minerva *gives him wit in plentious vaines,*
And Mars *a noble hart and valiant minde:*
    I meane Romani, *comming now addressed*   35
    With all the best, that learning hath professed.

11 Ardevol *Ed.*] Ardenol *Y.*

Two sunnes within my bankes shall now arise,
Shining as bright as Titan *in his sphere,*
And many spring tides in one yeere shall bee,
Decking my bankes and meadowes every where:
The hurtfull snowe, nor hard untempered ice   5
Shall hide my plaines, nor cover any tree
  When ecchoes in my woods or greenes reherse
  Vadillos *and* Pinedas *sweetest verse.*

The meetres of Artiede, *and* Clement, *so*
Famous shall be in their yoong tender yeeres,   10
That any thinking to excell the same,
But base to them and humble shall appeere:
And both amongst the wisest sort shall showe
Quicke and reposed wits with endlesse name.
  And after give us from their tender flowers   15
  Fruits of more woorth amongst more learned powers.

The fount, that makes Parnassus of such prize,
Shall be John Perez *of such woorthy fame,*
That from swift Tana *unto* Ganges *source,*
He shall dilate his admirable name: 20
To stay the hastie windes he shall suffice,
And rivers running with most swiftest course,
  Filling them all with woonder, that shall throng
  To heare his verse, and grave and solemne song.

The man to whom a woorthy name is due   25
Of right, for his abilitie and skill,
Whom all my sacred Nymphes in time shall knowe,
And all my Shepherdes shall with praises fill
For verse most high: amongst the learned crew
His honour and his praise shall daily growe: 30
  Almudevar *it is, whose shining wing*
  Unto the stars his golden praise must bring.

In vulgar toong the famous Espinose
Shall make the historie of Naples cleere,
After he hath reviv'd the memorie   35
Of the Centellas *highly linag'd heere*

With such a loftie style: That fame bestowes
His praise abroad, the which shall never die:
  And make this Poet, second unto none,
  To be renown'd in worlds but lately knowne.

But now I feele a certaine joy of minde,   5
That makes mine aged hart to leape apace,
But onely thinking of that great content,
That Bonavida *brings into this place:*
In gravest learning he shall leave behinde
The rest, whose glorie he shall still prevent: 10
  His fine and pithie verse, with Laurell *drest,*
  In every age shall sound from east to west.

Now Don Alonso *comes in place, who shall*
The Rebolledos *surname much increase*
In all the world, to raise his woorthy name   15
Above great Maro *he shall never cease,*
And seeme to have no humane wit at all,
But singing with most loftie verse: the same,
  His fine conceit, his art and vaine so high,
  It seemes he shall have robbed from the skie.   20

For end of this most sweete and pleasant song
And last conclusion of this generall skill,
I give you him, by whom dame Nature shall
The Circle of the world with woonder fill:
My simple praises should but doe him wrong   25
And all his vertues most heroicall,
  His valour, wit, nobilitie which graceth
  His bountie, faith and zeale which he imbraceth.

This is Aldana *monarch of such might,*
That jointly souldiours and brave verses makes: 30
That (with great reason) the most famous men
As far as Phebus *with his light awakes*
Doe doubte if he be Petrarke *Tuscans light,*
Or Petrarke *he: But yet admiring then,*
  To see that where fierce Mars *doth shew his face,*
  Apollo *milde should have so great a place.*   35

After this captaine there is none whom I
With my poore verse may honour and commend,
For next unto the golden sunne that star
That brightest shines, in darknes must depend:
And yet besides the short time doth denie,   5
To praise each one for poesie and war:
  Farewell, farewell, for unto you the rest
  Heereafter I will sing with cleerer brest.

This was the song of the river *Turia*, to the which the Shepherds
and Nymphes gave great eare, as well for the sweetnes of it, as 10
also for that the most famous men which were foretolde in it,
should be afterwards in the kingdome of *Valentia*. I could tell
you many other things, that I saw in those happie fields, but the
trouble that you have taken by my tediousnes will not permit me.
Marcelius and the Shepherds marvelled much at *Clenardas* report, 15
who having made an end of it, they perceived that they were
neere to *Dianas* Temple, where they began to discover the high
turrets of it, most stately reared above the tops of the trees. But
before they came to the great Palace, they saw a faire Nymphe
gathering sweete and fine flowers, whose name, and what suc- 20
ceeded by seeing of her, you shall know in the booke that followeth.

The end of the third Booke.

The fourth Booke of the third
Part of Diana.   25

THe complaints that men do ordinarily attribute to Fortune are
verie great, which would not be so many nor so grievous, if
they considered well the good that commeth oftentimes by her
mutabilities. He that now rejoyceth (having beene in a miserable
estate before) that Fortune is changed, hath no reason to checke 30
her, nor to call her wavering, when some contrary event doth
happen. But though she hath both in good, and in ill inconstancie
incident unto her, as part of her proper nature; yet a wise man
(how much soever he is touched with her) should not live with

affiance in the possession of worldly felicities, nor with despaire
in suffering adversities; but should rather moderate himselfe
with such wisedome, to entertaine pleasure as a thing not permanent, and griefe and sorrow as things that may have an ende in
time. Of such men God hath a particular regard, as of sorrowfull 5
and painefull *Marcelius*, delivering him from all his cares, by the
meanes and helpe of the most wise Ladie *Felicia*; who, divining
(as it were) in her minde, that *Marcelius*, *Diana* and others, shoulde
come to her Palace, caused in a maner that faire Nymphe to goe
foorth into that sweete meadow, to give them certaine newes and 10
signes, that strange things should come to passe, which by her
divine wisedome she did foresee were verie expedient and necessarie to be done. When *Marcelius* therefore and the rest were
come to the place, where the Nymph was gathering flowers, they
curteously saluted her, and she them againe. She asked them 15
whither they were going, and they said to *Dianas* Temple. Then
Arethea (for so was the Nymphe called) said unto them. My Ladie
Felicia, whose Nymphe I am, will be verie glad of your good
companie for the apparant signes of your good deserts, which by
your personages you seeme to testifie. And now since that the 20
Sunne hides it selfe in the West, I will goe backe with you
thither, where you shall be welcomed and feasted in the best sort
that may be. They gave her most hartie thankes, and went with
her towards the Temple, recovering great hope by the words and
promises of the Nymphe: and although *Polydorus* and *Clenarda* 25
had beene before in *Felicias* house, yet they never remembred
that they had knowen or seene her before: And the reason was,
bicause of the great number of Nymphes that the wise Ladie had
ever at her commaundement, diversly employed in divers parts
of her Court. Therefore they asked her her name, and she told 30
them that she was called *Arethea*. *Diana* asked her what newes she
knew in those parts? And she answered. The latest newes that is
here, is, that not two howers since there came to *Felicias* house
a strange Ladie in habit of a Shepherdesse; the which, being seene
by an ancient old man, that is also there, he knew her for his 35
daughter; and because she had beene a long time wandring up
and downe the world, and thought to be dead, the sudden joy
was so great that he received at her sight, that it caused a great
wonder amongst all those that were in the house. The olde mans
name (as I remember) is *Eugerius*, and his daughters *Alcida*. 40

Marcelius hearing these words, remained so sencelesse, with joy
and feare assayling him both at once, as any wise man may conjecture, and at last said. O happie travels, and fortunate troubles,
which come to their ende with so prosperous accidents! Ah ah,
and desiring to have passed on farther, his hart was so overcome, 5
and his toong so tyed, that in a traunce he fell downe to the
ground. *Diana*, *Ismenia*, and *Clenarda*, being next unto him, tooke
him up againe, and with comfortable wordes of hope recovered
his dismayed soule: And so comming to himselfe againe, he
thanked them many times. *Polydorus* and *Clenarda* were not a little 10
glad at those newes, seeing now that all their sorrowes should
have an ende by the happie comming of their sister *Alcida*. And
Diana and *Ismenia* were also verie joyfull, as well for their companions good hap, as also for the hope they had of their owne
good fortunes and helpe to receive it at her hands, who wrought 15
such miracles and woonders. *Diana*, bicause she would know
something of *Syrenus*, said thus unto her. The great hope of content that thou hast given me (faire Nymphe) by telling me of that,
which is in *Felicias* Palace for *Alcidas* comming, is not small; but
yet greater should I have, if thou wouldest tell me what Shepherds 20
of account are there also. There are many woorthie Shepherds
(answered *Arethea*) but those that I do best remember are *Sylvanus*
and *Selvagia*, *Arsileus* and *Belisa*, and one other more principall
then these, called *Syrenus*, whose vertues and deserts *Felicia* hath
in great estimation; but he is such an enimie to love, that he makes 25
all the rest that are there to woonder at him. *Alcida* is of like
qualitie and condition, in so much that ever since she came
thither, both of them have not beene asunder, discoursing of hate,
oblivion, and disdaine. And so I am verie certaine, that *Felicia*
made them come to her Court to marrie them togither, being both 30
of one minde, and their conditions being so semblable one to the
other. For though he be but a Shepherd, and she a noble Ladie,
Felicia yet by her supernaturall powers can give him valour,
force, riches, and wisedome, which is the truest nobilitie of all the
rest. And *Arethea* following on her speech, turning to *Marcelius*, 35
she said thus unto him. By this (Shepherd) thou seest how thy
joy is in hazard to fall to anothers lot; defer not therefore the
time, bicause if thou commest betimes, thou maist prevent *Syrenus*
of his match. But when *Diana* heard these words, she felt the
greatest griefe that might be, and had shewed it by teares and out- 40

cries, if bashfulnes and modestie had not beene an impediment to
it. *Marcelius* suffered the like paine for the same cause, and was so
tormented with it, that he thought to have dyed for verie anguish
of minde. So that on knife wounded *Marcelius* and *Dianas* hart,
and one jealousie molested their soules: *Marcelius* feared *Alcidas* 5
marriage with *Syrenus*; and *Diana* the marriage of *Syrenus* with
Alcida. The faire Nymph knew *Marcelius* and *Diana* very well,
and those that were with them, but she dissembled it very cunningly, as *Felicia* had told her how, telling *Marcelius* first a true
tale, to give him an unexpected joy; and after a fained matter, to 10
kindle his desire, and *Dianas* more, and also bi cause by these
bitter news, the gladnes that they afterwards received, might be
greater and more sweet. Being now come to a broad and most faire
Court, which was before the palace gate, they saw a reverend old
Lady comming out of it, apparelled with a long gowne of black 15
velvet, having a vaile on her head of white tynsell which hung
down over her shoulders, being accompanied with three most
faire Nymphes, representing a most venerable and divine Sybill.
This Ladie was *Felicia*, and her Nymphes were *Dorida*, *Cynthia*,
and *Polydora*. When *Arethea* was come before her Ladie and 20
Mistresse (but first telling her company that she was *Felicia*) she
kneeled downe and kissed her hands, and so did all the rest.
Felicia seemed to be verie glad of their comming, and with
a merie countenance said unto them. Woorthie Gentlemen, Lady,
and famous Shepherds, although the joy that I have of your 25
comming is great, yet the same that you shall reape by my sight
hereafter shall be no whit lesse. But bicause you are somewhat
wearie with your journey, go and take your rest, and forget your
griefes, bicause you cannot want the first in my house, and the
second with my great knowledge shall be soone amended. They 30
all humbly thanked her, shewing themselves verie glad of their
loving entertainment, and at last *Felicia* left them. Shee made
Polydorus and *Clenarda* to stay there, saying, that she had to talke
with them; and the rest being guided by *Arethea*, went to a chamber in the rich Palace, where they were feasted that night, and 35
served with all things needfull for their rest. This house was so
sumptuous and magnificent, and so full of all kinde of stately
riches, and of curious and costly gardens, that there was not
any other comparable unto it. But I will not trouble my selfe in
making any particular recount of the beautie and riches of it, 40

since that was declared at large in the first part of this worke.
I will onely tell how *Marcelius, Diana,* and *Ismenia,* were lodged in
two chambers in the Palace, hanged all about with rich Tapistrie,
curiously wrought with gold and silver, lodgings unacquainted
to simple Shepherds. They were there entertayned with a daintie
and plenteous supper, served with plate of gold and cristall, and
when they went to sleep layde in stately beds, whose bodies yet
(though with travell and paine they were not a little wearied)
with the softnes and sweetnes of them, and with the hope also
that *Felicia* had given them, were invited to a sweet and reposed
sleepe. On the other side *Felicia* in company of her three Nymphes,
and of *Polydorus* and *Clenarda* (telling them by the way, that they
should say nothing of *Marcelius, Dianas,* and *Ismenias* comming
thither) went to a most pleasant garden, where they sawe *Eugerius*
passing the time away with his daughter *Alcida. Don Felix* and
Felismena, Syrenus, Sylvanus, and *Selvagia, Arsileus* and *Belisa,* and
another Shepherd were sitting togither a pretie way off them
about a fountaine. *Alcida* had yet on the same pastorall weedes,
that she came apparelled with that day to the pallace, but she was
presently knowne by her brother and sister. The joy that the
brother and two sisters had to see themselves altogither, and the
gladnes that the father had to see himselfe and them so well and
happely met, moreover the great affection wherwith they embraced each other, the loving talke that passed betweene them, and
the sundry questions that they asked of one another, cannot be
with words nor writing declared. *Alcida* was rapt with joy to see
her brother and sister; but was gladder to see *Polydorus,* then
Clenarda, for the great presumption that she had, that *Marcelius*
went away with her, leaving her in the desolate Iland all alone.
But *Felicia* purposing to cleere all these mistes and errours, and
to make an end of so many hard fortunes, spake thus unto them.
Though Fortune hath never so much (faire *Alcida*) by many
kindes of injuries shewed herselfe thy mortall enimie, yet thou
canst not denie, but that with this content, that thou now en-
joyest, thou art fully revenged of all her wrongs. And bicause the
false imagination and deceit, wherein thou hast lived hitherto,
hating (without cause) thy loving *Marcelius,* if thou livest still in
it, is enough to alter thy hart, and to give him much sorrow and
greefe; it shall be therefore very needfull for thee to shake off
this conceit and injurious suspicion out of thy mind. That which

thou thinkest of *Marcelius*, is cleane contrarie, bicause it was not his fault when hee left thee in the Iland, but the deceite of a vile traytour and of Fortune, who now to satisfie the injurie that she hath done thee, hath brought thee hither unto me, which thou shalt finde to be as true as my mouth (never accustomed to faine 5 and lie) hath plainly and sincerely told thee. Thy sister *Clenarda* can make a large report unto thee of all that hath passed about this matter, harken to her, and beleeve her words, bicause I sweare unto thee, that all that she shall tell thee, is most true. Then *Clenarda* began to tell the whole matter and how it hapned, 10 purging *Marcelius* and herselfe, and reciting at large the treason and villany of *Sartofano*, and all the rest, as you have heard before. Which when *Alcida* heard, she thought herselfe very well satisfied, and then the long hatred, which she bare to *Marcelius*, went out of her hart with the deceit, the onely occasion of it. And then the 15 smothered love, and hidden fire began to revive in her brest, being cleerely ridde of her old suspicion, as also by the operation of those charming words that *Felicia* made in her soule, and being in that mind, she said unto *Felicia*. Mine errour I acknowledge (most honorable and sage Ladie) and the great benefite that you 20 have done me, by delivering me from it. But if I love now *Marcelius* (the miste of unjust suspect being driven from mine eies) and he being absent as he is indeed, I shal never the more for this happines attaine to the top of that joy which I hope for at thy hands; but shall rather be afflicted with so great greefe of minde, 25 that to remedie the same, I shall stand in neede of newe favours at thy gracious handes. It is a good token of love (answered *Felicia* againe) to take thought for the absence of the beloved, but let not this greeve thy minde, for I will be carefull for thy contentment: Now hath the Sunne hidden his beames, and it is 30 good time to take some rest. Goe therefore with thy father and sister to repose thy selfe, bicause we will to morrow take order for these affaires. When she had thus said, she went out of the garden, and so did *Eugerius* and his daughters, repayring to the chambers that *Felicia* had appointed for them in her pallace, which were 35 separated from that where *Marcelius* lay, and the rest of his company. *Don Felix* and *Felismena* with the other Shepherdes and Shepherdesses taried a pretie while about the fountain, and then went to supper, appointing to meet there the next morning following one hower before day, to take the fresh ayre of the 40

morning. So therfore as the hope of the pleasure of the next
morrowes meeting made them passe away the night with sleeping
but a little, they rose up all so earely in the morning, that before
the appointed hower they were ready at the fountaine with their
tuned instruments. *Eugerius* with his sonne and daughters ad-
vertised of the musicke, did also rise up, and went thither. They
beganne to play and sing, and to make much sport and pastime
by the light of the Moone, which with a full and bright face gave
them as cleere light as if it had beene day. *Marcelius, Diana,* and
Ismenia, laie in two chambers one joyning to the other, whose
windowes looked into the garden: And although they could not
see the fountain thorow them, by reason of the high and thick
Laurell trees which were about it, yet might they heare well what
they saide. So therfore when *Ismenia* (lying awake) heard the
noise they made, and the merriment and songs of the Shepherds,
she awaked *Diana,* and *Diana* knocking at the wall that was
betweene both their chambers awoke *Marcelius,* and so all of them
went to their windowes where they were neither seene nor
knowne. *Marcelius* gave attentive eare, if he might perhaps
heare *Alcidas* voice. *Diana* did diligently listen to heare her
Syrenus. Ismenia onely had no hope to heare her *Montanus,*
bicause she knew not that he was there. But yet her Fortune
was better then she was aware of, for at that very instant a
Shepherd sung to the sound of his Baggepipe this Sextine that
followes.   25

> *T*He faire, the fresh, the red, and rosie morning
>   Doth follow still the long and tedious night,
> And after darknes comes the sunshine day,
> When Nymphes goe foorth to walke the freshest meades,
> The aire resounding with their sweetest songs,   30
> And cheerefull notes of many chirping birdes.
>
> I am lesse happy then the pretie birdes,
> That are saluting of the merrie morning,
> With ratling foorth their sugred notes and songs:
> For in the morne I mourne, as in the night,   35
> Be this a desart or most fragrant meade,
> Be this a cloudie or most shining day.

In such a haplesse hower, and dismall day
So dead I was, that never can these birdes,
Which in the dawning joy both hill and meade,
Nor the Vermillion face of freshest morning
Drive from my soule a darke and deadly night,   5
Nor from my brest a lamentable song.

My voice shall never change her woonted song,
And for my selfe it never will be day:
But I will first die in eternall night,
Though more and more doe sing the warbling birdes,   10
And fairer rise the bright and purple morning,
To shine upon, and cherish this faire meade.

O irkesome garden! and O dolefull meade!
Since she, that cannot heare my plaining song,
And with her beames of beautie staines the morning,   15
Doth not give light unto my needefull day:
O trouble me no more you prating birdes,
For without her your morning is but night.

In that time of the still and silent night,
When in the townes, the hils, the vales, and meades,   20
All mortall men take rest, the beastes and birdes,
I most of all doe force my greevous song,
Making my teares even with the night, and day,
At noone, at night, and after in the morning.

One Morning *onely conquere must my* Night,   25
And if one Day *illustrate shall this* Meade,
Then will I heare with joy the Songs *of* Birdes.

By this time *Ismenia* that was harkening at the window, knew
that he that did sing, was her husband *Montanus*, and tooke so
great delight to heare him, as greefe in hearing of that which he   30
sung. For she thought, that the paine that (hee saide in his song)
he was troubled with, was for anothers sake and not for hers;
but she was by and by driven out of this doubt, for she heard
him (when he had made an end of his song) give a marvellous
great sigh, and saide. Ah wearied and sorrowfull hart! how ill   35
didst thou abuse thy selfe and her in giving credite to a simple
surmise, and how justly dost thou now suffer the sorrow, that

thine owne lightnes hath procured? Ah my beloved *Ismenia*! how
better had it bin for me, that thy zealous love had not caused
thee to seeke me thorow the worlde, bicause when I had come
backe againe to our towne (and knowing mine owne fault)
I might have found thee in it? Ah wicked *Sylveria*, how ill didst 5
thou requite him, that ever did thee good from his cradle? Alas
I woulde have thanked thee for the discoverie of the treacherie,
which afterwards thou toldest me, declaring to me the truth of
the matter, but that it came too late, which then availed no more,
nor nowe, but for my greater paine and greefe. *Ismenia* hearing 10
this, thought herselfe the happiest woman in the world, and was
so glad at this good fortune, as may be possiblie imagined. The
teares trickled downe her cheekes for joy, and like one that was
now neere unto the ende of her troubles she saide. Now is the
time of my happie daies come, and this house is onely made to 15
helpe those that live in distresse and woe. *Marcelius* and *Diana*
were woonderfull glad for *Ismenias* joy, and had by this, great
hope of their own. *Ismenia* would by and by have gone out of
her chamber into the garden, and even then when *Marcelius* and
Diana were perswading her to staie, thinking it better to attend 20
Felicias will and pleasure, they heard new songs about the fountaine, and *Diana* knew that it was *Syrenus* that sung them. *Ismenia*
and *Marcelius* held their peace, bicause they would not trouble
Diana, who giving an earnest eare to the voice of her beloved
husband heard him sing this song following.   25

Syrenus.

LOvers, with pride enjoy your full content,
  To see your selves in favour and in grace,
For I doe joy to see my torments spent,
  And joy to see them in oblivions place: 30
    I joy to see my captive hart so free,
    I joy to see my selfe in libertie.

For after suffring worldes of endlesse thrall,
  The favours of a proud and scornefull dame
So lately come, and seldome doe befall,   35
  That even the best, and greatest of the same
    Is, not to neede them, nor to be possest
    Of trifling toies a fond and fained jest.

Now laugh mine eies, and thanke Dianas *vaine,*
  Thanke her that brought you to this happy turne,
Her crueltie and hate your life did gaine,
    By her disdaine, by her unseemely scorne
      Your libertie, in bondage led away,   5
      You have redeem'd, thrise happy be that day.

For if by suffring torments for her sake,
  Ten thousand times more beautifull she weare,
And deerest love to me if she did make,
    Yet such content, as now in hating her,   10
      I should not have: And this doth joy my hart,
      That my disdaine doth beare so great a part.

O soveraine God! that once I might but knowe
  Greefe without hope to sease upon thy soule,
And that the God of love would wound thee so,   15
    And so thy scornefull hart with paines controule,
      That fully unreveng'd I might not be,
      For that great wrong which thou hast done to me.

For then I would (and lesse it were not meete)
  Be to thy greefe so cruell and so fierce,   20
That if with teares, and lying at my feete,
    Thou didst thy paines and torments all rehearse,
      And at my handes thy life if thou didst crave,
      Answere I would, Thy life I would not save.

God graunt thou maist for ever seeke me out,   25
  And (Shepherdesse) that I my selfe may hide:
That thou might'st say: O turne thee once about,
    And looke on me: and that I may deride,
      And answere thee, whom now I have forgot,
      Hence (Shepherdesse) away and vexe me not.   30

That thou maist say for thee I die in paining,
  And on my knees to thee I come a creeping,
What noveltie is this, O what disdaining?
    And I may goe, and leave thee thus a weeping,
      And answere thee for paines that I did borrow,   35
      I joy and laugh to see thee in this sorrow.

If this thou doubt'st with solemne oth I sweare,
  That while I live, I will doe this and more:
For now no paines, nor torments I doe feare,
  And suffer not, as I did once before:
    And I did never love so much thy name,
    As from my hart I now abhor the same.   5

And glad I am he hath forgot thee quite,
  That for thy sake was once so great a foole;
And for thy love did suffer such despite,
  And such fond lessons in blinde fancies schoole: 10
    And it is meete that he should suffer shame,
    That in these follies was so much to blame.

For cruell Love with Fortune doth agree,
  And tickle Fortune like to Cupid *wavers:*
Then (jolly Shepherdes) I would counsell yee   15
  Not to gape after Loves, and Fortunes favours:
    And if ye meane a sweete life to procure,
    Freedome imbrace, and captive Love abjure.

O that thou heard'st me now (ingrate Diane)
  To understand, what I doe say more cleere,   20
And how much more my soule doth yet retaine
  In plainer termes, if thou wert present heere,
    To tell thee, that I might unto thy face
    Degorge my minde unto thy great disgrace.

But yet it is the best (to joy my hart)   25
  For thee to shun the presence of my sight:
For I shall loose (no doubt) no little part
  Of that great joy, that pleasure, and delight
    Of my revenge, for it would pitie mee
    And greeve me too I thinke in seeing thee.   30

Then doe I wish, that I may never see
  Thy greevous presence, nor thy face againe,
Bicause unto my soule it needes must be
  A greater torment and more cruell paine,
    To see thee, when I sweare, I love thee not,   35
    Then when thou had'st my deerest love forgot.

It happened to *Diana* as to those which hearken to their owne
harmes; for in hearing *Syrenus* disdainfull resolution, she conceived so great griefe in her minde, that I am not able to expresse it,
and therefore thinke it better to leave it to the judgment of wise
men. Let it suffice you to know, that she thought to have dyed at 5
that present time, and therefore it was verie needfull for *Marcelius*
and *Ismenia* to comfort her up, and to incourage her with such
good reasons, as were sufficient for such an extreme griefe; one
of them was in telling her, that the knowledge and skill that
Felicia had (in whose house they were) was not so small, but that 10
it had remedied woes of greater paine and consequence, as she
had shewed but a little before by *Ismenia* as disdained of *Montanus*.
As they were thus talking togither, the golden morning beginning
to discover it selfe, the Nymphe *Arethea* came in to that chamber,
and with a cheerefull countenance said unto them. I wish as 15
fortunate and good daies to you (noble Gentleman and faire
Shepherdesses) as are due to your deserts and vertues. My sage
Ladie *Felicia* hath sent me hither to know, if you have slept more
contentedly this night then you were wont to do, and to bring
you along with me into the garden, where she hath to speake 20
certaine words with you. But you *Marcelius* must leave of these
Shepherds garments, and put on this apparell that I bring here,
fitter for your calling and degree. *Ismenia* would not stay for
Marcelius answer, for joy of the good newes, but said. The gladsome tydings that with thy sweete sight thou hast brought us this 25
morning (O happie Nymphe) God requite for us, since it lies not
in our power to recompence so great a debt and courtesie. The
content that thou wouldest know of us, is not little, with being
only in this house, and how much happier have we beene in it
this morning, when *Marcelius* and I have recovered our lives 30
welnie lost before, and *Diana* no small hope to the attayning of
her desires? But bicause we must obay the command of so great
and wise a Ladie as *Felicia* is, let us not delay the time to go into
the garden, and let her wisedome dispose of us at her best pleasure.
Then *Arethea* tooke the apparell that *Marcelius* should put on 35
from another Nymphe that brought it, and with her owne hands
helped to put it on, which was so rich, and garnished so bravely
with gold and precious stones, that it was of infinit value. They
went out of that quadrant, and all of them following *Arethea*,
by one of the Palace gates they went into the garden. This Orchard 40

of the one side was environed with an arme of a goodly river, of
the other side of it stoode most sumptuous and stately buildings
belonging to *Felicias* Palace, and the other two sides compassed
about with two wals, curiously plaistered with Jesmines, Wood-
bind, and other herbes and flowers passing delightfull to the eie. 5
But of the pleasantnes of this place, it is more copiously entreated
of in the fourth booke of the first part. Now after they were
come into it, they saw how *Sylvanus* and *Selvagia* separated from
the other company, were togither all alone in a little meadow that
was neere to the gate. There did *Arethea* leave them, willing them 10
to stay for *Felicia* there, bicause she was to go againe to the
Palace to tell that she had done the thing, that was given her in
charge. *Sylvanus* and *Selvagia* that were there, knew *Diana* by and
by, and marvelled much to see her there. *Selvagia* knew *Ismenia*
also, which was of her own towne, and so there was great courtesie 15
between them and many embracings, joyfull to see each other
there after so long a time. *Selvagia* then with a merie countenance
said unto them. Faire *Diana* is welcome, whose disdaine was an
occasion to make *Sylvanus* mine. And welcome also faire *Ismenia*,
who with thy deceit didst give me so much paine, that for remedie 20
of it I came hither, where I have changed it into a happy estate.
What good fortune hath brought you hither? That (said *Diana*)
which we receive of thy sight, and that, which we hope for at
Felicias hands. O happy Shepherdesse! how glad am I of the
content that thou hast gotten here: God confirme thy fortune so 25
prosperous, that thou maist enjoy it many yeeres. *Marcelius* offered
not to speake any thing amongst them, bicause he neither knew
Sylvanus nor *Selvagia*. But whilest the Shepherds were occupied
about their congratulations and curtesies, hee was beholding a
Gentleman and a Ladie, that hand in hand went walking up and 30
downe an Alley in the Garden, being verie merrie one with the
other. He tooke a certaine pleasure in beholding the Ladie, and
his minde gave him, that he had seene and knowne her before:
Wherefore to cleere himselfe of that doubt, comming to *Sylvanus*
he said. Although it is a point of discurtesie to interrupt your 35
friendly greetings, yet woulde I faine knowe (gentle Shepherd)
what Lord and Lady those are that walke there togither. Their
names (said *Sylvanus*) are *Don Felix*, and *Felismena*, husband and
wife. Then *Marcelius* hearing *Felismenas* name, altered his countenance and said. Tell me, I praie you, whose daughter *Felismena* 40

is, and where she was borne, if thou dost perhaps knowe, bicause I care not so greatly to enquire of *Don Felix*. I have heard her oftentimes tell (said *Sylvanus*) that she was borne in *Soldina* the cheefest citie of all *Vandalia*, her father being called *Andronius*, and her mother *Delia*. But I praie you Sir, do me the favour to let 5 me know what you are, and why you made this demand? My name (saide *Marcelius*) and all else that thou seekest at my hands, thou shalt knowe heereafter. In the meane time do me this curtesie, that since thou art acquainted with Lord *Felix* and *Felismena*, crave leave of them that I may speake a fewe words 10 with them, bicause I would aske her a question that may redounde (perhaps) to much joy and good on both sides. It likes me well (said *Sylvanus*) and then he went by and by to *Don Felix* and *Felismena* and told them, that a Gentleman not farre off would faine entreat with them in certaine affaires if they thought it not 15 troublesome unto them. They staied not a minute, but came to the place where *Marcelius* was. And after curteous salutations, *Marcelius* said to *Felismena*, I enquired (faire Lady) of this Shepherd thy countrey, name, and parents, who told me that which by thine owne report he knowes concerning the same, and bicause 20 I knowe a Gentleman which was borne in the same citie, who is also sonne to a Lord (if I be not deceived) whose name is like to thy Fathers; Tell me then (curteous Lady) if you have anie brother, and what his name is, bicause (it may be) he is the same, whom I knowe. With this *Felismena* gave a great sigh and saide. O noble 25 Gentleman! how much doth thy demand penetrate my hart? Know therefore, that I had a brother, borne with me at one birth, and being but a childe at twelve yeeres old, my father *Andronius* sent him to the king of *Portugales* court, where he lived many yeeres. This is as much as I can tell of him, and that which I told 30 *Sylvanus* and *Selvagia* that are heere present, on a time at the fountaine of the Sicamours, after that I had delivered the three Nymphes, and killed three Savages in the meadowe of the Laurell trees. From that time hitherto I have heard nothing of him, but that the king sent him as Captaine into the coast of *Africa*: and 35 bicause I have a good while since wandred up and downe the world, following mine owne destinies and fortune, I knowe not whether he be alive or dead. Then *Marcelius* could not stay himselfe any longer, but said. I have indeed (sweet sister *Felismena*) bin dead hitherto, bicause I have wanted thy good company, and 40

now am revived, in that I have beene so happie a man to see thee.
And in speaking these wordes he lovingly embraced her. *Felismena*
remembring well *Marcelius* kinde of gesture and his countenance
in her minde, did now cleerely see that he was the same indeed,
and so was undoubtedly resolved, that he was her owne brother. 5
The joyfull greeting that passed betweene the brother, sister, and
cousen, was great; and the gladnes that *Sylvanus* and *Selvagia*
tooke to see them so happely mette togither, not small. There
were many loving speeches exchanged, many teares of joy and
sorrow powred out, many demands and questions, hopes revived, 10
determinations concluded, and many wordes and things of joy
and rest mutually spoken and done. They spent in these congratulations one whole hower, which was little enough for the
large history and accidents that they had to discourse of after so
long an absence. But bicause they might better and more safely 15
talke of those matters, they sat themselves downe in that little
meadow under a ranke of Sicamours, whose wreathed boughes
loden with leaves, made a delightfull and coole shadow, defending
them from the heat of the radiant sunne, which was with some
heate mounted up the Hemispheare. Whilest *Marcelius*, *Don Felix*, 20
Felismena, *Sylvanus*, and the Shepherds were talking togither of
these matters, at the other end of the garden neere unto the
fountaine (as it is saide before) were *Eugerius*, *Polydorus*, *Alcida*,
and *Clenarda*. *Alcida* had that day left of her pastorall weedes as
Felicia had commanded, and was now apparelled and adorned 25
very richly with costly garments and jewels that she willed shoulde
be given her. But as *Syrenus* was also there, *Montanus*, *Arsileus*,
and *Belisa*, singing and sporting togither, they marvellouslie
delighted *Eugerius* and his sonne and daughters, that were harkening to them. And that which did most of all please them, was 30
a song which *Syrenus* and *Arsileus* did sing one against another
in dispraise and favour of *Cupid*: For they sung with an earnest
will and desire in hope of a brave christall cup, which *Eugerius*
had promised for a reward and prize to him that did sing
best. And so *Syrenus* to the sound of his Rebecke, and *Arsileus* 35
to the tune of his rurall Baggepipe, began to sing in maner
following.

Syrenus.

O Eies that are not now as once tormented,
   When first my star enveagled and disguis'd you:
O joyfull thoughts, and quiet minde absented,
O carelesse hart, now will I once advise you,   5
That since you made Diana discontented,
To see, love, thinke on you, let this suffice you,
   That I doe hold your counsell best of many,
   In vaine to see, nor love, nor thinke of any.

Arsileus.   10

O eies that have to greater light attained,
Looking upon that sunne, your onely treasure,
O joyfull thoughts, in thousand joies distrained,
O happy hart, the seate of secret pleasure:
Although Belisa would have once disdained   15
To see, to love, or thinke on me at leisure,
   Yet hold I this a heaven, as like was never
   To see, to love, and thinke on her for ever.

Syrenus would have replyed to Arsileus answer, if he had not
beene interrupted by Eugerius, who said. Since you must (jolly 20
Shepherds) receive your reward at my hands, it is good reason
that you sing in such sort, as may best content me. Sing thou
Syrenus first those verses which thy muse shall dictate unto thee:
and then thou Arsileus shalt sing as many againe, or those which
thou shalt best thinke good of. It pleaseth us well (said they) and 25
then Syrenus began thus.

Syrenus.

Et now the goodly spring tide make us merie,
   And fieldes, which pleasant flowers do adorne,
   And vales, meades, woods, with lively colours flourish,   30
Let plentious flockes the Shepherds riches nourish,
   Let hungrie woolves by dogs to death be torne,
   And lambes rejoice, with passed winter wearie:
     Let every rivers ferrie

In waters flowe, and silver streames abounding:
   And fortune, ceaslesse wounding,
Turne now thy face, so cruell and unstable,
   Be firme and favourable:
And thou that kill'st our soules with thy pretenses,   5
Molest not (wicked love) my inward senses.

Let countrie plainnes live in joies not ended,
   In quiet of the desart meades and mountaines,
   And in the pleasure of a countrie dwelling:
Let Shepherds rest, that have distilled fountaines   10
   Of teares: proove not thy wrath, all paines excelling,
   Upon poore soules, that never have offended:
      Let thy flames be incended
In hautie courtes, in those that swim in treasure,
   And live in ease and pleasure: 15
And that a sweetest scorne (my woonted sadnes)
   A perfect rest and gladnes
And hils and dales, may give me: with offences
Molest not (wicked love) my inward senses.

In what law find'st thou, that the freest reason,   20
   And wit, unto thy chaines should be subjected,
   And harmlesse soules unto thy cruell murder?
O wicked love, the wretch that flieth furder
   From thy extremes, thou plagu'st. O false, suspected,
   And carelesse boy, that thus thy sweetes dost season,   25
      O vile and wicked treason,
Might not thy might suffice thee, but thy fuell
   Of force must be so cruell?
To be a Lord, yet like a Tyrant minded,
   Vaine boy with errour blinded,   30
Why dost thou hurt his life with thy offences,
That yeeldes to thee his soule and inward senses.

He erres (alas) and fowly is deceived
   That cals thee God, being a burning fire,
   A furious flame, a playning greefe and clamorous,   35
And, Venus sonne (that in the earth was amorous,
   Gentle, and milde, and full of sweete desire)
   Who calleth him, is of his wits bereaved,
      And yet that she conceaved

By proofe, so vile a sonne and so unruly,
I say (and yet say truly)
That in the cause of harmes, that they have framed,
Both justly may be blamed:
She, that did breede him with such vile pretenses,   5
He, that doth hurt so much our inward senses.

The gentle sheepe and lambes are ever flying
The ravening woolves and beastes, that are pretending
To glut their mawes with flesh they teare asunder:
The milke white doves at noise of fearefull thunder   10
Flie home amaine, themselves from harme defending,
The little chicke, when puttocks are a crying:
The woods and meadowes dying
For raine, of heaven (if that they cannot have it)
Doe never cease to crave it: 15
So every thing his contrarie resisteth,
Onely thy thrall persisteth
In suffring of thy wrongs without defences,
And lets thee spoile his hart and inward senses.

A publike passion, natures lawes restraining,   20
And, which with wordes can never be declared:
A soule twixt love, and feare, and desperation,
And endlesse plaint, that shuns all consolation,
A spendlesse flame, that never is impaired:
A friendlesse death, yet life in death maintaining: 25
A passion, that is gaining
On him, that loveth well, and is absented:
Whereby it is augmented,
A jealousie, a burning greefe and sorrow.
These favours lovers borrow   30
Of thee fell Love, these be thy recompences,
Consuming still their soule and inward senses.

Arsileus, after that *Syrenus* had ended his song, began to tune his Bagpipe, and after he had played a little while upon it, answering everie staffe of his Competitor in order, he sung as 35 followeth.

Arsileus.

O Let that time a thousand monthes endure,
  Which brings from heaven the sweete and silver showres,
And joies the earth (of comforts late deprived)
  With grasse and leaves, fine buds, and painted flowres: 5
  Eccho returne unto the woods obscure,
  Ring foorth the Shepherds songs in love contrived:
    Let olde loves be revived,
  Which angrie winter buried hath of late:
    And that in such a state   10
  My soule may have the full accomplishment
    Of joy and sweete content:
  And since fierce paines and greefes thou dost controule,
  Good love doe not forsake my inward soule.

Presume not (Shepherds) once to make you mery   15
With springs, and flowres, or any pleasant song,
(Unlesse milde love possesse your amorous brestes)
  If you sing not to him, your songs doe werie,
  Crowne him with flowres, or else ye doe him wrong,
  And consecrate your springs to his behestes: 20
    I to my Shepherdesse
  My happie loves with great content doe sing,
    And flowres to her doe bring.
  And sitting neere her by the river side,
    Enjoy the brave springtide.   25
  Since then thy joies such sweetnesse doe enroule,
  Good love doe not forsake my inward soule.

The wise in ancient times a God thee nam'd
Seeing that with thy power and supreme might
Thou didst such rare and mighty woonders make: 30
  For thee a hart is frozen and inflam'd,
  A foole thou mak'st a wise man with thy light,
  The coward turnes couragious for thy sake:
    The mighty Gods did quake
  At thy commaund: To birdes and beasts transformed: 35
    Great monarches have not scorned

To yeeld unto the force of beauties lure:
Such spoiles thou dost procure
With thy brave force, which never may be toulde
With which (sweete love) thou conqu'rest every soule.

In other times obscurely I did live 5
But with a drowsie, base, and simple kinde
Of life, and onely to my profit bend me:
To thinke of love my selfe I did not give,
Or for good grace, good partes, and gentle minde
Never did any Shepherdesse commend me: 10
But crowned now they send me
A thousand garlands, that I woon with praise,
In wrestling daies by daies,
In pitching of the bar with arme most strong,
And singing many a song, 15
After that thou didst honour, and take hould
Of me (sweete love) and of my happy soule.

What greater joy can any man desire,
Then to remaine a captive unto love,
And have his hart subjected to his power? 20
And though sometimes he taste a little sower,
By suffring it, as milde as gentle dove,
Yet must he be, in lieu of that great hire
Whereto he doth aspire:
If lovers live afflicted and in paine, 25
Let them with cause complaine
Of cruell fortune, and of times abuse,
And let them not accuse
Thee (gentle love) That dost with blisse enfoulde
Within thy sweetest joies each loving soule. 30

Behold a faire sweete face, and shining eies,
Resembling two most bright and twinkling stars;
Sending unto the soule a perfect light:
Behold the rare perfections of those white
And Ivorie hands, from greefes most sure bars: 35
That minde wherein all life and glorie lies,
That joy that never dies,

That he doth feele, that loves and is beloved,
  And my delights approoved
To see her pleas'd, whose love maintaines me heere:
  All those I count so deere,
That though sometimes Love doth my joies controule,   5
Yet am I glad he dwels within my soule.

There was not one there amongst them all but tooke great
delight in the Shepherds songs. But *Eugerius* comming to give
his verdict, praise, and reward to him that had sung best, could
not so soone conclude of the matter: he stept aside to *Montanus* 10
to heare his opinion, whose judgement was, that one had sung as
well as another. Then *Eugerius* turning to *Syrenus* and *Arsileus*,
said. My opinion is (cunning Shepherds) that you are equall in
the subject of this contention, and that, if old *Palemon* were revived, and made an indifferent judge betweene you, hee could not 15
confesse (I thinke) any superioritie in your skill. Thou art *Syrenus*
worthie to beare away the cristall cup; and thou *Arsileus* deservest
it as well, so that I should offer you great wrong, if I did not define
who is conqueror, and who is conquered. To resolve my selfe
therefore of this doubt with *Montanus* opinion, I say that to thee 20
(*Syrenus*) is allotted the Cristall cup, and to thee (*Arsileus*) this
Calcedonian cup of no lesse value, which worthily thou hast
wonne. To both of you therefore I give cups of like value, both
of them of account amongst *Felicias* treasure, and by her bountifull hands bestowed on me. The Shepherds were well pleased at 25
the wise judgement, and rich rewardes of bountifull *Eugerius*,
to whom they gave many thankes. But *Alcida* by this occasion
calling to minde her passed times, said. If the deceitfull errour,
wherewith I have beene blinded so long, had endured till now,
I would not then consent that *Arsileus* should be rewarded equally 30
with *Syrenus*: But since I am now free from it, and wounded
afresh with the love of my betrothed *Marcelius*, for the paine
which I suffer for his absence, I like well of that which *Syrenus*
did sing; and for the joy and sweete delight which I expect,
I also commend *Arsileus* song. But take heed carelesse *Syrenus*, 35
that these complaints which thou makest of *Diana*, be not like to
those wherewith I blamed *Marcelius*, bicause thou maist not
repent thee of thy hardnes of hart and disdaine, as I have done.
Syrenus smiled at this and said: What greater blame may be laide

upon that Shepherdesse, who after she had forsaken me, married her selfe to a jealous, perverse, and unfortunate husband. Then *Alcida* answered. Unfortunate indeed he hath beene enough, since he cast his eies upon me: and bicause it comes fit to the purpose, I will tell thee that, which yesterday (by reason of *Felicias* discourses and affaires with me) I could not declare unto thee, when as we were talking about *Dianas* matters: and to this end especially, bicause thou mightest forget all injuries past, and shake off thy wrongfull oblivion, when thou shalt understand of the strange and unluckie accident, that by my contempt befell to miserable *Delius*. I have told thee before, how I was talking and singing with *Diana* at the fountaine of the Sicamours, and how jealous *Delius* came thither, and sorrowfull *Marcelius* after him in a Shepherds habit, at whose sight I was so grieved, that I fled from him incontinently into a wood that was hard by. But when I came to the other side of the wood, I heard a far off a voice that still cryed, *Alcida*, Oh *Alcida*, stay, stay: which made me to thinke that *Marcelius* followed me; and bicause I would not fall into his hands, I ran as fast as I could away. But by that which afterwards happened, I knew that it was *Delius*, husband to *Diana*, that came running after me. And bicause I had run a great way, and began to be wearie, I then went so easily, that he followed me in sight. I knew him, and staied to know what he would have, not thinking once of him, nor of the cause of his comming. And when he was before me, what by the faintnes of his running, and by the anguish of his minde that troubled him, he was not able to utter one word. At the last with rude and ill formed reasons he said, that he was in love with me, praying me after his homely manner to love him againe, and many other things (I know not what) which shewed his little wit, and simple behaviour. To tell the very truth I laughed at him, and the best I could, endevoured to comfort him, and to make him forget his folly, but it availed nothing; for the more I disswaded him from it, the more foole he was. In faith (Shepherd) I sweare unto thee, that I never knew man in my life so assotted with sudden love. But as I went on my waies, and he following me at an inch, we came to a village a mile distant from his towne, and there, when he perceived my rigour, and that I had flatly denied him, for verie griefe and anguish of minde he fell sicke. He was lodged there by a Shepherd that knew him, who as soone as morning came,

certified his mother of his malladie. *Delius* mother came thither
with a heavie hart in great haste, and found her sonne tormented
with a burning feaver. With much sorrow she lamented his case,
and did importune him to know the cause of his griefe, but no
other answer would he give her, but sob, sigh, and weepe. The 5
loving mother powring forth many a bitter teare, said unto him,
Oh my deere Son! what an unfortunate chance is this? Hide not
the secrets of thy hart from me, behold I am thy mother, and
(perhaps) I knowe some part of them alreadie. Thy wife told me
last night, that at the fountaine of the Sicamours thou didst for- 10
sake her, running after I knowe not what unknowne Shepherdesse,
tell me if thy greefe doth grow thereby, and be not afraid nor
ashamed to impart it to me; for ill may that malladie be cured, the
cause and beginning whereof is unknowne. Oh sorrowfull *Diana*!
thou didst this day go to *Felicias* temple to learn some newes of 15
thy husband, and he was neerer to thy towne, and weaker then
thou wert aware of. When *Delius* heard his mother speake these
words, he answered not a worde, but gave a great sigh, and then
redoubled his painefull agonie. For before he complained onely
of Love, but at these wordes with love and jealousie he was most 20
greevouslie molested. For when he remembred that thou (*Syrenus*)
wert here in *Felicias* pallace, and hearing that *Diana* was come
hither, fearing least her olde and mortified love might be rekindled againe in her, he fell into such a frantike madnes, that,
being assaulted with two most fierce and cruell torments, he 25
ended his life in a furious traunce, unto the greatest greefe of his
sorrowfull mother, kinsefolkes, and lamenting friends. In very
truth I could not chuse but be sorrowfull for his death, knowing
my selfe to be the chiefest cause of it, but I coulde have done no
lesse for safegard of mine owne content and honor. Onely one 30
thing greeved me not a little, that not contenting him with any
comfortable deede, I gave him not (at the least) some gentle
words, whereby he might not then (perhaps) have come to so
sudden a death. In the ende I came hither, leaving the poore soule
dead, and his kinsfolkes weeping for him, not knowing the cause 35
of his death. Thus have I digressed (yet to the purpose) to make
thee knowe what harme a cruell disdaine and forgetfulnes pro-
cureth, and also bicause thou shouldest understand of *Dianas*
widowhood, and consider with thy selfe, if now it were good for
thee to change thine intent, since she hath changed her condition 40

and estate. But I marvell much that *Diana* departing from her towne yesterday (as *Delius* mother saide) to come to this place, is not yet heere. *Syrenus* gave attentive eare to *Alcidas* words, and when hee heard of *Delius* death, his hart began somewhat to alter and change. There did the secret power also of sage *Felicia* worke 5 extraordinary effects, and though she was not present there, yet with her herbes and wordes, which were of great vertue, and by many other supernaturall meanes, she brought to passe that *Syrenus* began now againe to renewe his old love to *Diana*: which was no great marvell, considering that by the influence of his 10 celestiall constellation he was so much enclined to it, that it seemed *Syrenus* was not borne but onely for *Diana*, nor *Diana* but for *Syrenus*.

The provident and most wise Ladie *Felicia* was now in her magnificent and rich pallace, environed about with her chaste 15 Nymphes, working with soveraigne and secret verses the remedies, and content of all these Lovers. And as she sawe by her divine wisedome, that by this time *Montanus* and *Alcida* being by their imaginations deceived, had now acknowledged their errours, and that hard harted *Syrenus* had mollified his obstinate and rigorous 20 disposition, she thought it now high time utterly to confound olde errours, and to ease the long travels and troubles of her guestes, by exchanging them into joyfull and unexpected happines. Going therefore out of her sumptuous pallace, attended on by *Dorida*, *Cynthia*, *Polydora*, and manie other goodly Nymphes, 25 she came to the delightfull garden, where the Lordes, Ladies, Shepherds and Shepherdesses were: The first that she saw there, were *Marcelius*, *Don Felix*, *Felismena*, *Sylvanus*, *Selvagia*, *Diana*, and *Ismenia*, sitting in one of the corners of that little square meadow neere unto the great gate, as is aforesaide. When they sawe the 30 reverend Lady comming towards them, they all rose up, and kissed those hands, in which they had placed their cheefest hope and remedies. She courteously saluted them againe, making a signe unto them that they shoulde all follow her, which most willingly they did. *Felicia* attended on by this amorous traine, 35 crossing every part of this great and pleasant garden, came at the last to the other part of it to the fountaine, where *Eugerius*, *Polydorus*, *Alcida*, *Clenarda*, *Syrenus*, *Arsileus*, *Belisa*, and *Montanus* were. They all rose up, in honor of the sage Matron. And when *Alcida* espied *Marcelius*, *Syrenus Diana*, and *Montanus Ismenia*, they 40 were all astonished at the sight one of another, and verily thought they were in a dreame, standing like enchaunted persons, and not beleeving their owne eies. The wise Ladie commanding them all to sit downe againe, and shewing by her countenance that she was to entreat of important affaires, sat her downe in the middes of 5 them all, in a chaire of Ivorie, graven with gold and precious stones, and spake in this sort. Nowe is the hower come (renowned and faire assemblie) wherein with my hands I meane to give you all your long desired and happie contentment: for by divers strange meanes, and untroden waies I have made you come to my 10 Palace for no other intent and purpose. Since you are heere therefore altogither wel met, where the matters and meanes of your happie love and life to come must be determined, my desire is that you would follow my will, and obey my commands herein. Thou art *Alcida*, by the true testimonie and report of thy 15 sister *Clenarda*, cleerelie delivered from the suspicion of thy deceived imagination. And I knew well enough that, after thou hadst forsaken that cruell disdaine, the absence of thy *Marcelius* did not a little greeve thee. Come hither therefore, and offer thy selfe unto him, for this absence shall not be long, which hath 20 rather beene so short, that at that time when thou complainedst to me of it, *Marcelius* was in my pallace. Nowe thou hast him heere before thee, as firme and stedfast in his first love, that, if it pleased thee, and thy Father, brother and sister, he would thinke himselfe the happiest man alive, to solemnize this desired mar- 25 riage long since betrothed. The which besides that it must needes cause great joy and gladnes, being betweene such principall and noble personages, shall make it more perfect and absolute, by reason of *Felismena* his sisters presence, whom *Marcelius* after many yeeres past, hath happely found out in my Palace. Thou 30 *Montanus* by *Sylveria* herselfe, that betraied thee, art rid from thy erronious opinion. After which time thou didst weep continually for the losse of thy faithfull wife *Ismenia*, who now is come to live and die in thine armes, and to comfort all thy sorrowes, after that thorow out all Spaine, with many a wearie journey, and 35 many dangers, and troubles she hath sought thee out. But now last of all it resteth to remedie thy paines (faire *Diana*) before which time I meane to advertise thee of that which *Syrenus* and some of these Shepherds doe know by *Alcidas* report, although it will be but a sorrowfull tale in thine eares, and a grievous corosie 40

to thy pitifull hart. Thy husband *Delius* (faire Shepherdesse) as it
pleased the inexorable destinies, hath ended the course of his life.
For the losse whereof I know well (*Diana*) that thou hast great
cause to lament, but yet in the end all men are bound to pay this
tribute to Nature, and that which is so common a thing, ought not 5
extremely to grieve any one. Weepe not (faire *Diana*) for thou
breakest my hart asunder in seeing thee powre forth such dolorous
teares, drie up thine eies, comfort thy sorrowes, and cheere up
thy selfe. Put on no morning weeds, and make no long moan, for
too much lamentation and sorrow is not allowed in this house, 10
when as also the heavens have reserved for thee some better hap,
then that which thou had'st of late. And since there is no remedie
for that which is lately done, it belongeth to thy wisedome to
forget what is past, and to my skill and power, to give order to
things present. Heere is thy old lover *Syrenus*, whose hart by my 15
operations, and by the reason that bindes him to it, is become so
tender, gentle, and chaunged from his former hardnes, that now
for his great contentment, it onely behooveth him to conclude
a marriage with thee. That which I request of thee is, that thou
wilt obay my will in a thing which so greatly concerneth thy 20
happie and joyfull life: The which, although it may seeme to
offer some injurie to thy husband that is dead to marrie so soone
againe; yet being a thing practised by my decree and autoritie,
cannot any waies be deemed ill. And thou *Syrenus* since thou hast
begun to give place in thy hart to honest and vertuous Love, 25
make now an ende to yeelde up thy thoughts and deeds to it: and
let this merie and happie mariage be put in effect, to the fulfilling
of which, all the favourable stars are inclined. The rest of you,
which in this delightfull garden enjoy your happie content, rejoice
in your minds; make merie pastimes; play upon your tuned 30
instruments; sing sweete Ditties, and exercise your selves in
delightfull sports and conversation, in honour and memory of
these joyfull meetings, and happie marriages. Sage *Felicia* had no
sooner ended her speech, but all of them were verie willing to do
as she commanded them, liking well of her motion, and marvel- 35
ling at her singular wisedome. *Montanus* tooke his wife *Ismenia* by
the hand, thinking themselves thrise happie and fortunate; and
betweene *Marcelius* and *Alcida*, *Syrenus* and *Diana*, at that instant
a holy and virtuous marriage was solemnly celebrated with great
love, firmnes, and sumptuous accustomed ceremonies. 40

All the rest exceeding glad for these happie accidents, sung and
rejoiced with marvellous applause. Amongst the which, *Arsileus*
for the great good will that he bare to *Syrenus*, and for the friendship betweene them both, at the sound of his Rebecke, sung this
Caroll in memorie and joy of the new marriage betweene *Syrenus* 5
and *Diana*.

L *Et now each meade with flowers be depainted,*
   Of sundrie colours sweetest odours glowing:
Roses yeeld foorth your smels, so finely tainted,
  Calme windes, the greene leaves moove with gentle blowing: 10
    The christall rivers flowing
    With waters be increased:
    And since each one from sorrowes now hath ceased,
    (From mournefull plaints and sadnes)
    Ring forth faire Nymphes, your joyfull songs for gladnes. 15

Let springs and meades all kinde of sorrow banish,
  And mournefull harts the teares that they are bleeding:
Let gloomie cloudes with shining morning vanish,
  Let every bird rejoice, that now is breeding:
    And since by new proceeding,   20
    With marriage now obtained,
    A great content by great contempt is gayned,
    And you devoid of sadnes,
    Ring forth faire Nymphes, your joyfull songs for gladnes.

Who can make us to chaunge our firme desires,   25
  And soule to leave her strong determination,
And make us freeze in Ise, and melt in fires,
  And nycest harts to love with emulation:
    Who rids us from vexation,
    And all our minds commaundeth?   30
    But great Felicia, *that his might withstandeth*
    That fild our harts with sadnes,
    Ring forth faire Nymphes, your joyfull songs for gladnes.

Your fields with their distilling favours cumber
  (Bridegroome and happie Bride) each heavenly power   35
Your flockes, with double lambes increas'd in number,
  May never taste unsavourie grasse and sower:
    The winters frost and shower

Your kids (your pretie pleasure)
May never hurt, and blest with so much treasure,
To drive away all sadnes,
Ring forth faire Nymphes, your joyfull songs for gladnes.

Of that sweete joy delight you with such measure, 5
Betweene you both faire issue to ingender:
Longer then Nestor *may you live in pleasure:*
The Gods to you such sweete content surrender,
That may make milde and tender
The beasts in everie mountaine, 10
And glad the fields and woods and everie fountaine,
Abjuring former sadnes,
Ring forth faire Nymphes, your joyfull songs for gladnes.

Let amorous birds with sweetest notes delight you,
Let gentle winds refresh you with their blowing, 15
Let fields and forrests with their goods requite you,
And Flora *decke the ground where you are going:*
Roses, and vilets strowing,
The Jasmine and the Gilloflower
With many more: and never in your bower 20
To taste of houshold sadnes,
Ring forth faire Nymphes, your joyfull songs for gladnes.

Concord and peace hold you for aye contented,
And in your joyfull state live yee so quiet,
That with the plague of jealousie tormented 25
Ye may not be, nor fed with Fortunes *dyet:*
And that your names may flie yet
To hils unknowen with glorie,
But now bicause my brest so hoarse, and sorie
It faints, may rest from singing, 30
End Nymphes your songs, that in the clouds are ringing.

When *Arsileus* had made an end of his song, there was such
a generall rejoicing, that it woulde have cheered up the most
sorrowfull harts that ever were. Sweete and delightfull songs
resounded in every part of the garden, the tuned instruments 35
made more then earthly Harmonie, and it seemed that the

13 gladnes. *Ed.*] galdnes. *Y.*

blossomed trees, the gliding river, the pleasant fountaine, and the chirping birdes rejoyced at that feaste. After that they had a pretie while delighted themselves in this kinde of exercise, *Felicia* thinking it time to go to dinner, commanded that it shoulde be brought to the fountaine where they were. Whose commaunde the Nymphes obeying, presently busied themselves severally to provide for dinner; and setting the tables and cupbordes of plate under the shadowe of those greene trees, everie one sitting in order as *Felicia* appointed them, beganne to taste of those delicate and daintie meates that were served in, and most of them in plate of great value. Dinner being done, and returning to their former pleasures, they made much sport and merriment with many feastes and pastimes, which shall be set downe in the Booke following.

The end of the fourth Booke.

The fifth Booke of the third Part of Diana.

THese Lovers were so well pleased with their happie estate, everie one seeing himselfe in his desired companie, that they quite forgat their former troubles. But wee, that a farre off beholde and marke the paines and troubles that their contentment cost them, the dangers that they were in, and the mishaps and crosses that they had before they came to this happines, must be well advised and take good heed, that we put not our selves into like inconveniences, although our after reward and repose were more certaine then theirs; and the rather being so uncertaine and doubtfull, that for one that hath good happe, a thousand there are, whose long and painefull lives with desperate death have beene rewarded. But leaving this aside, let us entreate of those feastes and pastimes, which were made in *Felicias* garden for joy of the new espousals, and oblivion of old injuries and deceits, although it is not possible to set them downe in particular. *Felicia*, at whose command all were obedient, and in whose direction the whole order and substance of the feast consisted, willed the Shepherds (for their first pastime) to dance together, to the

tune of certaine songs that they themselves should sing: And so
sitting downe with *Eugerius*, *Polydorus*, *Clenarda*, *Marcelius*, *Alcida*,
Don Felix, and *Felismena*, she declared unto the Shepherds her
will and pleasure. Then they all rose up, and *Syrenus* taking *Diana*
by the hande, *Sylvanus Selvagia*, *Montanus Ismenia*, and *Arsileus* 5
Belisa, began to foote so brave and sweete a dance, as anie that the
fairest *Driades* and *Napees* with their yealowe haire like threedes
of fine Arabian golde hanging loose and blowen abroad with the
winde, were ever wont to dance in the greene and pleasant forrestes. There was no curteous contention amongst them, who 10
should begin to sing first: For *Syrenus*, who was the chiefest man
in all that feast, being somewhat ashamed of the small regard hee
had of *Diana* till that time, the thought whereof (he also suspected)
was likewise a hinderance unto him from justly excusing himselfe,
resolved in song to tell *Diana* his minde, which shame woulde not 15
permit him to acquaint her with in familiar talke. Therefore
without any more adoo (the rest answering him as it was decreed)
he sung as followeth.

I Should have dide, and never viewed thee
  (Faire Shepherdesse, unwoorthily forgot) 20
Since that I durst presume to live, and bee
Before thy sweetest sight, and love thee not.

A happy love, and fortune I should proove,
Both which my paines and sorrowes should abate,
If by remembring of thy deerest love, 25
I should forget the greefe of former hate.

For now the feare of death, and leesing thee,
I feare will be my guerdon and my lot,
Since that I durst presume to live, and bee
Before thy sweetest sight, and love thee not. 30

  Diana was of a contrarie opinion. For having satisfied her old
oblivion and disdaine that she had of *Syrenus* with a renewed and
entire love of him againe, and seeing herselfe sufficiently recompenced for her passed paines and greefes, she had now no cause
to lament the small care she had of him in times past, but rather 35
finding her hart filled with all content and joy that she could wish,

and free from all paine, by manifesting her gladnes and blaming
Syrenus needlesse excuse, she answered him with this song.

> *M*Y *soule doth leape for joy to have*
> *My wished love againe,*
> *For there's no other joy to crave,*   5
> *Nor greefe to give me paine.*
>
> *I doe not thinke of sorrowes past,*
> *Our love it may offend:*
> *Of any present greefe to taste,*
> *For hate that hath an end.*   10
>
> *Rejoice (my soule) such blisse to have,*
> *Since with so high a gaine,*
> *There is no other joy to crave,*
> *Nor greefe to give me paine.*

While *Diana* was singing her song, there came a most beautifull 15
Shepherdesse to the fountaine, but newly (as it seemed) come to
Felicias Palace, and being tolde, that the Ladie was in the garden,
she came thither to see her and to talke with her. Being come to
the place where *Felicia* was, she kneeling downe before her, kissed
her hands, and said unto her. Pardon (good Lady) my boldnes, 20
for comming into this presence without leave, since the desire
I had to see you, and the neede which I have of your skill and
wisedome, was so great, that I was forced hereunto. I bring with
me my hart surcharged with greefe, the remedie whereof is onely
in your handes, but it is so great, that it requireth some fitter 25
time, occasion, and place to tell it at large, bicause it is against
good manners to interrupt this merrie companie with matter of
sorrow and greefe. *Melisea* (for so was this Shepherdesse called)
was yet on her knees before *Felicia*, when she perceived a Shepherd comming along in an Alley of the Orchard towards the 30
fountaine, and in seeing him, saide. This is an other greefe (good
Ladie) so troublesome and painfull unto me, that for the deliverie
of the same also, I have no lesse neede of your gracious helpe and
favour. By this time the Shepherd (whose name was *Narcisus*)
came in presence of *Felicia*, and of those Lordes and Ladies that 35
were with her, and making lowe obeisance, he began to make

a great complaint against the Shepherdesse *Melisea* that was present there, saying, that he suffered great torments for her sake, and received not from her again one favourable or gentle word: Insomuch that in pursute of her love and company to that place, he had come very farre, and she not suffred him so much as to 5 declare his greefe to her cruell and disdainfull eares. *Felicia* commanded *Melisea* to rise up, and cutting off their troublesome contentions, saide. It is not now time to harken to long and tedious complaints, wherefore be content for this time *Melisea* and give *Narcisus* thy hand, and go both into that dance, and for the rest 10 wee will heereafter finde out a remedie at fitter time. The Shepherdesse would not gainsaie the Ladies command, but hand in hand with *Narcisus* she went to dance with the other Shepherds. And at this time happie *Ismenia* that was readie to sing, shewing by her outward countenance signes of inward content, which after 15 so long sorrow she injoyed, sung in this sort.

> *SUch joy I feele doth in my soule surmount,*
>   *That now againe I thinke it nothing strange:*
> *If that a pleasure of so great account*
> *Doth cost two thousand torments for exchange.*   20
>
> *Still did I looke, but still my comforts staied,*
>   *But when my soule did once enjoy the same,*
> *With their content and sweete delight I paied*
>   *My staying, and their tariance did not blame.*
>
> *Let paines therefore within my soule surmount,*   25
> *Sorrowes and plaints to me shall not be strange,*
> *If for a pleasure of so great account,*
> *They give me thousand torments in exchange.*

All the while that *Ismenia* was singing, and before, and after, she never cast her eies off her beloved *Montanus*. But he, who was 30 somewhat ashamed of his fonde conceit wherein he had lived so long, to the great griefe of his wife, durst never looke on her but by stealth, and at everie turne of the daunce, when she could not see him againe: the reason whereof was, bicause when sometimes he went about to looke her in the face, he was so much 35

21 *Still* Ed.] *Rtill* Y.

confounded with shame of his folly that was yet so fresh in his memorie, and was so much overcome with the light of those two radiant eies of her, which with great affection continually beheld him, that he was forced to cast his downe to the ground. Whereby seeing that he lost a great part of his delight, by not looking on 5 her, whom he accounted his chiefest felicitie, and making this the occasion and matter of the song, he sung to his beloved *Ismenia* in manner following.

TUrne thy faire eies (wherein my shame
I see) faire Shepherdesse, aside: 10
For looking on me with the same,
To looke on thee, I am denide.

With thy two sunnes so dost thou give,
And cast me beames with pearcing eie,
That though by seeing thee I live,   15
Yet when thou look'st on me I die:
Eies that are of such art and frame,
Thou must beware to keepe aside,
For looking on me with the same,
To looke on thee I am denide.   20

Like as the snowe unto the sunne,
And as the marke unto the flight,
As cloudes are with the windes undone,
As waxe before the fires light:
So doe thy fairest eies with shame   25
Confound me, and my soule devide:
For looking on me with the same,
To looke on thee I am denide.

Behold what mightie love is bent
To doe, and fortune doth ordaine   30
To make my sorrowes still augment
By the sweete guerdon of my paine.
Thine eies doe feede my amorous flame,
And sight of them my life doth guide:
But if thou view'st me with the same,   35
To looke on thee I am denide.

Melisea, who was all this while dauncing against her will with *Narcisus*, whom she could not abide, with a disdainfull song thought to be revenged on this griefe, and just to the purpose of those paines and griefes, wherewith the Shepherd said he died everie daie for her sake, making but a mocke and jest of them, did 5 sing thus.

> *Y*Ong Shepherd) *turne aside, and move*
>   *Me not to follow thee,*
> *For I will neither kill with love,*
>   *Nor love shall not kill mee.* 10
>
> *Since I will live, and never favour showe,*
> *Then die not for my love I will not give:*
> *For I will never have thee love me so,*
> *As I doe meane to hate thee while I live.*
>
> *That since the lover so doth prove* 15
> *His death, as thou dost see,*
> *Behold I will not kill with love,*
> *Nor love shall not kill mee.*

Narcisus tooke no meane griefe to heare the cruell song of his deerest Love, but encouraging himselfe with the hope that *Felicia* 20 had given him, and forced by the constancie and fortitude of his enamoured hart, he answered her with two staves, which he adjoyned to a certaine old song, that said thus.

> *I*F to be lov'd it thee offends,
>   *I cannot choose but love thee still:* 25
> *And so thy greefe shall have no end,*
> *Whiles that my life maintaines my will.*
>
> *O let me yet with greefe complaine,*
> *Since such a torment I endure:*
> *Or else fulfill thy great disdaine,* 30
> *To end my life with death most sure.*
> *For as no credit thou wilt lend,*
> *And as my love offendes thee still,*
> *So shall thy sorrowes have no end*
> *Whiles that my life maintaines my will.* 35

17 *Behold* Ed.] *Be bold* Y.   24 *be lov'd* Ed.] *belov'd* Y.

If that by knowing thee, I could
Leave of to love thee as I doe,
Not to offend thee, then I would
Leave of to like and love thee too,
But since all love to thee doth tend, 5
And I of force must love thee still,
Thy greefe shall never have an end,
Whiles that my life maintaines my will.

Melisea was so hardened in her crueltie, that *Narcisus* having
scarce ended the last words of his song, and before another did 10
sing, she replied in this manner.

*M*E *thinks, thou tak'st the woorser way,*
  (Enamoured Shepherd) and in vaine,
That thou wilt seeke thine owne decay,
To love her, that doth thee disdaine. 15

For thine owne selfe, thy wofull hart
Keepe still, else art thou much to blame,
For she, to whom thou gav'st each part
Of it, disdaines to take the same:

Follow not her that makes a play, 20
And jest of all thy greefe and paines,
And seeke not (Shepherd) thy decay
To love her, that thy love disdaines.

Narcisus could not suffer *Meliseas* song to passe without an
answer, and so with a milde grace he sung these new verses upon 25
an old song, that said.

*S*Ince *thou to me wert so unkinde,*
  My selfe I never loved, For
I could not love him in my minde,
Whom thou faire Mistresse dost abhor. 30

If viewing thee, I saw thee not,
And seeing thee, I could not love thee,
Dying, I should not live (God wot)
Nor, living, should to anger move thee.

But it is well that I doe finde
My life so full of torments: For
All kinde of ills doe fit his minde,
Whom thou (faire Mistresse) dost abhor.

In thy oblivion buried now   5
My death I have before mine eies,
And heere to hate my selfe I vow
As (cruell) thou dost me despise:

Contented ever thou didst finde
Me with thy scornes, though never (for   10
To say the truth) I joyed in minde,
After thou didst my love abhor.

The contention betweene *Narcisus* and *Melisea*, delighted them
all so much, that the generall rejoycing of that feast had beene
greatly augmented by it, had it not bin diminished with the mani- 15
fest apparance of the rigor that she shewed *Narcisus*, and with the
pitie that they had of those paines, which he suffered for hir sake.
After *Narcisus* had made an ende of his song, all of them turned
their eies to *Melisea*, thinking she would have replyed againe.
But she held her peace, not bicause she wanted nipping and cruell 20
songs to encounter and vexe the miserable Lover with, nor will to
reply; but bicause she would not be troublesome to all that merie
companie. *Selvagia* and *Belisa* were afterwards requested to sing,
who excused themselves, by alleaging their insufficiencie. Nay
that were not well (said *Diana*) that you should goe from the 25
feast without paying your shot. And this must not so smoothly
passe away (said *Felismena*) without the consent of us all heere,
who meane to participate the sweete delight of so delicate voices
as yours are. We will not be slacke (said they againe) to do you
anie service (little though it be) in this solemnitie; but pardon our 30
singing (I pray you) for in all other things we will be willing to do
our endevours. I will not for my part give my consent (saide
Alcida) to exempt you from singing, or at the least that some
others shall sing for you. Who can better do it (said they) then
Sylvanus and *Arsileus* our husbands. The Shepherdesses say well 35
(said *Marcelius*) and it would be best (me thinkes) if both did sing
one song, and one answere another in it, for it shall be lesse

troublesome to them, and more pleasant to us. All of them seemed
to take great delight at that kinde of singing, bicause they knew,
how the readines and livelines of their wits would be shewed and
tried by it. And so *Sylvanus* and *Arsileus* seeming to be well
content, leading their daunce about againe, sung in manner 5
following.

Sylv.	*SHepherd, why dost thou hold thy peace?*
	Sing: and thy joy to us report.
Arsil.	*My joy (good Shepherd) should be lesse,*
	If it were told in any sort. 10
Sylv.	*Though such great favours thou dost win,*
	Yet deigne thereof to tell some part:
	Arsil. *The hardest thing is to begin*
	In enterprises of such arte.
Sylv.	*Come, make an end, no cause omit* 15
	Of all the joies that thou art in,
	Arsil. *How should I make an end of it,*
	That am not able to begin.
Sylv.	*It is not just, we should consent,*
	That thou shouldst not thy joies recite, 20
	Arsil. *The soule that felt the punishment*
	Doth onely feele this great delight.
Sylv.	*That joy is small, and nothing fine,*
	That is not told abroad to many,
	Arsil. *If it be such a joy as mine,* 25
	It can be never told to any.
Sylv.	*How can this hart of thine containe*
	A joy, that is of such great force?
	Arsil. *I have it, where I did retaine*
	My passions of so great remorce. 30
Sylv.	*So great and rare a joy as this*
	No man is able to withhold,
	Arsil. *But greater that a pleasure is,*
	The lesse it may with words be told.
Sylv.	*Yet have I heard thee heeretofore* 35
	Thy joies in open songs report:
	Arsil. *I saide, I had of joy some store,*
	But not how much, nor in what sort.

Sylv.   *Yet when a joy is in excesse,*
        It selfe it will unfold,
      Arsil.   *Nay such a joy should be the lesse,*
            If that it might be told.

The Shepherds would have sung one verse or two more, when
a goodly companie of faire Nymphes (as *Felicia* had appointed)
came to the fountaine, and everie one playing upon her severall
instrument, made strange and delightfull harmonie. One of them
plaied on a Lute; another on a Harpe; another made a marvellous
sweet countertenour upon a Recorder; another with a peece of
a fine quil made the silver stringed Cyterne sweetely to sound;
others the stringes of the base Viall with rosined haires; others
with Virginals and Violins made delicate changes in the aire, and
filled it with so sweete musicke, that in a manner it astonished
them that heard it, and made them to marvell no lesse at it. These
Nymphes were strangely apparelled, and passing faire to behold,
everie one in her proper colours, their locks of golden haire
hanging loose to the wavering winde, with fine coronets on their
heads, and sweete flowers tied togither with threds of gold and
silver. The Shepherds seeing this melodious quier of angels, left
of the daunce that they had begun, and sat downe, giving attentive eare to the heavenly musicke, and concent of the sundrie
sweete instruments that they plaied on, which joyned sometimes
with cleere and delicate voices, mooved strange and rare delight.
Then came out by and by sixe Nymphes apparelled with crimosin
Satten, embrodered with flowers and leaves of gold and silver,
wearing rich caules upon their heads, which were filled and
wrought with Rubies and Emerauldes, from the which hung
downe upon their fairest browes Diamantes of incomparable
value, with pendants at their eares, of the rarest Pearles and
richest Diamonds that could be founde. They had crymosin
Buskins on their legs that were finely printed and gilt, with their
bowes in their hands, and their quivers of arrowes hanging
behinde their shoulders. In this sort they began to dance to the
sound that the instruments made, but with so brave a grace, that
it was a rare sight to behold them. And being in the middes of
their dance, there lept out on the sudden a stately white Hart,
marked all over with little blacke spots, which seemed very
pleasant to the eie: his painted hornes with golde were large,

high, and branchie. In breefe it was such an one, as *Felicia* could best devise to make that companie sport. When the Nymphes espied the Hart, they ranne rounde about him, and dancing neverthelesse without missing one straine of the musicke that plaied still, with a brave concord they began to shoote at him, the 5 which leaping from one side to another after the arrowes were once flien out, with manie nimble and pretie skips did the best to defend himselfe. But after they had a pretie while sported themselves with this pastime, the Hart beganne to breake out from them amongst the orchards and courts, the Nymphes pursuing 10 him amaine, untill they chased him out of the Garden, who with their joyfull cries and pleasant hallowing made a delicate noise, which the other Nymphes and Shepherds seconded with their voices, taking a most singular delight in this dance. And with this sport the Nymphes made an end of their musicke. In the meane 15 time sage *Felicia*, bicause there should not want some profitable lesson to be gathered out of those pleasures for the direction and instruction of life, meaning to trie their conceits about the obscure mysteries and significations of that dance, saide to *Diana*. Canst thou tell me (faire Shepherdesse) what is ment by the chase of this 20 goodlie Hart, besides the thing it selfe? To whom she saide againe, I am not so wise (gracious Ladie) that I am able to expounde mysteries, nor to dissolve your hard questions. Why then will I tell thee said *Felicia*, what matter is conteined under that invention. The Hart is mans hart, made faire with delicate thoughts, 25 and rich with quiet content. It submitteth it selfe to humane inclinations, which shoote mortall arrowes at it, but with discretion remooving it selfe into divers parts, and applying it selfe to honest exercises, it must defend it selfe from so many hurtfull arrowes, that ayme so cruelly at it. And when it is pursued of 30 them, it must flie away speedilie, thereby to save it selfe, though those humane and fraile inclinations which shoote such arrowes, will not cease to pursue it, and will never leave to accompanie it, untill it escapes out of the orchard of life. How can I understand (saide *Diana*) so difficult and Morall a conclusion, as this, when as 35 the questions and Riddles which wee Shepherdesses exercise and disport our selves with (to this but plaine and easie) I could never yet dissolve nor expound. Make not thy selfe so unskilfull (saide *Selvagia*) since I have knowne the contrarie in thee, and that there was never any Riddle so hard, but was easie enough in thy under- 40 standing. In good time (saide *Felicia*) for now we may wel try her cunning, which pastime wil affoord no lesse delight then the other before. Propound her therfore every one of you a Riddle, for I know *Diana* will acquite herselfe with you all. It liked them all well; but *Diana*, who had not such confidence in her cunning, 5 that she durst oppose her skil to such difficult questions as she thought they woulde propounde, but bicause she woulde obey *Felicia* and please her *Syrenus*, who seemed to take a pride and delight therein, she was content to take in hand the charge that they imposed upon hir. *Sylvanus*, who was very ready in pro- 10 pounding of Riddles, made the first, saying. Bicause I know well (faire Shepherdesse) that thy pregnant and lively wit is able to discover hard and hidden matters, and that thy skill is no lesse sufficient to compasse and attaine to intricate and high things, I will therefore (by thy favour) aske thee a question, by answering 15 which, I know thou wilt manifest thy delicate and ripe wit. Tell me therefore what this Riddle meanes?

A Riddle.

NEere to a Shepherd did a damsell sit,
  As leane as withered sticke by scorching flame: 20
Her body as full of eies as might be in it,
  A toong she had, but could not moove the same.
Her winde she drew above, and eke beneath,
  But from one part she never yet did change,
A wofull Shepherd came to kisse her breath, 25
  Then made she plaints most sorrowfull and strange:
The more the Shepherd put his mouth unto
  Her mouth in stopping it, she cried amaine,
  Opening her eies, and shutting them againe.
See now what this dumbe Shepherdesse could doe, 30
  That when her mouth he did but touch or kisse,
  He waxeth dumbe, but she still speaking is.

This Riddle (said *Diana*) although it be somewhat hard, shall not trouble my wit much, for I have heard thy selfe propound it 35 on a day at the fountaine of the Sicamours; and because there was no Shepherd there that could tell the meaning of it, thy selfe didst expound unto us, saying, that the Damosell was a Bagpipe or

a Fluite played upon by a Shepherd. And thou appliedst all the
parts of the Riddle to the effects that happen commonly in musicke.
All of them laughed to see how *Sylvanus* memorie had deceived
him, and how *Dianas* so readily found it out; wherefore *Sylvanus*
to acquite himselfe, and to be revenged of his shame, smiling 5
said. Marvell not at my weake memorie; for this forgetfulnes
seemes not so ill as *Dianas*, nor so hurtfull as that of *Syrenus*. Thou
hast now paide us home (said *Syrenus*) and better thou shouldest
have done, if our oblivions had not beene changed into so perfect
affections and happie estates as now they are. No more (said 10
Selvagia) for all is well spoken. But answere me *Diana* to that,
which I will aske thee, for I will trie if I can speake in a darker
language then my *Sylvanus* did : The Riddle is this.

A Riddle.

I Sawe a hill upon a day,   15
* Lift up above the aire:*
Which watered with blood alway
And tilled with great care,
* Herbes it brought foorth*
* Of mickle woorth.*   20

Pulling a handfull from that ridge
And touching but the same,
Which leaving neere unto a bridge,
Doth cause much sport and game,
* (A thing scarce of beleefe)*   25
* Lamenting without greefe.*

   Diana looking then towards her husband, said. Dost not thou
remember (my *Syrenus*) that thou hast heard this Riddle that night,
when we were togither in my uncle *Yranius* his house? And dost
not thou remember also how *Maroncius* sonne to (*Fernasus*) did 30
propound it? I remember verie well (said *Syrenus*) that he did put
it there, but told not (as I thinke) the signification of it. But then
I remember it (said *Diana*.) For he said, that the field was that
part of the horse from whence they pull out his longest haires,
wherewith the Rebeckes being strong, make a tuned noise, al- 35
though they suffer never the more any paine or hurt. *Selvagia*

said, that it was so, and that *Maroncius* Author of the Riddle, had told it for a fine one, although he had many more better then that. There are many pretie ones, said *Belisa*, and one of them is, that I will now put: wherefore call thy wits togither *Diana*, for this time thou shalt not escape scot free: and it is this.   5

A Riddle.

WHat bird is that so light,
    Her place that never changeth:
She flies by day and night,
In all the world she rangeth: 10
    Over the sea at once she flies,
    Mounting above the loftie skies.

She's never seene by eies,
And who doth seeke to show her
Hath beene accounted wise: 15
Yet sometimes we doe knowe her,
    Onely the wals by viewing well
    Of her close house, where she doth dwell.

Thy Riddle *Belisa* (said *Diana*) hath beene more unfortunate then the rest before; for I had not declared any of their significa- 20 tions, if I had not heard them before now, and this which thou hast put, as soone as I heard it, I understood it, which of it selfe is so easie and manifest, that any indifferent conceite (I thinke) is able to dissolve it. For it is verie cleere, that by the birde which thou speakest of, ones thought is understood, which flies with 25 such swiftnes, that is not seene of any body, but conjectured and knowen by the outward signes and gesture of the bodie, wherein it is included. I confesse my selfe overcommed (said *Belisa*) and have no more to say, but that I yeeld my reasons to thy discretion and wit, and my selfe to thy disposition and will. I will revenge 30 thee (said *Ismenia* to *Belisa*) for there comes an obscure probleme to my minde, that hath posed the wisest Shepherds, which I will propound, and thou shalt see how I will gravell *Diana*, who shall not be so fortunate (I thinke) in expounding it, as she hath beene in the rest, and looking upon *Diana*, she said.   35

A Riddle.

TEll me what Master he may be,
*   Whose Master is his man?*
Bound like a sencelesse foole is he,
*   Wittie, it nothing can.*   5
Unlearned, yet he doth abound
In learning grave and most profound:
When that I take him by the hand,
*   Although I heare him not,*
His meaning yet I understand,   10
*   Though him I have forgot.*
So wise is he, though wordes nor motions showing,
Yet thousand things he tels me woorth the knowing.

I would have beene well contented (said *Diana*) and thought
my selfe happie to have beene overcommed by thee (beloved 15
Ismenia) but since in beautie, and in other perfections and graces
thou goest far beyond me, I shall gaine no great praise and glorie
by overthrowing thy purpose, whereby thou thoughtest to have
entrapped me with thy Riddle. It is now two yeeres, since a certaine Phisition of *Leon* came to attend my Father in his sicknes, 20
and as he had a booke one day in his hands, he gave it me, and
I began to read. And the great profit occurring to my mind that is
commonly taken in reading of bookes, I told him, that they were
like doombe Masters, that were understoode without speaking.
Then to this purpose he told me this Riddle, wherein some rare 25
matters and excellent inventions of bookes are particularly set
downe and noted. In good sooth (said *Ismenia*) there can none of
us Shepherds overcome thee, wherefore our courage is quailed in
passing any farther in this contention, unlesse these Ladies heere
meane to give thee a fresh assault with their weapons, and to make 30
thee yeeld. *Alcida*, which till that time had held her peace, taking
great delight in hearing the musicke, and looking on the daunces
and sports, and to behold and devise with her beloved *Marcelius*,
being also very desirous to have one part in that sport, said:
Since thou hast (gracious *Diana*) subdued all the Shepherds with 35
thy skill, it is not reason that we should also passe safely away

22 occurring *Ed.*] occnrriug *Y.*

without our Riddles, the which although I know thou wilt as
easily dissolve (and mine especially) as thou hast done the rest;
yet bicause it may perhaps delight thee, I will propound it. When
I sayled on a time from *Naples* into *Spaine*, by the way the master
of the ship told it me, and I committed it to memorie, bicause me 5
thought it was a pretie one: and this it was.

A Riddle.

SHew me a horse of such a kinde,
    That in the strangest fashion
Doth never eate, but of the winde   10
    Doth take his sustentation:
Winged before, and wing'd behinde:
Strange things he doth, and wondrous deeds:
    And when he runs his race,
Upon his brest with haste he speedes.   15
    His reines with marvellous grace
Come from his sides that never bleedes.
    And in his course he doth not faile,
    If rightly he doth wag his taile.

When *Diana* had heard this Riddle, she was a pretie while 20
thinking with her selfe how she might expound it, and having
framed the discourse in her minde, which was necessarie for the
answere, and considered well of everie part in it; at the last, she
said. As it is great reason (faire Ladie) that I remaine conquered at
thy hands: So it is no lesse, that whosoever renders himselfe to 25
thy gentlenes, he yeelde himselfe also to thy discretion, whereby
I esteeme him not confounded, but happy. And if by the horse of
thy Enigma, a ship be not understoode, I confesse then that I cannot declare it. Thou hast overcome me more (said *Alcida*) with
thy answer, then I have done thee with my Riddle; for to confesse 30
it plainly unto thee I understood it not, before thou hadst subtilly
expounded it. By chaunce I have hit it, said *Diana* (as I thinke) and
not by any skill, speaking at randome, and not thinking to hit it so
neer. Howsoever thou didst it (said *Alcida*) it cannot otherwise
be but that it proceeded from thy readie wit and ripe judgement. 35
But I pray thee now (faire Shepherdesse) divine what my Sister
Clenardas Riddle is (which I know is no ill one) that she shall put

thee, if she can at the least remember it. And then turning her
selfe to *Clenarda*, she said unto her. Propound to this wittie
Shepherdesse (good sister) that Riddle, which one day in our citie
(if thou remembrest) thou didst put to *Berinthius* and *Clomenius*
our cosins, when we were merie togither in *Elisonias* house. I am 5
well content (said *Clenarda*) for I remember it well, and was
purposed to tell it: and this it is.

A Riddle.

*T*Ell me (good Sirs) what Bird is that that flies
  Three cubits high, and yet doth never rise,   10
With more then thirtie feete that mount and fall,
With wings that have no plume nor pens at all:
  Beating the aire, it neither eates, nor drinks,
  It neither cries, nor sings, nor speakes, nor thinks.
    Approching neere unto her cruell death,   15
    She wounds, and kils us with the stones she throwes:
    A friend to those that spend their deerest breath
    In spoiles, and thefts, in mortall wounds and blowes:
  Wherein she takes her pleasure and her fill,
  Hiding the men in waves that she doth kill.   20

    I should never expound this Riddle (said *Diana*) if I had not
heard the meaning of it by a Shepherd in my towne, who had
sometimes sailed. And yet I cannot tell whether I remember it or
not, but I thinke, he said that a Galley was understood by it,
which being in the middest of the dangerous waves, is neere to 25
death, and being accustomed to robbing and killing, casteth the
dead carcases into the Sea. By the feete he told me, that the oares
were ment, by the winges the sayles, and by the stones that it
threw, the pellets. We must in the end (saide *Clenarda*) goe one
equall with another, for one deserves no more praise then another. 30
Truely thy great knowledge *Diana* makes me to woonder much,
and thou canst receive no reward sufficient enough for so great
deserts, but onely by being *Syrenus* wife. These and other curteous
speeches they passed, when *Felicia*, beholding the fine wit, the
comely grace, the passing behaviour, and sweete actions of 35
Diana, and marvelling much at them, tooke off from her finger a
verie rich ring, set with a stone of infinite value, which she did

ordinarilie weare, and giving it her for a rewarde of her wittie answers to those Riddles, said. This shall serve for a token of that, which I meane to do for thee (faire Shepherdesse) keepe it therfore wel, for in time of thy need the vertue of it may not be a litle profitable unto thee. *Diana* and *Syrenus* both rendred humble 5 thanks to *Felicia*, for so great a gift, with devoutly kissing her reverend hands. Who after he had sufficientlie and curteously made an end of his thanks, said. I have noted one thing in all these Riddles, which is this, that the Shepherdesses and Ladies have propounded the most of them, and that the men have held their 10 peace in such sort that they have cleerely shewed, that in daintie and wittie conceits they have not so fine a vaine as women have. *Don Felix* then jesting said. It is no great marvell that in sharpnes of wit they excel us, when in all other perfections they come nothing neer us. *Belisa* coulde not digest *Don Felix* his merrie 15 jest, thinking (perhaps) that he ment it in good earnest, but looking upon all the women, said. We will agree (*Don Felix*) that men excell us, but therein we shew our goodnes, and our vertues in our voluntarie subjection to their will and skill. But yet knowe this, that there are women which for their vertues and deserts may be 20 paragoned to the woorthiest and wisest men, for though gold lies hidden and unknown, yet it looseth not therefore any part of that value and prize of that which is currant. For the truth and force of our praises is so great, that it maketh you publish them to your selves, which seeme to be our enimies. *Florisia* a Shep- 25 herdesse renowned for great knowledge and wisedome, was not (*Don Felix*) of your opinion, when in our towne on a day at a certaine marriage (where was a confluence of many Shepherds, men, and women, that from townes farre and nie had come to that feast) to the tune of a Rebecke, and of two Harpes, which three 30 Shepherds sweetely plaied on, she sung a song in the praise and defence of women, which not onely pleased them, but also delighted all the men there, of whom she spoke but little good. And if you are too perverse and obstinate in your opinion, it shall not be amisse to rehearse it to you, to make you leave of 35 your blinde errour. They laughed all hartely to see *Belisa* so cholericke, and made no small sport thereat. In the end old *Eugerius* and his sonne *Polydorus*, bicause they would not be deprived of that merrie song which they expected at *Belisas* handes, said unto her. The praise (faire Shepherdesse) and defence of women 40

is justly due unto them, and no lesse delightfull to us to heare it
with thy delicate voice repeated. It pleaseth me well (said *Belisa*)
if it like you, for there are many sharpe and stinging invectives, if
I could remember all the verses in it; but yet I will begin to recite
them, bicause I hope that in singing them, one will reduce another to 5
my minde. Then *Arsileus*, seeing that *Belisa* was preparing herselfe
to sing, began to tune his Rebecke, at the sound whereof she sung
the song, that she heard *Florisia* in times past sing, which was this.

Florisias *Song.*

*F*Lie storming verse out of my raging brest   10
  With furious anger, malice, and despite:
Indigned spirits, once at my request
  Powre foorth your wrath, and pen prepare to write
   With scornefull stinging and invective stile,
   Against a people brutish, base, and vile: 15
A vile, perverse and monstrous kinde of men,
  Who make it but their pastime, and their game,
With barbarous mouth and with uncivill pen
  To slaunder those, who lest deserve the same:
   Women I meane a workmanship divine,   20
   Angels in shape, and Goddesses in minde.

Thou wicked man that dost presume too hie
  Of thy perfections, but without desart,
False man I say, accustomed to lie,
  What evill canst thou thinke within thy hart,   25
   Or speake of her, whose goodnes more or lesse,
   Doth fill the world so full of happinesse,
But onely this, that woman was the cause,
  Though not alone, of one exceeding ill,
In bringing foorth (constrained by natures lawes)   30
  A man, whose mischiefes all the world doth fill:
   Who after that he is conceiv'd and borne,
   Against his mother proudly liftes his horne.

Whom if she had not borne, poore silly dame,
  With fewer greefes her life she might have lead,   35
For then he should not slaunder thus her name,
  And such a crowe she should not then have bred,

That being hatch'd, her dam would thus despise,
  And daily labour to plucke out her eies.
What man in all the world did ever knowe
  (Although the tendrest father he had beene)
Those cares, and greefes, that sorrow, and that woe,   5
    Which wives have for their husbands felt, and seene?
    And how the loving mother for her sonne
    With sorrow hath beene oftentimes undone?

Behold with what affection, and what joy,
  What gentlenes, and what intensive love,   10
The mother doth intreate her little boy?
    Which after doth a Traitour to her proove:
    Requiting ill her paines and love so kinde
    With powring sorrowes still into her minde.
What jealous feares, what fearefull jealousies,   15
  Doe haunt the mother for her cruell sonne?
What paine, when that in any paine he lies,
    What greefe, when that with greefe he is undone?
    What perfect gladnes, and what sweete content,
    When that he is to any goodnes bent?   20

Alas how pensive and how sad they ar,
  If that their husbands suffer any paine:
What sorrow, when they travell somewhat far,
    What moane, when that they come not soone againe:
    A thousand greefes to heare their losse of wealth,   25
    Ten thousand deathes to heare their want of health.
But men that are so full of false deceate,
  Our daily sorrowes never doe requite,
Or thinke of them, though they be never so great,
    But rather such their malice and despite   30
    Is; that our loving cares both great and small,
    Unjust suspects, and jealousies doe call.

The cause of which surmise is onely this,
  That as these wicked and detested men
Of custome are enclined to stray amisse,   35
    And in false love their wits and wealth to spend,
    Do thinke it now a burden to their lives,
    To be belov'd so truely of their wives.

Then since in loving them we ever finde
  Our selves apayde with hatefull scorne and blame,
I thinke it best, for easing of our minde,
  Quite to forget their nature, sexe, and name:
    Or else to leave our joies in looking on them,   5
    Or if we looke, not once to thinke upon them.

But yet it is a pretie jest to see
  Some kind of men, whose madnes is so great,
That if the woman will not wholly bee
  At their desires, then in a franticke heat   10
    They call her Tygresse, cruell, and unkinde,
    And traiteresse unto a loving minde.
Then shalt thou see these men unseemely call
  The modest women, whom they would have naught,
Coy and disdainfull to converse withall: 15
  And her that's chaste, unmanner'd and untaught.
    Those that be wise and sober, full of pride:
    And cruell those, whose honesties are tride.

I would to God that those dishonored names
  Did fit them all, as well as all the rest,   20
Then none of them should bide so many shames,
  Nor be deceiv'd by men, that love them lest:
    For being cruell, proude, and rusticall,
    They would not love, nay could not love at all.
For if the thing, which they so faine would have,   25
  By any meanes they cannot once obtaine,
Then do they wish for death, or for their grave:
  But yet the same no sooner they attaine,
    But make it but a sport and merie game,
    And straight forget that ere they lov'd the same.   30

They faine themselves most sorrowfull and sad,
  And wearied with a long and painfull life:
They still do tell the paines that they have had,
  And other lyes, which are with them so rife:
    They call themselves unhappie, poore, and blinde,   35
    Confounded slaves, yet all but words of winde.

O *how they can make Oceans of their eies!*
　And terme their flames their torments and their paines,
And breath out sighes, like vapours in the skies,
　And belch out sobs like Aetnas *burning vaines:*
　　And crie, lament, and mourne, and otherwhile　　　　5
　　Dissemble like the weeping Crocodile.

Sometimes they make themselves like conquered slaves,
　Sometimes themselves most valiant they do faine,
Sometimes great Lords, with many other braves,
　Sometimes throwen downe, and vanquished againe:　　　10
　　Their wounds their joyes, their paines their pleasures make
　　And happie comfort in their prisones take.
A thousand times they curse their haplesse stars,
　Despising life, and happie death implore:
Yet in the end so valiant in these wars　　　　15
　Of life and death, and other passions more,
　　That thousand deaths they say they passe and trie,
　　And yet they never make an end to die.

They give,　　they gaine,　　they heale,　　they wound,　　they plie,
their soule,　　their life,　　their harms,　　their harts,　　their teares,　20
they joy,　　they live,　　they burne,　　they paine,　　they die,
with hap,　　with hope,　　with heate,　　with greefe,　　with feares.
　　And so in all their loves, and what they say,
　　There is a strange confusion everie way.
And for this cause when Melibe *in vaine*　　　　25
　With daily suites his love to me did make,
By telling me his amorous greefe and paine,
　and everie other passion for my sake:
　　I answered him (good Shepherd) let not grieve thee,
　　I understand thee not, and lesse beleeve thee.　　　30

See therefore men how justly you deserve
　To leese our love defam'd by your abuse:
Since from this counsell we must never swerve,
　(As by the wisest dayly put in use)
　　To put no faith nor trust in any lyer,　　　　35
　　Nor love that man, whom love cannot inspire.

From this day therefore call us now no more
   Unpitifull and cruell homicides,
For tis no reason, that upon our score
   You should nicke up so many merie tides,
      Nor with our lives and honours (to our cost)   5
      Enrich your selves, and after make your boast.

For if (perhaps) a chaste and honest maide
   Should looke upon you in familiar sort,
Or talke with you, then straight it would be saide,
   That she is light, and then with false report   10
      Will judge her naught, by favouring with a kisse:
      Fie shamelesse men, why blush you not at this.
And in this sort the Shepherdesse and dame
   Of what degree soever that they bee,
On everie side doth suffer wrong and blame,   15
   Since that your wicked toongs in one agree
      To call them shamelesse, if they love you well;
      And cruell, if your love they do expell.

And now you hold us (which is worst of all)
   For such accursed women, and so naught   20
That all those ils which unto you befall,
   You say you have them onely by our fault.
      For your misfortunes, deaths, and other harmes
      You say they come by our enchants and charmes.
Nay they do rather happen unto you   25
   By want of wisedome and your simple sence,
And not by our beautie; for most true
   It is that Paris folly and offence
      Did cause the ruine of King Priames towne:
      And not faire Hellens beautie cast it downe.   30

But why so like dishonest women do you
   With lying toongs so basely us entreate?
When that so oft you do allure us to you
   With feastes, and maskes, and all of them so great,
      That scarce you let us rest in any sort,   35
      But forcibly do draw us to your sport.

Then of our honours, and of our estates
You have no care, and no respect at all,
For we no sooner gone out of your gates,
And from your feastes, which we regarded small,
But by and by your toongs do goe awrie, 5
Misterming us, that could not you denie.

And yet you are so blinded in this ill,
And troublesome, when that your suites you moove,
That you will have the woman (gainst her will)
To die in hot desire of your love. 10
So rude you be, that you are not content
To have some small and modest favour lent.
And thus the lives of these poore silly dames,
Which otherwise were modest, milde, and chaste,
And therewithall their honours, and good names, 15
Like traitours vile you conquer, spoile, and waste.
So that those women, that have gone astray,
By your meanes were brought unto decay.

But now what pen, what toong, or golden verse
Of women may the vertues rare set downe? 20
How may my simple skill and wit reherse
Their praises and perfections of renowne?
Their constancie, their love, and faith so pure,
Which in their harts remaines so firme and sure.
In many things the greatnes of their minde 25
They shew, contemning base and doubtfull feare:
As those, whose tender love hath beene so kinde
Unto their husbands, when they living were,
That all their moanes and sorrowes for their death
They ended soone, by stopping of their breath. 30

And if for vertue, and his chaste intent
Hippolytus *deserved any praise,*
On th'other side behold that excellent
And noble Roman Matrone *in her daies*
With stabbing dagger giving up the ghost, 35
I meane faire Lucrece, *for her honour lost.*

It was no doubt great valour in the youth,
As never like hath beene in all the rest,
Who vowing to his father faith and truth,
Deni'd his stepdames foule and fond request.
    All which admit: Hippolytus *is but one,*   5
    But thousands of Lucrecias *have beene knowne.*

Giftes have we more (our beauties set aside)
For in good letters famous have we bin:
And now to proove our judgements often tride,
And sharpnes of our finest wits therein,   10
    Let Sappho *and* Corynna *well suffice,*
    Who when they liv'd, for learning got the prise.
And learned men doe therefore banish us
Their schooles, and places where they do dispute,
For feare (if we should argue and discusse)   15
    With praise we should their arguments confute:
    Too proud therefore, they would not by their will,
    That women should excell them in their skill.

And if some authors, scorned in their loves,
Have written ill of women, in their hate,   20
Not this our credits any whit disprooves,
And can as lesse diminish our estates:
    Since they themselves have writ as ill of men,
    Beleeve not then their lying toongs and pen.
Yet this doth cause some small and little change,   25
And alteration in our great desarts:
For they must needes (and sure it is not strange,
Considering their vile malicious harts)
    In whatsoever they doe write or say,
    To speake the woorst of women that they may.   30

But yet among these Authors *thou shalt finde*
Most famous women, and most excellent:
Peruse their works but with indifferent minde,
And thou shalt see what numbers they present
    Of good and honest Dames, before thine eies,   35
    Of loving, faithfull, holy, chaste, and wise.

They doe adorne the world with goodly graces,
  And with their vertues give it golden light:
The shining beautie of their sweetest faces
  Doth fill each hart and eie with great delight.
    They bring all comforts, gladnes, peace, and joy,   5
    And drive away all sorrowes, and annoy.

By them (false men of bad and wicked mindes)
  You get great honour, glorie, and renowne:
And for their sakes, inventing sundry kindes
  Of verses, get sometimes the Laurell crowne: 10
    And for their love, in Martiall feates againe
    To golden praise and fame you doe attaine.
You therefore that imploy your wits and time,
  In searching out the course of others lives,
If that you finde some woman toucht with crime   15
  Amongst so many widowes, maides, and wives:
    Condemne not all for one poore soules offence,
    But rather hold your judgements in suspence.

And if so many Dames so chaste, and faire,
  Cannot subdue your proud and hautie harts,   20
Behold but one, whose vertues are so rare,
  To whom the heavens so many goods imparts,
    That onely she possesseth in her brest
    As many giftes, nay more then all the rest.
The bravest men, and most heroicall,   25
  And those that are most perfect in conceate,
I see this Lady far excell them all,
  With her divine perfections, and so great,
    Which Orpheus *did sing upon a day,*
    As on his harpe most sweetely he did play.   30

Saying: That in that happy land, where white
  And chalkie cliffes are steept in Brittish seas,
A morning star should rise exceeding bright,
  Whose birth will silver Cynthia *much displease,*
    In that her golden light, and beauties gleames   35
    Shall far surpasse her brothers borrowed beames.

And such a Lady shall she be indeede,
*   That she shall joy each hart with happy chaunce:*
Her woorthy house, wherein she shall succeede,
*   With titles of great praise she shall advaunce:*
*   And make the same more glorious and more knowne,*   5
*   Then ever did the Affrican his owne.*

Make triumphes then for birth of such a dame,
*   And let each hart be glad that hath beene sorie:*
Rejoice Meridian springs from whence she came;
*   You linage her, she honours you with glorie,*   10
*   Her name from East to West, from North to South*
*   Is well esteem'd and knowne in every mouth.*
Come then you Nymphes, resigne to her your powers,
*   Faire Nymphes that follow* Cynthia *in her chace,*
Come waite on her and strowe the ground with flowers,   15
*   And sing in honour of her matchlesse grace:*
*   And Muses nine that dwell in mount Parnasse*
*   Let verse nor song without her praises passe.*

Thou dar'st not Rome (in seeing her) presume
*   With* Brutus *stately Iland to compare,*   20
But sooner wilt thy selfe with greefe consume,
*   To see how far she doth excell those faire*
*   Ladies of Rome renowned in their daies,*
*   In every thing wherein they got most praise.*
In bountie Porcia *she shall much exceede,*   25
*   In wisedome passe* Cornelia Pompeies *wife,*
In honour Livia, *so have her stars decreed,*
*   And chaste* Sulpitia *in modestie of life:*
*   Her beautie and the vertues in her brest,*
*   Eugeria staines, and conquers all the rest.*   30

This is the Thought *that honours my desire,*
*   This is my* Parnasse *and* Aonian *spring,*
This is the Muse *that gives me holy fire,*
*   This is the* Phœnix *with her golden wing,*
*   This is the star, and power of such might,*
*   That gives me glorie, spirit, plume and light.*

Petrarke *had left his* Laura *all alone,*
  Folchet Aldagias *praise with loftie stile,*
Guilliaum *the* Countesse *of* Rossiglion,
  Raymbald *his Lady* Morie Verdefueille,
    To grace his verse, he would besides refuse   5
    The Countesse *of* Urgiel *for his Muse.*

Anacreon Euripile *defied*
  And Americ, Gentile, *Gascoignes light:*
Raymbald *the Lord of* Vacchieres *denied*
  Of Monferrato Beatrice *to delight*   10
    With sweetest verse to win her noble grace
    Sister unto the Marquis Boniface.
Arnoldo Daniel *had as much repented*
  Bovilles *praise his Lady long agon,*
Bernard *had never with his verse contented*   15
  The faire Vicountesse *of* Ventideon.
    (*Though these were Dames of beautie and renowne,*
    Gracing each Poet with a Laurell crowne.)

If they had seene this Lady in their time,
  Who all their giftes and beauties doth possesse,   20
They had strain'd foorth invention, verse, and rime,
  To celebrate so high a Patronesse.
    On her their thoughts and pens they had imployed,
    Happy so rare a Muse to have enjoyed.
This did Orpheus *sing with sweetest verse,*   25
  And Eccho *answered to his silver voice,*
And every time he did the same rehearse,
  The land and sea did presently rejoice
    To heare the joyfull newes of such an one,
    By whom their honour should be so much knowne.   30

Now then from this day foorth and evermore
  Let wicked men their false opinions leave,
And though there were not (*as there is*) *such store*
  Of woorthy Dames (*as vainly they conceive*)
    This onely one with honour shall recall,   35
    And amplifie the glorie of us all.

The praise and defence of women, and the brave grace and
sweet note wherewith *Belisa* sung it, pleased and delighted them
all passing well. Wherefore *Don Felix* acknowledging himselfe
overcommed, *Belisa* was well content, and *Arsileus* her husband
not a little proude. All the men there confessed all to be true that 5
was said in the song, and sung in the favour of women; and
all that to be false that was said and sung in the dispraise and
disgrace of men, and especially those verses which injuriously
invayed against their falshood, deceits, and dissembled paines
in love; with affirmation rather of their firmer faith and truer 10
torments, then they outwardly expressed. That which most of all
pleased *Arsileus*, was the answere of *Florisia* to *Melibeus*, bicause it
was no lesse pithie then pleasant; and also bicause he had sometimes heard *Belisa* sing a song upon that matter which delighted
him very much. Wherefore he praied her to rejoice so noble and 15
merie companie as that was, by singing it once againe. Who,
bicause she could not denie her deere *Arsileus*, although she was
somewhat wearie with her last song, to the same tune did sing it:
and this it was.

> *P**Oore** Melibee of love and hope forgot,*   20
> *Told to Florisia greefes that he had past,*
> *She answered him: I understand thee not,*
>   *And lesse beleeve thee (Shepherd) what thou saiest.*
>
> *He saith: My peerelesse Shepherdesse,*
>   *Behold the paine wherewith I die,*   25
> *Which I endure with willingnesse,*
>   *And seeke that greefe, which I would flie:*
> *My hot desires doe burne and die I wot,*
>   *Hope is my life, but feare the same doth waste:*
> *She answered him: I understand thee not,*   30
>   *And lesse beleeve thee (Shepherd) what thou saiest.*
>
> *He saith: The pale and pinching care*
>   *Hath beene so pleasant to my minde,*
> *That how much more fals to my share,*
>   *The more I doe desire to finde:*   35

8 injuriously *Ed.*] inluriously *Y.*

I crave no guerdon for my painefull lot,
But as I love, to be belov'd as fast:
She answered him: I understand thee not,
And lesse beleeve thee (Shepherd) what thou saiest.

He saith: My death should now redresse   5
My paines, but for the greevous ill
Which I should feele (faire Shepherdesse)
In leaving of to see thee still:
But if I see thee sad, a harder knot
Of greefes I feele, and greater death doe tast: 10
She answered him: I understand thee not,
And lesse beleeve thee (Shepherd) what thou saiest.

He saith: In seeing thee I die,
And when I see thee not, I paine,
In seeking thee, for feare I flie,   15
I have to finde thee out againe.
As old Proteus *was woont to change his cote,*
Figure, and shape which long time did not last:
She answered him: I understand thee not,
And lesse beleeve thee (Shepherd) what thou saiest.   20

He saith: I doe pretend to crave
No more good then my soule can get:
Bicause with that small hope I have,
(Me thinkes) I doe offend thee yet.
For suffring for thy sake the smallest jot   25
Of wounding greefe a thousand joies I tast:
She answered him: I understand thee not,
And lesse beleeve thee (Shepherd) what thou saiest.

Whilest *Belisa* was singing both her songs, *Felicia* commaunded a Nymphe to oversee and set in order a gallant sport and pastime, 30 which was prepared before, and which should presently insue, which she so well executed, that even then, when the Shepherdesse had ended her song, they heard a great noise and hurly burly in the river hard by, as it were the beating of oares in the water. Whereupon all of them went towards it, and being come to the 35 river side, they saw twelve little ships comming in two severall navies from the river beneath, bravely depainted with divers

colours, and verie richly set forth. Sixe of them bore sailes of
white and crimosin damaske, and their displayed flags in the tops,
and streamers in their poupes of the same colours : And the other
sixe, their sailes, flagges, and streamers of murrey sattin with
yellow shrouds and tackling to the same. Their oares were 5
bravely gilt all over; and they came decked, strowed, and adorned
with many sweete flowers, and garlands of Roses. In everie one
of them were sixe Nymphes apeece, apparelled with short moresco
gownes : they of the one fleete with crimosin velvet laid on with
silver lace and fringe; and they of the other, of murrey velvet 10
embrodered with curious workemanship of gold, having on their
armes a sleeve of golde and silver made fit unto them, and carrying their targets on their armes after the manner of the valiant
Amazones. They that rowed these fine ships, were certaine
Savages, crowned with garlands of Roses, and bound to their 15
seats with chaines of silver. There arose amongst them a great
noise of drums, trumpets, shagbotes, cornets, and of many other
sorts of musicke; at sound of which two and two togither with
a marvellous sweete concent keeping just time and measure,
entered into the river, which caused great woonder in them that 20
looked on. After this they parted themselves into two navies, and
out of both of them one ship apeece of defiance and answere
came out, the rest remayning beholders on either side. In each of
these two ships came a Savage apparelled with the colours of his
owne side, standing bolt upright in the forecastle, carrying on his 25
left arme a shield, which covered him from top to toe, and in his
right hand a launce, painted with the selfe same colours. They
both at one time hoysted saile, and with force of oares ran one
against the other with great furie. The Nymphes and Savages,
and they that favoured each partie, made great shootes and cries 30
to encourage their sides. They that rowed, emploied all their
force, the one side and the other striving to saile with greater
violence, and to make the stronger encounter. And the Savages
being welny met togither, and armed with their targets and
launces, it was the greatest delight in the world to see how they 35
were encouraged to this encounter, and how they sped in it:
For they stoode not so surely, nor had not so great dexteritie in
their fight, but that with the great violence that the ships met one
another, and with the pushes that they gave with their launces

14 fine *Ed.*] five *Y.*

upon their targets, they were not able to stande on their feete, sometimes falling downe upon the hatches, and sometimes into the river. Wherewith the laughter of them on the shoare encreased, and the rejoycing and triumphes of them, whose side had done best, and the musicke to encourage them on both sides. 5 The justers, when they fell into the water, went swimming up and downe, untill being helped by the Nymphes on whose side they fought, they made a fresh encounter, and falling into the water againe, redoubled the laughing of the beholders, and the sport with exceeding glee and meriment. In the end the ship with white 10 and crimosin sailes came on so fast, and with such force, and her champion so steadie in his place, that he stoode still on foote, bearing downe his adversarie before him into the river. Which when the Nymphes of his squadron perceived, made such triumphe, with hallowing, and ringing such a strange peale of musicke, that 15 the other side was halfe abashed, and dasht from any farther enterprise: But especially one proude and stoute Savage amongst the rest, who, being somwhat ashamed and angrie at their foile, said. Is it possible that there is any in our company of so small courage and strength, that is not able to abide so feeble and light 20 blowes? Unlocke this chaine from my legs, and let him that hath prooved himselfe so weake a juster, row in my place, and you shall see how I will make you conquerours, and confound our enemies in their owne foolish triumph. He had no sooner saide the word, but delivered from his chaine by a Nymphe, with 25 a brave courage he tooke his launce and target, and manfully stood upright in the prow of the ship. Then the Savages with valiant mindes began to row on both sides, and the Nymphes to make loude voices in the aire. The contrarie ship came with the same force as before, but her Savage had little need to set his 30 staffe in rest to get the victorie; for the champion that had braved it so much, before they met, with the great force and haste that the ship carryed him, could not possibly keepe himselfe on foote, but that with shield and speare he fell into the water, giving a manifest and cleere example, *That the proudest and most pre-* 35 *sumptuous fall most often into greatest disgraces.* The Nymphes tooke him up againe (who went swimming up and downe) although he little deserved it: But the five other ships spoken of before, remaining aside by themselves, seeing their captaine overcommed, what with choler, shame, and desire to regaine the victorie, and 40

their lost honours, came all rushing out at once. The other five
of white and crimosin did the like, and then the Nymphes
bestirred them in throwing perfumed pellets and muskebals of
white and red waxe, and painted egshels full of orange and rose
water, making such a shrill shoute, and fighting with so good 5
order and valour, that there they bravely figured a ship yeelding
it selfe, as if it had beene so in good earnest. At the end whereof
the ships with the murrey colours shewed themselves overcommed with striking saile, and yeelded to the other Nymphes,
who like valiant conquerours leaped into them by and by, and 10
then with the same musicke as before, came to the river banks,
where they disimbarked the conquerours, and those that were
vanquished, with the Savages their captives, making a goodly
shew with their severall and singular beauties. When this sport
was finished, *Felicia* with *Eugerius*, and the other companie fol- 15
lowing them, went backe againe to the fountaine, where they
were no sooner come, but they found a Shepherd, that during all
the time of the fight by water, had beene in the orchard, and had
sitten neere unto the fountaine. He seemed verie comely and
gracious in all their eies, but especially in *Felicias*, who knew him 20
incontinently, and said thus unto him.

Though couldest not have come at a better time (*Turianus*) for
remedie of thy greefes, and for encrease of this solace and sport.
We will hereafter take care for thy greefe, and helpe it at fitter
time, as for the rest, thou must shew this goodly companie, how 25
much thou canst delight with thy sweete singing. For now I see
thee with thy Rebecke out of thy scrip, as though thou wouldest
please this faire companie, sing something of thy *Elvinia*; for thou
shalt for this service see thy selfe hereafter well satisfied and
contented. The Shepherd was amazed to heare *Felicia* call him 30
by his name, and the Shepherdesse his love by hers, and that
she promised him some lightning of his paine: Wherefore meaning to requite such offers with rather obeying her commaund,
then onely with simple thankes to gratifie them, all of them being
set, and keeping silence, he began to play a while on his Rebecke, 35
and to sing that which followeth.

Provençall Rythmes.

*W*Hen that with thousand parti-coloured flowers
  The springtide comes in everie pleasant mead,
And glorious Titan, *free from winters showers,*
  With golden beames the fields doth overspread,   5
The Shepherds rich, and frollicke in their bowers,
  With pipes and songs their flockes to fields do lead:
    The nightingall with warbling throte
    Doth jug forth many a pleasant note,
      that makes the woods to ring: 10
    The fountaines cleere, as Christall glasse,
    About the which, upon the grasse
      The Nymphes do sit and sing:
But let Elvinia *turne her eies from all those sweete delights,*
Then doth continuall winter rage with stormy daies and nights.   15

When that the freezing Northren windes disgrace
  The fragrant flowers, the stately trees and tall
Of all their pride, and covereth every place
  With flakes of snow, which never cease to fall:
And nightingals their songs leave for a space,   20
  And desert fieldes, that have no greene at all:
    The daies are yrkesome short, and sad,
    The cold nights blow, as they were mad,
      With many a bitter blast:
    The cloudes as darke as any pitch,   25
    And thicke as lothsome mud in ditch,
      The aire do overcast:
But let Elvinia *walke the fields or where it please her best,*
There merie springtide doth returne her praises to protest.

If that the angrie heavens sometimes throw downe   30
  A fearfull lightning, or some cruell thunder,
The silly Shepherd, far from wood or towne,
  Begins to feare, to tremble and to wonder,
And if the hayle fall thicke upon the ground
  Like little stones, do beat and burst asunder   35
    The fruit, and leaves in everie place,
    And spoiles the flowers of their grace,

A strange, and pitious sight:
The Shepherd runs away amaine,
Leaving his sheepe upon the plaine
With swift and fearfull flight:
But let Elvinia *walke the fields her beautie everie where*   5
Doth cleere the heavens, and rids the Shepherds hart from trembling feare.

And if by chaunce I sing or pipe on hie,
  Under the shade of Elme or little hill,
The Song thrush and the heavenly Larke replie
  Unto my songs, with sweetest notes at will: 10
And when the fresh and Western windes in skie
  Breath forth an aire, so pleasant and so still:
    When everie joy, and sweete content,
    And everie day in pleasures spent
      Doth give me new delights,   15
    And free from feare with lively cheere
    In happines I spend the yeere,
      The pleasant daies and nights:
But if Elvinia *once do frowne, I am much more afraide*
Then if a burning lightning had my sences all dismaide.   20

If that Diana *goeth forth to chace*
  The savage beastes, with bended bow to tame,
With troups of Nymphes *that waite upon her grace*
  Whose thoughts chaste sports and exercise do frame:
And with the same with great delight do trace   25
  The woods and lawnes in seeking out some game,
    Hamadriades *and* Napees *faire*
    With strowing Roses, do prepare
      The way before their Queene:
    The Nymphes *that follow sweetly sing,*   30
    And hils and dales with triumphes ring,
      And woods both fresh and greene:
But if she come unto the wood, where my Elvinia *chaceth*
She makes her silent, quailes her pride, and beauties all disgraceth.

26 *game, Ed.] game.* Y.

And when her bodie whiter then the snow
She washeth in the fountaine christall bright,
If thither Cynthia *should but chaunce to goe,*
And see those parts so daintie and so white,
For shame she would cast downe her eies I know, 5
And so depart, confounded at that sight:
For in those fountaine waters cleere
So brave a figure doth appeere,
As like was never seene:
So faire a face, such golden haire 10
With rarest grace are shining there
As like hath never beene:
And bold Acteon *if he did but see her there alone,*
Had not beene turn'd into a Hart, but to a Marble stone.

A thousand times my song I will reply thee, 15
In everie place where I doe feed my sheepe,
But hence away, for pitie now go hie thee
Unto my Love, and tell her how I weepe.
See if thou canst but moove her hart
To some small pitie of my smart, 20
And of my little rest:
Go to my faire and fatall star,
Tell her what wounding thoughts do war
Within my painfull brest.
O happie man if that thou mightest this grace of Fortune trie, 25
To see Elvinia *change her minde, or else thy selfe to die.*

How much the sweete voice and gentle grace of this enamoured
Shepherd pleased them all, I am not able to expresse, whose song
was so melodious, and personage so faire and comely, that he
seemed to be *Apollo,* who had sometimes taken upon him a Shep- 30
herds shape for the love of a countrey wench, for they could not
judge any more like unto him for perfection in beauty, and
sweetnes in song: whereupon *Montanus* marvelling much, said.
Elvinia (gentle Shepherd) is not a little beholding to thee, of whom
thou haste so sweetely sung, not onely for the favour she hath 35
got, to be beloved of so gracious a Shepherd as thy selfe; but by
having her beauties, and virtues with thy delicate comparisons

13 *see her there* Ed.] *see there* Y.

and daintie verses so highly commended. And she being beloved
of thee, it cannot be otherwise imagined, but that her perfections
of bodie and vertues of minde are most rare and excellent. And
that which doth not a little helpe to the accomplishment of her
gifts, is the delight and dexteritie that she hath in hunting, for 5
which thou didst compare her with *Diana*; bicause it is one of the
brave qualities which make both Nymphes and Shepherdesses
to be thought more beautifull and gracious, and most worthie of
golden praises: For I my selfe did sometime know a Shepherd in
our towne, and my *Ismenia* and *Selvagia* knew him also verie well; 10
who being enamoured of a Shepherdesse (called *Argia*) was with
none of her passing graces more captivated, then with her singular
cunning in shooting and delight that she had in her bowe, which
was continually in her hande, and her quiver of steely headed
arrowes at her backe, wherewith shee hunted, wounded, and 15
killed, the nymble footed Does, wilde beastes, and simple birdes.
For which delight her loving Shepherd (named *Olympius*) did
sometimes sing a pretie Sonnet, made of the skill, beautie, and
cruelty of that Shepherdesse, fayning a challenge and contention
betweene her, the Goddesse *Diana* and *Cupid*, whether of them 20
three should shoote best, a fine and delicate conceit, which sometimes to delight me, I ever have by hart. With this *Clenarda* stept
foorth and said. It is reason *Montanus* that we enjoy part of that
delight with thee in hearing it: And nothing can please me better,
then to heare thee sing it for the great love and devotion that 25
I have to that exercise. I am content (said *Montanus*) if I shall not
seeme troublesome with it. That cannot cause any trouble
(saide *Polydorus*) which with so generall delight shall be heard.
Montanus then playing on his pipe sung *Olympius* Sonnet, which
was this.   30

> Diana, Love, *and my faire* Shepherdesse,
>   *Did in the field their chiefest cunning trie,*
>   *By shooting arrowes at a tree neere by,*
> *Whose barke a painted hart did there expresse:*
> Diana *stakes her beautie mercilesse,*   35
>   Cupid *his bowe,* Argia *her libertie:*
>   *Who shewed in her shot a quicker eie,*
> *A better grace, more courage, and successe:*

And so did she Dianas *beautie win,*
  And Cupids *weapons, by which conquer'd prize*
So faire and cruell she hath ever bin,
  That her sweete figure from my wearied eies,
    And from my painfull hart her cruell bowe   5
  Have stolne my life and freedome long agoe.

This Sonnet was marvellous delightfull to them all, and the
sweetnes, wherwith *Montanus* sung it, a great deale more. And
after they had discoursed of every particular part and matter of
it, *Felicia* seeing the night came on, and thinking she had feasted 10
and sported her guests that day sufficiently, made a signe by her
countenance, that she would say something; whereupon they
left of their mirth and talke for a while, and with attentive mindes
harkened unto her : and silence being kept, with her accustomed
gravitie, she thus began to speake.   15
I am undoubtedly perswaded (noble Lordes and Ladies, and
you worthy Shepherds) that, since the time that you came to my
house, you have no cause to complaine of my favours bestowed
on you, nor of the diligence and service of my Nymphes employed
for your sakes. For the desire which I had to please you all, was 20
so great, and the delight which I take to helpe distressed men to
their contentment, so proper to my nature, that (me thinks) if
I had done a great deale more for you, it had bin but little in
respect of that which your virtues deserve. Onely *Narcisus* with
the crueltie of *Melisea*, and *Turianus* with the disdaine of *Elvinia*, 25
remaine discontent amongst you all. Whom it shall now satisfie
to comfort themselves with hope of their future felicities, since
that my word (which was never stained with deceit and lye) hath
assuredly promised them a speedie and full contentment by those
meanes which shall be most expedient for them. I see old *Eugerius* 30
glad with his sonne, his daughters, and his sonne in law, and not
without cause, since for love of them he hath passed so many
dangers, and suffered such extreme paine, sorrow, and anguish
of minde. *Felicia* having ended her speech, *Eugerius* wondered
greatly at her wisedome, and the rest were satisfied and well con- 35
tent with so gentle and courteous instructions, wherby they
gathered out of them profitable lessons to lead from thence forth
a virtuous and happie life. And so all of them rising from their

30 *Eugerius* Ed.] *Engerius* Y.

places about the fountaine, and following the sage Ladie, went out of the garden into the Palace, everie one to their severall lodgings, accommodating their mindes to the joyfull feasts and princely sports of the next day following: The which, and that which happened to *Narcisus*, *Turianus*, *Taurisus*, and *Berardus*, with the delectable historie of *Danteus*, and *Duarda* the *Portugale* Shepherds (which for certaine respects is omitted heere) and many other things of great delight, pleasure, and profit, are handled in the second Part of this Booke.

All these three Partes were finished the first of May 1583.   10
Boto el amor en Yugo.

APPENDIX

The Spanish texts of Montemayor and Gil Polo used by Yong

IN trying to determine which editions of the Spanish Yong used for his translations, it is necessary to deal with Montemayor and Gil Polo separately, for Yong tells us himself in his preface that Banister gave him at first only 'the first and second part of *Diana* of *Montemayor* in Spanish',[1] and we are left to understand that he procured a copy of Gil Polo at a slightly later date.

Estrada lists twenty-one editions of Montemayor before 1582, the closing date for candidates, but we may ignore the first six of these, since it is not until the seventh, Valladolid, 1561, that the story of Abyndaraez is inserted into Book IV. Although all subsequent editions perpetuate this alteration, only two, according to Estrada, are direct descendants of Valladolid, 1561: Antwerp, Pedro Bellero, 1575 and Antwerp, Pedro Bellero, 1580.

In preparing his edition of Barcelona, 1561, Estrada has supplied the following omissions and better readings from Valladolid, 1561:

1. Barcelona lacks a leaf (Estrada, p. 14, l. 24–p. 16, l. 22).
2. Estrada, p. 18, l. 27 medio: Valladolid miedo.
3.   ,,   p. 31, l. 16 omitted: supplied from Valladolid.
4.   ,,   p. 49, l. 8 otra: Valladolid aora.
5.   ,,   p. 94, l. 3 Polydora: ,,   Dorida.
6.   ,,   p. 95, l. 1 Dandalia: ,,   Vandalia.
7.   ,,   p. 203, l. 21 end Book IV: ,,   Abyndaraez story.

He also notes, at p. 291, l. 10, but without emending his text, the more likely reading of 'clara' for 'cara'.

Since in each of these points Yong's translation follows the text of Valladolid, 1561, it seemed advisable to check his translation with the direct descendants of this edition. In doing this, I noted the following points in which his translation follows the text of Antwerp, 1575 against Estrada's edition of Barcelona, 1561:

1. Estrada, p. 12, l. 24 —¡ y que cabellos! —:   Ant. 75 omits.
2.   ,,   p. 18, l. 28 imaginación: ,,   ignorancia.
3.   ,,   p. 40, l. 19 cosas: ,,   casas.

[1] See above, p. 5.

4.	Estrada,	p. 66, l. 6 bolviesse a aquella:	Ant. 75	bolviesse, o aquella.
5.	„	p. 72, l. 23 Hermana Cinthia:	„	Cinthia.
6.	„	p. 120, l. 1 amor:	„	amo.
7.	„	p. 201, l. 10 aficiones:	„	affliciones.
8.	„	p. 230, l. 25 obligación:	„	condicion.
9.	„	p. 271, l. 12	„	omits.
10.	„	p. 287, ll. 20–21 Monte moro vello:	„	Montemor o velho.

Antwerp, 1580 agrees with Antwerp, 1575 in all these readings except the sixth, where Antwerp, 1580 reads 'amor' (but there may be differences between copies). The Antwerp editions also follow the readings given above of Valladolid, 1561 against Barcelona, 1561.

On this textual evidence one may venture the conjecture that Yong used one of the editions of Valladolid, 1561, Antwerp, 1575, or Antwerp, 1580. It is, however, possible to carry conjecture further by other means. Since Yong was handed Montemayor and Perez together, it is reasonable to look for an edition of Montemayor that is bound with or produced with one of Perez. Valladolid, 1561 is obviously impossible, since Perez's *Diana* was not published till 1564. Estrada notes that one sometimes finds bound with the Antwerp, 1575 a copy of Gil Polo, Antwerp, Gil Stelsio, 1574 (although this is not the case with the British Museum's copy of Antwerp, 1575), but mentions no edition of Perez in connexion with the Antwerp, 1575 and 1580 editions of Montemayor. He does, however, list an edition of Montemayor at Antwerp, 1581, which he has not seen himself, but has drawn from A. Palau y Dulcet, *Manual del Librero Hispano-Americano*, Barcelona, 1926. He suggests that this may be a reimpression of the Antwerp, 1580 edition. He may be right, but both the British Museum and the Bodleian own, as sets, copies of Montemayor, Antwerp, Pedro Bellero, 1580 together with Perez, Antwerp, Pedro Bellero, 1581. The Bodleian's pair (Art. 8°, M. 13, 14) is bound in old leather, with the same ornament stamped on each cover, and has been in the library's possession since before the publication of the 1605 catalogue. I was not, however, able to find any mention of it in the Benefactors' Register, so cannot prove provenance. The British Museum set (12490. a. 5) was acquired in May, 1871, and the Deputy Keeper informs me that the name 'Bourdonnieres' in a seventeenth-century hand is on the first paste-down. Possibly this set spent the earlier part of its life in France rather than England.

The coupling of the Antwerp, 1580 with an edition of Perez, the evidence that copies of this set were to be found in England at a very early date, and the probability that Banister, in 1582, would have offered Yong a recently acquired (and so, perhaps, recently published) book, all lead to the conclusion that Yong most probably used the Antwerp, 1580, 1581 set, printed by Pedro Bellero, for his translation of Montemayor and Perez.

Ferreres lists five editions of Gil Polo before 1583: Barcelona, 1564 (the copy text of his edition); Antwerp, 1567; Antwerp, 1574; Saragossa, 1577; Pamplona, 1578. Yong obviously did not use Barcelona, 1564, since it contains the long portion of Felicia's speech at the end of Book V, which Yong has omitted. Antwerp, 1567, Antwerp, 1574, and Saragossa, 1577 all omit this passage, and furthermore agree with Yong against Barcelona, 1564 in reading 'presencia' rather than 'preferencia'[1] and in omitting two quintains of *Florisias Song*.[2] However, all three editions contain the dedication to Doña Hieronyma de Castro y Bolea, and the four prefatory sonnets which Yong has omitted, although they do, like Yong, omit the 'Epistola a los lectores'. The most satisfactory way of determining which edition of Gil Polo Yong used would be to find a copy dedicated to Doña Maria de Austria,[3] instead of to Doña Hieronyma de Castro y Bolea, but this I have not yet succeeded in doing. I am tempted to suspect that there may have been a variant issue of one of the two Antwerp editions, because it seems more likely, first, that one of these would contain the alternative dedication, and second, that Englishmen in the 1570s and 1580s would be buying books from the Low Countries rather than from Spain.

[1] See above, p. 293, l. 30, and note.
[2] See note to p. 404, ll. 18–19.
[3] See above, p. 243, ll. 4–6, and note.

COMMENTARY

3. 1–3. *To . . . Lady Rich.* Sidney's Stella, Penelope Devereux (*c.* 1562–1607) married Lord Rich in 1581.

16. *Collin.* Nicolas Colin's translation of Montemayor's *Diana*, the first of the French translations, was first published at Rheims in 1578, at Antwerp in the same year, and several times thereafter (see Estrada, pp. xcvii–xcviii). See also **6.** 24–29, and note.

29. *deducted.* See *OED* Deduct *v.*† 7. To reduce. *Obs.*

5. 3–4. *About . . . countrey.* See above pp. lx–lxi.

9. *Edward Banister.* See above pp. lxi–lxii.

21. *discurring.* To run over or through. Yong is the only user of the word in this sense recorded in the *OED*.

22. *recordation.* A commemorative account. The *OED* records Yong as the first user.

6. 24–29. *Having compared . . . imitated.* According to Estrada, there are four editions of Colin's translation of Montemayor published together with Gabriel Chapuis's translations of Perez and Gil Polo: Tours, 1582; Paris, 1587; Tours, 1592 twice. Yong's estimate of their merits is just, but it is unlikely that he used even Colin as an aid to his own translation, since Colin most often agrees with the text which Estrada gives, where Yong departs from it.

30. *Edward Paston.* Possibly the grandson of Sir William Paston (1528–1610), the founder of North Walsham grammar school, but perhaps one of the Pastons of Appleton, from which family came the Edward Paston who was president of Douay College from 1688 to 1714.

8. 2–4. *To the . . . Quesa.* A Valencian lord, the son of Don Luis de Vilanova and Doña Juana Carroz, with lands in the province of León (see Estrada, p. xxi; Báez, p. 5).

21. *ampare.* Defence, protection, guard. The *OED* cites Yong as the only user of this word, taken directly from Spanish 'amparo'.

27 ff. *Maecenas, etc.* One stanza of *ottava rima* in both English and Spanish.

9. 1. *Don Gaspar Romani.* A Valencian poet, very little of whose work is known (see Báez, p. 7).

2 ff. *If Lady, etc.* Petrarchian sonnet. Sestet in Spanish cdedce, in English cdecde. Note the feminine rhymes of Yong's sestet, a type of rhyme he uses frequently, probably under the influence of the Spanish.

16. *Don Hieronymo Sant-Perez*. The Valencian poet who also contributed a laudatory sonnet (not translated by Yong) to Gil Polo's *Diana Enamorada*, and is extolled by Gil Polo in 'The Song of Turia' (see 348. 25, and note).

18 ff. *Parnasse, etc.* Shakespearian sonnet. In Spanish, Petrarchian.

24. *this Hill, whose Greatnes*. The pun on Montemayor's name is obscured in English (cf. Estrada, p. 5, l. 10).

11. 13. *rebecke* 'rabel' (Estrada, p. 9, l. 24). A primitive stringed instrument, the parent of the viol and violin, identical with the English 'fiddle'. After the invention of instruments of the viol and violin type it was banished to the streets of towns and to rustic festivities (Grove, vii. 69–70).

14. *scrip*. A small bag, wallet, or satchel, *esp*. one carried by a pilgrim, a shepherd, or a beggar (*archaic*). *OED*.

bagpipe 'çampoña' (Estrada, p. 10, l. 1). Minsheu glosses 'çampoña' as '*a bagpipe, an oten-pipe. Also a bell hanged about sheepe or gotes, a lowbell*'. For a Bagpipe, he says '*vide* çampóña, Cornamúsa, Gáita, Gáyta'. See Grove, i. 344–54 and plate. An instrument, in one or other of its forms, of widespread diffusion and very great antiquity. Its use was not restricted to rustic and popular music. Nero is said to have played one, Henry VIII owned one, and in medieval art bagpipers range from grotesque animals to angels.

19–21. *neither did . . . quiet rest*. Estrada sees in this comment a reference to Castiglione (Estrada, p. 10, note).

12. 9. *corsies* (= corrosive, *sb*.). Used figuratively to mean a cause of trouble and grief.

29–30. *memorie, how sure*. Yong omits 'destruydora de mi descanso' (cf. Estrada, p. 12, l. 16).

36. *haire tyed*. Yong omits '— ¡ y que cabellos! — '(cf. Estrada, p. 12, l. 24). This interjection is not found in the Antwerp, 1580 edition of the Spanish text.

13. 1. ff. *HAire in change, etc.* Yong keeps the Spanish form of the quatrain, abba, and uses a regular 7-syllabled trochaic metre.

This poem has also been translated by Sidney (whose version appears in *Englands Helicon*), by Thomas Wilson, and by Robert Southey in *Letters written during a short residence in Spain . . .* (Bristol, 1797). All three use the more common English quatrain abab, and a basically iambic metre. Wilson uses a clumpingly regular 6-syllabled line; Southey uses a 10-syllabled, heavily stressed line which considerably slows the movement of the poem. Sidney, whose version is by far the best of the four, lengthens the third line of each quatrain, a⁶b⁶a⁸b⁶, thus staving off monotony without doing violence to the light, swift movement of the poem.

1. *HAire in change what libertie*. Yong is speaking of the licence of change, of mutability.

13. 28. *In a love, etc.* Yong omits a quatrain after this line. Sidney translates

> Ah haire are you not griev'd,
> To come from whence you be,
> Seeing how once you saw I liv'd,
> To see me as you see?

32. The portrait of Donne which is the frontispiece to the 1635 edition of his poems quotes the Spanish of this line 'Antes muerto que mudado' as the motto on the crest.

33-36. Echoed by Byron in 'To Woman':

> This record will for ever stand,
> 'Woman, thy vows are trac'd in sand.'

14. 9-11. *O letter, . . . doe it?* Yong's translation is at fault. Freely rendered, the passage means that Syrenus would like to see the letter burnt, but somebody else would have to do it, since his free will is enslaved by love: he will be made miserable by reading the letter, but it is impossible for him to refrain from doing so. '— Ay, ¡carta, carta, abrasada te vea, por mano de quien mejor lo pueda hazer que yo, pues jamás en cosa mía pude hazer lo que quisiesse! ¡Malaya quien aora to leyere! Mas ¿quién podrá dexar de hazello?' (Estrada, p. 14, ll. 20-23).

38. *seven folde paine* 'las setenas' (Estrada, p. 15, l. 23), which Minsheu glosses '*the seaventh, seaven fold, a kind of fine or forfeyture imposed on men for breach of the kings prerogative of lawes, &c.*' Estrada says more specifically that it is a punishment for theft (Estrada, p. 15, note).

15. 24 ff. *I Am a lover, etc.* Yong has changed the *ottava rima* of the Spanish to the less demanding rhyme scheme ababccdd. There is a somewhat similar anatomy of love in the 'sonetto', 'What thing is Love?', in Greene's *Menaphon* (ed. G. B. Harrison, p. 104).

16. 25-28. *Love's not a thing.* The repetition is Yong's own.

17. 10. *ignorance.* Yong follows the text of Antwerp, 1580 'qualquiera ignorancia' (A9ʳ). Estrada (p. 18, l. 28) and Báez read 'imaginación'. Wilson gives 'imagination', Colin 'imagination'.

34. *loving thee.* Yong's translation makes sense, but Estrada (p. 19, l. 21) reads 'quererla', loving her.

18. 12. *novelties . . . conceites.* Estrada sees in this a possible allusion to Portuguese and Spanish discoveries in Asia and America (Estrada, p. 20, note).

19. 21 ff. *FOr a favour, etc.* Yong exactly follows the Spanish form of alternate quatrains and quintains. Sidney's translation 'Of this high grace with blisse conjoyn'd' (which is considerably closer to being poetry) keeps the quintain but alters the quatrain to abab.

27. *Face and eies, where Cupid stands* 'rostro y ojos soberanos' (Estrada, p. 22, l. 11). Cf. Sidney, 'In face and eyes unmatched being.'

21. 9 ff. *O Eies, etc.* Yong follows the stanza form of the Spanish with one minor variation: Yong: ABCABCCddEeFfGG
Spanish: ABCBACCddEeFfGG

34. *hap sway.* In support of the emendation, cf. 69. 29.

25. 20. *such store of peregrine beautie* 'tan gran hermosura' (Estrada, p. 29, l. 26), but cf. **146.** 25 where '*That matchlesse beautie sweete and peregrine*' translates 'Aquella hermosura peregrina' (Estrada, p. 183, l. 1). In both cases 'peregrine' means extraordinary or rare, senses not recorded in the *OED*. However, Covarrubias's *Tesoro de la Lengua Castellana* (1611) gives 'Cosa peregrina, cosa rara' (ed. Martín de Riquer, Barcelona, 1943, p. 863 a).

35. *Kit* 'rabel' (Estrada, p. 30, l. 13). Grove defines kit as 'a tiny violin', formerly carried by dancing-masters in their pockets, but notes 'In Florio (1598 and 1611), Beaumont and Fletcher, Ben Jonson, and Drayton, it seems evident that it is used without reference to size as a synonym for "crwth", "rebeck" or "pandora" ' (iv. 769–70).

26. 2 ff. *S Yrenus, what thought'st thou, etc.* The best that can be said for this poem is that one admires Yong's courage in attempting exactly to imitate the *tercetos esdrujolos* of the Spanish. Wilson attempts the same feat with no greater success. Sidney is more successful in his original *tercetos esdrujolos*, 'Dorus, tell me, where is thy wonted motion?' (*Arcadia*, Book II, ed. A. Feuillerat, i. 340).

16. *aboording.* Abord. To approach, come close to.

23. *rebounding.* Apparently either 'recoiling' or 'setting boundaries to', senses not recorded in the *OED*. Yong's 'rebounding them' and 'restraining them' are both drawn from 'rebolviéndose', cf. Estrada, p. 31, ll. 13–15:

> Mis tristes pensamientos muy solícitos
> de una parte a otra, rebolviéndose
> huyendo a toda costa el ser ilícitos.

27. *repell.* Apparently 'violently refuse', a sense not quite covered by any of the *OED* definitions of the word. Yong's translation and constructions in this poem are very strained.

29. *refell*, reject.

27. 2. *entendereth.* To make tender; to melt (the heart). First use recorded in the *OED* by Southwell in 1594.

14. *incended.* The *OED* defines incend as 'to set on fire' (first example 1597), or 'to heat, inflame (the body or its organs)' (first example 1533). The *OED* gives no quotation close to Yong's use of the word to describe the action of blushing.

28. *estraied*, strayed.

29. 2. (*if so . . . it*). Yong's insertion (cf. Estrada, p. 35, ll. 11–12).

29. 3. *I durst swear.* In support of the emendation, cf. Estrada, p. 35, l. 12 'yo osaría jurar'. The omission is an understandable error on the part of either Yong or the compositor. Cf. the omission of a word repaired in the 'Faultes escaped' at 92. 11.

11 ff. *MIne eies, etc.* Petrarchian sonnet in both English and Spanish.

31. 33. *pastaunce.* Recreation (pastime). Yong is misquoted in the last example recorded in the *OED*.

32. 37. *There are many houses.* Estrada (p. 40, l. 19) reads 'Ay muchas cosas', but Antwerp, 1580 and Báez both read 'casas'. Wilson gives 'cotages'; Colin 'maisons'.

34. 20. *Ismenia.* Presumably it is this name that led Dunlop to claim 'many of the incidents and names in the work of Eustathius have been transferred to the Spanish pastoral of Montemayor (*History of Prose Fiction*, 1896, i. 82). I can find no other similarity between the two works.

35. 40. *to make . . . laugh.* Yong's expansion (cf. Estrada, p. 44, l. 19 'por reírse conmigo').

36. 24. *onely for merriment.* Yong's insertion (cf. Estrada, p. 45, ll. 9-11).

37. 18-19. *since . . . Idea of fained Alanius* 'porque llevava en la imaginación los ojos del fingido Alanio' (Estrada, p. 46, ll. 10-11). Yong shows in his expanded translation an interestingly precise usage of Idea in the *OED* sense III. 8. a. 'The mental image or picture of something previously seen or known, and recalled by the memory.' The quotations, ranging from 1589 to 1764, are all concerned with the image of a desired person.

31-32. *For there . . . the hart.* The italics are Yong's. Estrada comments upon this passage as an example of Montemayor's psychological acuteness (Estrada, p. 46, note).

38. 36-38. *for as he . . . honour him.* Yong's translation is at fault. The Spanish text says nothing about Alanius's love for Selvagia, nor his beauties and deserts (cf. Estrada, p. 48, ll. 3-4).

41. 32-33. *or in . . . life.* Yong's insertion (cf. Estrada, p. 51, ll. 10-12).

42. 16. *buttals,* bounds or boundaries.

43. 13-14. *and lesse . . . discretion.* Yong's insertion (cf. Estrada, p. 53, ll. 5-6).

33. *Fiddle* 'rabel' (Estrada, p. 53, l. 26). See note to 11. 13. Minsheu gives '*a fiddle, vide* Rabel'.

35 ff. *NO more, etc.* Yong expands the *ottava rima* of the Spanish to 10-line stanzas ababcdcdee. This poem appears in *Englands Helicon*.

38. *dire Hardnes.* Cf. *Englands Helicon*.

44. 18. *before me: Englands Helicon* provides a comma, but the colon is more in keeping with the punctuation of the 1598 edition of *Diana*. Cf. **44.** 20.

45. 8. *adjured.* Bound by oath. (*Obs.*) Yong is the only user of the word in this sense recorded in the *OED*.

29 ff. *HOw fond am I, etc.* Yong has altered the eight short-lined quintains (abbab) of the Spanish to four 10-line stanzas of iambic pentameter with a linked rhyme scheme, ababbcacdd.

47. 1 ff. *FOolish love, etc.* Yong approximates the Spanish rhyme scheme of couplet aa, gloss bccbbaa (Yong: couplet aa, gloss bcbccaa), but considerably alters the metre, which in Spanish consists of 8-syllabled lines except for the sixth line of each stanza, which is 4-syllabled. Yong begins with a regular 8-syllabled couplet, then turns to common measure, but the rhymes of the fifth and sixth lines play against the metre, and the stanza is rounded off with a swinging fourteener (more properly fifteener, with the unstressed syllable at the end).

28 ff. *ALthough my quiet, etc.* Yong exactly follows the demanding rhyme scheme of the Spanish: ababcddcababeffeabab. The metre is iambic tetrameter. The next three poems are of similar form, although the printing of this one as one quatrain and two octaves obscures the likeness.

48. 3–4. *But God . . . jest it be.*

'mas, guárdeos Dios de olvidar
que es ayre ser olvidada'
(Estrada, p. 58, ll. 13–14).

Wilson gives

'Forgetfullness God keepe the fro
For tis a thing most dolorous'
(British Museum Add. MS. 18638, f. 35ᵛ).

49. 12 ff. *SHepherd, who can passe, etc.* Yong follows the Spanish rhyme scheme, except in changing the form of quatrain to abab from abba. The metre is truncated trochaic tetrameter. This poem appears in *Englands Helicon*.

17. *Leesing my affiance.* Losing my confidence.

50. 3 ff. *WEepe not, etc.* Yong follows the Spanish rhyme scheme, except in changing stanzas 1, 3, and 5 to abab from abba. The line length is varied: stanzas 1, 3, and 5 are 6868 syllables; stanza 2, 8888; stanza 4, 6886.

25 ff. *MY life, etc.* Yong follows the Spanish rhyme scheme, except in changing the form of quatrain to abab from abba. Stanzas 1, 3, and 5 are common measure, stanzas 2 and 4 decasyllabic (Yong's use of this form is commended by Saintsbury (*History of English Prosody*, ii. 133–4)). This poem appears in *Englands Helicon*.

51. 30. *knobbing.* Not in the *OED*, but cf. Knab, *v. Obs. exc. dial.* To bite lightly, to nibble (earliest recorded example 1668), and Knub, *v. dial. Obs.* To bite gently, nibble (earliest recorded example 1652).

52. 13–14. *to cloy . . . favours.* Yong's insertion (cf. Estrada, p. 63, l. 26–p. 64, l. 1).

31. *(disloyall Alanius).* Yong's insertion (cf. Estrada, p. 64, ll. 16–17).

53. 7. *Sextine* = sestine. The *OED* records only this usage by Yong before the nineteenth century. Montemayor's three sestinas are each called merely 'canción' (Estrada, p. 64, l. 31, p. 211, l. 34, p. 231, l. 5), but Gil Polo's is headed 'Sextina' (Ferreres, p. 181, l. 8). The earliest use recorded in the *OED* for 'sestine' is 1586 (Sidney's *Arcadia*), and for 'sestina' 1838 (and then mis-spelt).

8 ff. *WAters that fall, etc.* A strict sestina in both English and Spanish: I. 123456, II. 615243, III. 364125, IV. 532614, V. 451362, VI. 246531, Envoy 135 at the middle, 246 at the end of the lines.

54. 4. *O that he . . . Hill.* Cf. Estrada, p. 66, l. 6 '¡o, quien bolviesse a aquella dulce sierra!' Báez also gives this reading, but Antwerp, 1580 reads 'o quien bolviesse, o aquella dulce sierra' (C11).

24 ff. *TO heare me, etc.* Yong has expanded the *ottava rima* of the Spanish to a 10-line stanza ababcdcdee (all double rhymes) by such methods as adding pearle, dymond, and stars to the christall, rubie, and Allablaster of stanza 4. This poem is also translated by Googe (see Introduction, pp. lvi–lvii above).

55. 17. *twistall.* It is tempting to emend to 'twist all', but the forming of a single word to rhyme with 'christall' appears to be intentional.

33. *install.* Apparently a metaphorical usage of the *OED* sense 1.b. To place in any office or position, especially one of dignity or authority (earliest recorded example 1647).

57. 26. ff. *GOe now, etc.* Petrarchian sonnet of the same form in both Spanish and English.

58. 9. *Sylvanus.* Estrada, Báez, Antwerp, 1580, and Colin all read 'Selvagia' (cf. Estrada, p. 71, l. 14).

22. *periwig* 'lazáda' (Estrada, p. 71, l. 31). Yong's use of 'periwig' is misleading, since the Spanish implies merely an ornamental knot of hair, with no suggestion of false hair.

25. *consent.* Concent, Harmony (of sounds); accord or concord of several voices or parts; playing or singing together in harmony. The *OED* gives a separate entry for the 'erroneous' spelling consent. Minsheu gives 'Concénto, *a consent, a consort or concordance in musicke*'.

28. *fancie*, esp. in Music, a composition in an impromptu style (Estrada, p. 72, l. 3 'villancico', which Minsheu glosses 'a song').

29 ff. *COntents of love, etc.* The rhyme scheme in English and Spanish is

similar, but Yong has introduced the refinement of using the same rhyme words for the couplet at the end of the triplet and both stanzas. Yong has considerably altered the regular octosyllabic line of the Spanish: triplet a⁴b⁶b¹⁰, stanza c⁴d⁶c⁶d⁸d⁸b⁶b¹⁰.

59. 9. (*Cynthia*). Báez and Estrada (p. 72, l. 23) read 'Hermana Cinthia', Colin reads 'ma sœur Cinthie', but Antwerp, 1580 reads 'Cinthia' (D2ᵛ).

11. *I* = Ay.

25 and 26. For *Cynthia*, Estrada reads 'Dórida' (p. 73, ll. 12 and 13); 59. 30–31 for *Faire Cynthia* (*answered Polydora*) Estrada reads 'Cinthia le respondió: —Hermosa Dórida' (p. 73, ll. 19–20); 59. 35 for *Cynthia*, Estrada reads 'Dórida (p. 73, l. 23). Báez, Colin, and Antwerp, 1580 agree with Estrada, except that in Antwerp, 1580 on this one page (D3ʳ) Dórida is called Doria.

60. 1 ff. *The song of the Nymph*. Yong has expanded the quintains of the Spanish to 6-line stanzas ababcc, and altered the quatrains of Syrenus's and Diana's songs from abba to abab. The first twelve stanzas appear in *Englands Helicon* under the title 'Cinthia *the Nimph, her Song to faire* Polydora'.

70. 1. *My Master, etc*. Philip II.

35. *to saile is sent* 'a vender' (Estrada, p. 83, l. 28).

71. 24. *That one . . . heere* 'que me viste o que te vi' (Estrada, p. 84, l. 15).

73. 3. *excelse*. Lofty, high; fig. of high rank, character, or quality.

74. 29–30. Yong's addition, making explicit the 'remedie' that Diana found (cf. Estrada, p. 87, ll. 8–12).

31. For *Cynthia*, Estrada reads 'Dórida'; for *Doria*, Estrada reads 'Cinthia' (p. 87, ll. 13–14); 75. 6 for *Cynthia*, Estrada reads 'Dórida' (p. 87, l. 26). Báez, Antwerp, 1580, and Colin all agree with Estrada.

75. 12. *three . . . Savages*. These represent the ugliness and beastliness of unbridled passions, and provide a foil for the many aspects of beauty celebrated in the rest of the romance. (For further comment, see especially J. B. Avalle-Arce, *La novela pastoril española*, Madrid, 1959, pp. 71–75.)

76. 1. *sursault*. This word is common in Yong as a noun (a start, an attack) and as a verb (to attack suddenly). All the examples in the *OED* of sense b. are drawn from Yong. Yong is usually translating Spanish 'sobresalto', glossed by Minsheu as '*a sudden passion*'.

30–31. *and save . . . immanitie*. Yong's insertion (cf. Estrada, p. 89, ll. 20–22).

31. *immanitie*. Monstrous cruelty, atrocious savagery.

80. 30. *Vandalia*. Poetic name for Andalusia.

80. 39. *whose . . . pleased.* Yong's insertion (cf. Estrada, p. 97, ll. 8–11).

81. 33. *Unappassionate.* Uninfluenced by passion, dispassionate. The *OED* records no other example apart from this. See also **223. 6.**

82. 10–12. *or to . . . sorrowes.* Yong's insertion (cf. Estrada, p. 98, ll. 26–28).

88. 18. *Sackbot* 'sacabuche' (Estrada, p. 106, l. 6). An early name for the trombone. The form first appears in Spanish literature of the fourteenth century, the trombone having been evolved from the trumpet about the year 1300 (see Grove, vii. 350 and plate).

Cornets 'cornetas' (Estrada, p. 106, l. 6). A woodwind instrument popular from the tenth to the eighteenth centuries. Grove differentiates it from the modern brass valve instrument of the same name by using the spelling Cornett (see Grove, ii. 447–50 and plate).

27 ff. *SWeete Mistresse, etc.* Yong renders the 28 lines of the Spanish as seven quatrains abab. He has failed to grasp the principle of *romance continuo* (octosyllabic metre, with alternate assonants). For the use of assonance as a co-ordinating element in verse see R. M. Alden, *English Verse*, New York, 1903, pp. 113–15.

89. 17. *concent.* Harmony. See note to **58. 25.**

18. *Lute* 'dulçayna' (Estrada, p. 107, l. 15). Minsheu glosses dulçayna as '*a kinde of trumpet*'. Estrada's note, p. 107, describes it as a small trumpet with finger-holes. The Spanish for lute is 'laúd', as Yong knew (e.g. **134. 28**).

33 ff. *A Sonnet.* Petrarchian in both English and Spanish. The roman type points out the structure of the sonnet, by which the themes of 'Love', 'Fortune', 'Time', and 'Shee' are united in the last line.

35. *Appaying.* *OED* late form of APAY. 1. To satisfy, content, please. *arch.* †2. To repay, requite. *Obs.* Yong uses 'apay' in *OED* sense 1 at **191. 34**, and in *OED* sense 2 at **206. 13**, but here he is using 'appaying' together with 'spending' to translate 'Gastando' (Estrada, p. 108, l. 7), which requires that 'apay' should carry a meaning of extravagant wastefulness not covered by any of the senses given in the *OED*. Minsheu gives 'gastár, *to spend, to waste, to lay desolate, to consume*', and Covarrubias's long and amusing entry (*Tesoro de la lengua castellana*, ed. Martín de Riquer, Barcelona, 1943, p. 632 a) makes it quite clear that 'gastar' is strongly pejorative.

90. 11–12. *fower Lutes* 'quatro vihuelas de arco' (Estrada, p. 109, l. 1). Minsheu glosses vihuela de arco as '*a viall de Gamba, or a great viall that men set betweene their legs to play on*'. The first example of the use of 'viol da gamba' recorded in the *OED* is 1597, but Yong knew the name of the instrument, using it as a mistranslation of 'psalterio' (see note to **134. 29**).

12. *a paire of Virginals* 'un clavicordio' (Estrada, p. 109, l. 1). 'The household keyboard instrument of the 16th and early 17th centuries', which early writers seldom bothered to distinguish from a spinet, harpsichord, or clavichord. See Grove, ix. 2–19 and plates. Minsheu equates Virginals with the clavicordio.

18 ff. *A Song*. Yong alters the rhyme scheme of the quatrain from abba to abab, but follows the Spanish in using the same rhymes in stanzas 1, 3, and 5. He departs from the Spanish form in making stanzas 2 and 4 decasyllabic instead of octosyllabic.

92. 8. *watchet*. Light blue, sky blue.

16. *razed*. Slit.

94. 3. *an old Cannons maide* 'una criada de un canónigo viejo' (Estrada, p. 113, l. 22).

20. *Cachopines of Laredo*. A noble family renowned for their presumption and vanity. Alonso Cortes in his study of the family says that the name became synonymous with insolence and vulgarity (Estrada, p. 114, note).

95. 16. (*under . . . Lord*). Yong's insertion (cf. Estrada, p. 115, ll. 6–9).

97. 8. *besides, being*. 'Without being' would be a better translation. Cf. 'el qual bastará ser mal galardonado sin ser también mal agradecido' (Estrada, p. 117, ll. 20–21).

99. 2. *thy Master*. Estrada (p. 120, l. 1) and Antwerp, 1580 read 'tu amor' (an unlikely reading), but Báez and Antwerp, 1575 read 'tu amo', and Colin reads 'tõ maistre'.

100. 27. *lighting*. Alleviation, relief. The last example recorded in the *OED* is 1502.

101. 9–13. *My teares . . . another*. Yong has omitted two lines at the end of the Spanish sentence. Cf. 'A Celia le [Antwerp, 1580 'se'] llegaban al alma mis lágrimas, assí porque yo las derramava como por parecelle que si yo le [Antwerp, 1580 'la'] quisiera lo que a su amor devía, no solicitara con tanta diligencia favores para otro *y assí lo dezía ella muchas vezes con una ansia que parecía que el alma se le quería despedir*' (Estrada, p. 122, ll. 23–28).

102. 38–39. *because . . . kinsewomen*. Cf. 'por cierta visita en que estava ocupada' (Estrada, p. 124, ll. 18–19).

104. 32. *the greatest . . . worlde* 'todas las del mundo' (Estrada, p. 126, l. 26), referring to the 'muchas personas' who seek from Felicia a remedy for the griefs of love. Possibly Yong lost sight of the antecedent, but in any case his 'kings and estates' give a different impression of the nature of Felicia's fame from that conveyed by the Spanish.

105. 11 ff. *MY passion, etc.* Yong follows the Spanish rhyme scheme of theme aa and gloss bccbbaa, but goes one step further in using the same rhymes for the second stanza as for the first. Yong keeps the octosyllabic line for the aa couplets, but shortens the rest to six syllables.

105. 34 ff. *SAie Shepherdesse, etc.* Spanish octosyllabic abb, cddccbb: Yong decasyllabic except for the hexasyllabic second line, aba, cdcddaa.

106. 13 ff. *MIstresse, etc.* Yong follows the Spanish octosyllabic aa, bccbbaa.

111. 10. *do it: Of one.* A sentence of the Spanish has been omitted at this point: 'Pues ¿ qué podría yo hazer para darte algún alivio, si tu determinación me a de salir al encuentro ?' (Estrada, p. 135, ll. 7–9).

114. 9 ff. *Arsenius his letter.* Yong follows the Spanish form, except in altering the rhyme from abba to abab.

116. 29–**117.** 4. There is a play here on the ecclesiastical and legal connotations of the words 'substance' and (more particularly) 'circumstance' which Yong has failed to bring out (see Estrada, p. 142, note).

118. 12. *digresses.* Digressions. The *OED* records Yong as the first user of this word, the next being Fuller, 1655.

20. *exempted.* Withdrawn from care; unburdened. To whom immunity has been granted. The *OED* records Yong as the first user of this word. See also **244.** 12.

120. 21 ff. *A Sonnet.* Petrarchian in Spanish, but Yong varies the rhyme scheme of the octave: ababbaba.

121. 3 ff. *TO see thee, etc.* The printer's purpose in the arrangement of this poem is not quite clear. In both English and Spanish the poem consists of nine quatrains, of which 1, 3, 5, 7, and 9 have the same rhyme. Yong alters the rhyme from abba to abab, and lengthens the lines from 8 to 10 syllables.

122. 35–36. *calvelings.* Entered in the *OED* as calfling, with this phrase by Yong the only usage recorded.

123. 6 ff. *LOve passed, etc. Terza rima* in both Spanish and English.

124. 11. *O every . . . yeere* 'invierno, primavera, otoño, estío' (Estrada, p. 152, l. 27). Yong was perhaps confused by the reading of Antwerp, 1580 'invierno, primavera, otro estio'.

126. 37. *paragonned.* Paralleled, compared. Now archaic or poetic. The first use recorded in the *OED* is 1586 (Sidney's *Arcadia*).

127. 3–4. *as the sun . . . brightnes.* Yong's insertion (cf. Estrada, p. 156, ll. 12–16).

129. 18–19. *without . . . house.* Yong has omitted a phrase. Cf. 'sin más pensar, como muger sin sentido, me salí de casa de mis padres' (Estrada, p. 159, ll. 12–13).

29–30. *(or . . . tragedie).* Yong's insertion (cf. Estrada, p. 159, ll. 24–25).

130. 26–28. *But what . . . paine.* Yong has omitted a half-sentence of the Spanish that is necessary to the sense of the passage. Cf. 'Mas ¿qué dolor puede aver que no se acabe o acabe al mismo que lo padece? *Y no me tengas por tan loca que piense consolarte,* mas a lo menos podría mostrarte el camino por donde pudiesses algún poco aliviar tu pena' (Estrada, p. 160, ll. 26–30).

131. 8. *The fourth Booke,* which is devoted to considerations of beauty, wisdom, virtue, and the nature of love in the setting of the Temple of Diana presided over by Felicia, is the philosophic core of the novel. Chastity is here represented as loyalty in love (cf. Introduction, p. lvii, n. 5 above). The choice of Diana as goddess of chastely loyal lovers was probably suggested by such Neoplatonic allegorizations of the classical myths concerning Diana as are found, for example, in Leone Ebreo, and in Cartari, who discusses Diana as she appears in her more fruitful identities such as Lucina and Isis (*Le Imagini con la Spositione de i Dei de Gliantichi,* Venetia, 1556, ff. xxiii–xxviii). Felicia's name is probably intended to suggest the happiness achieved in that union with the highest beauty and wisdom which is the ultimate end of love according to Renaissance Neoplatonic theory (see, for example, Leone Ebreo's third dialogue). Ideally Montemayor's lovers are presented as seeking happiness in the chastely fruitful union of marriage with those they love because they see in them some reflections of the divine beauty and wisdom.

16. *and cheered . . . rest.* Yong's insertion (cf. Estrada, p. 162, ll. 7–11).

34. *brinked.* Apparently 'edged' ('cercados', Estrada, p. 163, l. 1). The *OED* records no verbal or adjectival use of 'brink'.

131. 35–**132.** 2. *In the middes . . . behold it.* Yong omits the rest of the Spanish sentence, which continues 'porque los chapiteles que por encima de los árboles sobrepujavan, davan de sí tan gran resplandor que parecían hechos de un finíssimo crystal' (Estrada, p. 163, ll. 4–7).

132. 32–33. *but to blesse . . . content.* Yong's insertion (cf. Estrada, p. 164, ll. 4–5).

133. 9. *checkey worke.* Patterned like a chess-board. See *OED* 'Chequerwork' and 'Checky, chequee'.

31. *Jeat.* Should be bronze or brass: 'arambre' (Estrada, p. 165, ll. 18–19).

32 ff. *WEll let her life, etc.* One stanza of *ottava rima* in both Spanish and English.

134. 24. *inestimate.* Inestimable. The *OED* records 1614 Rowlands *Fooles Bolt* as the only use of this word.

29. *base Vial de Gamba* 'un psalterio' (Estrada, p. 167, l. 1). Minsheu gives '*a Viall de Gamba, vide* Vihuéla de árco' (see note to **90.** 11–12), and 'Saltério, *a psalter or psalme booke, or a musicall instrument called a psalterie*'. A psaltery was a dulcimer, played with the fingers or a plectrum instead of by hammers, the prototype of the spinet and harpsichord (see Grove, vi. 983–4).

135. 2 ff. *THe authours, etc.* Quintains, in Spanish ababb, in Yong abaab.

(R. M. Alden, *English Verse*, New York, 1903, does not give a specimen of Yong's rhyme scheme.) Yong's rhyme scheme emphasizes the arrangement of long and short lines, the Spanish plays against it.

138. 1. *the other Shepherdesse.* 'Todas las pastoras y pastores' (Estrada, p. 171, l. 7). An odd slip on Yong's part.

10–11. *in countermaund of,* as a counteraction or counterbalance to. The *OED* does not give this sense for the noun, but cf. Countermand, *v.* †7. *fig.* To counteract, to frustrate, to counterbalance. *Obs.* First example of use Fuller, 1645.

138. 29–139. 15. *A faire petticoate . . . infinite price.* Yong has enlarged upon the details of Felismena's dress (cf. Estrada, p. 172, ll. 2–21).

139. 3. *tablet Diamonds* = table diamonds (i.e. cut with a table or large flat upper surface surrounded by small facets; especially a thin diamond so cut having a flat under-surface).

30. *Moysaical* = mosaical, of which the first use recorded in the *OED* is 1586 (Sidney's *Arcadia*). Moysaical is given as a variant spelling only for the word of totally different origin meaning pertaining to Moses.

140–55. For full notes on the historical personages mentioned in these pages, both men and women, see Báez.

140. 14. *manie dead mens heads.* Yong's translation is at fault. Cf. 'muchas cabeças de Moros' (Estrada, p. 173, l. 29–p. 174, l. 1).

140. 16.–142. 14. The inscriptions *I Am Cid* to *Don Luys, etc.* Yong follows the Spanish verse forms with minor rearrangements of rhyme in quatrains and quintains.

141. 13. *many enfolded Auncients.* Ensigns, or flags (cf. 'muchas vanderas', Estrada, p. 175, l. 9.)

142. 5. *subscription.* Something written or inscribed underneath. The earliest example recorded in the *OED* is 1631.

20. *Medea.* Should be Penelope. The mistake is Montemayor's.

32. *Coronella.* María Coronel, a Castilian lady of the fourteenth century, to whose name were attached many legends (Estrada, p. 178, note).

143. 15. *Retracted.* Portrayed, drawn. This word is not in the *OED*. Spanish 'retratadas' (Estrada, p. 178, l. 22). Minsheu gives 'Retratádo, *pourtraied, pictured out*' and 'Retratár, *to pourtray, to draw out plots, to picture proportionably. Also to goe backe from that he hath spoken*'.

144. 3–4. *Cyconians, Cyparisus, Atis.* See Ovid, *Met.* x–xi.

9 ff. *Orpheus his song. Ottava rima* in both Spanish and English.

29. *illustrate.* To shed lustre upon; to render illustrious.

145. 27–28. *Daughters . . . Cristiane.* Yong's translation is mistaken. Cf.
son hijas del infante Lusitano
Duarte, valeroso y gran cristiano. (Estrada, p. 181, ll. 29–30)

147. 3. *Manriq.* This and the other mistakes in the spellings of proper names corrected at **148.** 23, **150.** 24, and **152.** 34, are most probably printer's errors. See Yong's own correction of Vigue to Vique **150.** 16 in the 'Faultes escaped'.

19–20. *The Lady Bettrice . . . knowne.* Cf.
doña Beatriz Sarmiento y Castro es una
con la hermosa hermana qual ninguna. (Estrada, p. 183, ll. 31–32)
Yong makes the same slip in the next stanza but one.

29–30. *The Lady Anne . . . place.* Cf.
Doña Anna Osorio y Castro está cabe ella
de gran valor y gracia acompañada. (Estrada, p. 184, ll. 9–10)

148. 24. *From Atlas unto Maurus.* Cf. 'del Bórea al Austro, al Euro' (Estrada, p. 185, l. 8).

152. 10. *sublimate.* Refined, elevated. The earliest recorded example in the *OED* is 1607.

154–55. *Epitaphs. Ottava rima* in both Spanish and English.

156–60. The discussion of love and reason is drawn from the end of Leone Ebreo's first Dialogue of Love (Leone Ebreo, *The Philosophy of Love*, tr. F. Friedeberg-Seeley and J. H. Barnes, 1937, pp. 57–64).

157. 8. *alienation* 'enagenamiento' (Estrada, p. 196, l. 13). Montemayor is closely echoing Ebreo's phrase 'enajenado de si mismo', quoted by Estrada (p. 195) in Garcilasso de la Vega's translation. Both *OED* sense 1 'the action of estranging or state of estrangement in feeling or affection' and sense 2 'The action of transferring the ownership of anything to another' are helpful in arriving at an understanding of the total self-abnegation of the lover, but no definition given in the *OED* quite covers this usage.

9–10. *Euripides . . . beloved.* Báez searched the works of Euripides in vain for this quotation, but cites parallels from Fr. Luis de León, Alemán, and Calderón (Báez, p. 222, note). Montemayor is here merely repeating Leone Ebreo (*The Philosophy of Love*, tr. F. Friedeberg-Seeley and J. H. Barnes, 1937, p. 58).

158. 23. *impropriate.* To make oneself proper or natural to, become one with (cf. 'buelve ageno de si todo hombre y proprio de la persona amada', Estrada, p. 199, ll. 10–11). This sense is not recorded by the *OED*, the closest being †1. †b. To instal (a person) as proprietor. *Obs. rare.* 1627–77 Feltham *Resolves.*

159. 16–17. *full . . . mind.* Estrada (p. 201, l. 10) reads 'muchos trabajos y aficiones', but Báez reads 'afliciones', Antwerp, 1580 'affliciones'.

159. 17. *desires. Thou.* Yong has omitted a sentence and a half of the Spanish text at this point, where it is explained that the troubles of love proceed more from unsatisfied desire than from love itself: 'pero después de conseguida la cosa desseada, se les buelve en descanso y contentamiento. De manera que todos los males que passavan más proceden de desseo [que] de amor que tengan a lo que dessean' (Estrada, p. 201, ll. 11–15).

160. 32. *And supper being ended.* Montemayor's text of Book IV ends at this point, with the company dispersing to the rooms prepared for them. The story of Abyndaraez first appears in the edition of Valladolid, 1561, and then in most subsequent editions.

162. 22 ff. *FIrst in Granada, etc.* Yong does his best to complicate the simple form of this 'dittie' by linking the rhymes of the three quatrains ababacac-dbdb (Spanish abbacddcbaba).

164. 8. *belaied. intr.* To lay *about one.* Yong is the only user of the word in this sense recorded in the *OED*.

170. 1–2. *her image . . . verie hart* 'su ymagen y trasunto, y la más ver-dadera, trasladada en mis entrañas' (Estrada, p. 210, ll. 39–40).

171. 4. *trustles.* Having no trust or confidence. The *OED* cites Yong as the first user of the word in this sense.

12 ff. *IF thy soft Haires, etc.* Yong has substituted the rhyme scheme ababcc for the sestina, but the original end words of the sestina are marked (with one or two exceptions) by roman type.

19. *the flight . . . Haire* 'flecha del metal de los cabellos' (Estrada, p. 211). Minsheu gives 'Flecha, *f. an arrow, a shaft'.* Yong probably had in mind a flight-arrow, but perhaps also the sense 'A volley of missiles, especially arrows'. (*OED*, sense 8. c.)

174. 14–15. *and refreshed . . . trees.* Yong's insertion (cf. Estrada, p. 214, l. 4).

30. *inopinate.* Not thought of; unlooked for; unexpected. The *OED* records Yong as the first user. See also **270.** 37.

175. 13. *not any to.* A possible reading, but more probably 'not to any' (cf. Estrada, p. 214, l. 34).

176. 15. *Centrinels.* Obsolete variant of 'sentinel'.

179. 30. *for . . . resolution.* A misleading translation. Cf. 'que assí lo quiero yo' (Estrada, p. 218, l. 13).

180. 18. *and appalled.* In support of the emendation, cf. **268.** 14–15 and **283.** 8.

32–33. *bicause the signe . . . them.* Yong's insertion (cf. Estrada, p. 219, ll. 4–6).

181. 29. *mutuall.* Emended from *mutall,* since the *OED* defines *mutal* as 'changeable', and lists only one use of the word (1562).

182. 13. *affinitie.* Voluntary social relationship; companionship, alliance, association.

185. 13–14. *from thine owne house heere.* An expression of courtesy. Cf. **180.** 11–12. 'Come in therefore, and rest you in your owne house, the which from henceforth, as also the master of it, accept for none other.'

24. *condigne.* Worthily deserved, merited, fitting, appropriate; adequate.

189. 10–11. *which . . . masters.* Yong's insertion (cf. Estrada, p. 228, l. 13).

191. 12. *my manner and condition.* Estrada (p. 230, l. 25) reads 'mi obligación', but Báez and Antwerp, 1580 read 'mi condicion', Colin 'ma coustume'.

13–14. *and my selfe . . . sake.* Yong's insertion (cf. Estrada, p. 230, l. 26).

30 ff. *O Vainest hopes, etc.* Double sestina in both English and Spanish.

194. 9. *deduct.* Lead. This usage is not recorded in the *OED*. See also **340.** 9, and cf. **3.** 29 and note.

196. 39–**197.** 2. *to kisse . . . senses.* Yong's insertion (cf. Estrada, p. 237, l. 23).

197. 6–8. *Thou hast . . . have it.* Yong's translation is misleading. It is not the joy, but the sorrow, which Arsileus least deserved to have. Cf. 'Verdaderamente, hermosa pastora, vos avéis alegrado un coraçon, el más triste que yo e pensado ver y el que menos merecía estarlo' (Estrada, p. 237, ll. 29–31).

199. 15 ff. *WHen that I, etc.* Yong has converted the difficulties of an irregular Spanish verse form (odd lines unrhymed, even lines of an identical rhyme) to simple truncated trochaic quatrains, but has expanded one group of 4 lines (Estrada, p. 242, ll. 4–7) to two quatrains (**200.** 13–20). This poem also appears in *Englands Helicon.*

206. 1 ff. *NOw Love, etc. Terza rima* in both Spanish and English. This poem also appears in *Englands Helicon.*

4. *recures.* To bring back to a normal state or condition; to restore after loss, damage, exhaustion, etc.

209. 1–2. *that shal . . . againe.* Yong's insertion (cf. Estrada, p. 254, ll. 18–19).

17. *Good . . . tarie.* The pun is lost in translation. Cf. 'VENTURA, VEN Y TURA' (Estrada, p. 255, l. 4).

209. 20 ff. *The Glosse.* The Spanish stanza is composed of two quintains, Yong's of five couplets.

211. 24–25. *by reason of . . . eye brinkes.* Cf. 'las lágrimas a los ojos' (Estrada, p. 257, l. 26).

25. *eye brinkes.* This combination is not recorded in the *OED*, the closest being 'eye-brim'.

214. 35–**215.** 1. *For the infinite . . . my selfe.* The sense is obscure in both English and Spanish. Apparently Amarillis is saying that Filemon's knowledge that she has other suitors might have aroused his jealousy, although she has refused all other suits, and furthermore he should know that she would not do anything injurious to her good name. (Cf. Estrada, p. 262, ll. 14–19.)

216. 31. *feele?* Yong omits two questions in which Filemon points out the difference between his love and Amarillis's when tested by absence. '¿O qué más muestra de amor que no ser ella causa de olvidarte? ¿y qué mayor señal del poco que conmigo tenías que avelle tú perdido de todo punto con mi ausencia?' (Estrada, p. 264, ll. 23–26).

218. 5–6. *which . . . more.* Yong's insertion (cf. Estrada, p. 266, l. 25).

36 ff. *I See thee, etc.* Yong has converted the abba quatrains of the Spanish to couplets, although his form could be regarded as aabb quatrains. The poem is printed in quatrains in *Englands Helicon*.

220. 28 ff. *PAssed contents, etc.* Yong shortens the first line of the Spanish ('Passados contentiamentos') and lengthens the last line of each stanza to 10 syllables, but otherwise follows the Spanish form AbB, CDDCCbB. Yong has omitted the second line of the last stanza, 'no ay passión ni avrá turbarme' (Estrada, p. 271, l. 12); this line is also omitted in the edition of Antwerp, 1580, N8ᵛ. This poem appears in *Englands Helicon*.

221. 15. *layes.* A place of lying or lodging; lair, couch (of animals).

222. 33. For *Diana,* Estrada reads 'Sireno'. For Estrada's distribution of the barbed comments in this lively little quarrel, see Estrada, p. 272, l. 29–p. 274, l. 12.

223. 6. *Unappasionately.* Unmoved by passion, dispassionately. The *OED* records no other example apart from this. See also **81.** 33.

35. *Pipe* 'flauta' (Estrada, p. 274, l. 15). Minsheu gives 'Flaúta, *f. a pipe of a reed, a flute, a fife*'.

224. 7 ff. *IF teares, etc.* Yong exactly follows the Spanish verse form: two 15-line groups of *terza rima*; five quintains abccb, the last line of each repeated as the first line of the next; four 8-line stanzas abccabdd (R. M.

Alden, *English Verse*, New York, 1903, has no specimen of this form); 12 plus 7 lines of *terza rima*.

225. 16. *accoyd.* Accoy. To still, calm, quiet, or appease; *hence,* to soothe or coax (the alarmed or shy), to tame, silence, or daunt (the forward or bold).

227. 24. *wrest.* Obsolete variant spelling of 'wrist'.

228. 25. *plat* = plot. A piece of ground, a patch. See also **230.** 2.

229. 3. *plaine. The.* Yong omits mention of the sumptuous bridge. 'Por encima del qual estava la más sumptuosa y admirable puente que en el universo se podía hallar' (Estrada, p. 281, ll. 18–20).

32–33. *browne-abram* 'no muy ruvios' (Estrada, p. 282, l. 15). Minsheu gives 'Rúvio, or Róxo, *red of colour*'. Abram (or Abraham) is a corruption of AUBURN. The earliest example in the *OED* of the spelling Abraham is 1599, of Abram 1607.

230. 2. *Oke* 'fresno' (Estrada, p. 282, l. 24). Yong regularly mistranslates fresno as 'oak' instead of 'ash'.

36–37. *the hedge of Fremoselle* 'al soto de Fremoselle' (Estrada, p. 283, l. 32). A proper name?

232. 10 ff. *TImes change, etc.* Yong has converted the Portuguese abba quatrain to abab, but otherwise follows the repeated rhyme scheme. The abab quatrains (1, 3, and 5) are in common measure, 2 and 4 are octosyllabic (cf. the group of poems **47–51**).

233. 24. *Montemor, or Velho.* Estrada reads 'Monte moro vello' (p. 287, ll. 20–21), i.e. 'old moor's mountain', which justifies the point Duarda is making, but Antwerp, 1580 reads 'Montemor o velho', which should be translated 'Montemor the old'. Possibly Montemayor was deliberately punning between Spanish and Portuguese.

32–33. *and of . . . Shepherdes.* Yong's insertion (cf. Estrada, p. 288, ll. 2–4).

234. 4. *Who . . . Felismena.* Yong omits 'con muchas lágrimas' (cf. Estrada, p. 288, l. 15).

27 ff. *SIghes, etc.* Yong follows the Portuguese verse form except in altering abba to abab. The metre is octosyllabic (cf. **232, 47–51**).

235. 21–22. *speake . . . deeds.* Yong's insertion (cf. Estrada, p. 290, ll. 14–15).

235. 36–**237.** 7. *If the teares . . . fondly lost.* The conversation between Danteus and Duarda is in Portuguese (cf. Estrada, p. 290, l. 34–p. 292, l. 19).

236. 2. *Like . . . swanne.* Yong's insertion (cf. Estrada, p. 291, ll. 4–5).

236. 8. *cleere.* Estrada (p. 291, l. 10) gives 'cara', but Valladolid, 1561 and Antwerp, 1580 give 'clara'.

238. 1. *transpiercing.* The first use recorded in the *OED* is 1594 (Drayton's *Idea*).

17. *forgetnesse.* Forgetfulness. The *OED* records two examples: Caxton in 1474, and the *Daily News* in 1892. Possibly all three examples are merely the result of a moment of forgetness on the part of the compositors.

21–22. *exiled . . . owne* (cf. Estrada, p. 295, ll. 21–22). Felismena no longer has her liberty, because Felix chose to use his liberty, in forgetting the ties of his love for her.

239. 38. *the substance . . . thoughts.* Yong's insertion (cf. Estrada, p. 297, ll. 8–9).

243. 4–6. *To the . . . fuentes.* All copies that I have located of the first five editions of *Diana Enamorada* are dedicated to Doña Hieronyma de Castro y Bolea. However, since the practice of multiple dedications was not uncommon in the sixteenth century, it is possible that some copies, perhaps of the editions of Antwerp, 1567 or Antwerp, 1574, were dedicated to Doña Maria de Austria. This title probably designates the sister of Philip II who married Maximilian II, and who was at one time patroness of Montemayor (see, for example, *Enciclopedia universal ilustrada*, Espasa-Calpe, S.A., Madrid, xxxiii. 30). The same title is, however, used of a sister of Maximilian II (see K. Brandi, *The Emperor Charles V*, tr. C. V. Wedgwood, 1939, p. 423).

7–24. *If you . . . admiration.* This passage is substituted for the first 7½ lines of the usually found dedication to Doña Hieronyma (cf. Ferreres, p. 8, ll. 3–10).

28. *patrocinie,* patronage.

244. 3–4. Yong has omitted the 'Epistola a los lectores' and four prefatory sonnets (cf. Ferreres, pp. 9–13).

245. 4. *which . . . her.* Yong's insertion (cf. Ferreres, p. 17, l. 3).

6 ff. *LOng have I, etc.* Yong has expanded the octosyllabic quintains of the Spanish to 6-line stanzas (ababcc) of iambic pentameter, with double rhyme throughout. The expansion results in a fairly free treatment of the sense; e.g. the conceit of the winds in the first two stanzas has been inserted by Yong.

247. 11. *affreighted.* Apparently 'weighed down', 'overloaded'. Not in the *OED*, but cf. Freighted, *pple.* and *ppl. a.* 1852 MRS. STOWE *Uncle Tom's C.* xxxi, The boat moved on—freighted with its weight of sorrow; and b. 1850 W. IRVING *Goldsmith* xxvi. 257 Just arrived from College . . . full freighted with academic gleanings.

26. *unknowen.* Should be 'known' (cf. Ferreres, p. 20, ll. 6–8).

248. 30. *condolent.* Sorrowing for another, compassionate. Yong is the first recorded user of this word in the *OED*, the next being Johnson in 1763.

250. 19 ff. *THat mighty Love, etc.* Petrarchian sonnet in both Spanish and English.

28. *gives,* gyves.

251. 16 ff. *LOve is not, etc.* Petrarchian sonnet in both Spanish and English. An anonymous translation of this poem appears in the British Museum MS. Add. 23229, f. 122. b. (For a description of this manuscript see H. J. C. Grierson, *Poems of John Donne,* 1912, II. lxxxii.)

> Love is not blind but I, that doe direct
> My mynd through wayes of so much misery
> Nether is hee a child but in effect
> Tis I, at once who feare, hope, laugh and cry.
> His flames are nought but my too hot desires
> His wings my soaring thoughts that never rest
> And who the sharpenes of his darts admires
> Interprets fals his owne resistles brest
> Nor did his fable chayns eare ty a hart
> That did not yeeld before a blow was strooke
> Though some whose Mistris scornd his smal desart
> Swore it was Cupids doome [wil b.c.], and so mistooke
>   For my part Ime resolved that hee that can
>   Thinke him a God, is himselfe lesse then Man.

253. 18 ff. *HE that in freedome, etc.* Yong has converted the Spanish Petrarchian sonnet to three 6-line stanzas ababcc, by elaborating but not adding to the sense.

254. 31. *Rythmes.* Not Rhythm in the modern usage, but a graphic variant of Rhyme (Rime), and so pronounced.

31 ff. *Provençal Rythmes.* Yong follows the Spanish stanza form ABBAC-cddeeFF.

256. 12. *reposedly.* Now obsolete or rare. The *OED* cites Yong's translation of Guazzo for 'reposed', but the first use it records of the adverb is 1598 (Florio).

256. 33, **257.** 8–9, 20. Yong has given a religious flavour to these lines which is not present in the Spanish : *their holy wordes* 'el hablar' (Ferreres, p. 34, l. 3); *Their faith's not vaine, But good and plaine* 'todo es llaneza | bondad, simpleza' (Ferreres, p. 34, ll. 12–13); *With that that God hath sent* 'con lo que tiene' (Ferreres, p. 35, l. 1).

259. 10 ff. *I Cannot be, etc.* In Spanish a regular Petrarchian sonnet, but Yong's form is unusual : abbacddceffeff.

259. 16. *affection* 'afición' (Ferreres, p. 37, l. 16). Ferreres (p. 37, note) says that other editions read 'aflicción', but the editions of Antwerp, 1567, Antwerp, 1574, and Saragossa, 1577 read 'aficion'.

261. 12. *quote out.* Apparently 'mark, point out', a figurative use not recorded in the *OED*. Spanish 'señalar' (Ferreres, p. 40, l. 3), which Minsheu glosses '*to note, to marke, to point at*'.

263. 11. *charie.* Careful in preservation of.

20 ff. *Marcelius his letter, etc. Terza rima* in both Spanish and English, but the last four lines of the Spanish have been expanded by Yong to six (cf. Ferreres, p. 45, ll. 3–6).

265. 6. *hart-breake.* The *OED* glosses as 'heart-breaking' (*Obs.*) and gives two examples (1586 and 1599). Neither the definition nor the illustrative quotations exactly correspond to Yong's usage, which could most precisely be rendered as 'written with a broken heart'. This whole verse line is an addition by Yong to the sense of the Spanish (cf. Ferreres, p. 45, ll. 3–6).

11. *posie.* Syncopated form of poesy, a poetical production.

16–23. *manie . . . togither.* Considerably expanded (cf. Ferreres, p. 45, ll. 14–17).

21. *impresa.* An emblem or device. The first example cited in the *OED* is Greene's *Menaphon* (1589), the second *Diana*. All forms of the word are first recorded in the very late sixteenth or early seventeenth centuries. Impresas are not mentioned at this point by Gil Polo (Ferreres, p. 45, ll. 14–17). Cf. note to **344.** 31.

23. *for . . . togither* 'por espacio de algunos años' (Ferreres, p. 45, l. 17).

267. 23. *a hideous . . . monsters* 'un espantable ruido de las sacudidas maromas' (Ferreres, p. 48, ll. 4–5). Minsheu gives 'Sacudído, *shaken off*' and 'Maróma, *a cable for a ship*'.

37. *tottered.* Battered and shaken; in a tottering condition. The earliest example recorded in the *OED* is 1615.

269. 30–31. *not forgetting . . . ship.* Not abandoning her bow and quiver 'no dexando en la nave su arco y aljaba' (Ferreres, p. 50, ll. 31–32). Yong has become muddled in trying to say that Clenarda did not forget her bow and quiver and leave them in the ship.

270. 35. *Sartofano.* Ferreres, Antwerp, 1567, Antwerp, 1574, and Saragossa, 1577 read 'Bartofano' (Ferreres, p. 52, l. 13 et seq.).

271. 16. *inhabited.* Not dwelt in, uninhabited. The earliest example recorded in the *OED* is 1614.

272. 12. *hand and foote.* In support of the emendation, cf. **274.** 11–12.

21–22. *to steere . . . place* 'encaminasse la proa hazia Levante' (Ferreres' p. 54, l. 19).

274. 33 ff. *O Sandie desart, etc.* Petrarchian sonnet in both Spanish and English. This is the only poem which R.C. (in *The Troublesome and Hard Adventures in Love*, 1652) translates from Gil Polo. His version runs as follows:

> Thou sandie medow, desart all and dry,
> Thou sable, like the plumes of snow-white swans,
> Thou sea that shrowdest Neptune in his court,
> And art acquainted with my flowing tears,
> Thou furious wind and variable air,
> Molested with my grievous sad complaints;
> Where painted and engraven doth remain,
> Th'exceeding torment of my helpless grief;
> All ye make true report of my intent,
>   For seeing that mine own Marcelio
>   Is with Clenarde fled I left alone,
>   And sith his faith and all my hope withall,
>   Is with his sails committed to the wind;
>   Bear witness that Alcida thus forsaken,
>   Henceforth will never fancy person more;
>   For fear to enter in such dangerous seas
>   And eke to fall from freedome to like foil,
>   From pleasing rest to such disquiet toil. (E3ᵛ)

276. 23. *Shepherdesses and Nymphes* 'los pastores y pastoras' (Ferreres, p. 59, l. 3).

26–29. *and in . . . offered.* Yong's insertion (cf. Ferreres, p. 59, ll. 5–6).

277. 34 ff. *NOw that the sunne, etc.* Yong treats his original with considerable freedom. He expands the first two stanzas (*ottava rima* in Spanish) to 14 lines each (12 of iambic pentameter and a final couplet of fourteeners); he then follows the Spanish for four stanzas of *ottava rima*; he expands the next two stanzas to 12 lines from 11, using six rhymes instead of four; he copies the next two stanzas of 8 and 9 lines with internal rhyme; he converts the four last 13-line stanzas of the Spanish to 16, 17, 14, and 14 lines respectively, making no attempt to follow the rhyme scheme except in the final couplets.

279. 6. *wills.* In support of the emendation, cf. Ferreres, p. 62, l. 18: 'Amor quiere que viva confiado'.

281. 18. *raves.* The act of raving; frenzy, great excitement. The *OED* cites Yong as the first user of this word.

282. 17. *homely.* The derogatory usage of this word as applied to persons is first recorded in the *OED* in 1590 (Shakespeare, *The Comedy of Errors*).

283. 10–11. *shepherds.* Ferreres notes (p. 67) that he has emended the 1564

text to 'los pastores' from 'las pastoras', but without stating his authority. Antwerp, 1567, Antwerp, 1574, and Saragossa, 1577 all read 'las pastoras'. Possibly Yong himself made the necessary emendation.

283. 23 ff. *THe cause, etc.* Yong changes the abba quatrain of the Spanish to abab, and makes no attempt to follow the Spanish in identical rhymes in the odd stanzas. This poem appears in *Englands Helicon*.

284. 1. *Behold* 'Mira' (Ferreres, p. 69, l. 3). The misprint 'Bebold' is corrected in *Englands Helicon*.

13. *Behold* 'Cata' (Ferreres, p. 69, l. 15). Minsheu gives 'Cáta, *or* Míra, *beholde, see, looke, lo here, at hand, here, take heede*'. *Englands Helicon* reads 'Be bold;', although the editors had properly corrected the earlier misprint of b for h (**284.** 1).

32 ff. *ENd now, etc.* Yong follows the rhyme scheme (ababcdcdabab) of the Spanish, but evolves his own metre of 5-stress 11-syllable lines, except for the third and eleventh, which are 3-stress 7-syllable.

285. 19 ff. *AH such, etc.* Yong alters the Spanish abba quatrain to abab, and lengthens the lines from octosyllabic to decasyllabic.

287. 25 ff. *AWake a little, etc.* Yong precisely follows the exacting Spanish rhyme scheme and approximates the varying line lengths, except in the final stanza, which he expands from AbbCcDD to ABABCDCD.

291. 6 ff. *INconstant love, etc.* Yong has expanded the Spanish 11-line stanza to 12 lines, and evolved his own somewhat simplified lyric stanza: Spanish AbCBaCcDdEE; Yong ABABcdcDEFeF.

293. 19–20. (*to be . . . Marcelius*). Yong's insertion (cf. Ferreres, p. 81, ll. 27–30).

30. *presence* 'preferencia' (Ferreres, p. 82, l. 6) but the editions of Antwerp, 1567, Antwerp, 1574, and Saragossa, 1577 read 'presencia'.

294. 38–39. (*with . . . spoken*). Yong's insertion (cf. Ferreres, p. 83, ll. 25–27).

295. 5 ff. *A Sonnet.* Petrarchian in both Spanish and English, but Yong alters the sestet from cdecde to cddcee.

296. 17 ff. *A Sonnet.* Petrarchian in both Spanish and English, but Yong alters the sestet from cdecde to cdcdee.

297. 26. *he . . . counterfaite* 'cree que lo desdeña' (Ferreres, p. 87, ll. 9–10).

298. 35. *harpe* 'lira' (Ferreres, p. 88, l. 29). Although the harp and lyre (simrila in principle and both of great antiquity) are separate instruments, they were not apparently always considered distinct in the sixteenth and seventeenth centuries. See Grove, v. 453–6. Minsheu gives 'Lira, *f. a harpe*' and '*a Harpe,* *vide* Hárpa, Lira'. Yong regularly translates harpa as harp, e.g. 59. 35 (Estrada, p. 73, l. 24).

299. 1 ff. *A Sonnet.* Petrarchian in both Spanish and English, but Yong alters the sestet from cdecde to cddcee.

300. 20–21. *and in . . . Sylvanus.* Yong's translation is careless. Selvagia was born in Ismenia's town, married in Diana's. 'y en la tuya, hermosa Diana, está casada con el pastor Sylvano' (Ferreres, p. 91, ll. 1–2).

33. *Filenus* 'Fileno' (Ferreres, p. 91, l. 16). Spelt *Phylenus* at 42. 17, from 'Philenio' (Estrada, p. 51, l. 34).

301. 26 ff. *Filenus letter to Ismenia.* Yong has expanded the quatrains of the Spanish to 6-line stanzas ababcc, thereby slightly obscuring the comparison which Gil Polo invited with Montemayor's *Arsenius his letter* 114).

31. *shent.* Disgraced, lost, ruined; stupefied.

306. 27. *Amphion.* Son of Jupiter and Antiope, so skilled in music that he is said to be the inventor of it, and fabled to have moved stones and raised the walls of Thebes at the sound of his lyre.

308. 14–15. *hanged her selfe* 'perderse' (Ferreres, p. 98, l. 17). It is possible that a copy of a Spanish text reads 'penderse', but I have not come across one.

311. 4–5. *that his . . . felt it.* Awkward translation. Cf. 'que el ánimo y los braços se le cayeron y el puñal se le salió de las manos sin sentirlo' (Ferreres, p. 102, ll. 3–5).

313. 18. *awaite.* A lying in wait or waylaying with hostile intent; ambush, ambuscade; a snare, plot. Yong is translating 'conjuración' (Ferreres, p. 105, l. 8) which Minsheu glosses *'a conspiracie, a conjuration, a trecherie'*.

28–30. *by making . . . withall.* Expanded from 'haziéndome importunas fiestas' (Ferreres, p. 105, ll. 19–20).

314. 7. *since* 'dos días después' (Ferreres, p. 106, ll. 4–5).

315. 4. *the pastorall Arcadia.* Reference to Sannazaro.

316. 27. *(I hope).* Yong's insertion (cf. Ferreres, p. 109, ll. 20–21).

317. 4 ff. *THe coole, etc.* In Spanish this poem is headed 'tercetos esdrucciolos' and the first four stanzas, of 15, 15, 12, and 12 lines, are in this metre. Yong seems to have started out with some idea of following the Spanish, but then evolved his own lyric stanzas, the first two of 18 lines ABABCBCDCdEFe-FFGhG, and the second two of 14 lines ababcdcdefefgg. Yong then follows the complex scheme of the Spanish until the last two stanzas which he expands from *ottava rima* to 10-line stanzas ababcdcdee. Gil Polo is imitating Montemayor's 'Si lagrimas no pueden ablandarte', whose form Yong followed exactly in 'If teares cannot with tendernesse relent thee' (224).

317. 19. *salutiferous*. The earliest usage of this word recorded in the *OED* is 1604.

30. *sovenaunce*. Remembrance; memory.

321. 8. *geason*. Rare, scarce, uncommon.

34–36. *Marcelius . . . bushes*. Mistranslation. It should read '*Marcelius*, who was with the Shepherds behinde the shrubs and bushes, heard the talke of the Gentleman and the Damosell' (cf. Ferreres, p. 117, ll. 6–8).

323. 13. *Neapolitan Syncerus*. Sannazaro.

324. 30. *hoisting*. Not recorded in the *OED* as an adjective.

325. 5 ff. *WElcome thy friendes, etc*. Yong has expanded the Spanish sonnet to four 6-line stanzas ababcc, without making any significant additions to the content.

27–28. *That I may wash . . . hate*. The waters of the river Turia will wash away the abhorred sea-water: 'para que cuando en Turia yo me lave | estas malditas aguas aborrezca' (Ferreres, p. 122, ll. 22–23).

326. 21. *tew*. Implements, tools, etc. for work generally, but especially fishing-tackle. (*Obs.*)

327. 6–7. *we . . . boate* 'los sacamos de su batel' (Ferreres, p. 124, ll. 24–25). Yong's insertion of 'both' is misleading. There were 'two Marriners' (**327.** 11) with Clenarda.

328. 22 ff. *Nereas Song*. Yong has expanded the quintains of the Spanish to 6-line stanzas $a^8a^8b^6c^8c^8b^6$ (R. M. Alden, *English Verse*, New York, 1903, gives no specimen of this stanza).

330. 33. *Alnade*. Yong has missed the reference to Bacchus and the manner of his birth. The usual meaning of the Spanish 'alnado' is stepchild, but Ferreres (p. 129, note) points out that here it means born before the proper time (ante natu > antenado > alnado). The whole stanza has been misinterpreted by Yong. The reference is to the capture of Bacchus by mariners (see Ovid, *Met.* iii. 605 ff.).

34. *Dishivered*. Shivered to pieces.

336. 12 ff. *MY greevous sighes, etc*. and *The glosse*. Yong has expanded the Spanish 10-line stanzas (groups of two quintains) to 12-line stanzas of varied line length. The rhyme scheme is the same in each (ababccdedeff), but the line lengths are not exactly repeated.

338. 1 ff. *The Song* and *The glosse*. As in the preceding poem, Yong has altered the quintains of the Spanish to a less regular stanza, but this time without expansion. Perez wrote two glosses on the same song, which, in

Yong's translation, both appear in *Englands Helicon*: 'Eclipsed was our Sunne' and 'If that the gentle winde'.

339. 21 ff. and **340.** 4 ff. *HAving no cause, etc.* and *STep after step, etc.* Yong has not quite achieved the rigorous artifice of the Spanish, which uses 5 homonyms in sonnets of the strict Petrarchian form, but he has managed 7, with a Petrarchian sestet in each sonnet.

342. 15 ff. *The Song of Turia.* Yong has abandoned the *ottava rima* of the Spanish in favour of an 8-line stanza of his own devising abcbacdd (R. M. Alden, *English Verse*, New York, 1903, gives no specimen of this form). For biographical notes on the poets and scholars mentioned in this poem see Ferreres; the edition of *Diana Enamorada* of Madrid, 1778; and (for notes in English) Gaspar Gil Polo, *Diana Enamorada* together with the English translation by Bartholomew Yong, ed. etc. by R. L. and M. B. Grismer, Minneapolis, 1959.

23. *The Father of flouds* 'el Pado' (Ferreres, p. 145, l. 2). The Po.

344. 17. *musicall.* Melody, sweet music ('la excelsa melodía' Ferreres, p. 149, l. 5). Not recorded in the *OED*, but cf. B. *sb.* †1 b. A musical performance. 1579 SPENSER, *Sheph. Cal.*

28. *Phebe,* Phoebus ('Apolo', Ferreres, p. 149, l. 15).

31. *emprese.* Empress, *sb.*² *Obs.* A motto or significant device. The *OED* refers to Impress and Impresa, and notes that the form in *em-* is treated separately since it may come from the Spanish. Both here and at **347.** 16 Yong is translating 'empresa' (Ferreres, p. 150, l. 1 and p. 159, l. 5). Where Yong has no lead from the Spanish he uses the Italian form 'impresa' (see **265.** 21 and note).

346. 28. *rebound.* To send *out,* exalt, celebrate, by a re-echoing sound.

347. 36. *Marius.* An error for Maro ('Marón', Ferreres, p. 161, l. 4). Yong does not make the same mistake **351.** 16.

348. 25. *Praising alwaies 'Semper* loando' (Ferreres, p. 163, l. 4). Yong missed the pun on the name of Jeronimo Semper (otherwise known as Samper, Sampedro, Sent Pere, Sanpere, and (by Yong) Sant-Perez). See also **9.** 16 and note.

355. 4. *on.* Listed by the *OED* as a still current variant spelling of 'one'.

358. 26 ff. *THe Faire, the fresh, etc.* A regular sestina in both Spanish and English.

360. 24–25. *her beloved husband.* Yong is anticipating a little. Cf. 'su amado' (Ferreres, p. 184, l. 15).

360. 27 ff. *LOvers, with pride, etc.* Yong has expanded the octosyllabic quintains of the Spanish to decasyllabic 6-line stanzas ababcc.

362. 24. *Degorge.* Disgorge.

363. 30–32. *Marcelius . . . desires.* Yong's careless translation exaggerates Marcelius's happiness. Cf. 'yo he cobrado vida y Marcelio y Diana esperança de tenella' (Ferreres, p. 187, ll. 27–28).

366. 7. *cousen* 'cuñado' (Ferreres, p. 191, l. 6). Minsheu gives 'cuñádo, *m. a brother-in-law, a sisters husband, or brother to my wife*'.

367. 2 ff. *O Eies, etc.* Two stanzas of *ottava rima* in both Spanish and English.

28 ff. *LEt now, etc.* Yong's stanza form ABCCBAaDdEeFF (with the exception of the second stanza ABCBCAa) closely approximates the Spanish ABCBACcDdEeFF. This poem appears in *Englands Helicon.*

369. 12. *puttocks.* A bird of prey; usually applied to the kite or glede; sometimes to the common buzzard.

24. *spendlesse.* That cannot be spent or consumed. The *OED* cites Yong as the only user.

35. *staffe.* A 'verse' or stanza of a song. Now STAVE. The *OED* cites Yong as the first user. See also **385.** 22 and note.

370. 2 ff. *O Let that time, etc.* In the first stanza Yong exactly follows the Spanish form ABCBACcDdEeFF, but varies the arrangement of the rhymes of the first seven lines in the other five stanzas. This poem appears in *Englands Helicon.*

372. 14. *Palemon.* Possibly the noted Roman grammarian of the time of Tiberius, but more probably the Palemon who is invited to judge the contest between Menalcas and Damoetas in Virgil's third Eclogue. The conclusion of Virgil's contest, also, is that each is worthy of the prize.

376. 6–7. *graven . . . stones.* Yong's insertion (cf. Ferreres, p. 203, ll. 24–25).

378. 4–5. *this Caroll.* Substituted by Yong for the title of the Spanish poem 'Versos franceses' (Ferreres, p. 206, l. 9).

7 ff. *LEt now each meade, etc.* Yong's stanza form ABABBbcCdD (not illustrated in R. M. Alden, *English Verse*, New York, 1903) is the same as that used by Sidney in 'Let mother earth now decke her selfe in flowers' (see above p. xli), and closely approximates the Spanish ABBAacCdD. The last word of each stanza in Spanish is 'canto', but with a different preceding rhyme each time: Yong has been able to find only one rhyme for 'gladnes', and therefore does not always translate exactly. Yong has made the variation in the final line of the last stanza more striking by altering the rhyme also. This poem appears in *Englands Helicon.*

378. 8. *Of sundrie . . . glowing.* Grammatically this line does not make sense, although it does convey a suitable impression. Yong has not translated the Spanish 'retumbe el hueco bosque de vozes deleitosas' (Ferreres, p. 206, l. 11).

31–32. *But great . . . sadnes.* A successful substitution for Gil Polo's classical reference:

> sino la gran Felicia, que obrado ha más hazañas,
> que la Thebana Manto?   (Ferreres, p. 207, ll. 6–7)

379. 17. *Flora.* Introduced by Yong (cf. Ferreres, p. 208, l. 6).

20–21. *With many . . . sadnes.* By the need to introduce his rhyme word 'sadnes', Yong has been driven to abandon Gil Polo's continued list of flowers:

> la madreselva hermosa y el arrayán florido,
> narcisso y amaranto: (Ferreres, p. 208, ll. 9–10)

31. *that in the clouds are ringing.* Yong's addition. (Cf. 'dad fin, hermosas ninfas, al deleitoso canto', Ferreres, p. 208, l. 20.)

381. 19 ff. *I Should have dide, etc.* Yong expands to decasyllabic quatrains ababcdcdabab the octosyllabic quatrains abbacddcabba of the Spanish.

382. 3 ff. *MY soule, etc.* Yong alters the octosyllabic quatrains of the Spanish to common measure, but follows the rhyme scheme, apart from altering the middle stanza from cddc to cdcd.

383. 17 ff. *SUch joy, etc.* Yong expands the octosyllabic quatrains of the Spanish to decasyllabic quatrains. The rhyme schemes are identical.

384. 9 ff. *TUrne thy faire eies, etc.* Octosyllabic quatrains with the ab rhyme repeated in the odd stanzas in both Spanish and English, but Yong has converted the abba scheme to abab.

385. 7 ff. *YOng shepherd, etc.* The first and third stanzas (abab) are in common measure, the second (cdcd) is decasyllabic. The Spanish is octosyllabic abbacddcabba. G. Saintsbury comments with approval on the metre of this poem (*A History of English Prosody*, ii. 133 and 133–4 note). The poem also appears in *Englands Helicon*.

17. *Behold.* There is no support in Spanish for either 'Behold' or 'Be bold' ('ni quiero matar de amor', Ferreres, p. 217, l. 24), but cf. 284. 1 and 284. 13, and notes.

22. *staves.* A 'verse' or stanza of a poem, song, etc. = STAFF. The earliest example recorded in the *OED* is 1659.

24 ff. *IF to be lov'd, etc.* Octosyllabic quatrains (Spanish abba, English abab) with the ab rhymes repeated in odd stanzas in both Spanish and English. This poem appears in *Englands Helicon*.

386. 12 ff. *ME thinks, etc.* Octosyllabic quatrains, in Spanish abbacddcabba, in English ababcdcdabab. This poem appears in *Englands Helicon*.

386. 27 ff. *SInce thou, etc.* Octosyllabic quatrains, in Spanish abbacdcdabba, etc., in English ababcdcdabab, etc. This poem appears in *Englands Helicon.*

388. 7 ff. *SHepherd, why, etc.* Yong alters the Spanish abba quatrain to abab, and does not attempt to reproduce the repetition of the ab rhymes in the odd stanzas. Yong follows the Spanish octosyllabic line except in the final quatrain, which he converts to common measure. This variation has been 'corrected' in *Englands Helicon.*

389. 10. *Recorder* 'flauta' (Ferreres, p. 223, l. 2). Minsheu gives '*a Recorder or flute, vide* Flaúta'. For a description of the early varieties of flutes, see Grove, FIPPLE FLUTE, iii. 140–1, and RECORDER, vii. 73–78.

11. *Cyterne* 'cítara' (Ferreres, p. 223, l. 3). The cittern or cithern, a fig-shaped instrument of the guitar family, very popular in western Europe from the end of the fifteenth to the early eighteenth century. See Grove, ii. 312.

12. *base Viall* 'lira' (Ferreres, p. 223, l. 4). Minsheu gives '*a Viall to play on, vide* Vihuéla', and '*Lira, f. a harpe*' (see note to 298. 35).

13. *Virginals and Violins* 'los albogues y chapas' (Ferreres, p. 223, l. 5). Yong did not know the Spanish words, and has mistaken the character of the music. For Virginals see note to 90. 12. 'Violin' does not appear in Minsheu. The first example of its use recorded in the *OED* is 1579, in Spenser's *The Shepheardes Calender.* Minsheu gives '*Albógue, a pipe, a flute*'. Ferreres (p. 223, note) cites *Don Quixote*, 2nd part, chap. lxvii: ' "And if to these different musics we have the albogue too, we shall have all kind of pastoral instruments." "What is albogue?" quoth Sancho. "It is," said Don Quixote, "a certain plate made like a candlestick; and being hollow, gives, if not a very pleasing or harmonious sound, yet it displeaseth not altogether, and agrees well with the rustic tabor and bagpipe; and this word albogue is Moorish, as all those in our Castilian tongue are that begin with *al*" ' (tr. T. Shelton, Macmillan, 1900, iii. 292). Ferreres (p. 223, note) was unable to find the meaning of 'chapa' as a musical instrument, but Minsheu gives '*Chápas, f. a cimball, a clapper, rattles, an instrument made with two plates. Also thin plates, spangles*'.

18–20. *with . . . silver.* Yong's translation is not clear. The coronets were made of roses (omitted by Yong) and flowers tied with gold and silver threads (cf. Ferreres, p. 223, ll. 10–12).

30–31. *with pendants . . . founde.* Yong's insertion (cf. Ferreres, p. 224, l. 2).

391–6. *Riddles.* Yong has not been over-careful to reproduce the metre of the riddles. The first, a Petrarchian sonnet in Spanish, he alters to a Shakespearian sonnet; the second and fourth he converts from quintains to 6-line stanzas ababcc; in the third he alters the rhyme scheme from abcabc to ababcc; in the fifth and sixth he expands the two quintains of the Spanish to 12 lines, one ababacdcdcee; the other aabbccdedeff. These six riddles, in

Yong's translation, have been copied into a manuscript commonplace book in the University Library at Cambridge (Dd. 5. 75, f. 46ʳ⁻ᵛ), which is described as a *Collection of English Verses 1581–1612*.

392. 15. *hill* 'soto', which Yong at **392.** 33 more correctly translates 'field' (cf. Ferreres, p. 227, l. 21 and p. 228, l. 7).

397. 30. *two Harpes* 'unas chapas' (Ferreres, p. 234, l. 9). According to Minsheu, chapas are cymbals. See note to **389.** 13.

398. 9 ff. *Florisias Song.* Yong has expanded the octosyllabic quintains of the Spanish to decasyllabic 6-line stanzas ababcc; omitted two quintains, and, almost at the end, substituted eleven stanzas of his own for six of the Spanish (see below). The following may serve as examples of his methods of expansion: **398.** 15–16 *Against a people . . . kinde of men*, cf. 'la gente bestial' (Ferreres, p. 235, l. 7); **398.** 21–22 *Women I meane . . . minde*, cf. 'mujeres' (Ferreres, p. 235, l. 9).

12. *indigned.* Excited to indignation, offended.

401. 4–6. Aetna and the crocodile are Yong's own similes (cf. Ferreres, p. 238, ll. 21–25).

19–22. *They give . . . with feares.* Much expanded by Yong. Cf.

Dan y cobran, sanan, hieren
la alma, el cuerpo, el coraçón,
gozan, penan, viven, mueren.   (Ferreres, p. 239, ll. 6–8)

402. 24. *enchants.* Enchantments. The only recorded use of this noun in the *OED* is 1634.

404. 18–19. At this point Yong has omitted two quintains of the Spanish (see Ferreres, p. 242, l. 9–p. 243, l. 4), in which the courage of Camilla and Penthesilea is vaunted above that of Mutius Scaevola: he merely burnt his hand, while they cut off their breasts. Ferreres (p. 242, l. 9 note) states that all editions except the first lack three quintains at this point, but Antwerp, 1567, Antwerp, 1574, and Saragossa, 1577 lack only the two which Yong omits.

405. 29. *Orpheus* 'Proteo' (Ferreres, p. 244, l. 17).

31–**407.** 24. These 66 lines in praise of Queen Elizabeth are substituted for 30 lines in Spanish (Ferreres, p. 244, l. 18–p. 246, l. 2) of praise of Doña Hieronyma de Castro y Bolea, to whom *Diana Enamorada* is usually dedicated (see above **243.** 4–6, note). Yong has incorporated most of Gil Polo's material (e.g. the comparisons with Roman ladies), but adapted it to his purpose. The references to Petrarch and the Provençal poets are Yong's own (see note below).

407. 1–18. The chief source for the lives of the Provençal poets is

Nostredame. There were two editions of Nostredame's *Lives* printed in 1575, one in French, *A Lyon pour Alexandre Marsilij*, one in Italian, *In Lione, Appresso d'Alesandro Marsilij*. The French edition, together with some manuscript versions, has been edited for the Librairie Ancienne, *Les Vies des plus célèbres et anciens poètes provençaux*. Édition préparée par C. Chabaneau et publiée avec introduction et commentaire par J. Anglade (Paris, 1913). The forms which Yong uses of the names are closer to the Italian than to the French, and the mention of Petrarch leads one to suppose that Yong was introduced to the names of the Provençal poets by Petrarch's mention in his *Triumph of Love* of six of the seven poets named by Yong. Yong obviously did not use the very poor and muddled English translation of Petrarch's *Triumphs* by Henry Parker (1565?). He may have seen a fully annotated Spanish translation *Los Triumphos de Francisco Petrarcha, agora nuevamente traduzidos en lengua Castellana . . .*, Salamanca, 1581, but I have found no single source for all the information and the precise forms of the names he gives.

407. 25. *Orpheus* 'Proteo' (Ferreres, p. 246, l. 3).

408. 20 ff. *POore Melibee, etc.* Basically quatrains grouped as 8-line stanzas. Yong changes the Spanish abba form to abab, but follows the Spanish in repeating the ab rhymes in the odd quatrains. Yong follows the Spanish octosyllabic line in the even quatrains, but expands the odd quatrains to decasyllabic lines.

   20. *POore . . . forgot.* This melodious line is Yong's own (cf. 'Contando está Melibeo', Ferreres, p. 247, l. 9).

410. 14. *fine.* Emended from 'five', since all twelve ships were rowed by 'Savages'. Yong's 'They that rowed these fine ships' translates 'Los remeros' (Ferreres, p. 249, l. 16).

   15–16. *Savages . . . silver.* The crowned and chained Savages perhaps suggest unruly sexual passions kept in order by the bonds of marriage.

   17. *drums, trumpets, shagbotes, cornets* 'clarines, chirimías, cornetas' (Ferreres, p. 249, l. 19). Minsheu gives '*a Drum, vide* Atambór, Cáxa' and '*a Trumpet, vide* Anafil, or Trompéta, Bozína, Trómpa'. He does not enter Shagbot (a variant spelling of Sackbut. See note to 88. 18). For cornets see note to 88. 18. Minsheu's definitions of the Spanish words are unhelpful: 'Clarín, *m. a certaine musicall instrument*', 'Chirrimía, *f. an instrument of musicke*'. Either 'trumpets' or 'shagbotes' would seem an acceptable translation of 'clarines' (clarions), but Yong has not translated 'chirimías'. *Enciclopedia universal ilustrada*, Espasa-Calpe, S.A., Madrid, describes 'chirimía' as a wind instrument similar to the clarinet, of considerable antiquity and of Arab origin, mentioning that the instrument was used by the jugglers of King Juan I, 1350–93 (xvii. 546).

413. 1 ff. *Provençall Rythmes.* In the earlier example of this verse form (pp. 254–7) Yong exactly followed the Spanish stanza ABBACcddeeFF, but here he evolves his own even more complex stanza $ABABABc^8c^8d^6e^8e^8d^6F^{14}F^{14}$. The final fourteeners are particularly effective.

414. 27. *Hamadriades and Napees.* Wood-nymphs and nymphs haunting wooded dells. The *OED* for Napaea (*rare*) cites only Shelton's *Quixote* (1612) and Drummond of Hawthornden's *Forth Feasting* (1617).

415. 13. *see her there.* The emendation is warranted not only for the sense but also by Yong's care for his metre, as evinced in the correction in the 'Faultes escaped' for **224.** 25.

416. 31 ff. *DIana, Love, etc.* A Petrarchian sonnet in both Spanish and English, but Yong alters the sestet from cdecde to cdcdee.

417. 34. *minde.* At this point Yong has omitted 3½ pages of the Spanish text (Ferreres, p. 257, l. 30–p. 261, l. 14). The drastic cutting of Felicia's philosophical speech on love makes the awed wonder of her audience a little incomprehensible. According to Ferreres (p. 257, note), this passage has been omitted from all editions after the first.

418. 9. *Booke.* Yong omits the end of the Spanish sentence, 'que antes de muchos días, plaziendo a Dios, será impresa' (Ferreres, p. 261, ll. 27–28). He also omits the Laus Deo and final laudatory sonnet. The sonnet is also omitted from Antwerp, 1567, Antwerp, 1574, and Saragossa, 1577.

11. *Boto el amor en Yugo.* This tag is not found in the Spanish text, but is an addition of Yong's own. That Yong felt a particular affection for it appears from its occurrence together with his signature on the title-page of Guillaume de La Perrière's *Morosophie* (see above, p. lxii and illustration on p. lxi). In view of Yong's fondness for playing on his name, evinced in his manner of signing his translation of Boccaccio's *Amorous Fiammetta* (see above, p. lxii), it is not surprising to find the tag yields a good anagram—Bartolomeo Younge. The ambiguous meaning of the tag also demonstrates Yong's liking for word-play. Minsheu gives 'Botár, or Votár, *to put foorth, to thrust foorth, to vowe, to dimme the colour, to dull the edge*', and 'Yúgo, *m. a yoake*'. *Enciclopedia universal ilustrada*, Espasa-Calpe, S.A., Madrid, mentions a liturgical use of 'Yugo' referring to the nuptial veil anciently used at one point of the marriage ceremony (lxx. 812). It is, besides, a common figure of speech to refer to the nuptial tie as the marriage yoke. I therefore take the primary sense of the tag to be 'I vow (or vote for) love in marriage', which makes a very suitable comment upon Gil Polo's celebration of the joys of love crowned in marriage. It is, however, possible to find in the tag a more cynical meaning, quite in keeping with Yong's sense of humour and his bachelor status: 'I dim the colour (or blunt the edge) of love in marriage (by marrying).'

CHECK-LIST OF WORDS GLOSSED
OR ANNOTATED IN THE
COMMENTARY

aboording	see note to	26. 16
accoyd	,,	225. 16
adjured	,,	45. 8
affiance	,,	49. 17
affinitie	,,	182. 13
affreighted	,,	247. 11
alienation	,,	157. 8
ampare	,,	8. 21
appay	,,	89. 35
Auncients	,,	141. 13
awaite	,,	313. 18
belaied	,,	164. 8
brinked	,,	131. 34
browne-abram	,,	229. 32–33
buttals	,,	42. 16
calvelings	,,	122. 35–36
Centrinels	,,	176. 15
charie	,,	263. 11
checkey worke	,,	133. 9
concent	,,	89. 17
condigne	,,	185. 24
condolent	,,	248. 30
consent	,,	58. 25
corsies	,,	12. 9
countermaund	,,	138. 10–11
deduct	,,	194. 9
deducted	,,	3. 29
degorge	,,	362. 24
digresses	,,	118. 12
discurring	,,	5. 21
dishivered	,,	330. 34
emprese	,,	344. 31
enchants	,,	402. 24
entendereth	,,	27. 2
estraied	,,	27. 28
excelse	,,	73. 3
exempted	,,	118. 20
eye brinkes	,,	211. 25
fancie	,,	58. 28

flight	see note to	171. 19
forgetnesse	,,	238. 17
geason	,,	321. 8
Hamadriades	,,	414. 27
hart-breake	,,	265. 6
hoisting	,,	324. 30
homely	,,	282. 17
Idea	,,	37. 19
illustrate	,,	144. 29
immanitie	,,	76. 31
impresa	,,	265. 21
impropriate	,,	158. 23
incended	,,	27. 14
indigned	,,	398. 12
inestimate	,,	134. 24
inhabited	,,	271. 16
inopinate	,,	174. 30
install	,,	55. 33
knobbing	,,	51. 30
layes	,,	221. 15
leesing	,,	49. 17
lighting	,,	100. 27
Moysaical	,,	139. 30
musicall	,,	344. 17
Napees	,,	414. 27
paragonned	,,	126. 37
pastaunce	,,	31. 33
patrocinie	,,	243. 28
peregrine	,,	25. 20
plat	,,	228. 25
posie	,,	265. 11
puttocks	,,	369. 12
quote out	,,	261. 12
raves	,,	281. 18
razed	,,	92. 16
rebound	,,	346. 28
rebounding	,,	26. 23
recordation	,,	5. 22
recures	,,	206. 4
refell	,,	26. 29
repell	,,	26. 27
reposedly	,,	256. 12
retracted	,,	143. 15
rythmes	,,	254. 31
salutiferous	,,	317. 19
scrip	,,	11. 14
Sextine	,,	53. 7
shent	,,	301. 31

sovenaunce	see note to	317. 30
spendlesse	,,	369. 24
staffe	,,	369. 35
staves	,,	385. 22
sublimate	,,	152. 10
subscription	,,	142. 5
sursault	,,	76. 1
tew	,,	326. 21
tottered	,,	267. 37
transpiercing	,,	238. 1
trustles	,,	171. 4
unappassionate	,,	81. 33
unappassionately	,,	223. 6
watchet	,,	92. 8

LIST OF MANUSCRIPTS AND BOOKS

I. MANUSCRIPTS

Collection of English Verses 1581–1612, Cambridge University Library, MS. Dd. 5. 75.

Hunter, Joseph, *Chorus vatum Anglicanorum*, British Museum, Add. MSS. 24487–92.

'Love is not blind', Anon. translation in British Museum, Add. MS. 23229.

Miscellaneous verses collected by Edward Banister 1583–1603, British Museum, Add. MS. 28253, ff. 1–13.

Wilson, Thomas, *Diana de Monte mayor done out of Spanish by Thomas Wilson Esquire, In the yeare 1596*, British Museum, Add. MS. 18638.

(This manuscript has been printed by Sir H. Thomas, *Revue Hispanique*, 1 (1920), 367–418.)

II. EDITIONS AND TRANSLATIONS OF THE *DIANAS* CONSULTED

For bibliographies of Montemayor and Gil Polo see the editions by Estrada and Ferreres.

Gil Polo, Gaspar, *Primera parte de Diana Enamorada. Cinco libros que prosiguen, los siete de la Diana de Jorge Monte Mayor, etc.*, Juan Stelsio: Anvers, 1567.

—— —— Gil Stelsio: Anvers, 1574.

—— —— Juan Millan: Çaragoça, 1577.

—— —— Madrid, 1778.

—— —— ed. R. Ferreres, *Clásicos Castellanos*, Madrid, 1953.

—— —— together with the English translation (1598) by Bartholomew Yong. Edited with Notes and Glossary by R. L. and M. B. Grismer, Minneapolis, 1959.

Montemayor, Jorge de, *Los siete libros de la Diana, etc.*, Pedro Bellero: Anvers, 1575.

—— —— *agora nuevamente añadida, etc.*, Pedro Bellero: Anvers, 1580.

Perez, Alonso, *Segunda parte de la Diana de George de Monte Mayor*, Pedro Bellero: Anvers, 1581.

(The preceding two entries are usually listed as one edition of Montemayor in two parts.)

Montemayor, Jorge de, *Los siete libros de la Diana*, ed. F. L. Estrada, *Clásicos Castellanos*, 2nd ed., Madrid, 1954.

—— —— ed. E. Moreno Báez, Madrid, 1955.

—— (A. Perez and G. Gil Polo), *La Diane de G. de Montemayor. Divisee en trois parties, & traduites d'Espagnol en François* [Part 1 by N. Colin, parts 2 and 3 by G. Chapuis], *Reveuë & corrigee, etc.*, Tours, 1592.

Vega Carpio, Lope da, *The Pilgrim, or the Stranger in his own Country; also Diana, a Pastoral Romance, by G. de Montemajor*, 1738.

III. LITERARY WORKS

Apollonius of Tyre. The Old English Apollonius of Tyre, ed. Peter Goolden, Oxford English Monographs, Oxford, 1958.

Bandello, Matteo, *Novelle,* 3 parts, Lucca, 1554.

—— *Le Novelle,* A cura di G. Brognoligo, 2da ed. riveduta, 3 vols., Bari, 1928–31.

Beaumont, F., and Fletcher, J., *The Works,* ed. The Revd. A. Dyce, 11 vols., 1843–6.

—— —— ed. A. Glover and A. R. Waller, 10 vols., Cambridge English Classics, Cambridge, 1905–12.

Blount, Thomas, *The Academie of Eloquence,* 1654.

Boccaccio, Giovanni, *Ameto, comedia delle nimphe fiorentine . . . con la dichiaratione de i luoghi difficili di messer Francesco Sansovino, etc.,* Vinegia, 1545.

—— *Amorous Fiammetta . . . Fyrst written in Italian by . . . Iohn Boccace . . . And now done into English by B. Giovano* [i.e. B. Yong], 1587.

—— —— ed. E. Hutton, Navarre Society, 1926.

—— —— ed. K. H. Josling, 1929.

Browne, William, *Poems,* ed. G. Goodwin with an introduction by A. H. Bullen, 2 vols., Muses' Library, 1894.

Byron, George Gordon, Baron Byron, *The Poetical Works,* ed., with a memoir, by E. H. Coleridge, 1905.

Castiglione, Baldassare, *The Book of the Courtier. Done into English by Sir T. Hoby,* with an Introduction by W. Raleigh, The Tudor Translations, 1900.

Cervantes Saavedra, Miguel de, *The history of the valorous & witty knight-errant Don Quixote of the Mancha,* translated T. Shelton, 3 vols., Library of English Classics, London and New York, 1900.

—— *The complete works,* ed. J. Fitzmaurice-Kelly, translated J. Ormsby, 12 vols., Glasgow, 1901–3.

?C[odrington], R[obert], *The Troublesome and Hard Adventures in Love . . . by . . . M. Cervantes; . . . translated . . . By R.C., Gent.,* 1652.

Crowne, John, *Pandion and Amphigenia; or the coy lady of Thessalia; with sculptures,* 1665.

Davenant, Sir William, *The Dramatic Works,* 5 vols., Edinburgh, 1872–4.

Davison, Francis, *A Poetical Rhapsody* (1602), ed. H. E. Rollins, 2 vols., Cambridge, Mass., 1931–2.

Dickenson, John, *Prose and verse,* ed., etc., by A. B. Grosart, Manchester, 1878.

Donne, John, *Poems. With elegies on the author's death,* 1635.

—— *The Poems,* ed. H. J. C. Grierson, 2 vols., Oxford, 1912.

—— *The Life and Letters . . .* collected by E. Gosse, 2 vols., 1899.

Ebreo, Leone, *The Philosophy of Love,* translated F. Friedeberg-Seeley and J. H. Barnes, 1937.

—— *Dialoghi d'Amore.* A cura di S. Caramella, Bari, 1929.

Eliot, John, *Ortho-epia Gallica,* 1593.

Englands Helicon, ed. A. H. Bullen, revised ed. 1899.

—— ed. H. E. Rollins, 2 vols., Cambridge, Mass., 1935.

Eustathius Macrembolites, *Ismene and Ismenias*, translated from the French by L. H. Le Moine, 1788.

Florian, Jean-Pierre Claris de, *Estelle, roman pastoral*, 2de ed. Paris, 1788.

Fontenelle, Bernard Le Bovier de, *Œuvres*, 3 vols., Paris, 1818.

Googe, Barnabe, *Eglogs, epytaphes, & sonettes, 1563*, ed. E. Arber, Arber's English Reprints, 1871.

Greene, Robert, *The Life and Complete Works in Prose and Verse*, ed. A. B. Grosart, 15 vols., 1881–6.

—— *Menaphon*, and *A Margarite of America*, by Thomas Lodge, ed. G. B. Harrison, Oxford, 1927.

Guazzo, Stefano, *The civile Conversation . . . divided into foure bookes, the first three translated out of French by G. Pettie . . . the fourth . . . now translated out of Italian into English by Barth. Young, of the middle Temple, Gent.*, 1586.

—— —— with an Introduction by Sir E. Sullivan, 2 vols., The Tudor Translations, 1925.

Heliodorus, *An Æthiopian history. Englished by T. Underdowne* (1587), with an Introduction by C. Whibley, The Tudor Translations, 1895.

Hoskins, John, *Directions for speech and style*, ed. H. H. Hudson, Princeton University Press, 1935.

Jonson, Ben, *Works*, ed. C. H. Herford and P. Simpson, 11 vols., Oxford, 1925–52.

—— *Notes of Ben Jonson's Conversations with William Drummond of Hawthornden*, ed. D. Laing, Shakespeare Society, 1842.

Killigrew, Thomas, *Comedies and tragedies*, 1664.

La Perrière, Guillaume de, *La morosophie*, Lyon, 1553.

Leo the Jew. *See* Ebreo, Leone.

Lodge, Thomas, *The Complete Works, etc.*, with a memoir by E. Gosse, 4 vols., Glasgow, for the Hunterian Club, 1875–88.

—— *Rosalynde*, ed. W. W. Greg, 1907.

Longus, *Daphnis and Chloe*: the Elizabethan version from Amyot's translation by A. Day. Reprinted from the unique original (1587) and edited by J. Jacobs, The Tudor Library, 1890.

Lower, Sir William, *Dramatic Works and Translations*, ed. W. B. Gates, Philadelphia, 1932.

Lyly, John, *The Complete Works*, ed. R. Warwick Bond, 3 vols., Oxford, 1902.

Markham, Gervase, *The English Arcadia, alluding his beginning from Sir P. Sydneys ending*, 1607.

—— *The second and last part of the first booke of the English Arcadia*, 1613.

Milton, John, *Complete Prose Works*. General editor: D. M. Wolfe. Vol. 1– , London and New Haven, Conn., 1953– .

Montemayor, Jorge de, *El Cancionero*, ed. A. G. Palencia, *Sociedad de Bibliófilos Españoles*, Madrid, 1932.

Montreux, Nicolas de, *Honours academie: or the pastoral of Julietta*, translated R. T[ofte], 1610.

Nostredame, Jehan de, *Les Vies des plus célèbres et anciens poètes provençaux*. Édition préparée par C. Chabaneau et publiée avec introduction et commentaire par J. Anglade, Librairie Ancienne, Paris, 1913.

Nostredame, Jehan de, *Le vite delli più celebri et antichi primi Poeti Provenzali*, *etc*. In Lione, Appresso d'Alesandro Marsilij, 1575.

Ovid, *Metamorphoses*, with English translation by F. J. Miller, 2 vols., Loeb Classical Library, 1916.

Parry, Robert, *Moderatus, the most delectable historie of the blacke knight*, 1595.

Petrarch, Francis, *The tryumphes of Fraunces Petrarcke*, translated by Henrye Parker, knyght, Lorde Morley [?1565].

—— *Los Triumphos de Francisco Petrarcha, agora nuevamente traduzidos en lengua Castellana, etc.*, Salamanca, 1581.

Playford, John, *Select Musicall Ayres and Dialogues*, 1653.

Ponce, Bartholome, *Primera parte de la Clara Diana a lo divino, repartida en siete libros*, Çaragoça, 1599.

Reynolds, John, *The Flower of Fidelitie*, 1650.

Rich, Barnabe, *Riche his Farewell to Militarie profession*, ed. J. P. Collier, Shakespeare Society, 1846.

Sannazaro, Jacopo, *Arcadia*. A cura di E. Carrara. Collezione di classici italiani, Torino, 1948.

Shakespeare, William, *The Plays*, with notes by Samuel Johnson and George Steevens, 4th ed., 15 vols., 1793.

—— *The Complete Works*, ed. G. B. Harrison, New York, 1952.

—— *The Two Gentlemen of Verona*, ed. R. Warwick Bond, The Arden Shakespeare, 1906.

—— *A Midsummer Night's Dream*, ed. H. Cuningham, The Arden Shakespeare, 2nd ed., 1922.

—— *As You Like It*, ed. J. W. Holme, The Arden Shakespeare, 2nd ed., 1920.

—— *The Tempest*, ed. F. Kermode, The New Arden Shakespeare. Corrected ed., 1961.

Sidney, Sir Philip, *The Complete Works*, ed. A. Feuillerat, 4 vols., Cambridge, 1912–26.

—— *The Poems*, ed. W. A. Ringler, Jr., Oxford English Texts, Oxford, 1962.

—— *An Apology for Poetry*, ed. G. Shepherd, 1965.

Sorel, Charles, *The Extravagant Shepherd*, translated John Davies, 2nd ed., 1654.

Southey, Robert, *Letters written during a short residence in Spain and Portugal, etc.*, Bristol, 1797.

Spenser, Edmund, *The Works*. A variorum edition, ed. E. Greenlaw and others, 11 vols., Baltimore, 1932–58.

Spingarn, J. E., ed. *Critical Essays of the Seventeenth Century*, 3 vols., Oxford, 1908–9.

Turberville, George, *Epitaphes, epigrams, songs and sonets, etc.* (1567). Reprinted J. P. Collier, 1867.

d'Urfé, Honoré, *L'Astrée*, 5 vols., Paris, 1647.

—— *The history of Astrea. The first part*, translated John Pyper, 1620.

—— *Astrea, a romance*, translated by a person of quality [J. Davies of Kidwelly], 3 vols. in 2, 1657, 58.

Vauquelin de la Fresnaye, Jean, *L'Art poétique* (1605), ed. G. Pellissier, Paris, 1885.

Virgil, *Works*, with an English translation by H. R. Fairclough. Revised ed., 2 vols., Loeb Classical Library, 1935, 46.

Wroth, Lady Mary, *The Countesse of Mountgomeries Urania*, 1621.

IV. CRITICAL WORKS

A. *Books*

Alden, R. M., *English Verse. Specimens illustrating its principles and history*, New York, 1903.

Anders, H. R. D., *Shakespeare's Books*, Berlin, 1904.

Avalle-Arce, J. B., *La novela pastoril española*, Madrid, 1959.

Baker, E. A., *The History of the English Novel*, reprinted, 10 vols., New York, 1950.

Bouterwek, Fridericus, *History of Spanish and Portuguese Literature*, translated Thomasina Ross, 2 vols., 1823.

Bullen, A. H. (ed.), *Poems Chiefly Lyrical from Romances and Prose Tracts, etc.*, 1890.

Bullough, Geoffrey, *Narrative and Dramatic Sources of Shakespeare*, vol. 1– , 1957– .

Buxton, John, *Elizabethan Taste*, 1963.

Case, R. H., *English Epithalamies*, The Bodley Head Anthologies, London and Chicago, 1896.

Courthope, W. J., *A History of English Poetry*, 6 vols., London and New York, 1895–1910.

Cross, W. L., *The Development of the English Novel*, New York and London, 1899.

Danby, J. F., *Poets on Fortune's Hill*, 1952.

Davis, W. R., and Lanham, R. A., *Sidney's Arcadia*, New Haven and London, 1965.

Dunlop, J. C., *History of Prose Fiction*, new ed. revised by H. Wilson, 2 vols., 1896.

Ellis, G., *Specimens of the Early English Poets*, 5th ed., corrected, 3 vols., 1845.

Empson, W., *Some Versions of Pastoral*, 1935.

Fletcher, H. F., *The Intellectual Development of John Milton*, 2 vols., Urbana, 1956.

Genouy, H., *L'Élément pastoral dans la poésie narrative et le drame en Angleterre de 1579 à 1640*, Thèse, Lyon, Montpellier, 1928.

—— *L'"Arcadia" de Sidney dans ses rapports avec l'"Arcadia" de Sannazaro et la 'Diana' de Montemayor*, Thèse complémentaire, Lyon, Montpellier, 1928.

Gerhardt, Mia, *La Pastorale. Essai d'analyse littéraire*, Assen, 1950.

Greg, W. W., *Pastoral Poetry and Pastoral Drama*, 1906.

Harbage, Alfred, *Thomas Killigrew, Cavalier Dramatist, 1612–83*, Philadelphia, 1930.

—— *Sir William Davenant, Poet, Venturer, 1606–68*, Philadelphia, 1935.

—— *Cavalier Drama*, Modern Language Association of America, general series, New York, etc., 1936.

Hazlitt, W. C., *Shakespeare's Library*, 6 vols., 1875.

Hume, M. A. S., *Spanish Influence on English Literature*, 1905.

Hunter, G. K., *John Lyly. The Humanist as Courtier*, 1962.

Hunter, Joseph, *New Illustrations of the Life, Studies and Writings of Shakespeare*, 2 vols., 1845.

Jusserand, J., *The English Novel in the Time of Shakespeare*, translated E. Lee . . ., revised and enlarged ed., 1908.

Kalstone, D., *Sidney's Poetry: Contexts and Interpretations*, Cambridge, Mass., 1965.

Kelly, J. Fitzmaurice-, *A New History of Spanish Literature*, 1926.

Lewis, C. S., *English Literature in the Sixteenth Century Excluding Drama*, Oxford, 1954.

Marsan, J., *La Pastorale dramatique en France*, Paris, 1905.

Menedez y Pelayo, *Origenes de la Novela*, 4 vols., Madrid, 1905.

Moorman, F. W., *William Browne. His Britannia's Pastorals and the pastoral poetry of the Elizabethan age*, Strassburg, 1897.

Myrick, K. O., *Sir Philip Sidney as a Literary Craftsman*, 2nd ed., Lincoln, Nebraska, 1965.

Newdigate, B. H., *Michael Drayton and his Circle*, Oxford, 1941.

Pruvost, R., *Robert Greene et ses romans*, Paris, 1938.

Raleigh, Sir W., *The English Novel*, 1894.

Randall, D. B. J., *The Golden Tapestry: A Critical Survey of Non-chivalric Spanish Fiction in English Translation (1543–1657)*, Durham, North Carolina, 1963.

Reynier, G., *Le Roman sentimental avant l'Astrée*, Paris, 1908.

Roche, T. P., Jr., *The Kindly Flame: A Study of the Third and Fourth Books of Spenser's Faerie Queene*, Princeton, 1964.

Saintsbury, G., *History of English Prosody*, 3 vols., 1923.

Schlauch, M., *Antecedents of the English Novel 1400–1600: from Chaucer to Deloney*, Warszawa and London, 1963.

Schönherr, J. G., *Jorge de Montemayor und sein Schäferroman die 'Siete libros de la Diana'*. Inaug. diss. . . . Leipzig, Halle, 1886.

Seccombe, T., and Allen, J. W., *The Age of Shakespeare (1579–1631)*, 2 vols., 1909.

Smith, Hallett, *Elizabethan Poetry*, Cambridge, Mass., 1952.

Thompson, J., *The Founding of English Metre*, 1961.

Ticknor, G., *History of Spanish Literature*, 3 vols., 1849.

Tieje, A. J., *The Theory of Characterization in Prose Fiction prior to 1740*. University of Minnesota Studies in Language and Literature, no. 5, Dec. 1916.

Tillyard, E. M. W., *The English Epic and its Background*, 1954.

Underhill, J. G., *Spanish Literature in the England of the Tudors*. Columbia University Studies in Literature, New York, 1899.

Ungerer, G., *Anglo-Spanish Relations in Tudor Literature*, Bern, 1956.

Vyvyan, J., *Shakespeare and Platonic Beauty*, 1961.

Wedgwood, C. V., *Seventeenth-Century English Literature*, Home University Library, 1950.

Wilson, J. H., *The Influence of Beaumont and Fletcher on Restoration Drama*, Ohio State University Press, Columbus, Ohio, 1928.

Wolff, S. L., *The Greek Romances in Elizabethan Prose Fiction*, New York, 1912.

B. *Articles*

Anderson, D. M., 'Sir Thomas Wilson's Translation of Montemayor's *Diana*', *Review of English Studies*, N.S. vii (1956), 176–81.

Atkinson, W. C., 'Studies in Literary Decadence, III, The Pastoral Novel', *Bulletin of Spanish Studies*, iv (1927), 117–26, 180–6.

Avalle-Arce, J. B., 'The *Diana* of Montemayor: Tradition and Innovation', *PMLA*, lxxiv (1959), 1–6.

Cory, H. E., 'The Golden Age of the Spenserian Pastoral', *PMLA*, xxv (1910), 241–67.

Covington, F. F., 'Biographical Notes on Spenser', *Modern Philology*, xxii (1924), 63–66.

Duncan-Jones, K. D., 'Sidney's Urania', *Review of English Studies*, N.S. xvii (1966), 123–32.

Greenlaw, E., 'Shakespeare's Pastorals', *Studies in Philology*, xiii (1916), 122–54.

Harrison, T. P., Jr., 'Googe's "Eglogs" and Montemayor's "Diana"', *University of Texas Studies in English*, no. 5 (Oct. 1925), 68–78.

—— 'A Source of Sidney's "Arcadia"', *University of Texas Studies in English*, no. 6 (Dec. 1926), 53–71.

—— 'Shakespeare and Montemayor's "Diana"', *University of Texas Studies in English*, no. 6 (Dec. 1926), 72–120.

—— 'Bartholomew Yong, Translator', *MLR*, xxi (1926), 129–39.

—— 'A Probable Source of Beaumont and Fletcher's *Philaster*', *PMLA*, xli (1926), 294–303.

—— 'The *Faerie Queene* and the *Diana*', *Philological Quarterly*, ix (1930), 51–56.

Hebel, J. W., 'Drayton's *Sirena*', *PMLA*, xxxix (1924), 814–36.

Kelly, J. Fitzmaurice-, 'The Bibliography of the *Diana Enamorada*', *Revue Hispanique*, ii (1895), 304–11.

Krappe, E., '*Two Gentlemen of Verona* and Montemayor', *Notes and Queries*, N.S. ix, no. 4 (April 1962), 143.

Lascelles, M. M., 'Shakespeare's Pastoral Comedy', *More Talking of Shakespeare*, ed. J. Garrett (1959), 70–86.

Mathews, E. G., 'Gil Polo, Desportes, and Lyly's "Cupid and my Campaspe"', *MLN*, lvi (1941), 606–7.

—— 'John Donne's "Little Rag"', *MLN*, lvi (1941), 607–9.

—— 'English Translations from Spanish: A Review and a Contribution', *Journal of English and Germanic Philology*, xliv (1945), 387–424.

Mincoff, M., 'Shakespeare and Lyly', *Shakespeare Survey*, xiv (1961), 15–24.

Muñoz Rojas, J. A., 'Apuntes para un estudio de las relaciones literarias de Donne con España', *Homenaje a Walter Starkie*, Barcelona, 1948, 225–42.

Pruvost, R., '*The Two Gentlemen of Verona*, *Twelfth Night*, et *Gl'Ingannati*', *Études anglaises*, XIIIᵉ année (1960), 1–9.

Randall, D., '*The Troublesome and Hard Adventures in Love*: An English Addition to the Bibliography of *Diana*', *Bulletin of Hispanic Studies*, xxxviii (1961), 154–8.

Rennert, H. A., 'The Spanish Pastoral Romances', *PMLA*, VII. iii (1892), 1–119.

Reyher, P., 'A. de Vigny, Shakespeare, and George de Montemayor', *Revue de l'Enseignement des langues vivantes* (1920), 1–7.

Reyher, P., 'The Two Gentlemen et Twelfth Night: leurs sources communes', Revue de l'Enseignement des langues vivantes (1924), 438–48.

Salmon, V., 'Early Seventeenth-Century Punctuation as a Guide to Sentence Structure', Review of English Studies, N.s. xiii (1962), 347–60.

Schevill, R., 'On the Influence of Spanish Literature upon English in the Early Seventeenth Century', Romanische Forschungen, xx (1907), 604–34.

Smith, Homer, 'Pastoral Influence in the English Drama', PMLA, xii (1897), 355–460.

Solé-Leris, A., 'The Theory of Love in the two Dianas: A Contrast', Bulletin of Hispanic Studies, xxxvi (1959), 65–79.

—— 'Psychological Realism in the Pastoral Novel: Gil Polo's Diana Enamorada', Bulletin of Hispanic Studies, xxxix (1962), 43–47.

Thorndike, A. H., 'The Pastoral Element in the English Drama before 1605', MLN, xiv (1899), 228–46.

Tobler, R., 'Shakespeare's Sommernachtstraum und Montemayor's Diana', Shakespeare Jahrbuch, xxxiv (1898), 358–66.

Wardropper, B. W., 'The Diana of Montemayor: Revaluation and Interpretation', Studies in Philology, xlviii (1951), 126–44.

V. REFERENCE WORKS

Brandi, K., The Emperor Charles V, translated C. V. Wedgwood, 1939.

Butler, Charles, The English Grammar, 1633.

Cartari, V., Le Imagini con la Spositione de i Dei de Gliantichi, Venetia, 1556.

Case, A. E., A Bibliography of English Poetical Miscellanies 1521–1750, Oxford, 1935.

Clifford, Henry, The Life of Jane Dormer, Duchess of Feria, ed. The Revd. J. Stevenson, S.J., 1887.

Covarrubias, Sebastian de, Tesoro de la lengua castellana o española según la impresión de 1611, con las adiciones de Benito Remigio Noydens publicadas en la de 1674, ed. Martín de Riquer, Barcelona, 1943.

Enciclopedia universal ilustrada Europeo-Americana, 70 tom., Apéndice, 10 tom. Supl. anual., 1934– , Bilbao, etc., c. 1910– .

The Encyclopedia Britannica, eleventh edition, 29 vols., 1910–11.

Esdaile, A., A List of English Tales and Prose Romances printed before 1740, 1912.

Feuillerat, A., (ed.), Documents relating to the Office of the Revels in the time of Queen Elizabeth, Louvain, 1908.

Greg, W. W., A Bibliography of the English Printed Drama to the Restoration, 4 vols., 1939–59.

Grove, Sir George, Grove's Dictionary of Music and Musicians, 5th ed., ed. Eric Blom, 9 vols. and suppl., 1954, 61.

McKerrow, R. B., An Introduction to Bibliography, 2nd impression, with corrections, Oxford, 1928.

—— general editor, A Dictionary of Printers and Booksellers in England, Scotland and Ireland, and of Foreign Printers of English Books 1557–1640, 1910.

Middle Temple. Middle Temple Records: Minutes of Parliament, ed. C. H. Hopwood, 4 vols., 1904–5.

—— Register of Admissions to the Honourable Society of the Middle Temple 1501–1944, compiled by H. A. C. Sturgess, 3 vols., 1949.

Minsheu, John, *A dictionarie in Spanish and English, first published into the English tongue by Ric. Percivale Gent. Now enlarged and amplified, etc.*, 1599.

Nouvelle biographie générale, 46 tom., Paris, Firmin Didot Frères, 1855–66.

Trimble, W. R., *The Catholic Laity in Elizabethan England 1558–1603*, Cambridge, Mass., 1964.

Wheatley, H. B., and Cunningham, P., *London Past and Present*, 3 vols., 1891.

INDEX OF FIRST LINES OF POEMS

A faire maide wed to prying jealousie 338
A farewell they departure call, 62
Ah such an one I ever was, since that 285
Although my quiet it doth let, 47
As many stars as *Heaven* containeth, strive 299
Awake a little, light of cleerest day, 287
Bernard of *Carpio* I am, 141
Beware good Love, beware, it is not well 338
Contents of love, 58
Diana, Love, and my faire *Shepherdesse,* 416
Don Luys of *Villanova* I am named, 142
End now my life, with daily paines affrighted, 284
Even as (O death) the Planets should remaine 155
Faire Shepherdesse, The cause was Love, 301
Faire Shepherdesse whose hap and fare, 114
First in Granada I was borne, 162
Flie storming verse out of my raging brest 398
Foolish love, ah foolish lover, 47
For a favour of such woorth 19
Goe now my thoughts, where one day you were going, 57
Haire in change what libertie, 13
Harke *Felismena* to the sweetest song 144
Having no cause, why in the deepest sound 339
Heere Lady *Katherine* entombed lies, 154
Hernand Gonçales of *Castile* I am 140
He that in freedome jets it proude and brave, 253
How fond am I to hope for any rest 45
I am a lover, but was never loved, 15
I am *Cid* th'honour of Spaine, 140
I am *Fonseca* whose brave historie 141
I cannot be by Loves wrath more tormented, 259
I sawe a hill upon a day, 392
I see thee jolly Shepherd merry, 218
I should have dide, and never viewed thee 381
If Lady LAURAS memorie unstained 9
If teares cannot with tendernesse relent thee, 224
If thy soft *Haires* be threds of shining gold, 171
If to be lov'd it thee offends, 385
Inconstant love and cruell, which hast lately 291
In this cleere Sunne with golden beames that shineth, 120
In those most happy fieldes and plaines, 328
Let not thy Graces rare, 336

Let now each meade with flowers be depainted, 378
Let now the goodly spring tide make us merie, 367
Long have I felt a silent paine of sorrow, 245
Love is not blinde, but I, which fondly guide 251
Love passed by me with his bowe unarm'd, 123
Lovers, with pride enjoy your full content, 360
Mæcenas was to *Maro* of great fame 8
Me thinks, thou tak'st the woorser way, 386
Mine eies, once have I seene you more contented, 29
Mistresse thou hast forgotten me, 106
My greatest valours they shall see, 141
My greevous sighes and sorrowfull teares 336
My life (yoong Shepherdesse) for thee 50
My painefull yeeres impartiall *Love* was spending 89
My passion (*Love*) thou dost disdaine, 105
My soule doth leape for joy to have 382
Neere to a Shepherd did a damsell sit, 391
Neere to the river bankes, with greene 60
No more (O cruell Nymph) now hast thou prayed 43
Now Love, and fortune turne to me againe, 206
Now that the sunne doth hide his golden beames 277
O eies that are not now as once tormented, 367
O eies, that see not him, who look'd on yow 21
O let that time a thousand monthes endure, 370
O Love thou gav'st me not the joy, 64
O sandie desart, and drie barren meade, 274
O vainest hopes, Alas, how many *Daies* 191
Parnasse, O sacred mount and full of glorie, 9
Passed contents, 220
Poore *Melibee* of love and hope forgot, 408
Saie Shepherdesse, what hath deprived thee 105
Shepherd, who can passe such wrong 49
Shepherd, why dost thou hold thy peace? 388
Shew me a horse of such a kinde, 395
Sighes, since you lighten not my hart, 234
Since thou to me wert so unkinde, 386
Step after step I followe death in sight 340
Such joy I feele doth in my soule surmount, 383
Sweete Mistresse harken unto me 88
Syrenus, what thought'st thou when I was viewing thee 26
Tell me (good Sirs) what Bird is that that flies 396
Tell me what Master he may be, 394
That majestie so princely, grave, and sweete, 263
That mighty Love, though blinde of both his eies, 250
That sweetest harme I doe not blame, 90
The authours of subjections 135
The cause why that thou dost denie 283
The coole fresh winde, *Taurisus*, that inviting us 317

The faire, the fresh, the red, and rosie morning   358
They say *Love* sware, he never would be frend,   295
Times change and shall (as we doe see)   232
To heare me wearied is the cleerest river,   54
To see thee I lift up my happie eies,   121
Turne thy faire eies (wherein my shame   384
Water (faire Springs, and purest running streames)   342
Waters that fall from top of these steepe *Hils*,   53
Weepe not my dolefull eies,   50
Welcome thy friendes from swelling seas that rore   325
Well let her life that enters heere be waighed,   133
What bird is that so light,   393
What motions, times and changes,   209
When cruell absence woundes a soule with paine,   296
When that I poore soule was borne,   199
When that with thousand parti-coloured flowers   413
While *Titan* in his Coach with burning beames   254
Yong Shepherd) turne aside, and move   385